BIRDS

OF THE WORLD

COLIN HARRISON AND
ALAN GREENSMITH

DR. K.E.L SIMMONS
Editorial Consultant

DORLING KINDERSLEY
London • New York • Stuttgart

A DORLING KINDERSLEY BOOK

Note on Classification
The arrangement of bird families in this book is based on the recently published work of
Richard Howard and Michael Moore. For the names of genera and species, the authors
have drawn on the work of Charles G. Sibley and Burt Monroe.

Editor Edward Bunting
Art Editor Chris Walker
Editorial Assistant Jeanette Cossar
Design Assistant Christina Betts
Production Caroline Webber
Picture Research Catherine O'Rourke

First published in Great Britain in 1993
by Dorling Kindersley Limited,
9 Henrietta Street, London WC2E 8PS

Copyright © 1993
Dorling Kindersley Limited, London

A CIP catalogue record for this book is available from the British Library

ISBN 0-7513-1032-8 hardcover
ISBN 0-7513-1033-6 flexiback

Computer page make-up by
The Cooling Brown Partnership, Great Britain

Text film output by
P4 Graphics Limited, Great Britain

Reproduced by
Colourscan, Singapore

Printed and bound by
Kyodo Printing Co., Singapore

CONTENTS

INTRODUCTION

Birds have always been important for humans. We have long striven to imitate their ability to fly, now at last with some success. Through the ages, images of birds have appeared in art and design, from illuminated manuscripts to coins and banknotes. Birds play a major role in our economy in the form of poultry, and they have given rise to important leisure pursuits, such as birdkeeping, falconry, and birdwatching.

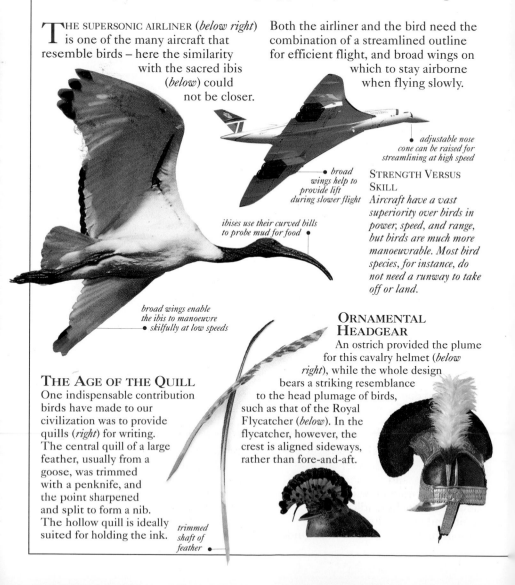

THE SUPERSONIC AIRLINER (*below right*) is one of the many aircraft that resemble birds – here the similarity with the sacred ibis (*below*) could not be closer.

Both the airliner and the bird need the combination of a streamlined outline for efficient flight, and broad wings on which to stay airborne when flying slowly.

• adjustable nose cone can be raised for streamlining at high speed

• broad wings help to provide lift during slower flight

ibises use their curved bills to probe mud for food •

broad wings enable the ibis to manoeuvre • skilfully at low speeds

STRENGTH VERSUS SKILL
Aircraft have a vast superiority over birds in power, speed, and range, but birds are much more manoeuvrable. Most bird species, for instance, do not need a runway to take off or land.

THE AGE OF THE QUILL
One indispensable contribution birds have made to our civilization was to provide quills (*right*) for writing. The central quill of a large feather, usually from a goose, was trimmed with a penknife, and the point sharpened and split to form a nib. The hollow quill is ideally suited for holding the ink.

trimmed shaft of feather •

ORNAMENTAL HEADGEAR
An ostrich provided the plume for this cavalry helmet (*below right*), while the whole design bears a striking resemblance to the head plumage of birds, such as that of the Royal Flycatcher (*below*). In the flycatcher, however, the crest is aligned sideways, rather than fore-and-aft.

SYMBOLS OF POWER AND WEALTH

GERMAN ARMY
BADGE FROM
WORLD WAR I

US ARMY
DISTINGUISHED
SERVICE MEDAL AND CROSS

US ARMY CAP BADGE
WITH EAGLE

US CONGRESSIONAL
MEDAL OF HONOR

SINGAPORE $500 NOTE WITH
SYMBOLIC GOLDEN ORIOLE

CANADIAN $1 COIN WITH
GREAT NORTHERN DIVER

NEW ZEALAND $20 NOTE
WITH NEW ZEALAND PIGEON

GAME, FARM, AND AVIARY BIRDS

Birds have been important to human society since the most ancient times. Early peoples ate birds and their eggs, and made tools and needles from the bones. The best species for eating would have included gamebirds (*see pp. 108-117*). The first of these to be domesticated was the Red Junglefowl (*see p. 114*), which is the wild ancestor of the chicken now known all over the world. In more recent times, other gamebirds were domesticated including the Wild Turkey (*see p. 108*), and some guineafowl. Another family of birds that has proved suitable for captive breeding is that of the swans, geese, and ducks (*see pp. 73–85*). Farm geese were developed from captive Greylag Geese (*see p. 74*), and all farm ducks are domestic forms of the Mallard (*see p. 79*). Birds have for a long time provided feathers for our use. Goose quills, and the smaller crow quills, were used for writing, while down from ducks is still made into quilts and duvets. Feathers from various bird species are used to guide the flight of arrows. Birds are also prized for their decorative value. Fanciers breed and show hundreds of varieties of chickens and ducks; doves and peafowl are kept in gardens; and countless species are kept in aviaries.

FALCONRY

Since the Middle Ages, birds of prey have been tamed, carried on an arm, and restrained with a hooded cowl on the head, and leashes on the legs and feet. When released, trained birds will fly after and kill selected prey. The Peregrine Falcon is the commonest bird used; other species used in falconry include the Saker Falcon, Goshawk, Harris's Hawk, and the smaller Merlin.

leather hood covers the eyes

leg leashes are known as "jesses"

HOW THIS BOOK WORKS

THE BOOK is arranged according to the major groups of birds: non-passerines, which include the largest birds, and passerines, which include the "songbirds". Each entry describes a separate species or "kind" of bird. The entries are arranged in order of their scientific classification. Birds that belong to the same family are grouped together. Within each family, closely related birds are placed near together. Readers can find a bird by its habitat and behaviour via the Key on pages 18–37, or by its Latin or English name in the Index. Each entry systematically covers appearance, habitat, food, nest, and distribution, thus giving the most basic identification features. In many entries additional details, such as song, calls, or behaviour, are also provided.

PLUMAGE ILLUSTRATIONS

Except when stated otherwise, the bird photograph in an entry shows the adult male. Many birds also have other plumages (*see pp. 12–13*), and the most important of these are shown in illustrations beside the photograph.

SUBSPECIES   FEMALE   JUVENILE   MALE CREST

SUBSPECIES   FEMALE   JUVENILE   WING PATCH   MALE TAIL

DISTRIBUTION MAPS

These show where the bird is likely to be seen, either all year round or at certain times. For example, Purple Martins breed in North America and winter in Brazil: the map also shows the area through which they pass in transit. By contrast, in the west of their range, Eurasian Robins stay all year, but in the east they are migrants, wintering in the south and west. The Australian Brush-Turkey is a non-migrant, resident all year round.

PURPLE MARTIN

EURASIAN ROBIN

BRUSH-TURKEY

SCALE SILHOUETTES

These show the bird next to a copy of this book. For reasons of space, birds above 50cm (20in) long are shown on a smaller scale, so that the book appears in two different sizes. All birds are measured fully stretched out, from beak to tail tip. In species where male and female look different, the male is illustrated.

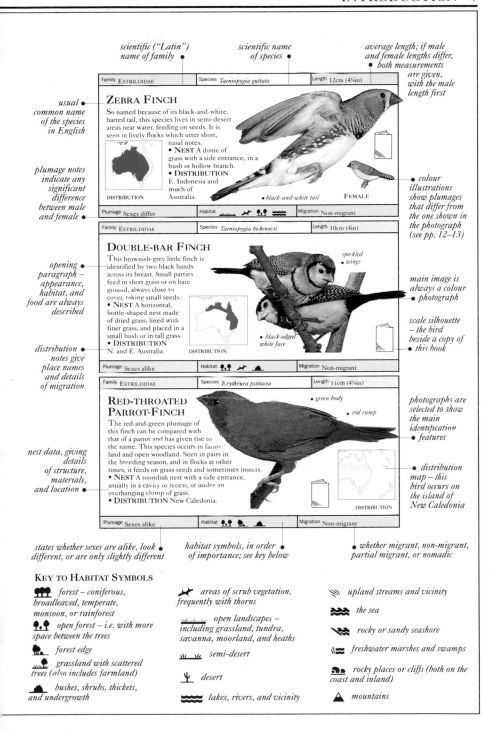

scientific ("Latin") name of family

scientific name of species

average length; if male and female lengths differ, both measurements are given, with the male length first

| Family ESTRILDIDAE | Species *Taeniopygia guttata* | Length 12cm (4¾in) |

usual common name of the species in English

ZEBRA FINCH

So named because of its black-and-white, barred tail, this species lives in semi-desert areas near water, feeding on seeds. It is seen in lively flocks which utter short, nasal notes.

• **NEST** A dome of grass with a side entrance, in a bush or hollow branch.

• **DISTRIBUTION** E. Indonesia and much of Australia.

plumage notes indicate any significant difference between male and female

DISTRIBUTION

• *black-and-white tail* FEMALE

colour illustrations show plumages that differ from the one shown in the photograph (see pp. 12–13)

| Plumage Sexes differ | Habitat | Migration Non-migrant |

| Family ESTRILDIDAE | Species *Taeniopygia bichenovii* | Length 10cm (4in) |

opening paragraph – appearance, habitat, and food are always described

DOUBLE-BAR FINCH

This brownish-grey little finch is identified by two black bands across its breast. Small parties feed in short grass or on bare ground, always close to cover, taking small seeds.

• **NEST** A horizontal, bottle-shaped nest made of dried grass, lined with finer grass, and placed in a small bush or in tall grass.

• **DISTRIBUTION** N. and E. Australia.

speckled • wings

• black-edged white face

DISTRIBUTION

main image is always a colour photograph

scale silhouette – the bird beside a copy of this book

distribution notes give place names and details of migration

| Plumage Sexes alike | Habitat | Migration Non-migrant |

| Family ESTRILDIDAE | Species *Erythrura psittacea* | Length 11cm (4¼in) |

RED-THROATED PARROT-FINCH

The red-and-green plumage of this finch can be compared with that of a parrot and has given rise to the name. This species occurs in farm-land and open woodland. Seen in pairs in the breeding season, and in flocks at other times, it feeds on grass seeds and sometimes insects.

• **NEST** A roundish nest with a side entrance, usually in a cavity or recess, or under an overhanging clump of grass.

• **DISTRIBUTION** New Caledonia.

• green body

• red rump

nest data, giving details of structure, materials, and location

photographs are selected to show the main identification features

distribution map – this bird occurs on the island of New Caledonia

DISTRIBUTION

| Plumage Sexes alike | Habitat | Migration Non-migrant |

states whether sexes are alike, look different, or are only slightly different

habitat symbols, in order of importance; see key below

whether migrant, non-migrant, partial migrant, or nomadic

KEY TO HABITAT SYMBOLS

forest – coniferous, broadleaved, temperate, monsoon, or rainforest

open forest – i.e. with more space between the trees

forest edge

grassland with scattered trees (also includes farmland)

bushes, shrubs, thickets, and undergrowth

areas of scrub vegetation, frequently with thorns

open landscapes – including grassland, tundra, savanna, moorland, and heaths

semi-desert

desert

lakes, rivers, and vicinity

upland streams and vicinity

the sea

rocky or sandy seashore

freshwater marshes and swamps

rocky places or cliffs (both on the coast and inland)

mountains

ANATOMY OF BIRDS

BIRDS ARE ANIMALS that can fly, and virtually every feature of a bird shows that it is highly adapted for this purpose. The body is short, strong, and compact, the internal organs being protected by the breastbone and the pelvis. The breastbone is broad and flattened, to carry large flight muscles. The legs are strong and springy, and muscular at the point where they join the body. They must provide the push for take-off, and cushion the shock on landing. Anatomically, a bird's wings correspond to human hands, but most of the "finger" bones are absent in birds. The wings carry the large fans of feathers that are used in flight, but folded away when at rest. Since a bird has no hands, its bill must be adapted for all feeding. The tail has evolved into a short row of bones carrying the large, adjustable fan of tail feathers.

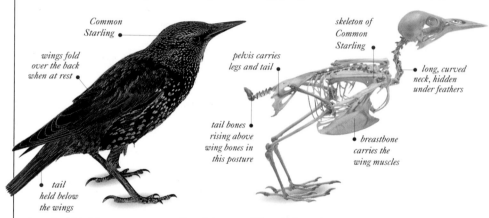

Common Starling

wings fold over the back when at rest

tail held below the wings

pelvis carries legs and tail

tail bones rising above wing bones in this posture

skeleton of Common Starling

long, curved neck, hidden under feathers

breastbone carries the wing muscles

A typical bird has a neat, streamlined shape, formed by its feather-covered body and wings; its bill is covered by a hard sheath; and it has bare, scale-covered legs and feet.

The skeleton has a thinner structure and is lightly made to aid flight. The bill lacks the smooth sheath of the living bird; and the wings and tail look short and bony.

FOUR FEATHER TYPES

Contour feathers are small and cover the body, while down feathers form a layer underneath providing extra insulation. Flight feathers are long and stiff; there are two types, tail feathers, which are often symmetrical, and wing feathers, which are unevenly shaped. The feathers on this page are not to scale – many birds have wing feathers, for instance, that would be taller than this book.

CONTOUR   DOWN   TAIL   WING

SHAPE AND MOVEMENT

The shape of a bird, and of its various parts, are clues to the way in which it lives. The bill, for instance, is always very precisely adapted to a bird's particular method of feeding. Similarly, a bird's way of flying, standing, or moving on the ground – for instance whether it hops or walks – are related to its way of life. The way a bird clings to its perch is always closely adapted to the kind of vegetation, or the sort of place, in which it normally lives. People who watch birds learn to take an interest in shape and movement, for they help to indicate the overall category in which to place the bird being watched. This can be combined with other information to help identify the bird.

CORMORANT: SHARP BILL OF A FISH EATER

SUNBIRD: DOWNCURVED BILL FOR PROBING FLOWERS FOR NECTAR

HERON: A STRONG, DAGGER-LIKE BILL FOR STABBING AND SEIZING

WARBLER: A SLENDER, INSECT-EATING BILL

GOLDFINCH: EATS SEEDS WITH ITS STRONG BILL

TOUCAN'S LONG BILL REACHES OUT FOR FRUIT

DUCK'S BILL FILTERS FOOD FROM WATER

FLESH-EATER'S SHARP, HOOKED BILL

Look carefully at flight silhouettes: forest raptors (a) have rounded wings; martins (b) have narrow, tapering wings.

The tapering wings and narrow tail of a falcon (c) contrast with the broad, splayed wings and broad tail of an eagle (d).

Terns (e) have long, elegant wings; albatross wings (f) are very long, with an extended inner section.

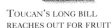

Look, too, at posture and gait. Some birds like the Reed Warbler (g) cling to vertical stems. Pipits (h) always walk; pittas (i) travel by hops and leaps along the ground.

Many birds, including most finches, perch upright (j) on a level branch. Wagtails (k) run after insects on the ground, using their tails as rudders or brakes when turning.

Look for birds that clamber up trees, using sharp claws, like this treecreeper (l). The Water Rail (m) has long legs and a narrow body for squeezing through marsh vegetation.

VARIATIONS WITHIN SPECIES

A SPECIES is a "kind" of bird, a number of related individuals that can interbreed and produce fertile young. However, there are many species in which the birds do not all look alike. Male and female adults are often differently coloured. Young birds look different from adults, which may give them better camouflage or may prevent unnecessary fighting for territory. This page shows how "family members" (male, female, and juvenile) can look different; the opposite page shows other ways in which a species can vary: it may have subspecies (local forms) or two or more colour phases.

Sexes alike: the Cape Grassbird (*right*) is an example. Males often have a different song.

male   *female*

Pattern similar but male has brighter hues than female, e.g. Eurasian Bullfinch (*right*).

male   *female*

Pattern similar but female has brighter hues than male, e.g. Eurasian Dotterel (*right*).

male   *female*

Sexes totally different: fairy-wrens (*right*) are an example of this category. The full difference is seen only in the breeding season.

male   *female*

Sexes totally different in breeding plumage, but the male goes into a third plumage (the "eclipse") for part of the non-breeding season. Eclipse males look like females, but with slight differences. This occurs in many duck species, e.g. Pintail (*right*).

male

eclipse   *female*

Male is significantly larger than female: the Great Bustard (*right*) is one example.

male   *female*

Female is significantly larger than male, as in the Red-tailed Hawk (*right*) and other birds of prey.

male   *female*

Male has a longer tail than the female (often only in breeding birds), as in the Blue Peafowl (*below and right*).

female

male

male   *female*   *juvenile*

Juvenile has a similar pattern to the female, but is duller, e.g. Northern Cardinal (*above*).

Juvenile is totally unlike the adult, as in the Black-crowned Night-Heron (*right*) and many other herons.

adult   *juvenile*

SUBSPECIES

Many species have distinct local forms, known as subspecies. These look different from one another, though often in only a minor way. They can be distinguished by colour, size, song, or sometimes by features like bill shape or tail length.

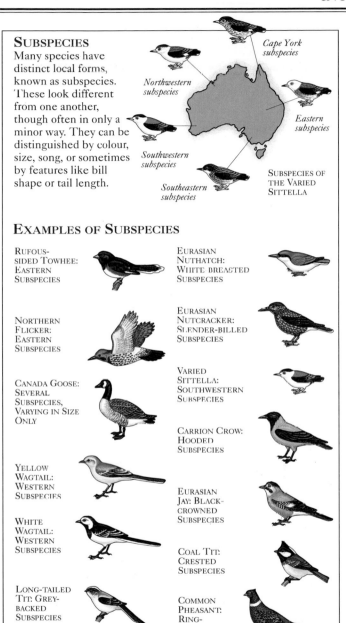

Cape York subspecies

Northwestern subspecies

Eastern subspecies

Southwestern subspecies

SUBSPECIES OF THE VARIED SITTELLA

Southeastern subspecies

COLOUR PHASES

In some species, differently coloured individuals occur regardless of geographical area, e.g. the blue and white colour phases of the Snow Goose.

EXAMPLES OF SUBSPECIES

RUFOUS-SIDED TOWHEE: EASTERN SUBSPECIES

NORTHERN FLICKER: EASTERN SUBSPECIES

CANADA GOOSE: SEVERAL SUBSPECIES, VARYING IN SIZE ONLY

YELLOW WAGTAIL: WESTERN SUBSPECIES

WHITE WAGTAIL: WESTERN SUBSPECIES

LONG-TAILED TIT: GREY-BACKED SUBSPECIES

FOX SPARROW: DARK, WESTERN SUBSPECIES

EURASIAN NUTHATCH: WHITE BREASTED SUBSPECIES

EURASIAN NUTCRACKER: SLENDER-BILLED SUBSPECIES

VARIED SITTELLA: SOUTHWESTERN SUBSPECIES

CARRION CROW: HOODED SUBSPECIES

EURASIAN JAY: BLACK-CROWNED SUBSPECIES

COAL TIT: CRESTED SUBSPECIES

COMMON PHEASANT: RING-NECKED SUBSPECIES

DARK-EYED JUNCO: OREGON SUBSPECIES

EXAMPLES OF PHASES

EURASIAN HONEY BUZZARD: RUFOUS PHASE

PAPUAN LORIKEET: BLACK PHASE

COMMON CUCKOO: RUFOUS PHASE

EUROPEAN SCOPS OWL: RUFOUS PHASE

GOULDIAN FINCH: YELLOW-HEADED PHASE

WATCHING BIRDS IN THE GARDEN

BIRDWATCHING USUALLY BEGINS at home. In any garden, there are bound to be a number of birds that are already present; it doesn't take much work to adapt a garden so that it offers the best for birds and brings in more than the usual handful of species.

Some things are particularly likely to help: providing the birds with water, both for drinking and bathing; giving them maximum variety in the habitats on offer; arranging possible nest-sites; and providing food, at the appropriate time and in the appropriate way.

NEST-BOXES

Birds that use nest-boxes range in size from tiny passerines like tits, robins, and nuthatches to some ducks and birds of prey. All the boxes shown here are for small passerines; other species need boxes of different sizes and designs.

small flowerpot base, suitable for drinking water •

larger flowerpot base also makes a good bath •

• *birds like to bathe in shallow water*

WATER CONTAINERS

Many passerines like water to be provided in a raised site, such as a bird table. A site preferred by other birds is a shallow pool on the ground, with good all-round visibility.

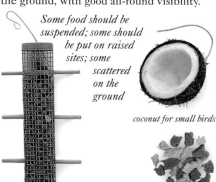

Some food should be suspended; some should be put on raised sites; some scattered on the ground

coconut for small birds

peanut dispenser

bread is a useful stop-gap in winter

BIRD TABLES

In colder climates, many people build food tables to feed birds in winter. This prevents food from being lost in the snow, or taken by scavengers. Shown here are two views of a simple table that can be made at home.

strong pole for support •

• *tray to support food*

"bird pudding"

mixed loose seeds

fat and seed ball

WATCHING BIRDS IN THE FIELD

THE THOUGHT OF learning how to find and identify birds out in the wild seems a daunting one, but once you have been there to look for them, perhaps with someone who knows the birds of the area, your skill will develop rapidly. You will very soon get used to looking carefully at the shapes and colours of birds, and to watching their actions. The type of country in which the birds occur, their location (whether high or low in the trees, or down on the ground, for instance), and any song they may perform, are all useful clues.

BINOCULARS
Lightweight types are the most practical, with magnifications of 7 to 10. Higher powers can make you spend too much time aiming and focusing.

well-balanced, lightweight model

BIRD PHOTOGRAPHY
The most suitable type of camera for photographing birds is a 35mm SLR model. Practise on garden birds first, to acquire the skills of judging distance, focusing in the time available, and steadying the camera for the shot.

short lens for normal use

WATCHING FROM A HIDE
Birds are often alarmed at the sight of people, but hiding behind or within a simple structure is usually enough to put them at their ease. A temporary, moveable hide, in the form of a simple tent (*above left*) can be concealed with branches and foliage. It may look like laziness, but a parked car (*left*) is one of the best hides, as the birds usually fail to realize that it contains humans.

NOTEBOOK
If you can make a quick sketch of a bird, there is no better way to train your eye for detail. It also provides a record of the birds that you have seen, and forms a log of your activities, which will be helpful when planning future trips.

LONG LENSES
To photograph small or distant birds, you will need a high-powered lens (e.g. 200mm focal length or more), and for best results a tripod to keep it steady.

PERMANENT HIDES
Purpose-built hides, often seen in nature reserves for wildfowl, can accommodate many visitors.

BIRD PROTECTION IN THE BREEDING SEASON
Remember that birds are sensitive to disturbance. Nothing should be done that will frighten them or alter the surroundings of their nest. Once frightened, they may abandon the nest, and this could set their breeding back a whole year.

IDENTIFYING BIRDS IN FLIGHT

FLIGHT IS A helpful identification feature for many birds. Some whole groups of species can be recognized by the pattern of their normal, everyday flight. During courtship, birds perform special display flights, and these, too, can help in identification. When a bird opens its wings, the markings it reveals may provide crucial information as to what species you are looking at.

Steady flight with regular wingbeats, along a direct path, is typical of an enormous range of species, ranging from crows (*above*) to geese, pigeons, and smaller birds as well.

Some small birds, such as finches (*above*), economize in energy by rising on a wingbeat, closing the wings to the body, and swooping until the next wingbeat.

Some larger birds (*above*) often soar and glide without flapping their wings, rising a little each time they turn into the wind.

Some large birds (*right*) have an energy-saving style of flight, in which bursts of strong wingbeats alternate with long, level glides.

Woodpeckers (*above*) have an undulating style of flight. They ascend with several wingbeats, then swoop downwards on closed wings like finches.

DISPLAY FLIGHTS
Birds that are breeding often perform aerobatic display flights to attract a mate or show their presence to rivals. This is specially common in open-country birds.

Flying from the treetops, the Common Wood-Pigeon (*below*) rises steeply with loud, clapping wing beats, then planes downwards.

The male Meadow Pipit (*below*) rises from the ground in a steep, fluttering flight, during which he utters weak "tip" calls. Then he parachutes down again, uttering one long trill.

The Northern Lapwing (*above*) has an erratic, tumbling display, with wild calls.

Some large eagles (*right*) perform swoops and dives high in the air. They close their wings to dive, turn up again briefly, and then continue the plunge before finally levelling out.

"Pendulum" displays (*right*) are seen in some birds of prey and some hummingbird species.

MARKINGS ON THE WINGS

The moment a bird takes to the air it is likely to display vivid markings on the spread wings and tail. These include white or coloured patches, bars, or stripes, which were hidden while the bird was still on the ground. Other birds feeding nearby, often in a mixed-species flock, notice the change in appearance and interpret it as a warning of danger and the need to fly away. The pattern also enables each bird to recognize members of its own species, which it will then follow to safety. We, too, are able to use the pattern, together with details like song or behaviour, to identify the species.

ALARM SIGNAL On taking off, the male Chaffinch reveals a vivid pattern (*above*).

WING PATCHES

Look for the flash of wing patches. These are panels of a conspicuous, vivid colour, as seen on the female Evening Grosbeak (*right*).

WING STRIPES

These are bands of a bright, contrasting colour that show along the extended wing when the bird is seen in flight, as in the Eurasian Goldfinch (*right*).

WINGS OF WADERS AND DUCKS

| GREATER YELLOWLEGS | COMMON REDSHANK | EURASIAN OYSTERCATCHER | RUDDY TURNSTONE | BEACH THICK-KNEE | PIED AVOCET |

In waterside shorebirds, also known as waders (*above*), most species have their own characteristic patterns of white on the wing. These become visible when the birds fly.

As well as having patterns of white stripes on the wing, some ducks (*below*) also have a speculum – a white or vividly coloured panel located on the inner flight feathers.

| MALLARD | CINNAMON TEAL | COMMON SHELDUCK | SMEW | MANED DUCK | GREATER SCAUP |

IDENTIFICATION KEY

THE FAMILIES to which birds belong are not always useful as guides to how they will look when seen in the field. A good number of families include birds that are very unlike one another in vital respects such as colour, shape, habitat, or behaviour. This key solves the problem by setting up categories that are not based on family, but on habitat and feeding manner. Key users should always bear in mind that categories like this cannot be watertight – birds are living creatures and can rarely be tied down to a single habitat or style of behaviour. This means that you may need to try alternative ways through the key. Stage 1 (*opposite*) divides all birds into five basic types. Choose the relevant one and follow its symbol into Stage 2, where the basic types are divided into helpful categories. Silhouette images lead from here into Stage 3 (*pages 22–37*), giving possible identifications.

STAGE 2: WALKING AND WADING BIRDS

LARGE FLIGHTLESS BIRDS
Very big birds, some taller than humans, mostly with long legs and necks. Some live in open country and survive by their ability to walk or run long distances.

SMALLER FLIGHTLESS BIRDS
Birds from pigeon- to chicken-size thatlive on the ground and hide in vegetation or in burrows; some are nocturnal.

STAGE 2: WATERBIRDS

WATERBIRDS SWIMMING WITH WEBBED FEET
Birds mostly feeding at the surface; some reach beneath the surface and some dive to pursue fish or other prey.

WATERBIRDS SWIMMING WITHOUT WEBBED FEET
Mostly surface feeders, though some dive. Some have lobes on their toes as swimming aids.

STAGE 1

This part of the key will enable you to identify the broad, basic type to which a bird belongs. Most birds fit into one of the first four categories, enabling you to move on immediately to Stage 2. A few belong to the category of Specialized Feeders. To understand this group, turn to the relevant parts of Stage 2 (*bottom of pages 20–21*) and Stage 3 (*pages 36–37*); this will make it clear which birds belong to this category.

WALKING
AND WADING
BIRDS

WATERBIRDS

FRUIT-EATERS,
NECTAR-FEEDERS,
AND SEED-EATERS

HUNTERS ON
LAND AND IN
TREES

SPECIALIZED
FEEDERS

SMALLER RUNNERS WITH SHORT BILLS

Ranging from pigeon- to chicken-size, these are birds that spend most or all of their time on the ground, often feeding on seeds, but can fly when necessary.

SMALLER RUNNERS WITH LONG BILLS

Pigeon- to chicken-sized birds with slender bills for probing the ground and feeding on insects. Most of them can fly when necessary.

MEDIUM-SIZED RUNNERS

These are turkey-sized birds that live for most of the time on the ground, though all are able to fly. A number of them are seen nesting and roosting in the branches of large trees.

LARGE, LONG-LEGGED WADING BIRDS

Nearly all these birds wade in shallow waters or marshes – the rest feed in grassland. All can fly. Most have long necks for reaching down to feed.

WATERBIRDS THAT SNATCH FROM THE AIR

Birds that locate their prey by flying over water, and snatch it from the surface or just below, without swimming.

WATERBIRDS THAT PLUNGE-DIVE FROM THE AIR

Birds that generally spot prey while flying over water, then plunge beneath the surface to seize it or chase after it.

WATERBIRDS THAT DIVE FROM THE SURFACE

Surface-swimmers that submerge to hunt. Most swim with their feet, some with their wings.

WATERBIRDS THAT ALIGHT ON THE SURFACE

Birds that settle from the air to take food from the surface; some make a shallow dive.

STAGE 2: FRUIT-EATERS, NECTAR-FEEDERS, AND SEED-EATERS

FRUIT-EATERS

This category consists mainly of tree-dwelling birds. Most eat the fruit where it grows on the branch, some without plucking it. Some birds merely remove the flesh from the inside of large, soft fruits. Fruit-eating bills are adapted in various ways. Some are very long and enable the bird to reach fruit without having to walk on thin twigs; others are shorter and stouter, and are useful for cutting or grasping fruit.

STAGE 2: HUNTERS ON LAND AND IN TREES

ACTIVE HUNTERS

Birds of this category seek out their prey and pounce on it in a sudden, aggressive attack, also pursuing it if necessary. Some are seen patrolling in flight, watching with keen eyes for any movement. Some watch from a perch before swooping down on prey. This group includes many nocturnal hunters.

TREETRUNK AND BRANCH FORAGERS

These birds hunt insects that are hidden in cracks in the bark of treetrunks or branches, or rest on the bark. Some also chisel out grubs of insects that bore into rotten wood.

GROUND FEEDERS

These are flying birds that take food from the surface of the ground or just below.

STAGE 2: SPECIALIZED FEEDERS

CARRION-EATERS

Birds of this category feed on dead animals that they have not killed. Some soar high overhead and scan the ground with their keen eyes to locate carcases.

AERIAL FEEDERS

Smaller members of this group feed by catching flying insects. Larger members, such as the frigatebirds, piratically rob other birds of their prey in mid-flight.

NECTAR-FEEDERS

A number of birds feed by inserting their bills into flowers and sucking out nectar. Some of these are also capable of eating fruit, such as the lorikeets. Many also eat pollen, and have brush-tipped tongues for this purpose. Others are more specialized for nectar-feeding and have tubular tongues. Most nectar-feeders also eat small insects that they find in or beside the flowers. Many also feed on fruit.

SEED-EATERS

Included in this category are the seed-eaters known to cage and aviary bird enthusiasts – the finches, waxbills, weavers, sparrows, and buntings. Seeds are taken both from vegetation and from the ground. There are many pigeons, parrots, larks, and members of the crow family that also take seed. Acorns and nuts are large seeds and birds that feed on them, such as jays and nutcrackers, also appear here.

INVERTEBRATE PROBERS

A rich supply of insects and other invertebrates is found in the soil, especially beneath the turf in grassland. This category consists of birds that exploit this resource, probing the ground with their long, strongly made bills. All birds in this category can fly.

SIT-AND-WAIT HUNTERS

A very large number of species adopt the policy of sitting at some vantage point and watching, ready to swoop to the ground or fly out after prey when they see it.

INSECT GLEANERS

Birds of this category feed by moving through tree foliage, undergrowth, or low-growing plants, and taking small creatures from twigs and leaves at random. Any insect that happens to be resting on a leaf, or clinging underneath, is seized as soon as it is noticed. These birds often hunt in flocks.

INSECT PURSUERS

A number of passerines are small equivalents of the "Active Hunters", moving around in search of insects and pouncing on them or chasing them on sight.

SPECIALIZED EXPLOITERS OF ANIMALS

A number of birds rely on other animals to provide their food. Herds of animals attract parasites and disturb ground insects on which birds can feed. Army ants cause small creatures to flee in panic. The honeyguides rely on any animal, including man, that will break open bees' nests.

OPPORTUNISTS

Some species do not restrict themselves to a particular type of food or method of finding it. They are able to eat many different types of food, and quickly take advantage of any food supply as soon as the opportunity occurs. They may be seen feeding, like other birds, on insects, fruit, or seeds; they may hunt small animals or eat carrion, or they may scavenge at rubbish dumps.

STAGE 3

This part of the key brings you closer to identifying the bird you are considering. The categories from Stage 2 are broken down, either to a precise species or to a small group that may contain it. This handbook contains descriptions of 819 species, out of some 9,600 known to exist altogether – in other words, one in 11 of the world's birds. Within these limits, bird species have been specially selected so that the book covers the full range of diversity. In many cases Stage 3 is able to

WALKING AND WADING BIRDS

LARGE FLIGHTLESS BIRDS

Ostrich **39**

Rheas **38**

Emperor Penguin **44**

SMALLER FLIGHTLESS BIRDS

Kiwis **42t**

Mesites **118t**

Smaller Penguins **45–46t**

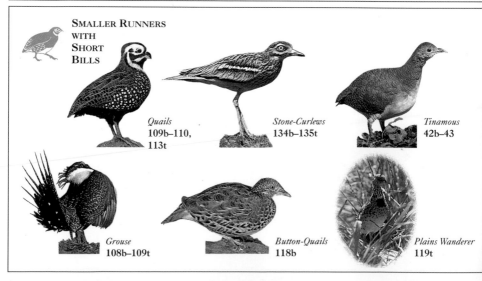

SMALLER RUNNERS WITH SHORT BILLS

Quails **109b–110, 113t**

Stone-Curlews **134b–135t**

Tinamous **42b–43**

Grouse **108b–109t**

Button-Quails **118b**

Plains Wanderer **119t**

offer a precise identification, as in the case of the Emu or the Kakapo lower down on this page. In other cases, Stage 3 refers you to a group of species, such as "Pheasants" at the bottom of this page. This means that your bird is either one of the pheasants mentioned in the book (to which page references are given) or a similar-looking species which has not been included in the book. In a group reference of this kind, the name of the type of bird is always given in the plural.

Cassowaries 40

Emu 41

ABBREVIATIONS
Page references
use abbreviations
to indicate the part
of the page to
which they apply:

t = top of the page
m = middle
b = bottom

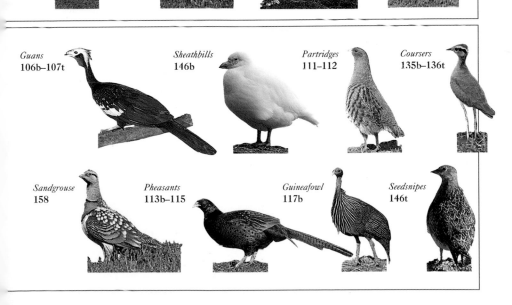

Kagu
128b

Takahe
127t

Kakapo
185b

Weka
124t

Guans
106b–107t

Sheathbills
146b

Partridges
111–112

Coursers
135b–136t

Sandgrouse
158

Pheasants
113b–115

Guineafowl
117b

Seedsnipes
146t

STAGE 3

WALKING AND WADING BIRDS (continued)

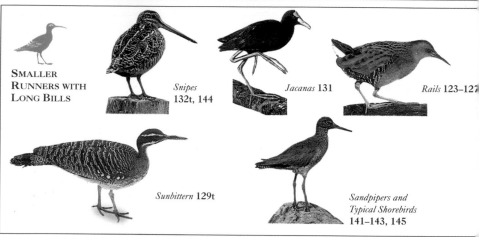

SMALLER RUNNERS WITH LONG BILLS

Snipes 132t, 144

Jacanas 131

Rails 123–127

Sunbittern 129t

Sandpipers and Typical Shorebirds 141–143, 145

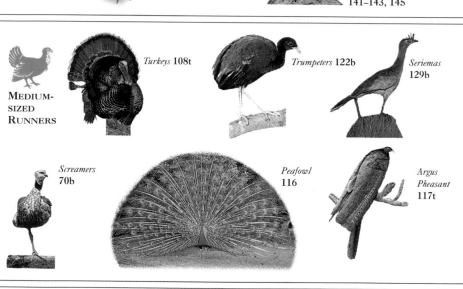

MEDIUM-SIZED RUNNERS

Turkeys 108t

Trumpeters 122b

Seriemas 129b

Screamers 70b

Peafowl 116

Argus Pheasant 117t

LARGE, LONG-LEGGED WADING BIRDS

Flamingos 71

Shoebill 64

Limpkin 122t

Hoopoe 228b

Crab-Plover 132b

Avocets and Stilts
133b–134t

Plovers
137b–140

Oystercatchers
133t

Megapodes
105b–106t

Ground-
Hornbills 231b

Secretary Bird
100

Curassows
107b

Crowned
Pigeon 166t

Bustards
130

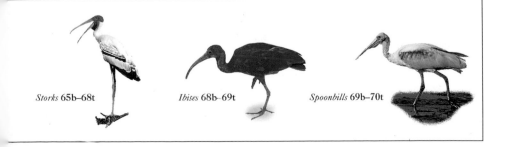

Storks 65b–68t

Ibises 68b–69t

Spoonbills 69b–70t

STAGE 3

WALKING AND WADING BIRDS (*continued*)

LARGE, LONG-
LEGGED WADING
BIRDS (*continued*)

Herons
58b–63

Hammerkop
65t

Cranes
119b–121b

WATERBIRDS

WATERBIRDS
SWIMMING
WITHOUT
WEBBED FEET

Moorhens
126

Coots 127b

Finfoots
128t

WATERBIRDS
THAT SNATCH
FROM THE AIR

Fish-Eagles 90–91t

Osprey
88b

Fish-Owls
198t

WATERBIRDS THAT
PLUNGE-DIVE
FROM THE AIR

Gannets 55t

Tropicbirds
53b

*Brown
Pelican* 54b

*Diving-
Petrels* 52b

WATERBIRDS THAT
DIVE FROM THE SURFACE

Divers
46b

Ducks
81b–86t

Penguins
44–46t

WATERBIRDS

Swans
73

Ducks
76–86t

Geese **72t,
74t–75**

Pelicans
54

WATERBIRDS
SWIMMING WITH
WEBBED FEET

Dippers **280m**

Phalaropes **143m**

Storm-Petrels
52t–52m

Frigatebirds
58t

Skimmers
155b

Terns **152t,
154–155t**

Kingfishers
219b–222

Boobies **55b**

Sea-Terns
152b–153

Cormorants
56t–57t

Auks
156–157

Darters
57b

Grebes **47**

STAGE 3

WATERBIRDS (continued)

WATERBIRDS THAT ALIGHT ON THE SURFACE

Gulls 148–151

Albatrosses 48–49t

FRUIT-EATERS, NECTAR-FEEDERS, AND SEED-EATERS

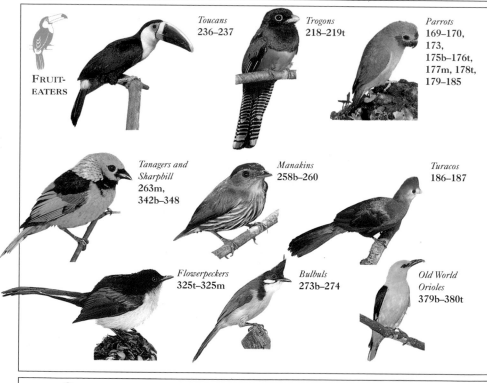

FRUIT-EATERS

Toucans 236–237

Trogons 218–219t

Parrots 169–170, 173, 175b–176t, 177m, 178t, 179–185

Tanagers and Sharpbill 263m, 342b–348

Manakins 258b–260

Turacos 186–187

Flowerpeckers 325t–325m

Bulbuls 273b–274

Old World Orioles 379b–380t

NECTAR-FEEDERS

Hummingbirds 210–217t

Sunbirds 326m–328t

Honeyeaters 329m–333

Shearwaters
51b, 53t

Petrels
49b–51t, 52

Skuas **147**

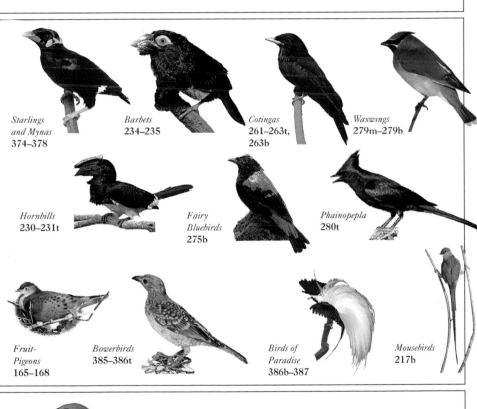

Starlings and Mynas
374–378

Barbets
234–235

Cotingas
261–263t, 263b

Waxwings
279m–279b

Hornbills
230–231t

Fairy Bluebirds
275b

Phainopepla
280t

Fruit-Pigeons
165–168

Bowerbirds
385–386t

Birds of Paradise
386b–387

Mousebirds
217b

Honeycreepers
347b–348

Hawaiian Honeycreepers
352b–353m

Parrots
169–170, 178t

STAGE 3

FRUIT-EATERS, NECTAR-FEEDERS, AND SEED-EATERS *(continued)*

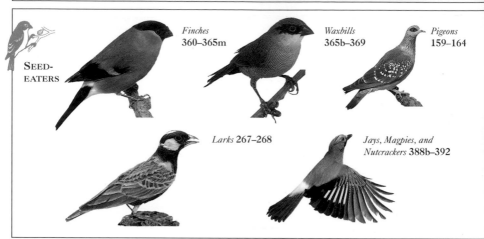

SEED-EATERS

Finches
360–365m

Waxbills
365b–369

Pigeons
159–164

Larks 267–268

Jays, Magpies, and
Nutcrackers 388b–392

HUNTERS ON LAND AND IN TREES

ACTIVE HUNTERS

Owls 194–203t

Typical Birds of Prey
88b–90t, 91–99

Falcons
101b–105t

GROUND FEEDERS

Wagtails
and Pipits
270b–272t

Dunnocks
283m–283b

Crows
393–395

Pittas
264–265t

Larks
267–268

Kea
185t

Tapaculos
251m

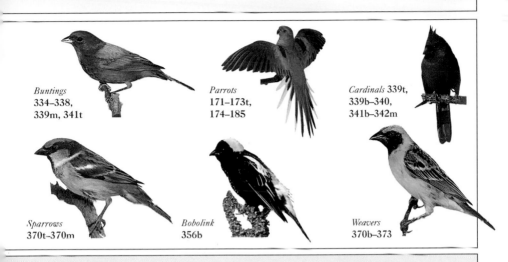

Buntings
334–338,
339m, 341t

Parrots
171–173t,
174–185

Cardinals 339t,
339b–340,
341b–342m

Sparrows
370t–370m

Bobolink
356b

Weavers
370b–373

Shrikes 276–278

Skuas 147

*Australian
Ground Feeders*
266b,
294b–295t,
314t, 382

Hoopoe
228b

*Ground-
Rollers* 227b

Cuckoos
191–193t

Pigeons
159–164

Lyrebirds
266t

Starlings
374 377

STAGE 3

HUNTERS ON LAND AND IN TREES (continued)

**TREETRUNK
AND BRANCH
FORAGERS**

Woodpeckers
238–243

Woodcreepers
245

Pearled Treerunner
247t

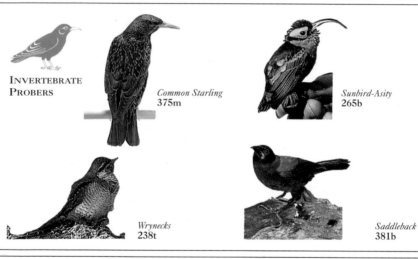

**INVERTEBRATE
PROBERS**

Common Starling
375m

Sunbird-Asity
265b

Wrynecks
238t

Saddleback
381b

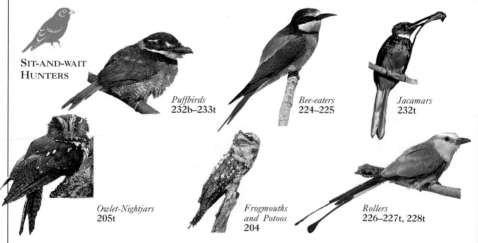

**SIT-AND-WAIT
HUNTERS**

Puffbirds
232b–233t

Bee-eaters
224–225

Jacamars
232t

Owlet-Nightjars
205t

*Frogmouths
and Potoos*
204

Rollers
226–227t, 228t

Wood-
Hoopoes
229

Nuthatches
323t–323m

Sittellas
323b

Treecreepers
324

Wrens
280b–283t

New World Blackbirds
355m–358

Thrashers
285

Choughs
393t

Motmots
223b

Drongos
380b–381t

Trogons
218–219t

Todies 223t

Kingfishers
219b–222b

Tyrant Flycatchers
251b–258m

Flycatchers
308b–309, 314b

STAGE 3

HUNTERS ON LAND AND IN TREES *(continued)*

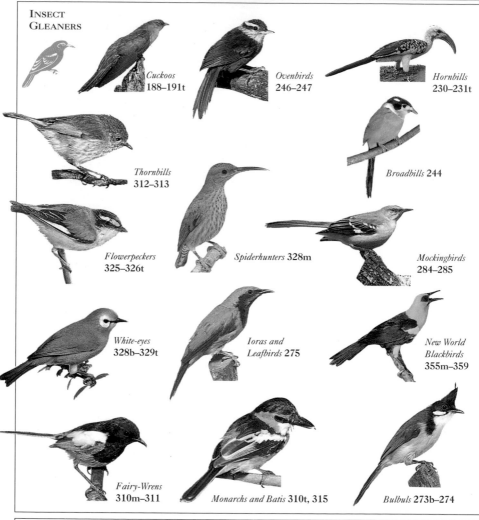

INSECT GLEANERS

Cuckoos 188–191t

Ovenbirds 246–247

Hornbills 230–231t

Thornbills 312–313

Broadbills 244

Flowerpeckers 325–326t

Spiderhunters 328m

Mockingbirds 284–285

White-eyes 328b–329t

Ioras and Leafbirds 275

New World Blackbirds 355m–359

Fairy-Wrens 310m–311

Monarchs and Batis 310t, 315

Bulbuls 273b–274

INSECT PURSUERS

Antbirds 248–250

Shrikes 276–278

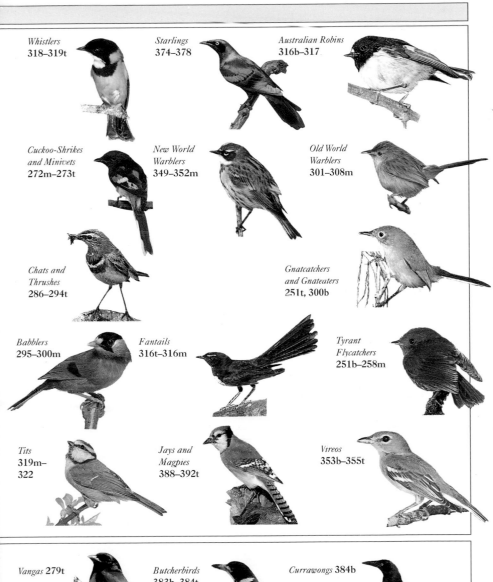

Whistlers
318–319t

Starlings
374–378

Australian Robins
316b–317

Cuckoo-Shrikes
and Minivets
272m–273t

New World
Warblers
349–352m

Old World
Warblers
301–308m

Chats and
Thrushes
286–294t

Gnatcatchers
and Gnateaters
251t, 300b

Babblers
295–300m

Fantails
316t–316m

Tyrant
Flycatchers
251b–258m

Tits
319m–
322

Jays and
Magpies
388–392t

Vireos
353b–355t

Vangas 279t

Butcherbirds
383b–384t

Currawongs 384b

STAGE 3

SPECIALIZED FEEDERS

CARRION-EATERS

New World Vultures 86b–88t

Kites 89b

Giant Petrels 49b

Crows and Magpies 391, 394–395

AERIAL FEEDERS

Swifts 208–209

Frigatebirds 58t

Oilbird 203b

Pratincoles 136b–137t

Nightjars 205m–207b

SPECIALIZED EXPLOITERS OF ANIMALS

Cattle Egret 61b

Honeyguides 233b

Oxpeckers 379t

Antbirds 249m–250

Old World Vultures
91b–92

Sheathbills
146b

Caracaras 101t

Marabou Stork 67

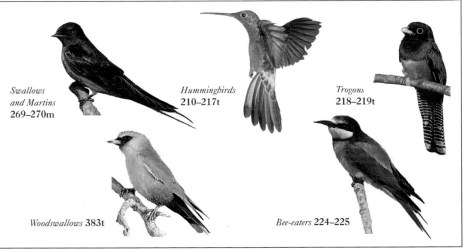

Swallows
and Martins
269–270m

Hummingbirds
210–217t

Trogons
218–219t

Woodswallows 383t

Bee-eaters 224–225

OPPORTUNISTS

Magpies and
Crows 392t, 394–395

Caracaras
101t

Starlings
and Mynas
375m, 377t

NON-PASSERINES

N EARLY HALF THE BIRD species in the world, including all the larger ones, belong to the 99 non-passerine families. The non-passerines occupy a varied range of habitats, and include birds of freshwater and the sea, birds that are almost permanently airborne, flightless birds, and species dwelling mainly on the ground, and some that are adapted to perching in trees or bushes. Non-passerines often build very simple nests, or the eggs may be laid on bare ground or rock. The young are helpless in some species, but in others they are down-covered, active chicks that can run and feed themselves almost from hatching. Non-passerines vary in voice, but few produce the complicated and musical songs typical of many passerine birds.

Family RHEIDAE	Species *Rhea americana*	Length 130cm (51in)

GREATER RHEA

This large, flightless bird lives on open plains, particularly where grass is tall and bushes are plentiful. Here it feeds on the leaves, roots, and seeds of plants, together with insects and other small animals. Although it never flies, the Greater Rhea comes nearest to doing so when it races over the open grassland, holding its wings up to gain a very slight lift. It can also swim, and flocks visit lakes or rivers to drink and to bathe. This species is always sociable, except for older males, which sometimes withdraw from the flock to live alone. In the breeding season, rival males fight, mainly with heavy kicks. Males also display, to deter rivals or to attract females, ruffling their wings and uttering low, roaring calls. A male normally mates with several females, which he then leads to the nest. Up to a dozen females will visit the same nest, normally producing 15 to 30 eggs, sometimes more than 60. The male incubates the eggs alone, covering as many as he can, and cares for the downy young.
• **NEST** A shallow hollow in the ground, sparsely lined with grass.
• **DISTRIBUTION** South America in open country from Brazil south of the Amazon to C. Argentina.

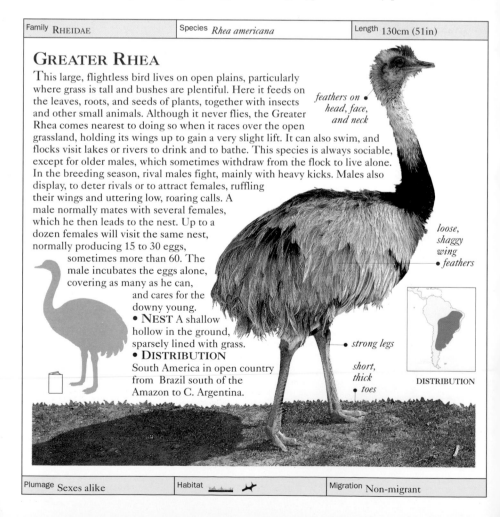

feathers on head, face, and neck

loose, shaggy wing feathers

strong legs

short, thick toes

DISTRIBUTION

Plumage Sexes alike	Habitat	Migration Non-migrant

Family STRUTHIONIDAE	Species *Struthio camelus*	L. 250cm (98in)/200cm (79in)

OSTRICH

The world's largest and tallest bird species, the Ostrich
stands at an average height of 2.5m (8ft 2in). It is flightless,
with drooping, loose-textured feathers on its wings and tail.
Large, strong legs enable it to walk about with easy strides
and to run fast, with a top speed of some 64km/h (40mph). The
Ostrich inhabits open landscapes such as desert, semi-desert,
and grassland, living by its keen sight and its ability to cover long
distances to reach safety or a food supply. It feeds on the leaves,
stems, flowers, and seeds of plants, plucked with its blunt-tipped
and proportionally small bill. Breeding males are seen squatting
in their sexual display posture, waving their wings and necks.
A male that has successfully defended his territory pairs
with a female, which lays her eggs in
a shallow nest. The male Ostrich
may also mate with as many as
five subordinate females,
which add their eggs to the
clutch. As many as 40
eggs may accumulate
but the dominant
female pushes out all
but 20, which include
her own. She incubates
these with the help of
the male. The downy young
are tended by both parents,
sometimes later merging with
other broods.

• **NEST** A hollow, some 3m (9ft
10in) across, scraped with the feet and
formed by body pressure in sandy soil.

• **DISTRIBUTION** Across Africa from
Senegal to Ethiopia, and
south as far
as Tanzania;
separate
population in
southern Africa.

• **REMARK**
Ostriches are farmed
in southern Africa for
their wing and tail plumes.
The former wild population
in the Arabian Peninsula
is now extinct.

bristles •
on head
and face

FEMALE

• *fine, downy
wing plumes*

• *no feathers
on the upper leg*

*two large
toes on*
• *each foot*

DISTRIBUTION

Plumage Sexes differ	Habitat	Migration Non-migrant

Family CASUARIIDAE	Species *Casuarius casuarius*	Length 183cm (72in)

SOUTHERN CASSOWARY

This is a sturdily built, heavy, flightless bird
that lives in rainforests among thick, tropical
vegetation. Its feathers are coarse in texture
and some end in long, hair-like filaments.
The wings are tiny, and in place of flight
feathers they carry only a few quills. The
bare skin on the head and neck, and the
wattles that hang from the neck, are coloured
red and blue in a pattern that varies with age.
On top of the head there is a horn-like casque
which may give protection when the birds dash
with lowered heads through dense vegetation,
as they frequently do when alarmed. The
bill is narrow and is normally used for
feeding on fallen fruit, sometimes also
on green plants, seeds, and some small
animals. This species utters a variety
of calls including deep booms, roars,
hisses, and low, rumbling sounds.
Individuals live alone for much of
the time. The female is slightly
larger than the male, with
brighter head and neck
colours, and a slightly taller
casque. When breeding, a
female sometimes pairs with
more than one male, laying a
clutch of eggs for each. The
downy chicks are boldly striped,
and are cared for by the male for
the first nine months of life.
  • **NEST** A shallow hollow in
  the leafy floor of the forest,
    sometimes sparsely
    lined with grass and
    fallen leaves.
  • **DISTRIBUTION**
  Rainforests in New Guinea
  and N.E. Australia.
  • **REMARK** The large,
  blade-like claw on the
  outer toe is used in
  aggressive fights.

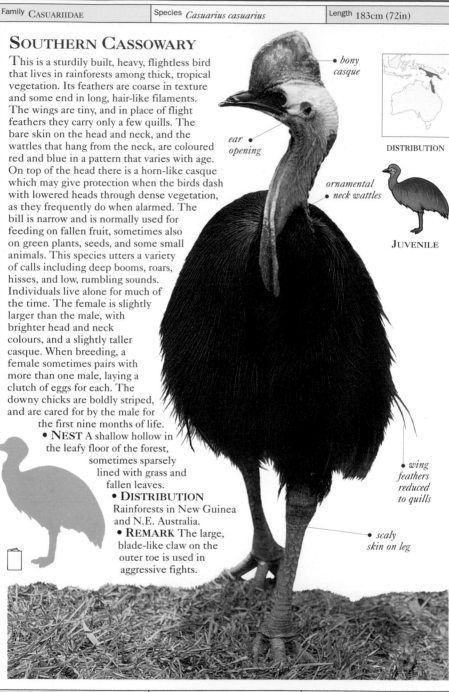

bony casque

ear opening

DISTRIBUTION

ornamental neck wattles

JUVENILE

wing feathers reduced to quills

scaly skin on leg

Plumage Sexes differ slightly	Habitat	Migration Non-migrant

Family DROMAIIDAE	Species *Dromaius novaehollandiae*	Length 210cm (83in)

EMU

A large, flightless bird, the Emu lives in a variety of open-country habitats, ranging from semi-desert to grassland and open woodland. Its wings are very small and are usually hidden in the Emu's long, loose, shaggy feathers. Females are slightly larger than males, and have stronger blue coloration on the bare skin of the head and neck. The Emu can run at up to 48km/h (30mph), though it normally walks. Pairs or small parties feed on plants including grasses, also taking insects. The call is low and booming. Males incubate the eggs and care for the striped, downy chicks.

• **NEST** A slight hollow in the ground, either bare or lined with trampled-down vegetation.

• **DISTRIBUTION** Australia except for the wetter coastal areas and thick forests.

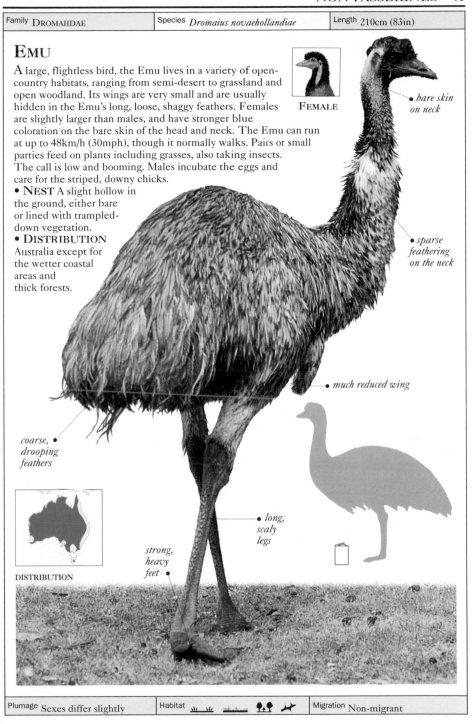

FEMALE

• *bare skin on neck*

• *sparse feathering on the neck*

• *much reduced wing*

coarse, drooping feathers •

• *long, scaly legs*

strong, heavy feet •

DISTRIBUTION

Plumage Sexes differ slightly	Habitat	Migration Non-migrant

Family APTERYGIDAE	Species *Apteryx australis*	Length 70cm (28in)

BROWN KIWI

This flightless, forest-dwelling bird is nocturnal, hiding by day in a burrow or cavity, and feeding at night. Its eyesight is poor but it has a good sense of smell and its nostrils are placed at the tip of the bill. Sensory bristles at the base of the bill also help to locate food. The Kiwi probes the soil for worms and other invertebrates, also eating some seeds and berries. It can run fast, but is always unobtrusive. The call is a high, whistling sound. The female lays one or two large eggs, each about a fifth of her body weight. The male incubates these, hatching out the feathered, active young.

coarse, hairy plumage •

• **NEST** A bare hollow in a burrow in the ground, in a hole among tree roots, or in a hollow log.
• **DISTRIBUTION** Thinly distributed in New Zealand.

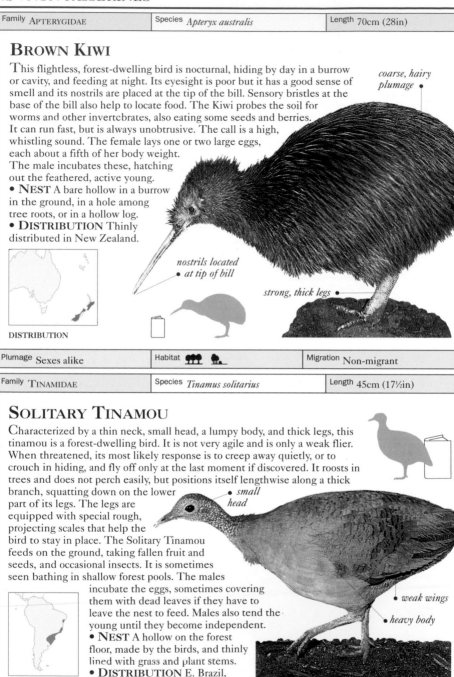

nostrils located • at tip of bill

strong, thick legs •

DISTRIBUTION

Plumage Sexes alike	Habitat	Migration Non-migrant

Family TINAMIDAE	Species *Tinamus solitarius*	Length 45cm (17½in)

SOLITARY TINAMOU

Characterized by a thin neck, small head, a lumpy body, and thick legs, this tinamou is a forest-dwelling bird. It is not very agile and is only a weak flier. When threatened, its most likely response is to creep away quietly, or to crouch in hiding, and fly off only at the last moment if discovered. It roosts in trees and does not perch easily, but positions itself lengthwise along a thick branch, squatting down on the lower part of its legs. The legs are equipped with special rough, projecting scales that help the bird to stay in place. The Solitary Tinamou feeds on the ground, taking fallen fruit and seeds, and occasional insects. It is sometimes seen bathing in shallow forest pools. The males incubate the eggs, sometimes covering them with dead leaves if they have to leave the nest to feed. Males also tend the young until they become independent.

• small head

• weak wings

• heavy body

• **NEST** A hollow on the forest floor, made by the birds, and thinly lined with grass and plant stems.
• **DISTRIBUTION** E. Brazil, S.E. Paraguay, and N. Argentina.

DISTRIBUTION

Plumage Sexes alike	Habitat	Migration Non-migrant

Family TINAMIDAE	Species *Eudromia elegans*	Length 40cm (16in)

ELEGANT TINAMOU

The slender, upward-curving crest
helps to identify this tinamou, which
is adapted to living in open country, dry
grassland, scrub, and woodland. It is capable of
running fairly fast across open ground, but if
alarmed it is more likely to crouch and hide,
waiting until danger is past. If approached
directly it makes a short, low flight on
whirring wings as a last resort. At times
the Elegant Tinamou is a solitary-living
species, but after the breeding season
it is seen in family parties, and these
sometimes combine to form small flocks.
The male incubates the eggs. The young
are downcovered and can run and feed
within minutes of hatching. They soon
leave the nest, under the supervision of
the male. The diet consists of seeds, fruit,
and other parts of plants, as well as insects.
• **NEST** A hollow in the ground, made by
the birds, often situated close to a low bush.
• **DISTRIBUTION** Much of Argentina;
also scattered, small populations in E. Chile.

thin crest

slender neck

DISTRIBUTION

camouflage
plumage

Plumage Sexes alike	Habitat	Migration Non-migrant

Family TINAMIDAE	Species *Crypturellus undulatus*	Length 30cm (12in)

UNDULATED TINAMOU

A common bird within its range, this tinamou occurs in forest, scrub,
and secondary growth (where trees have regrown after forest clearance).
It lives on the ground among low vegetation. Pairs and families
maintain contact with whistling calls. The diet
consists of seeds, berries, and insects. Studies
suggest that the male may mate with
several females, which move in a
group from one male to another.
Each male guards a single nest,
in which he incubates eggs
from all his partners.
• **NEST** A hollow in the
ground, situated among grass
and low vegetation.
• **DISTRIBUTION**
Amazon Basin in Brazil
and adjoining countries.

wavy
markings

plump body

DISTRIBUTION

Plumage Sexes alike	Habitat	Migration Non-migrant

Family SPHENISCIDAE	Species *Aptenodytes forsteri*	Length 115cm (45in)

EMPEROR PENGUIN

This is the largest and most heavily built of all the penguins. It puts on a deep layer of fat all over its stout body during the times of year that it spends feeding in the sea. Propelled by flipper-like wings, the Emperor pursues fish and squid to depths as great as 265m (870ft). On ice or snow, it walks upright, or drops on its belly and toboggans along, helped by its flippers. Emperor Penguins breed in colonies on the Antarctic ice, each recognizing its mate or parents by individual variations in the nasal, trumpeting call. After pairing in early winter, the female lays an egg and leaves for coastal waters. The male incubates the egg for two months, by standing upright and supporting it on his feet. Males huddle together for warmth through the blizzards of the polar winter. The female returns from the sea just as the young one hatches, and she feeds it with regurgitated food. The male, having lost almost half his original weight, then walks to the sea to feed for some weeks, before returning to help rear the chick.

• **NEST** No nest. The single egg, and chick, rest on the feet behind a fold of feathered belly skin.

• **DISTRIBUTION** Antarctic coasts.

DISTRIBUTION

JUVENILE

• *well-insulated body*

• *dense, fur-like plumage*

• *protective fold of skin*

• *chick resting on the feet*

• *uptilted feet support the chick*

short, stiff tail •

Plumage Sexes alike	Habitat	Migration Partial migrant

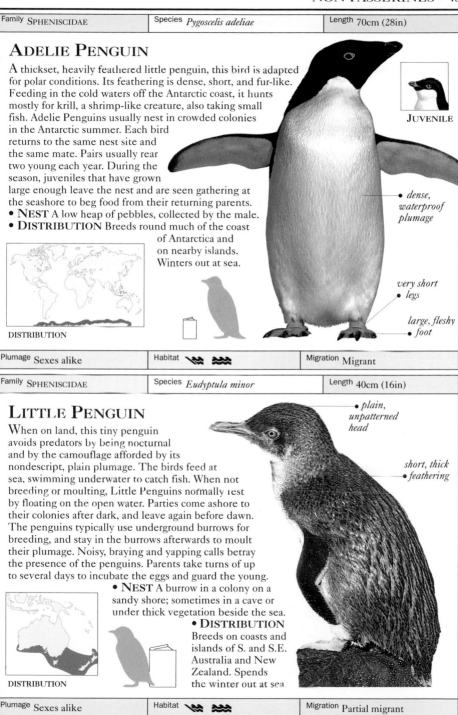

Family SPHENISCIDAE	Species *Pygoscelis adeliae*	Length 70cm (28in)

ADELIE PENGUIN

A thickset, heavily feathered little penguin, this bird is adapted for polar conditions. Its feathering is dense, short, and fur-like. Feeding in the cold waters off the Antarctic coast, it hunts mostly for krill, a shrimp-like creature, also taking small fish. Adelie Penguins usually nest in crowded colonies in the Antarctic summer. Each bird returns to the same nest site and the same mate. Pairs usually rear two young each year. During the season, juveniles that have grown large enough leave the nest and are seen gathering at the seashore to beg food from their returning parents.
• **NEST** A low heap of pebbles, collected by the male.
• **DISTRIBUTION** Breeds round much of the coast of Antarctica and on nearby islands. Winters out at sea.

JUVENILE

• *dense, waterproof plumage*

• *very short legs*

• *large, fleshy foot*

DISTRIBUTION

Plumage Sexes alike	Habitat	Migration Migrant

Family SPHENISCIDAE	Species *Eudyptula minor*	Length 40cm (16in)

LITTLE PENGUIN

When on land, this tiny penguin avoids predators by being nocturnal and by the camouflage afforded by its nondescript, plain plumage. The birds feed at sea, swimming underwater to catch fish. When not breeding or moulting, Little Penguins normally rest by floating on the open water. Parties come ashore to their colonies after dark, and leave again before dawn. The penguins typically use underground burrows for breeding, and stay in the burrows afterwards to moult their plumage. Noisy, braying and yapping calls betray the presence of the penguins. Parents take turns of up to several days to incubate the eggs and guard the young.
• **NEST** A burrow in a colony on a sandy shore; sometimes in a cave or under thick vegetation beside the sea.
• **DISTRIBUTION** Breeds on coasts and islands of S. and S.E. Australia and New Zealand. Spends the winter out at sea.

• *plain, unpatterned head*

• *short, thick feathering*

DISTRIBUTION

Plumage Sexes alike	Habitat	Migration Partial migrant

Family SPHENISCIDAE	Species *Spheniscus humboldti*	Length 68cm (27in)

HUMBOLDT PENGUIN

With a banded pattern on its breast and face, and a raucous, braying call, this bird is easily recognized as one of the "jackass" penguins that occur in South Africa, South America, and the Galapagos Islands. It feeds in the cold but fish-rich Humboldt Current, taking anchovies, pilchards, and other surface-shoaling fish, as well as squid. The penguins hunt in groups or small flocks, diving simultaneously to chase and herd the fish underwater. Breeding success or failure is linked to the season's supply of fish. Humboldt Penguins nest in large colonies of burrows, using caves if they can find no suitable soil for burrowing. Like most nestling penguins, the two downy young grow and fatten until they look a little larger than their parents, before moulting into their first adult plumage.

- **NEST** A bare hollow in a burrow, cave, or rock crevice, situated close to the sea.
- **DISTRIBUTION** Peru and N. Chile.
- **REMARK** Commercial quarrying for fertilizer has destroyed many colonies of burrows and taken away the soil, forcing the birds to nest in caves or rock crevices.

bare, orange skin •

• black breast band DISTRIBUTION

wing is reduced to • a flipper JUVENILE

short, webbed • toes

Plumage Sexes alike	Habitat 〰〰	Migration Non-migrant

Family GAVIIDAE	Species *Gavia immer*	Length 91cm (36in)

GREAT NORTHERN DIVER

This bird is easily detected in its northern breeding grounds, where its wailing, laughing calls echo across the freshwater lakes on whose shores and islands it nests. Head and body are streamlined for chasing fish underwater, but the bird walks clumsily when it comes ashore to nest.

WINTER

DISTRIBUTION

- **NEST** A low heap of plant materials by the water.
- **DISTRIBUTION** Breeds in N. North America, Greenland, and Iceland. Winters on coasts of N.W. Europe and North America.

strong, dagger bill •

striped neck patch •

Plumage Sexes alike	Habitat 〰 ⅃⅃⅃ 〰	Migration Migrant

| Family PODICIPEDIDAE | Species *Podilymbus podiceps* | Length 38cm (15in) |

PIED-BILLED GREBE

A small grebe with a stout bill, this bird is usually found on streams and ponds. In spring it occurs in pairs or family parties, but in winter larger groups gather on lakes and larger ponds. The birds swim rapidly underwater, catching fish and insects.
• **NEST** A heap of decayed plant material, lying in shallow water or afloat among growing waterplants.
• **DISTRIBUTION** Breeds in much of the Americas. Populations in the north and south migrate to warmer areas in winter.

short, deep bill

long neck

DISTRIBUTION

plump, rounded body

WINTER

| Plumage Sexes alike | Habitat 〰〰 ⸾≈ | Migration Partial migrant |

| Family PODICIPEDIDAE | Species *Podiceps cristatus* | Length 48cm (19in) |

GREAT CRESTED GREBE

Ornamented with crests on their crowns and chestnut "tippets" on the sides of their heads, pairs of this species display together on lakes and rivers. The birds hunt for fish, insects, and other aquatic animals underwater.
• **NEST** A heap of plant materials, floating in shallow water or among waterplants.
• **DISTRIBUTION** Breeds in much of Eurasia, and in Africa and Australasia. Populations in the north of the Eurasian range winter as far south as the Mediterranean and N. India.

DISTRIBUTION

slim, dagger bill

WINTER

| Plumage Sexes alike | Habitat 〰〰 ⸾≈ 〰〰 | Migration Partial migrant |

Family DIOMEDEIDAE	Species *Diomedea exulans*	Length 135cm (53in)

WANDERING ALBATROSS

This gigantic seabird has long, narrow wings with a span of some 3m (9ft 9in). It flies effortlessly over the southern oceans, where strong winds and gales are usual. Saving energy by soaring on the wind, the Wandering Albatross often travels for dozens, or even hundreds, of miles while prospecting for a good food source. A typical feeding site would be an area of water in which upward currents bring nutrients to surface waters. The bird feeds mainly at night, reaching down from the surface for prey, or on rare occasions making shallow dives. Squids and other cephalopods are the main food. During the night, these and other marine animals rise to the surface. The albatross stores food as an oily liquid in its stomach, either to be digested later or to be regurgitated for its young. Wandering Albatrosses nest in small colonies on the exposed tops and slopes of small, oceanic islands from which they can easily launch themselves off into the wind. Adults display to one another by spreading their wings, waving their heads, and rapping their bills together, amid frequent, braying calls. Pairs thus formed stay together for life. The single egg is incubated for 11 weeks by both parents in turn. The young bird is fed on fish and regurgitated oil for up to ten months, before it flies. Breeding normally takes place every two years. The young bird spends its first ten years at sea until it is mature enough to breed. By then its plumage will have changed gradually, through a series of moults, from chocolate-brown to mainly white. The birds live on average for about 30 years.
• **NEST** A large, drum-shaped mound scraped together out of earth and plant materials, with a small hollow in the top.
• **DISTRIBUTION** Oceans and islands surrounding Antarctica, and coasts of the southern continents.

DISTRIBUTION

JUVENILE

snowy white plumage of fully mature bird •

very long, narrow wing •

Plumage Sexes alike	Habitat 〰️ 〰️	Migration Migrant

Family DIOMEDEIDAE	Species *Phoebetria palpebrata*	Length 85cm (34in)

LIGHT-MANTLED SOOTY ALBATROSS

FLYING ADULT

ADULT IN GROUND DISPLAY

DISTRIBUTION

Three features identify this small albatross: its plumage is mostly dark, its back is pale grey, and, when seen in flight, its tail forms a perfect wedge shape. It glides for long distances with spread wings. To feed, it floats on the sea and catches fish, squid, and crustaceans. Courtship behaviour includes paired flights and face-to-face ground displays in which the white eye-crescent and bill-stripe are shown off. The birds nest in scattered pairs on ledges of steep slopes on islands in the southern oceans.
• NEST A tall mound scraped together out of soil and plant materials, with a deep, cupped hollow on the top.
• DISTRIBUTION Oceans and islands around Antarctica, and the southern coasts of South America, Australia, and New Zealand.

Plumage Sexes alike	Habitat	Migration Migrant

Family PROCELLARIIDAE	Species *Macronectes giganteus*	Length 95cm (37in)

SOUTHERN GIANT PETREL

A heavy, albatross-sized petrel, this bird looks slightly hump-backed in flight. On land, it walks with far greater agility than other petrels, which creep on lowered legs. Southern Giant Petrels feed both at sea and on the shore. Birds are seen fighting over carrion, such as a beached whale, or killing smaller seabirds. Breeding colonies are situated on islands or on mainland shores.
• NEST A shallow depression in the ground, bordered with pebbles or dry vegetation.
• DISTRIBUTION Breeds on coasts and islands of Antarctica. Winters on the southern oceans.

NORMAL PHASE

• *drab, mottled plumage*

WHITE PHASE

webbed feet •

DISTRIBUTION

Plumage Sexes alike	Habitat	Migration Migrant

Family PROCELLARIIDAE	Species *Fulmarus glacialis*	Length 47cm (18½in)

NORTHERN FULMAR

A stout-bodied seabird with a rounded head and thick bill, this species occurs in colour phases (*see p. 13*) from grey-and-white to dark blue-grey. It flies strongly, alternating a few quick wingbeats with a glide on stiffly spread wings. When feeding, it catches fish at the sea surface, or dives to depths up to a few metres, taking small animals drifting in the plankton. Flocks also gather around fishing boats for offal. Fulmars nest on coastal cliffs, singly or in noisy colonies.
• **NEST** Eggs are laid on a bare ledge on a cliff or crag.
• **DISTRIBUTION** Breeds on N. Atlantic and N. Pacific coasts. Disperses out to sea in winter.

DARK PHASE

DISTRIBUTION

wings held level for gliding

bird manoeuvring in an updraught over nest site

tubular nostrils on the bill

legs lowered for landing

Plumage Sexes alike	Habitat	Migration Migrant

Family PROCELLARIIDAE	Species *Daption capense*	Length 39cm (15½in)

CAPE PETREL

With its chequered plumage, this seabird was likened to a pigeon by seamen aboard the whaling vessels around which it flocked: hence its traditional name, the Cape Pigeon. Its flight pattern consists of rapid wingbeats alternating with stiff-winged glides. To feed, it swims and reaches down or dives for small fish and other animals in the plankton. Cape Petrels breed in small groups or colonies on shores and islands.
• **NEST** A shallow depression in a layer of loose rock fragments, on a rocky ledge or in a crevice.
• **DISTRIBUTION** Breeds on islands and coasts of southern continents. Winters on the southern oceans.

FLYING ADULT

DISTRIBUTION

chequered plumage

Plumage Sexes alike	Habitat	Migration Migrant

Family PROCELLARIIDAE	Species *Pterodroma cookii*	Length 33cm (13in)

COOK'S PETREL

Seen in fast, erratic flight over the ocean, this petrel can be recognized by its bold wing markings. It floats on the sea to feed, taking small marine animals that form the plankton. From a tiny breeding range it journeys extensively over the ocean. When breeding, it comes ashore by night to avoid predators.
• **NEST** A hollow in a burrow, usually high on a forested slope.
• **DISTRIBUTION** Breeds on two small islands at opposite ends of New Zealand. Winters at sea over much of the Pacific Ocean.

FLYING ADULT

• *dark wing mark*

• *tubular nostrils on the bill*

• *weak legs*

DISTRIBUTION

Plumage Sexes alike	Habitat	Migration Non-migrant

Family PROCELLARIIDAE	Species *Pachyptila turtur*	Length 27cm (10½in)

FAIRY PRION

This small petrel flies over the ocean for much of its life. It feeds in flocks by night, skimming the sea surface with its bill to scoop up small crustaceans, squid, and other animals. The bill is equipped with fine plates (lamellae) which filter these animals from the water. Fairy Prions land by night at their breeding colonies, which are always situated on small islands. Incoming birds utter soft, cooing calls as they arrive, and if their breeding partners are in the burrow they reply with similar calls. On land, they walk clumsily on weak legs, in a low, crouching gait.
• **NEST** A burrow dug with the bill and feet in soil, often hidden among vegetation, or a hollow in a rock crevice.
• **DISTRIBUTION** Breeds on coasts of southern continents. Winters at sea.

FLYING ADULT

• *long wings*

weak • *legs*

DISTRIBUTION

Plumage Sexes alike	Habitat	Migration Migrant

Family HYDROBATIDAE	Species *Oceanites oceanicus*	Length 17cm (6¾in)

WILSON'S STORM-PETREL

This sparrow-sized seabird flutters across the oceans with its legs dangling and often pattering along the sea surface. It feeds by picking tiny crustaceans, fish, and molluscs from the water.
• NEST A hollow in a burrow, in a colony located on a slope overlooking the coast.
• DISTRIBUTION Breeds on Antarctic coast and on islands in the southern oceans. Winters out on the oceans.

legs are weak on land •

DISTRIBUTION

Plumage Sexes alike	Habitat	Migration Migrant

Family HYDROBATIDAE	Species *Hydrobates pelagicus*	Length 15cm (6in)

EUROPEAN STORM-PETREL

ADULT RESTING

A small, dark seabird with a white rump and fluttering flight, this species flies low over the water, often pattering with its feet on the surface. It feeds on small animals picked from the plankton, and follows fishing boats for offal. Breeding colonies are on offshore islands, and the birds visit their nest burrows at night, uttering harsh, churring calls.
• NEST A hollow in a burrow.
• DISTRIBUTION Breeds on islands in N.E. Atlantic and in W. Mediterranean. Winters out at sea.

DISTRIBUTION   FLYING ADULT

Plumage Sexes alike	Habitat	Migration Migrant

Family PELECANOIDIDAE	Species *Pelecanoides urinatrix*	Length 23cm (9in)

COMMON DIVING-PETREL

This seabird flies over the ocean, plunging through waves to pick up marine animals.
• NEST A hollow at the end of a burrow in a colony on a slope beside the coast.
• DISTRIBUTION Breeds on islands and mainland coasts of the southern oceans except on Antarctica. Disperses and winters out at sea.

compact • *body*

FLYING ADULT

hooked • *bill*

DISTRIBUTION

Plumage Sexes alike	Habitat	Migration Migrant

Family PROCELLARIIDAE	Species *Puffinus puffinus*	Length 34cm (13½in)

MANX SHEARWATER

A dark-backed seabird with a white underside, the Manx Shearwater flies low over the sea, making rapid, tilting glides, alternating with quick wingbeats. The shearwater feeds at the surface or in shallow plunge-dives, taking small fish, squid, crustaceans, and offal from fishing boats. Nesting colonies are located on hilly offshore islands. Flocks are seen floating offshore, waiting to visit their nests after dark. They eventually go ashore, amid a chorus of crowing calls.
• **NEST** A hollow, sometimes lined with grass, in a burrow or occasionally in a rock crevice or cavity.
• **DISTRIBUTION** Breeds along coasts of N. Atlantic Ocean. Winters in mid-ocean, as far south as S. Atlantic Ocean.

narrow, tapering wings

DISTRIBUTION

ADULT

Plumage Sexes alike	Habitat 〰〰 〰	Migration Migrant

Family PHAETHONTIDAE	Species *Phaethon lepturus*	Length 80cm (31in)

WHITE-TAILED TROPICBIRD

This beautiful seabird flies gracefully with its streamlined body, slender tail, and long wings. It feeds by plunge-diving into the sea for fish, squid, and crustaceans. Both sexes have long, white tail-streamers which they show off in acrobatic display flights over the nesting area.
• **NEST** Eggs are laid in a crevice, on bare ground, or underneath overhanging rocks.
• **DISTRIBUTION** Breeds on islands in the Pacific, Atlantic, and Indian Oceans. Disperses out to sea.

strong, dagger bill

FLYING ADULT

very long wing

DISTRIBUTION

JUVENILE

Plumage Sexes alike	Habitat 〰〰	Migration Migrant

| Family PELECANIDAE | Species *Pelecanus crispus* | Length 170cm (67in) |

DALMATIAN PELICAN

The distinctive features of this pelican are white plumage with blackish wing tips, a short crest, and a pink or orange pouch beneath the bill. The species is sociable, and flocks often feed cooperatively by driving a school of fish into the shallows, then reaching underwater to scoop up fish and water together. This fills their bill pouches, which they drain by raising their heads. Breeding colonies are located in swamps.
• **NEST** A platform of grass and twigs on a floating mat of vegetation.
• **DISTRIBUTION** Breeds in Eurasia from the Adriatic Sea to C. China. Winters as far south as Egypt and N. India.

small, curly crest

bill pouch

DISTRIBUTION

strong, swimming legs

JUVENILE

| Plumage Sexes alike | Habitat | Migration Migrant |

| Family PELECANIDAE | Species *Pelecanus occidentalis* | Length 115cm (45in) |

BROWN PELICAN

This is one of two species of pelican that plunge-dive for fish, hurtling down from the air with spread wings that are stretched back as the bird hits the water. It is common along sea coasts and estuaries, often becoming tame. Its diet consists mainly of fish, sometimes taken from the surface but mostly by plunge-diving. Nesting colonies are usually located on coastal islands.
• **NEST** A hollow in the ground, lined with feathers and debris; or a mound of mixed materials; or a stick platform in a bush or tree.
• **DISTRIBUTION** Pacific coast of the Americas from W. Canada to N. Peru, and Atlantic coast from N. USA to N. Brazil. Northern populations migrate southwards within this range.

brown breeding plumage on back of neck

expandable bill pouch

DISTRIBUTION

JUVENILE

| Plumage Sexes alike | Habitat | Migration Migrant |

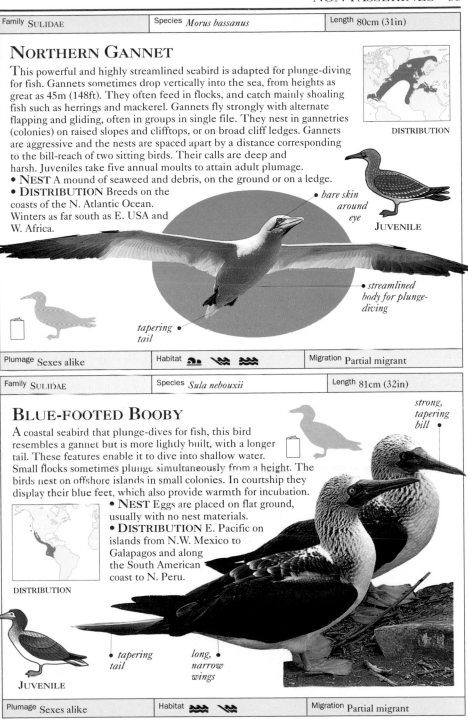

Family SULIDAE	Species *Morus bassanus*	Length 80cm (31in)

NORTHERN GANNET

This powerful and highly streamlined seabird is adapted for plunge-diving for fish. Gannets sometimes drop vertically into the sea, from heights as great as 45m (148ft). They often feed in flocks, and catch mainly shoaling fish such as herrings and mackerel. Gannets fly strongly with alternate flapping and gliding, often in groups in single file. They nest in gannetries (colonies) on raised slopes and clifftops, or on broad cliff ledges. Gannets are aggressive and the nests are spaced apart by a distance corresponding to the bill-reach of two sitting birds. Their calls are deep and harsh. Juveniles take five annual moults to attain adult plumage.

DISTRIBUTION

• NEST A mound of seaweed and debris, on the ground or on a ledge.
• DISTRIBUTION Breeds on the coasts of the N. Atlantic Ocean. Winters as far south as E. USA and W. Africa.

• *bare skin around eye*

JUVENILE

• *streamlined body for plunge-diving*

tapering tail •

Plumage Sexes alike	Habitat	Migration Partial migrant

Family SULIDAE	Species *Sula nebouxii*	Length 81cm (32in)

BLUE-FOOTED BOOBY

strong, tapering bill •

A coastal seabird that plunge-dives for fish, this bird resembles a gannet but is more lightly built, with a longer tail. These features enable it to dive into shallow water. Small flocks sometimes plunge simultaneously from a height. The birds nest on offshore islands in small colonies. In courtship they display their blue feet, which also provide warmth for incubation.

• NEST Eggs are placed on flat ground, usually with no nest materials.
• DISTRIBUTION E. Pacific on islands from N.W. Mexico to Galapagos and along the South American coast to N. Peru.

DISTRIBUTION

JUVENILE

• *tapering tail*

long, narrow wings

Plumage Sexes alike	Habitat	Migration Partial migrant

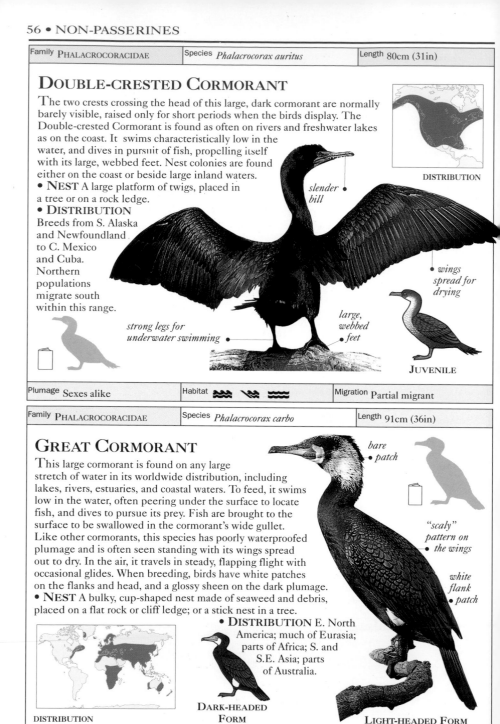

| Family PHALACROCORACIDAE | Species *Phalacrocorax auritus* | Length 80cm (31in) |

DOUBLE-CRESTED CORMORANT

The two crests crossing the head of this large, dark cormorant are normally barely visible, raised only for short periods when the birds display. The Double-crested Cormorant is found as often on rivers and freshwater lakes as on the coast. It swims characteristically low in the water, and dives in pursuit of fish, propelling itself with its large, webbed feet. Nest colonies are found either on the coast or beside large inland waters.
• **NEST** A large platform of twigs, placed in a tree or on a rock ledge.
• **DISTRIBUTION** Breeds from S. Alaska and Newfoundland to C. Mexico and Cuba. Northern populations migrate south within this range.

DISTRIBUTION

slender bill

wings spread for drying

strong legs for underwater swimming

large, webbed feet

JUVENILE

| Plumage Sexes alike | Habitat | Migration Partial migrant |

| Family PHALACROCORACIDAE | Species *Phalacrocorax carbo* | Length 91cm (36in) |

GREAT CORMORANT

This large cormorant is found on any large stretch of water in its worldwide distribution, including lakes, rivers, estuaries, and coastal waters. To feed, it swims low in the water, often peering under the surface to locate fish, and dives to pursue its prey. Fish are brought to the surface to be swallowed in the cormorant's wide gullet. Like other cormorants, this species has poorly waterproofed plumage, and is often seen standing with its wings spread out to dry. In the air, it travels in steady, flapping flight with occasional glides. When breeding, birds have white patches on the flanks and head, and a glossy sheen on the dark plumage.
• **NEST** A bulky, cup-shaped nest made of seaweed and debris, placed on a flat rock or cliff ledge; or a stick nest in a tree.
• **DISTRIBUTION** E. North America; much of Eurasia; parts of Africa; S. and S.E. Asia; parts of Australia.

bare patch

"scaly" pattern on the wings

white flank patch

DISTRIBUTION

DARK-HEADED FORM

LIGHT-HEADED FORM

| Plumage Sexes alike | Habitat | Migration Partial migrant |

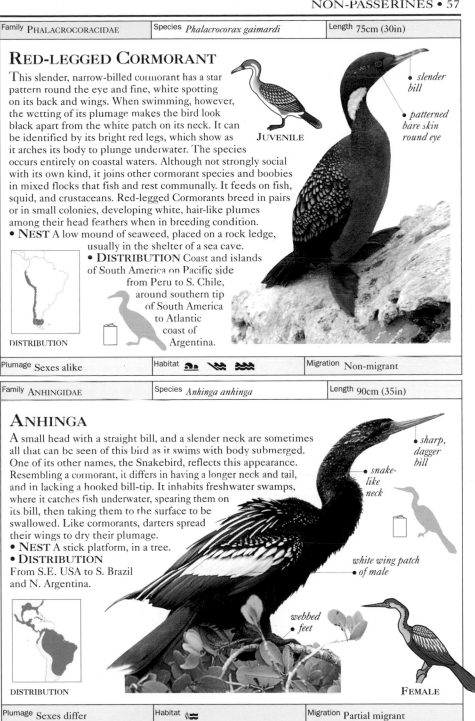

Family PHALACROCORACIDAE	Species *Phalacrocorax gaimardi*	Length 75cm (30in)

RED-LEGGED CORMORANT

This slender, narrow-billed cormorant has a star pattern round the eye and fine, white spotting on its back and wings. When swimming, however, the wetting of its plumage makes the bird look black apart from the white patch on its neck. It can be identified by its bright red legs, which show as it arches its body to plunge underwater. The species occurs entirely on coastal waters. Although not strongly social with its own kind, it joins other cormorant species and boobies in mixed flocks that fish and rest communally. It feeds on fish, squid, and crustaceans. Red-legged Cormorants breed in pairs or in small colonies, developing white, hair-like plumes among their head feathers when in breeding condition.

JUVENILE

• slender bill

• patterned bare skin round eye

• **NEST** A low mound of seaweed, placed on a rock ledge, usually in the shelter of a sea cave.
• **DISTRIBUTION** Coast and islands of South America on Pacific side from Peru to S. Chile, around southern tip of South America to Atlantic coast of Argentina.

DISTRIBUTION

Plumage Sexes alike	Habitat	Migration Non-migrant

Family ANHINGIDAE	Species *Anhinga anhinga*	Length 90cm (35in)

ANHINGA

A small head with a straight bill, and a slender neck are sometimes all that can be seen of this bird as it swims with body submerged. One of its other names, the Snakebird, reflects this appearance. Resembling a cormorant, it differs in having a longer neck and tail, and in lacking a hooked bill-tip. It inhabits freshwater swamps, where it catches fish underwater, spearing them on its bill, then taking them to the surface to be swallowed. Like cormorants, darters spread their wings to dry their plumage.
• **NEST** A stick platform, in a tree.
• **DISTRIBUTION** From S.E. USA to S. Brazil and N. Argentina.

• sharp, dagger bill

• snake-like neck

white wing patch • of male

webbed • feet

DISTRIBUTION

FEMALE

Plumage Sexes differ	Habitat	Migration Partial migrant

Family FREGATIDAE	Species *Fregata minor*	Length 100cm (39in)

GREAT FRIGATEBIRD

This bird is often seen soaring and gliding on the winds over coast and sea, with long wings extended. It feeds in the air, either swooping to snatch fish from the sea, or piratically attacking other seabirds and forcing them to drop or disgorge their food for its own consumption. When breeding, male Great Frigatebirds inflate their red throat sacs in display.
• **NEST** A frail platform of twigs, placed in a low bush or tree, usually on an island.
• **DISTRIBUTION** Breeds along coastlines of C. America, S. Brazil, E. Africa, S.E. Asia, and N. Australia, and on islands in the Pacific, S. Atlantic, and Indian Oceans.

long, hooked bill

FEMALE

DISTRIBUTION

Plumage Sexes differ	Habitat	Migration Partial migrant

Family ARDEIDAE	Species *Ardea cinerea*	Length 97cm (38in)

GREY HERON

black, drooping crest

The large, grey figure of this heron, resting with its head hunched on its shoulders or standing alert, with neck outstretched, is a regular sight beside lakes, ponds, rivers, or marshes. To feed, it either stands still, or wades slowly and watchfully, its angled neck allowing the head to dart forward to seize a fish or any small animal. The heron flies with slow beats of its large, broad wings, its head tucked back on its shoulders and its legs extended. It is usually silent, but occasionally utters a harsh call.
• **NEST** A platform of sticks, to which more material is added each year.
• **DISTRIBUTION** Eurasia, Africa, and Asia.

black shoulder patch

JUVENILE

long legs

long, thin toes

DISTRIBUTION

Plumage Sexes alike	Habitat	Migration Non-migrant

Family ARDEIDAE	Species *Ardea herodias*	Length 127cm (50in)

GREAT BLUE HERON

The largest of the American herons, this
bird occurs in both freshwater and saltwater
habitats, hunting in marshes and still or slow-
flowing water for fish, frogs, and other creatures.
Sometimes it wades up to its belly in search of
fish. It also hunts on dry land, stalking prey in
open habitats, or standing still to watch for it.
Mice, gophers, and other animals are taken.
• **NEST** A shallow platform made of sticks, in a
colony in trees, bushes, or at ground level in a marsh.
• **DISTRIBUTION** Breeds in much of North and
Central America. Northern populations migrate south
for the winter, some travelling as far as Venezuela.
• **REMARK** A pure white form, known as the
Great White
Heron, occurs
in the
Caribbean
and in
S.E. USA.

lowered •
crest

black
shoulder
• *patch*

JUVENILE

large, •
abroad wings

DISTRIBUTION

Plumage Sexes alike	Habitat	Migration Partial migrant

Family ARDEIDAE	Species *Egretta novaehollandiae*	Length 65cm (26in)

WHITE-FACED EGRET

A slender heron, often standing very upright, this bird
occurs on offshore reefs, coastal mudflats, rivers, lakes,
marshes, and dry grassland. On dry land or in water, it
walks slowly, stopping to stab at its prey, or stands and
watches for it. Prey includes fish, frogs, shrimps, and
sometimes lizards and small birds. The White-faced Egret
also benefits from plagues of grasshoppers or mice that
occur in parts of its range. Like many herons, it sometimes
establishes a temporary feeding territory, which it defends
against others of its kind. Its usual call is a loud, single croak
but it also utters low, guttural notes. When not breeding, it is
sometimes found in open landscapes, but pairs always nest in
trees. Breeding birds perform displays at the nest in which
they raise the spiky plumes that grow
from their heads, necks, and backs. They
nest in pairs or in loose groups of pairs.
• **NEST** A large structure of sticks
and twigs with a central hollow
on top, situated in a tree.
• **DISTRIBUTION** S. New
Guinea, New Caledonia,
Australia, and New Zealand.

• *typical*
upright
stance

JUVENILE

spiky plumes that
are raised when
• *the bird displays*

DISTRIBUTION

Plumage Sexes alike	Habitat	Migration Non-migrant

Family ARDEIDAE	Species *Ardea goliath*	Length 150cm (59in)

GOLIATH HERON

This is the tallest and largest heron in the world. It occurs at the edges of large lakes and swamps, where it can wade deeper than other herons. Other habitats include mudflats, mangrove swamps, rivers, and papyrus swamps. When not breeding, birds are either solitary or live in pairs. A Goliath Heron tends to fish over the same areas daily. It often hunts among thickly crowded floating vegetation on tropical waters, or wades up to its belly in open water, either stalking slowly or standing still to watch for prey. When about to strike, it lowers its body, head, and back-curved neck, to crouch near water level. The neck has a kink which can suddenly straighten, shooting the head forwards. Prey is mostly impaled on the sharp point of the bill, or sometimes seized in the bill. Fish, frogs, small mammals, reptiles, and invertebrates are taken. Like other herons, the Goliath has special patches of downy feathers on its lower body. These constantly break down to a powder, which the heron works into its plumage with its bill as part of the preening process. The powder absorbs fish-slime, and the heron cleans both off together with the comb-shaped claw of its front middle toe. The call of the Goliath is a deep, repeated, raucous note. Flight is slow and heavy, with the legs sagging slightly. Goliath Herons usually nest in pairs, sometimes at the edge of mixed colonies of birds of other species.

• **NEST** A platform of sticks and reed stems, placed on top of growing swamp vegetation, in a bush, in a low tree, or on the ground.

• **DISTRIBUTION** Parts of Africa, Arabian Peninsula, and the Indian subcontinent.

DISTRIBUTION

resting posture with • folded neck

• brown "shoulder" patch

• marbled pattern on the neck of mature bird

plumes • hanging from nape

• bird often rests with one leg raised

JUVENILE

• long, wading leg

comb-like claw on the middle front toe, • used in feather care

Plumage Sexes alike	Habitat	Migration Non-migrant

Family ARDEIDAE	Species *Egretta thula*	Length 60cm (24in)

SNOWY EGRET

The pure white plumage of this species, and the fine plumes that hang from its head, neck, and back, are justly famed for their beauty. Both sexes acquire this decoration at the start of the breeding season, and raise their plumes in display to one another at the nest. At other times, Snowy Egrets are simply small, white herons with black bills and bright yellow feet. They live mainly in marshes, either fresh or saltwater. They feed in the daytime, dashing about in search of fish and any small marsh animals. At times they rake or stir the bottom of the water with their feet, to disturb prey. Snowy Egrets gather in large flocks to roost in trees, and also nest in colonies in trees.
• **NEST** A platform made of sticks and twigs, placed in a tree.
• **DISTRIBUTION** Breeds in USA and through the Americas as far as S. Chile. Northern and southern populations migrate to warmer regions for winter.
• **REMARK** The species was hunted nearly to extinction by the end of the 19th century. Public protests led to the formation of bird protection societies.

crest in lowered position

fine display plumes

yellow feet

DISTRIBUTION   JUVENILE

Plumage Sexes alike	Habitat	Migration Partial migrant

Family ARDEIDAE	Species *Bubulcus ibis*	Length 50cm (20in)

CATTLE EGRET

stout bill

A small, stocky heron with a short neck and a stout bill, this species specializes in associating with grazing animals in open country. It is often seen walking on the ground amidst a herd of cattle, catching the insects that the animals disturb with their feet, picking flies off them, and flying up to use them as temporary perches. Apart from insects, it takes any other small animal that it finds. Cattle Egrets roost communally in trees or on the ground near water, and nest in colonies in trees or bushes, in reedbeds or other swamps, or on rocky islands.
• **NEST** A shallow cup nest of sticks and reed stems, in a tree.
• **DISTRIBUTION** North and South America, S. Europe, Africa, and Asia to Australia.

typical hunched posture

strong, walking legs

large feet with long toes

BREEDING PLUMAGE

DISTRIBUTION

Plumage Sexes alike	Habitat	Migration Non-migrant

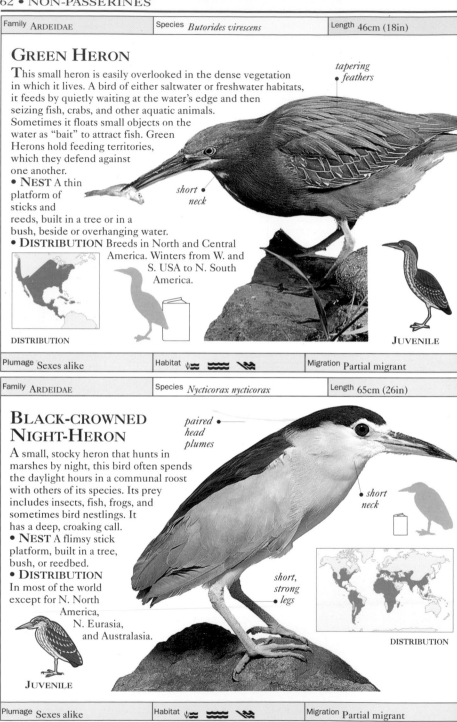

| Family ARDEIDAE | Species *Butorides virescens* | Length 46cm (18in) |

GREEN HERON

This small heron is easily overlooked in the dense vegetation in which it lives. A bird of either saltwater or freshwater habitats, it feeds by quietly waiting at the water's edge and then seizing fish, crabs, and other aquatic animals. Sometimes it floats small objects on the water as "bait" to attract fish. Green Herons hold feeding territories, which they defend against one another.

tapering feathers

short neck

• **NEST** A thin platform of sticks and reeds, built in a tree or in a bush, beside or overhanging water.
• **DISTRIBUTION** Breeds in North and Central America. Winters from W. and S. USA to N. South America.

DISTRIBUTION

JUVENILE

| Plumage Sexes alike | Habitat | Migration Partial migrant |

| Family ARDEIDAE | Species *Nycticorax nycticorax* | Length 65cm (26in) |

BLACK-CROWNED NIGHT-HERON

paired head plumes

A small, stocky heron that hunts in marshes by night, this bird often spends the daylight hours in a communal roost with others of its species. Its prey includes insects, fish, frogs, and sometimes bird nestlings. It has a deep, croaking call.

short neck

• **NEST** A flimsy stick platform, built in a tree, bush, or reedbed.
• **DISTRIBUTION** In most of the world except for N. North America, N. Eurasia, and Australasia.

short, strong legs

DISTRIBUTION

JUVENILE

| Plumage Sexes alike | Habitat | Migration Partial migrant |

| Family ARDEIDAE | Species *Cochlearius cochlearius* | Length 50cm (20in) |

BOAT-BILLED HERON

Looking like a night-heron apart from its capacious bill, this bird is adapted for night hunting, even in total darkness. Its prey consists of small creatures such as fish, shrimps, and insects, and the Boat-bill is believed to be able to feel these in the dark with its bill, which is touch-sensitive. As soon as contact is made the bill opens, drawing in a current of water, and with it the prey. The Boatbill feeds at the edges of mangrove creeks, beside other tidal inlets, and in either fresh or partly saltwater lagoons, lakes, and marshes. It roosts and nests in trees or bushes, either in pairs or in small groups of pairs.

large eye for feeding at night

• **NEST** A frail platform made of twigs, placed in mangroves or other swamp trees.

• **DISTRIBUTION** From Mexico to N. Argentina.

JUVENILE

DISTRIBUTION

| Plumage Sexes alike | Habitat | Migration Non-migrant |

| Family ARDEIDAE | Species *Tigrisoma lineatum* | Length 75cm (30in) |

RUFESCENT TIGER-HERON

The strongly streaked, black-and-yellow plumage of juveniles, as well as the markings of the adults, give the tiger-herons their name. This shy heron is found in extensive tropical rainforest. It occurs beside slow-moving, marshy waters or lowland rivers, and also in swamps and mangroves. Rufescent Tiger-Herons hunt alone and mainly at night, prowling slowly or waiting motionless to catch shrimps and insects. When disturbed, birds usually freeze motionless to escape detection, but if forced to break cover, they take refuge in the trees.

stout bill

camouflage plumage

• **NEST** A frail platform of twigs and plant stems, usually built high in a tree.

• **DISTRIBUTION** From E. Honduras to Paraguay and N. Argentina.

JUVENILE

long, green legs

ADULT

DISTRIBUTION

| Plumage Sexes alike | Habitat | Migration Non-migrant |

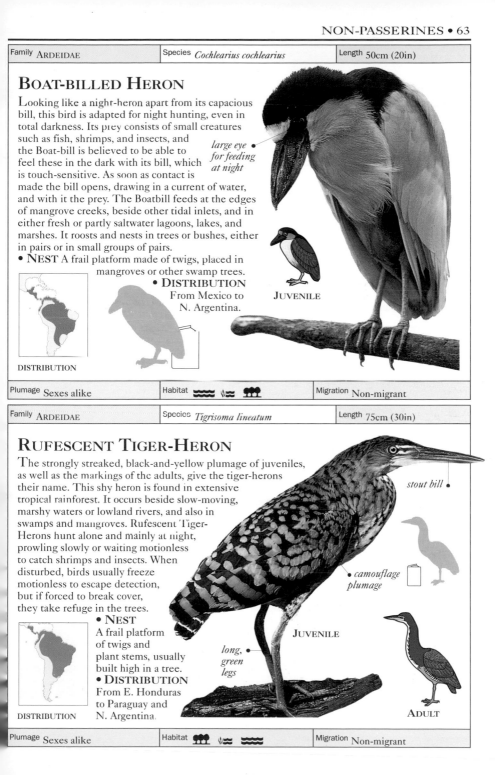

Family BALAENICIPITIDAE	Species *Balaeniceps rex*	Length 120cm (47in)

SHOEBILL

This large, stork-like bird, recognized by its enormous, hook-tipped bill, occurs only in the freshwater swamps of East and Central Africa. Shoebills live singly or in pairs, remaining for most of the time in a small area of marshland. They sometimes feed in wet grassland or shallow water, but their favoured hunting grounds are deep marshes and rivers or lakes that are choked with vegetation. When hunting, a Shoebill walks slowly and deliberately, often climbing over floating waterplants, spreading its weight on long, straight toes. The bird pauses to watch the water for prey such as lungfish, catfish, frogs, water snakes, or small turtles. On sighting a victim the Shoebill lunges forwards and down, stretching its neck and whole body and spreading its wings. If it succeeds in making a catch, it usually also grabs a mass of waterweed together with the prey, and has to separate out the food by turning it over in its bill. The flight of the Shoebill is slow but strong, with heavily beating wings and with the head resting back on the shoulders. The legs are extended behind. Shoebills are also seen circling and soaring on rising air currents to gain height. The species nests in isolated pairs among tall vegetation, usually over water. Parent birds are seen bringing water in their bills, to pour over the small young in hot weather.
- **NEST** A bulky platform of rushes, grasses, and leaves, in thick vegetation, with the base usually in water.
- **DISTRIBUTION** In African freshwater marshes from S. Sudan to Zambia and S.E. Zaire.

small tuft on the crown

FLYING ADULT

large head

DISTRIBUTION

typical upright posture

large, broad wing

long toes for spreading weight

Plumage Sexes alike	Habitat	Migration Non-migrant

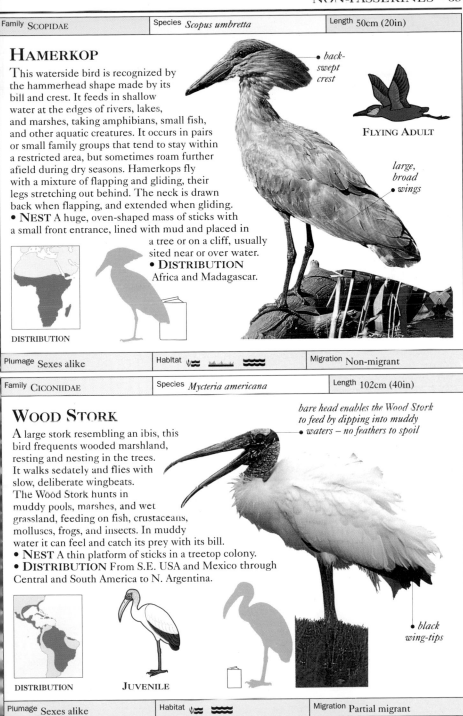

Family SCOPIDAE	Species *Scopus umbretta*	Length 50cm (20in)

HAMERKOP

This waterside bird is recognized by the hammerhead shape made by its bill and crest. It feeds in shallow water at the edges of rivers, lakes, and marshes, taking amphibians, small fish, and other aquatic creatures. It occurs in pairs or small family groups that tend to stay within a restricted area, but sometimes roam further afield during dry seasons. Hamerkops fly with a mixture of flapping and gliding, their legs stretching out behind. The neck is drawn back when flapping, and extended when gliding.
• **NEST** A huge, oven-shaped mass of sticks with a small front entrance, lined with mud and placed in a tree or on a cliff, usually sited near or over water.
• **DISTRIBUTION** Africa and Madagascar.

• back-swept crest

FLYING ADULT

large, broad • wings

DISTRIBUTION

Plumage Sexes alike	Habitat	Migration Non-migrant

Family CICONIIDAE	Species *Mycteria americana*	Length 102cm (40in)

WOOD STORK

A large stork resembling an ibis, this bird frequents wooded marshland, resting and nesting in the trees. It walks sedately and flies with slow, deliberate wingbeats. The Wood Stork hunts in muddy pools, marshes, and wet grassland, feeding on fish, crustaceans, molluscs, frogs, and insects. In muddy water it can feel and catch its prey with its bill.
• **NEST** A thin platform of sticks in a treetop colony.
• **DISTRIBUTION** From S.E. USA and Mexico through Central and South America to N. Argentina.

bare head enables the Wood Stork to feed by dipping into muddy • waters – no feathers to spoil

• black wing-tips

DISTRIBUTION   **JUVENILE**

Plumage Sexes alike	Habitat	Migration Partial migrant

Family CICONIIDAE	Species *Mycteria leucocephala*	Length 102cm (40in)

PAINTED STORK

Recognized by pink tints on the wings
and back, and a finely checquered
panel on the inner wing, this stork
occurs on freshwater lakes, marshes,
and paddy fields. Its feeding method is
specially adapted for very muddy waters.
When wading, the stork swings its partly
opened bill from side to side underwater, snapping it shut
if it touches a fish. Frogs and other small creatures are also
caught in this way. The Painted Stork feeds by day, often in
groups at a good food source, and roosts in larger flocks at
night. It nests in colonies, normally in trees that stand in or
close to water. Nests are packed together at close quarters,
and the site is frequently
shared with other stork species
as well as egrets, ibises,
and cormorants.
• **NEST** A large platform built
of sticks, with a shallow hollow
at the centre, situated in a tree.
• **DISTRIBUTION** Indian
subcontinent, S.W. China, and
part of S.E. Asia.

baldness allows the bird to dip into muddy water without feather fouling

downcurved bill

checquered inner wing

pink outer wing

long legs for wading

JUVENILE

DISTRIBUTION

Plumage Sexes alike	Habitat	Migration Partial migrant

Family CICONIIDAE	Species *Ciconia ciconia*	Length 115cm (45in)

WHITE STORK

This stork is typically seen wading in shallow water in streams, pools, and
marshes, where it hunts frogs and other small creatures. It also feeds in grassland
and rice fields, taking any small prey it finds. The White Stork flies slowly with
steady wingbeats and occasional glides, its neck and legs extended. It also circles
and soars on rising air currents to gain height, especially during migration. After
breeding in scattered pairs or small groups, it migrates and winters in flocks.
• **NEST** A large stick platform with a central hollow, lined with stems and
grass and situated in a tree or on a building.
• **DISTRIBUTION** Breeds in scattered
areas from Europe to N. India. Winters
in parts of Africa, Pakistan, and India.

typical flight posture

red bill

broad, rounded wings

DISTRIBUTION

Plumage Sexes alike	Habitat	Migration Migrant

Family CICONIIDAE	Species *Leptoptilos crumeniferus*	Length 150cm (59in)

MARABOU STORK

A large, scavenging stork, this species lives in grassland and marshes, sometimes near human habitation. It feeds on animal carcases of all sizes, sometimes competing with vultures, and also searches rubbish dumps. Live prey is often taken, including insects, fish, rats, and small birds. Flamingo colonies are raided for eggs, young, and even adult birds. The Marabou's bald head enables it to eat messy foods such as carrion with minimal fouling of the feathers. Attached to the bare neck is a dangling, inflatable wattle, which is used in various forms of display behaviour. The Marabou flies heavily on slowly beating wings, also soaring to considerable heights on rising air currents. It roosts in flocks and nests in large colonies. Courtship behaviour includes a ritual slow raising and lowering of the head, with a variety of mooing, grunting, and whistling calls.

• **NEST** A large mass of sticks with a hollow at the centre, which is lined with smaller twigs and green leaves. The nest is situated in a colony in a tree or on a cliff.

• **DISTRIBUTION** Much of Africa south of the Sahara.

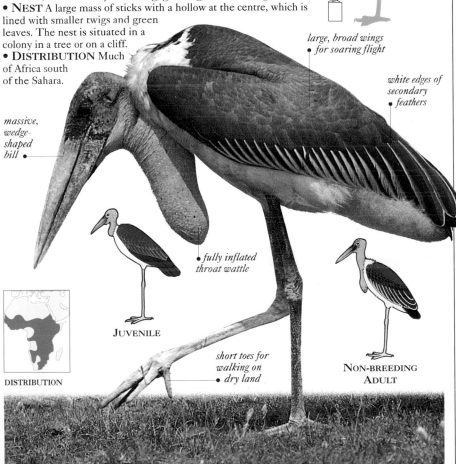

large, broad wings for soaring flight

white edges of secondary feathers

massive, wedge-shaped bill

fully inflated throat wattle

JUVENILE

DISTRIBUTION

short toes for walking on dry land

NON-BREEDING ADULT

Plumage Sexes alike	Habitat	Migration Non-migrant

Family CICONIIDAE	Species *Ephippiorhynchus senegalensis*	Length 145cm (57in)

SADDLE-BILLED STORK

Like other wading storks, this species is tall
and long-legged, with a long, thick bill and strong
colours. It occurs on any kind of water where it can
fish. The Saddlebill has several feeding methods.
It stands in water and stabs fish on sight; it walks
among waterplants and jabs at random; or it may
sweep its bill through muddy water to catch fish
by touch. Occasionally it stirs up the mud with
one foot to disturb fish. Saddlebills roost in
pairs in trees, and nest in scattered pairs.
In courtship, they run with wings spread,
displaying their boldly marked plumage.
• NEST A platform of sticks, lined with
reeds, sedges, and earth, on a bush or
tree, usually near water.
• DISTRIBUTION
Much of Africa south
of the Sahara Desert.
• REMARK
The female is
smaller in body size
(typically 130cm/51in)
and the eye has a yellow iris.

distinctive, FEMALE
• red leg joints

large bill
with yellow
• saddle

DISTRIBUTION

Plumage Sexes alike	Habitat	Migration Non-migrant

Family THRESKIORNITHIDAE	Species *Threskiornis aethiopicus*	Length 75cm (30in)

SACRED IBIS

Birds with downcurved bills are mostly
specialized for probing in soil or mud for food,
but the Sacred Ibis is very much a general
feeder. It frequents marshy ground, the
edges of lakes or rivers, grassland (especially
after grass fires), cultivated fields, and even rubbish dumps
at the edges of towns. It hunts any kind of small animal,
as well as eggs and nestlings of other birds, and also eats
carrion and offal. The Sacred Ibis flies on broad, black-tipped
wings with neck extended, alternately flapping and gliding,
often in flocks in V-formation. It feeds and roosts in large or
small flocks, and nests in crowded colonies. Young birds lack the
long bill. They feed direct from the throat of the parent bird.
• NEST A platform made of twigs and sticks,
lined with grass and leaves, and placed
in a tree, in a bush, or on the ground.
• DISTRIBUTION Africa south of
the Sahara, N. Yemen, and S. Iraq.
• REMARK This bird used
to be held sacred
by the ancient
Egyptians.

• bare, black
skin on head
and neck

JUVENILE

decorative
plumes on
• the back

DISTRIBUTION

Plumage Sexes alike	Habitat	Migration Migrant

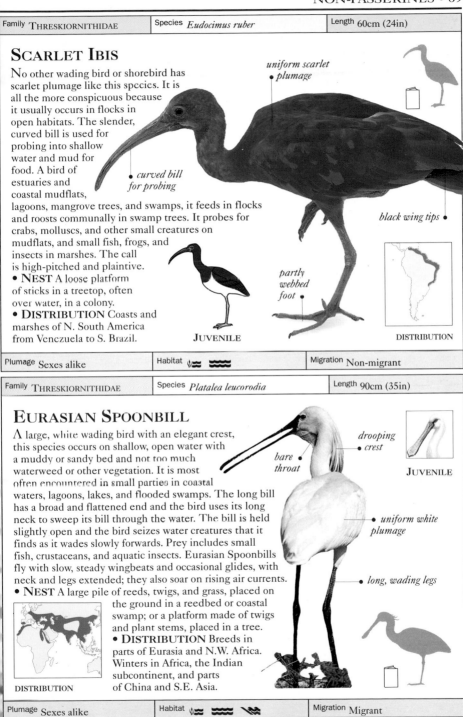

Family THRESKIORNITHIDAE	Species *Eudocimus ruber*	Length 60cm (24in)

SCARLET IBIS

No other wading bird or shorebird has scarlet plumage like this species. It is all the more conspicuous because it usually occurs in flocks in open habitats. The slender, curved bill is used for probing into shallow water and mud for food. A bird of estuaries and coastal mudflats, lagoons, mangrove trees, and swamps, it feeds in flocks and roosts communally in swamp trees. It probes for crabs, molluscs, and other small creatures on mudflats, and small fish, frogs, and insects in marshes. The call is high-pitched and plaintive.
• **NEST** A loose platform of sticks in a treetop, often over water, in a colony.
• **DISTRIBUTION** Coasts and marshes of N. South America from Venezuela to S. Brazil.

uniform scarlet
• plumage

• *curved bill for probing*

black wing tips •

partly webbed foot •

JUVENILE

DISTRIBUTION

Plumage Sexes alike	Habitat	Migration Non-migrant

Family THRESKIORNITHIDAE	Species *Platalea leucorodia*	Length 90cm (35in)

EURASIAN SPOONBILL

A large, white wading bird with an elegant crest, this species occurs on shallow, open water with a muddy or sandy bed and not too much waterweed or other vegetation. It is most often encountered in small parties in coastal waters, lagoons, lakes, and flooded swamps. The long bill has a broad and flattened end and the bird uses its long neck to sweep its bill through the water. The bill is held slightly open and the bird seizes water creatures that it finds as it wades slowly forwards. Prey includes small fish, crustaceans, and aquatic insects. Eurasian Spoonbills fly with slow, steady wingbeats and occasional glides, with neck and legs extended; they also soar on rising air currents.
• **NEST** A large pile of reeds, twigs, and grass, placed on the ground in a reedbed or coastal swamp; or a platform made of twigs and plant stems, placed in a tree.
• **DISTRIBUTION** Breeds in parts of Eurasia and N.W. Africa. Winters in Africa, the Indian subcontinent, and parts of China and S.E. Asia.

drooping crest •

bare throat

JUVENILE

• *uniform white plumage*

• *long, wading legs*

DISTRIBUTION

Plumage Sexes alike	Habitat	Migration Migrant

Family THRESKIORNITHIDAE	Species *Ajaia ajaja*	Length 80cm (31in)

ROSEATE SPOONBILL

bare green skin on head

broad, flat bill-tip

The elegance of this spoonbill's rose-coloured plumage contrasts with its bizarre-looking, bare green head. The species often forms flocks that wade in shallow coastal waters, mangrove creeks, lagoons, flooded marshlands, and swamps. The birds fish by sweeping their broad-tipped bills from side to side through the water, seizing any small fish that they chance to contact.
• **NEST** An untidy structure of twigs and sticks, lined with leaves, in a colony in the treetops.
• **DISTRIBUTION** From S. USA to C. Argentina.

scarlet wing patch

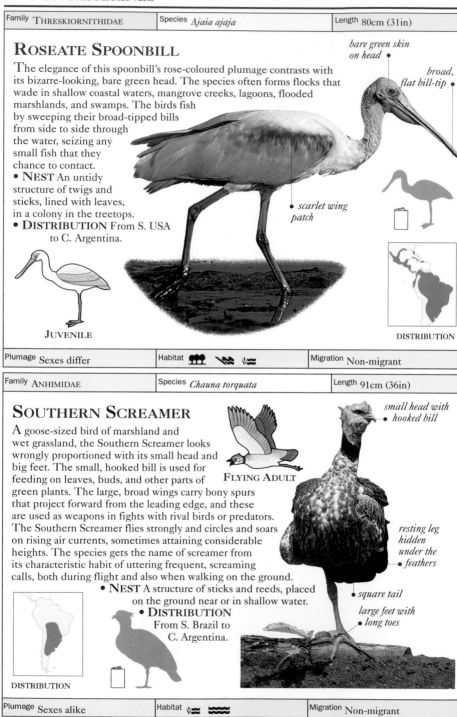

JUVENILE

DISTRIBUTION

Plumage Sexes differ	Habitat	Migration Non-migrant

Family ANHIMIDAE	Species *Chauna torquata*	Length 91cm (36in)

SOUTHERN SCREAMER

small head with hooked bill

A goose-sized bird of marshland and wet grassland, the Southern Screamer looks wrongly proportioned with its small head and big feet. The small, hooked bill is used for feeding on leaves, buds, and other parts of green plants. **FLYING ADULT** The large, broad wings carry bony spurs that project forward from the leading edge, and these are used as weapons in fights with rival birds or predators. The Southern Screamer flies strongly and circles and soars on rising air currents, sometimes attaining considerable heights. The species gets the name of screamer from its characteristic habit of uttering frequent, screaming calls, both during flight and also when walking on the ground.
• **NEST** A structure of sticks and reeds, placed on the ground near or in shallow water.
• **DISTRIBUTION** From S. Brazil to C. Argentina.

resting leg hidden under the feathers

square tail

large feet with long toes

DISTRIBUTION

Plumage Sexes alike	Habitat	Migration Non-migrant

Family PHOENICOPTERIDAE	Species *Phoenicopterus ruber*	Length 145cm (57in)

GREATER FLAMINGO

This tall, slender bird is seen on shallow lakes
and coastal waters. It specializes in feeding
in lakes with a high concentration of either
saline or alkaline salts. These waters
contain sufficient food to feed a large
number of birds, but the food is usually
very small, consisting of insects, shrimp-
like animals, and tiny plants including
diatoms and algae. The Greater
Flamingo wades in the shallow water,
reaches down with its long neck, and
sucks in the water through its upturned
bill. Inside the bill, small animals are
collected on a comb-like arrangement of fine
plates (lamellae) between which the water
passes. Suitable lakes are few and far between,
and the birds must travel long distances from
one feeding site to another, often in large flocks.
• **NEST** A cone of mud with
a hollow top, in a dense colony
on a mudflat or salt lake.
• **DISTRIBUTION** Scattered
locations in the Caribbean,
Africa, S.W. Europe, and Asia.

*elongated
plumes used in
• display*

*folded
• wing*

FLYING ADULT

JUVENILE

DISTRIBUTION

*blunt,
angled
bill •*

*chick is
down-
covered
and has
a straight
• bill*

*webbed
feet •*

Plumage Sexes alike	Habitat 〰〰 〰 〰〰	Migration Migrant

Family ANATIDAE	Species *Anseranas semipalmata*	Length 85cm (34in)

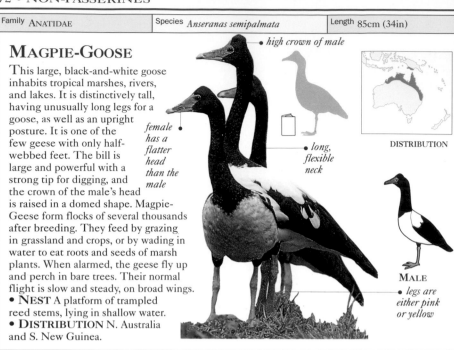

high crown of male

MAGPIE-GOOSE

This large, black-and-white goose inhabits tropical marshes, rivers, and lakes. It is distinctively tall, having unusually long legs for a goose, as well as an upright posture. It is one of the few geese with only half-webbed feet. The bill is large and powerful with a strong tip for digging, and the crown of the male's head is raised in a domed shape. Magpie-Geese form flocks of several thousands after breeding. They feed by grazing in grassland and crops, or by wading in water to eat roots and seeds of marsh plants. When alarmed, the geese fly up and perch in bare trees. Their normal flight is slow and steady, on broad wings.
• **NEST** A platform of trampled reed stems, lying in shallow water.
• **DISTRIBUTION** N. Australia and S. New Guinea.

female has a flatter head than the male

long, flexible neck

DISTRIBUTION

MALE
• *legs are either pink or yellow*

Plumage Sexes alike	Habitat	Migration Partial migrant

Family ANATIDAE	Species *Dendrocygna eytoni*	Length 60cm (24in)

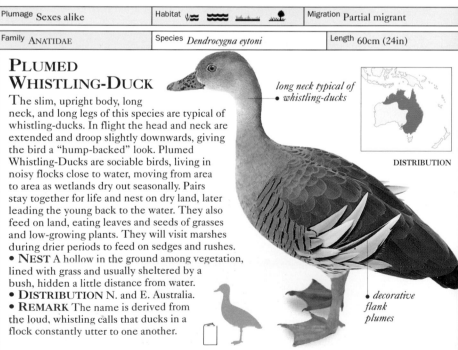

PLUMED WHISTLING-DUCK

The slim, upright body, long neck, and long legs of this species are typical of whistling-ducks. In flight the head and neck are extended and droop slightly downwards, giving the bird a "hump-backed" look. Plumed Whistling-Ducks are sociable birds, living in noisy flocks close to water, moving from area to area as wetlands dry out seasonally. Pairs stay together for life and nest on dry land, later leading the young back to the water. They also feed on land, eating leaves and seeds of grasses and low-growing plants. They will visit marshes during drier periods to feed on sedges and rushes.
• **NEST** A hollow in the ground among vegetation, lined with grass and usually sheltered by a bush, hidden a little distance from water.
• **DISTRIBUTION** N. and E. Australia.
• **REMARK** The name is derived from the loud, whistling calls that ducks in a flock constantly utter to one another.

long neck typical of whistling-ducks

DISTRIBUTION

decorative flank plumes

Plumage Sexes alike	Habitat	Migration Partial migrant

Family ANATIDAE	Species *Cygnus olor*	Length 152cm (60in)

MUTE SWAN

This species occurs on freshwater lakes and rivers, and is the largest and heaviest swimming bird in this habitat. It is identified by the red colour of the bill in adult birds, contrasting with the grey bills of juveniles, and with the yellow bills of adults of other swan species in its range. Its body is streamlined for swimming and its legs are short and strong. The neck is long and flexible enough to reach underwater for aquatic plants and roots, which are the bird's main food. The diet also includes worms, shellfish, and other small animals. It leaves the water to graze, but is slow and ungainly on dry land, and never ventures far from water. The Mute Swan flies on tapering wings, with its neck stretched forwards. Pairs stay together for life. When not breeding, the birds are sociable, forming flocks on lakes, rivers, and estuaries, but nesting pairs defend their territories vigorously against other swans. As its name implies, this species is silent, apart from hisses, grunts, and throaty noises.

DISTRIBUTION

• **NEST** A large mound of plant material placed in reeds, on a small island, on the shore of a lake, or beside a river or stream.
• **DISTRIBUTION** Scattered areas across Eurasia. Introduced in areas of North America, South Africa, Australia, and New Zealand.

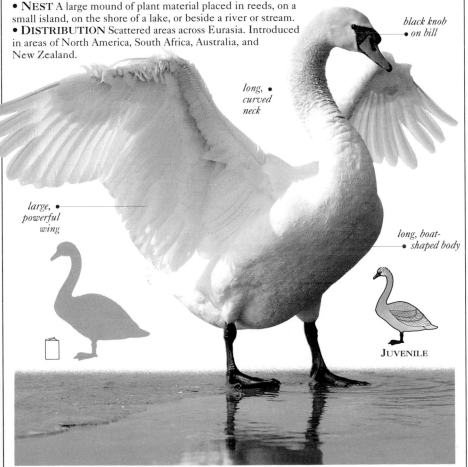

black knob • on bill

long, • curved neck

large, • powerful wing

long, boat- • shaped body

JUVENILE

Plumage Sexes differ slightly	Habitat 〰〰 〰〰	Migration Non-migrant

Family ANATIDAE	Species *Anser anser*	Length 90cm (35in)

GREYLAG GOOSE

This goose is seen swimming on rivers, lakes, and marshes, and walking or running in grassland and pasture. It is strongly built and has a short, stout bill that can demolish leaves and stems, and dig up roots for food. Its flight is strong and direct, showing conspicuous, blue-grey wing-coverts, and birds often travel in V-formation. The Greylag is an alert, suspicious goose, raising the alarm at the slightest disturbance with loud, harsh calls.
• NEST A shallow, natural depression in the ground, lined with leaves and an inner cup of feather down.
• DISTRIBUTION Across Eurasia apart from N. Russia and N. Siberia. Winters as far south as N. Africa, Iran, India, and China.
• REMARK Farm geese (often white) are the domesticated form of the Greylag Goose.

EASTERN FORM

"ribbed" neck feathers

WESTERN FORM

DISTRIBUTION

Plumage Sexes alike	Habitat	Migration Partial migrant

Family ANATIDAE	Species *Anser caerulescens*	Length 70cm (28in)

SNOW GOOSE

An Arctic goose breeding in marshy parts of the tundra, this species feeds by digging up roots and bulbs, and also grazes on buds and leaves. It is sociable, even in the breeding season, when pairs nest only a short distance apart. After breeding, the geese migrate in flocks, sometimes several thousand strong, to winter on marshes and coastal grassland. The call is a harsh cackle.
• NEST A natural hollow in the ground, lined with leaves and an inner down cup.
• DISTRIBUTION Breeds in Arctic zone of North America. Winters as far south as Mexico.
• REMARK There are two colour phases (*p. 13*): white, and "blue" (grey, tinged blue in parts).

"BLUE" PHASE

short, strong bill

snowy white plumage

WHITE PHASE

DISTRIBUTION

Plumage Sexes alike	Habitat	Migration Migrant

Family ANATIDAE	Species *Anser canagicus*	Length 65cm (26in)

EMPEROR GOOSE

A dark goose with a white head, this species breeds near the coast in the Arctic tundra and winters in family parties on rocky shores and islands. It feeds on a mixed diet that includes green plants, seaweed, and shellfish.
• **NEST** A hollow lined with down and moss.
• **DISTRIBUTION** Breeds in coastal tundra of Alaska and N.E. Siberia. Winters as far south as W. USA and Kamchatka.
• **REMARK** The head and neck are sometimes stained orange by iron salts in the water in which the birds dip for food.

JUVENILE

ORANGE STAIN

heavy body •

• *barred pattern*

short legs •

DISTRIBUTION

Plumage Sexes alike	Habitat	Migration Migrant

Family ANATIDAE	Species *Branta canadensis*	Length 115cm (45in)

CANADA GOOSE

Mainly dark, with white markings on the face and breast, this goose is becoming increasingly common. Originally a bird that lived mainly in tundra and prairie grassland, it has become more willing in recent decades to explore new breeding areas. Canada Geese have expanded into freshwater sites in woodland, and have multiplied in towns, where their diet of grass and other low-growing plants is always available. Flocks fly in V-formation, often not far above the ground, uttering loud, honking calls.
• **NEST** A natural hollow in dry ground close to water, lined with a little grass and down feathers.
• **DISTRIBUTION** Breeds throughout N. America and in E. Siberia. Winters as far south as New Mexico, E. China, and Japan. Introduced in N.W. Europe.
• **REMARK** There are several subspecies, some little larger than a Mallard (*see p. 79*).

white "chin-strap" •

• *white tail coverts*

• *short, strong legs*

DISTRIBUTION

Plumage Sexes alike	Habitat	Migration Migrant

Family ANATIDAE	Species *Branta ruficollis*	Length 55cm (22in)

RED-BREASTED GOOSE

This rare goose is a migrant to the Arctic, breeding on mountain tundra and feeding mainly on grasses and sedges. Other foods include broadleaved plants, roots, tubers, and, in winter, cultivated grain. Migrating birds fly in ragged groups or in slanting lines, rather than in the V-formation well-known in other species of geese. The frequent call is a harshly piercing, double note.

• **NEST** A hollow, lined with down and feathers, in the top of a raised piece of ground. Pairs often choose a site close to the nest of a Peregrine Falcon (*see p. 105*). Surprisingly, this relationship gives protection to the geese, as the falcon attacks or deters any predators that approach the nest intending to attack the geese or steal their young.

flank feathers overlapping the wing

chestnut coloured breast

• **DISTRIBUTION** Breeds in Arctic Siberia. Winters near the Black, Caspian, and Aral Seas.

• **REMARK** Endangered, mainly due to being heavily hunted in its winter range.

DISTRIBUTION

Plumage Sexes alike	Habitat	Migration Migrant

Family ANATIDAE	Species *Alopochen aegyptiacus*	Length 75cm (30in)

EGYPTIAN GOOSE

This bird lives in marshes, lakes, and rivers where it sometimes swims and dives, but is more usually seen on land. It grazes on grass, also eating leaves and seeds of plants including crops, and possibly occasional insects. The female can be distinguished by her trumpet-like quacking in contrast with the male's soft, husky calls. Pairs mate for life, forming flocks after breeding which perch and roost in trees.

• **NEST** A hollow in the ground under vegetation, or a hole in a cliff, cave, or tree.

• **DISTRIBUTION** Upper Nile Valley and Africa south of the Sahara; introduced in England.

• **REMARK** Although it is called a goose, this bird is really a species of shelduck.

shaggy neck feathers

GREY PHASE

glossy green patch (speculum) on hind edge of wing

DISTRIBUTION

Plumage Sexes alike	Habitat	Migration Partial migrant

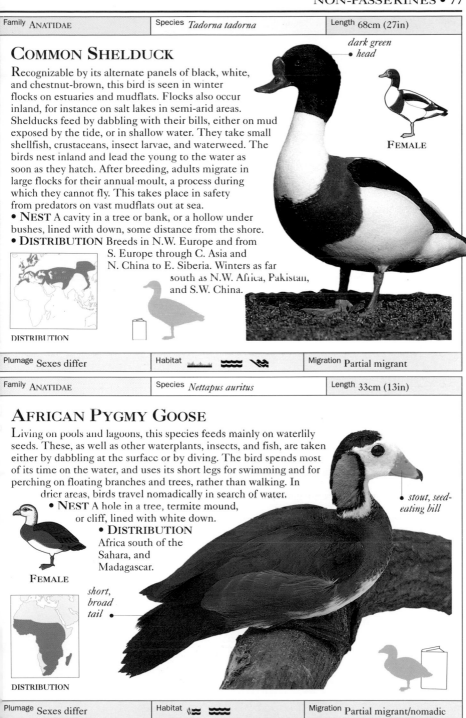

| Family ANATIDAE | Species *Tadorna tadorna* | Length 68cm (27in) |

dark green
• head

COMMON SHELDUCK

Recognizable by its alternate panels of black, white, and chestnut-brown, this bird is seen in winter flocks on estuaries and mudflats. Flocks also occur inland, for instance on salt lakes in semi-arid areas. Shelducks feed by dabbling with their bills, either on mud exposed by the tide, or in shallow water. They take small shellfish, crustaceans, insect larvae, and waterweed. The birds nest inland and lead the young to the water as soon as they hatch. After breeding, adults migrate in large flocks for their annual moult, a process during which they cannot fly. This takes place in safety from predators on vast mudflats out at sea.
• **NEST** A cavity in a tree or bank, or a hollow under bushes, lined with down, some distance from the shore.
• **DISTRIBUTION** Breeds in N.W. Europe and from S. Europe through C. Asia and N. China to E. Siberia. Winters as far south as N.W. Africa, Pakistan, and S.W. China.

FEMALE

DISTRIBUTION

| Plumage Sexes differ | Habitat | Migration Partial migrant |

| Family ANATIDAE | Species *Nettapus auritus* | Length 33cm (13in) |

AFRICAN PYGMY GOOSE

Living on pools and lagoons, this species feeds mainly on waterlily seeds. These, as well as other waterplants, insects, and fish, are taken either by dabbling at the surface or by diving. The bird spends most of its time on the water, and uses its short legs for swimming and for perching on floating branches and trees, rather than walking. In drier areas, birds travel nomadically in search of water.
• **NEST** A hole in a tree, termite mound, or cliff, lined with white down.
• **DISTRIBUTION** Africa south of the Sahara, and Madagascar.

stout, seed-
• eating bill

FEMALE

short,
broad
tail •

DISTRIBUTION

| Plumage Sexes differ | Habitat | Migration Partial migrant/nomadic |

Family ANATIDAE	Species *Aix sponsa*	Length 47cm (18½in)

WOOD DUCK

This species lives in wooded lakes and rivers and feeds on acorns, nuts, seeds, green plants, and small invertebrates. It is one of the few ducks that perch readily on branches. Another characteristic feature is that it nests in trees. Soon after hatching, the ducklings jump down from the nest at their mother's call, and follow her to the water.
• **NEST** A tree-hole or nest-box, lined with down.
• **DISTRIBUTION** North America to Cuba.

crest raised in display

bare, red eye-ring

finely spotted breast

white edges of flank feathers

FEMALE

DISTRIBUTION

Plumage Sexes differ	Habitat 〜〜 🌲	Migration Partial migrant

Family ANATIDAE	Species *Aix galericulata*	Length 47cm (18½in)

MANDARIN DUCK

A shy, woodland duck, this species rests by day in shrubs overhanging water, and feeds in woodland streams and lakes at dusk. The male has a sweeping, bushy crest on its head and one enlarged, orange feather on each inner wing. The Mandarin prefers broadleaved woodland, especially oak, eating acorns and other seeds, nuts, plants, land snails, insects, and small fish.
• **NEST** A hole in a tree, lined with down, often situated over water.
• **DISTRIBUTION** Breeds in E. Asia. Winters as far south as S. China.
• **REMARK** Introduced as an ornamental bird in S. England, which now has a significant part of the world population.

crest raised in display

sail-shaped inner wing feather

FEMALE

DISTRIBUTION

Plumage Sexes differ	Habitat 〜〜 🌲	Migration Partial migrant

Family ANATIDAE	Species *Anas crecca*	Length 37cm (14½in)

COMMON TEAL

This small dabbling duck often swims inconspicuously on shallow pools where marsh vegetation provides partial cover. If disturbed, it rockets up from the water in rapid flight, revealing a green, white, and black wing patch (the speculum). It feeds on a wide range of plants and small animals, mainly eating seeds in winter and animal food in summer. As in other dabbling ducks, males utter whistling calls but females quack.
• **NEST** A depression in dry grass, lined with down, among marsh plants.
• **DISTRIBUTION** Breeds in North America and Eurasia. Winters as far south as Central America, Africa, India, and S.E. Asia.

green, white, and black • wing patch (speculum)

• bird rising in steep, rapid flight

DISTRIBUTION

FEMALE

Plumage Sexes differ	Habitat 〰〰 〰	Migration Partial migrant

Family ANATIDAE	Species *Anas platyrhynchos*	Length 58cm (23in)

MALLARD

A dabbling duck that seems unaffected by human disturbance and changing conditions, the Mallard occurs on all inland waters, large or small. It prefers those with plenty of vegetation. To feed, it swims with its bill dabbling in the water surface. As water passes through the bill, small food items such as seeds, leaves, insects, and worms, are strained out by a comb-like arrangement of plates. The Mallard also upends to reach down to the mud or weeds for food, and it grazes on land.
• **NEST** A hollow in the ground or in a raised site, such as a pollarded tree, lined with stems, leaves, feathers, and down.
• **DISTRIBUTION** Breeds in much of North America and Eurasia. Winters as far south as Mexico, N. Africa, and S.E. Asia.
• **REMARK** The farmyard duck, in its many different breeds, is the domestic form of the Mallard.

• blue and white wing patch (speculum)

DISTRIBUTION

FEMALE

two curled • tail feathers

Plumage Sexes differ	Habitat 〰〰 〰	Migration Partial migrant

Family ANATIDAE	Species *Anas acuta*	L. 65cm (26in)/50cm (20in)

NORTHERN PINTAIL

A slim dabbling duck identified by the male's long, tapering tail feathers, this species flies rapidly, its wings making a swishing sound. Occurring mainly in pairs and small parties on open, shallow waters, the Pintail avoids reedbeds and tall marsh plants. It rests on the water by day and feeds at night. The usual feeding method is to upend in the water and reach down for roots, seeds, and tubers, but birds also go ashore to graze, or dabble in surface waters for seeds and small animals. Northern Pintails usually migrate to the coast in winter.

• **NEST** A hollow, lined with vegetation and down.
• **DISTRIBUTION** Breeds in North America and Eurasia. Winters as far south as Central America, Africa, and India.

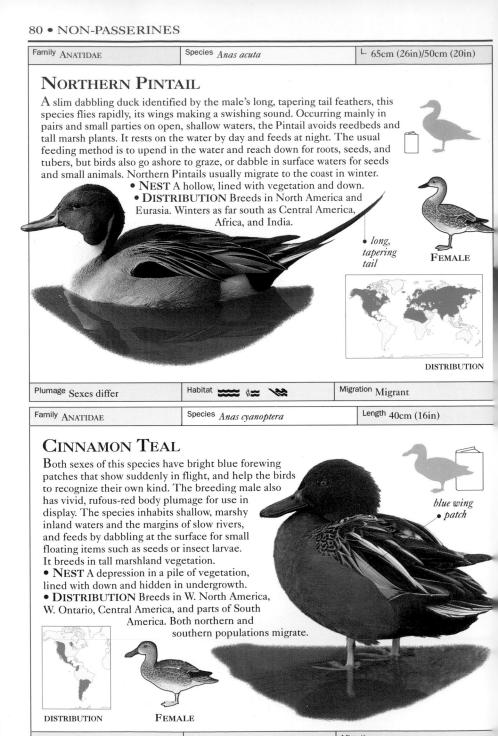

long,
tapering
tail

FEMALE

DISTRIBUTION

Plumage Sexes differ	Habitat	Migration Migrant

Family ANATIDAE	Species *Anas cyanoptera*	Length 40cm (16in)

CINNAMON TEAL

Both sexes of this species have bright blue forewing patches that show suddenly in flight, and help the birds to recognize their own kind. The breeding male also has vivid, rufous-red body plumage for use in display. The species inhabits shallow, marshy inland waters and the margins of slow rivers, and feeds by dabbling at the surface for small floating items such as seeds or insect larvae. It breeds in tall marshland vegetation.

• **NEST** A depression in a pile of vegetation, lined with down and hidden in undergrowth.
• **DISTRIBUTION** Breeds in W. North America, W. Ontario, Central America, and parts of South America. Both northern and southern populations migrate.

blue wing
• *patch*

DISTRIBUTION   FEMALE

Plumage Sexes differ	Habitat	Migration Migrant

| Family ANATIDAE | Species *Malacorhynchus membranaceus* | Length 42cm (16½in) |

PINK-EARED DUCK

This dabbling duck often inhabits regions where dry conditions are usual, and survives by finding places where rain has caused temporary flooding. These waters contain microscopic animals on which the duck feeds. It moves through shallow water, using its bill to trawl for food. Special flaps at the side of the bill-tip help to draw in water, which then passes over a series of fine plates that strain out the tiny animals, before being expelled at the sides. When the flooded areas dry out, the ducks travel around nomadically in search of new feeding grounds.

pink ear patch

fleshy flap hanging from the bill

- **NEST** A hole in a treetrunk or stump, lined with down.
- **DISTRIBUTION** W. and E. (mainly southeast) Australia.

DISTRIBUTION

| Plumage Sexes alike | Habitat | Migration Nomadic |

| Family ANATIDAE | Species *Aythya valisineria* | Length 53cm (21in) |

CANVASBACK

FEMALE

A diving duck of open water on lakes, rivers, estuaries, and coasts, this species is identified by the long, sloping outline of its forehead and bill. The legs are strong and set widely on the body for underwater swimming. The Canvasback dives to feed on waterplants or shellfish, reaching depths of 9m (29ft 3in). The species is common and sociable, forming large flocks in winter. It nests inland on small areas of water, such as prairie pools and marshes, and migrates after breeding to estuaries and the sea. Flocks fly strongly and fast, often forming slanting lines.

long, sloping forehead

- **NEST** A mound of dried reeds and sedges, lined with down, and situated on the ground.
- **DISTRIBUTION** Canada and N. and W. USA. Winters as far south as Mexico.

DISTRIBUTION

| Plumage Sexes differ | Habitat | Migration Migrant |

Family ANATIDAE	Species *Aythya fuligula*	Length 43cm (17in)

TUFTED DUCK

A slender crest dangling over the nape identifies this diving duck. Naturally a bird of deep, open water on lakes and rivers, it has adapted itself to live in built-up areas. Of all the birds seen in an urban setting, the Tufted Duck is unique for two features: males have black plumage with white sides and bellies; and both sexes have yellow, button eyes. Tufted Ducks swim well underwater, sometimes to depths of 14m (45ft), and feed on a wide range of tiny aquatic animals and plants.
• **NEST** A hollow lined with grass and down, usually in vegetation close to water.
• **DISTRIBUTION** Breeds in Eurasia. Winters as far south as S. Sudan and N. India.

FEMALE

DISTRIBUTION

yellow
• *iris*

tail slopes down into the water

• *white flank patch*

Plumage Sexes differ	Habitat 〰️ 〰️	Migration Migrant

Family ANATIDAE	Species *Somateria spectabilis*	Length 55cm (22in)

KING EIDER

This stout sea duck dives for shellfish in cold, coastal waters at all times of year. The feathering is dense, with a thick layer of down. Males have an unusual, bulging forehead.
• **NEST** A hollow lined with down, which the birds pluck from their undersides.
• **DISTRIBUTION** Breeds in N. Alaska, Canada, and Eurasia. Winters as far south as S. Alaska, New England, and Kamchatka.

FEMALE

DISTRIBUTION

high •
forehead bulge

decorative, upward-curving • *feathers*

• *plumes drooping from the shoulder*

Plumage Sexes differ	Habitat 〰️ 〰️ 〰️	Migration Migrant

Family ANATIDAE	Species *Histrionicus histrionicus*	Length 42cm (16½in)

HARLEQUIN DUCK

The brilliant, fragmented pattern of this duck's plumage is a subtle camouflage against clear, moving waters. The Harlequin breeds beside cold, fast-flowing streams and rivers, feeding on the aquatic insects that cling to rocks and shingle. It flies strongly and low, following watercourses. After breeding it migrates to the sea, where it dives for shellfish, crustaceans, and other food.

DISTRIBUTION

• NEST A hole in a tree or bank, lined with down.
• DISTRIBUTION Breeds in Alaska, Canada, Greenland, Iceland, E. Siberia. Winters on coasts.

FEMALE

short neck

tapering, short bill

strong, compact build for swimming in rough water

Plumage Sexes differ	Habitat 〰〰 〰 〰	Migration Migrant

Family ANATIDAE	Species *Melanitta nigra*	Length 48cm (19in)

BLACK SCOTER

The orange bill patch of the male, and the pale cheeks of the female, identify the Black Scoter. The species spends much of the year at sea. Large flocks float in shallow coastal waters, or fly low over the water in straggling formations. Birds dive, often simultaneously, to feed on mussels and other marine animals.

DISTRIBUTION

FEMALE

• NEST A down-lined hollow on the ground.
• DISTRIBUTION Breeds in tundra of North America and Eurasia. Winters as far as California, N. Africa, and China.

stocky build of a sea-diving duck

stiff, tapering tail

orange patch on bill

Plumage Sexes differ	Habitat 〰〰 〰	Migration Migrant

Family ANATIDAE	Species *Bucephala clangula*	Length 50cm (20in)

COMMON GOLDENEYE

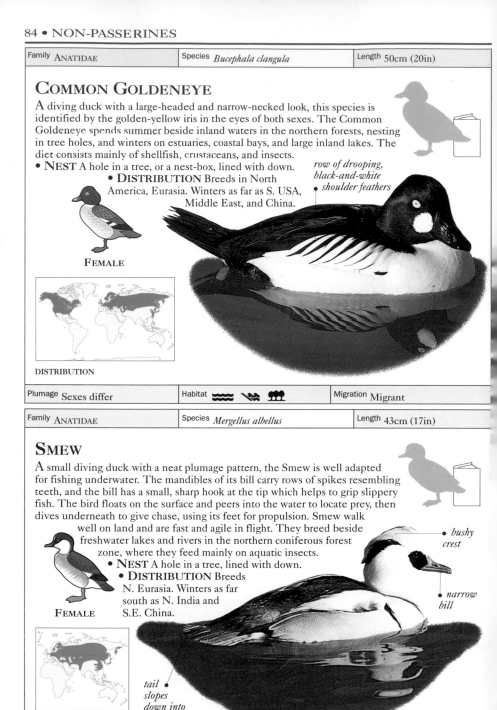

A diving duck with a large-headed and narrow-necked look, this species is identified by the golden-yellow iris in the eyes of both sexes. The Common Goldeneye spends summer beside inland waters in the northern forests, nesting in tree holes, and winters on estuaries, coastal bays, and large inland lakes. The diet consists mainly of shellfish, crustaceans, and insects.

• NEST A hole in a tree, or a nest-box, lined with down.
• DISTRIBUTION Breeds in North America, Eurasia. Winters as far as S. USA, Middle East, and China.

row of drooping, black-and-white • shoulder feathers

FEMALE

DISTRIBUTION

Plumage Sexes differ	Habitat	Migration Migrant

Family ANATIDAE	Species *Mergellus albellus*	Length 43cm (17in)

SMEW

A small diving duck with a neat plumage pattern, the Smew is well adapted for fishing underwater. The mandibles of its bill carry rows of spikes resembling teeth, and the bill has a small, sharp hook at the tip which helps to grip slippery fish. The bird floats on the surface and peers into the water to locate prey, then dives underneath to give chase, using its feet for propulsion. Smew walk well on land and are fast and agile in flight. They breed beside freshwater lakes and rivers in the northern coniferous forest zone, where they feed mainly on aquatic insects.

• NEST A hole in a tree, lined with down.
• DISTRIBUTION Breeds N. Eurasia. Winters as far south as N. India and S.E. China.

bushy crest

narrow bill

FEMALE

tail • slopes down into the water

DISTRIBUTION

Plumage Sexes differ	Habitat	Migration Migrant

Family ANATIDAE	Species *Mergus merganser*	Length 65cm (26in)

GOOSANDER

This large, fish-eating duck is adapted for fast underwater swimming in pursuit of its prey. Its body is streamlined and the bill is long and narrow. Each mandible carries a row of backward-pointing spikes on each side. These, and the hooked bill-tip, help to grip slippery fish. Goosanders fish in estuaries, lowland rivers, lakes, and in the fast-flowing rivers and streams of the uplands. They fly fast and low, often following the course of a river. Young birds start by learning to hunt aquatic insects, then graduate to fish. Goosanders live in family parties or small flocks, often roosting in larger numbers on the ground or in trees.
• **NEST** A cavity in a tree, bank, rock crevice, or stone wall.
• **DISTRIBUTION** Breeds in N. North America and Eurasia. Winters as far south as S. USA and C. China.

DISTRIBUTION

• sleeked-back crest on nape

FEMALE

Plumage Sexes differ	Habitat	Migration Migrant

Family ANATIDAE	Species *Oxyura leucocephala*	Length 46cm (18in)

WHITE-HEADED DUCK

A diving duck of freshwater habitats, upper estuaries, and lakes where fresh and salt water mix, this is one of the "stiff-tailed" species. The tail normally trails on or below the surface, but is held up vertically in display. The White-headed Duck prefers open, shallow waters, with a fringe of reeds, feeding on waterplants and aquatic animals. It rarely goes ashore, walking clumsily when it does so.
• **NEST** A hole in a tree or a hollow in the ground.
• **DISTRIBUTION** Breeds in scattered areas from S. Spain to Middle East and C. Asia. Eastern populations migrate as far south as N.W. India.

FEMALE

DISTRIBUTION

tail lying in the water •

• blue bill with a swollen base

Plumage Sexes differ	Habitat	Migration Partial migrant

Family ANATIDAE	Species *Biziura lobata*	L. 68cm (27in)/53cm (21in)

MUSK DUCK

This large diving duck has a rounded back, a stout head, and a heavy bill from which an unusual, disc-shaped lobe is suspended. It gets its name from the musky scent of its plumage. The Musk Duck feeds mainly on small aquatic animals, ranging in size from insects to frogs. It rarely leaves the water, moving with difficulty on land.

• **NEST** A hollow among plants at the water's edge; occasionally a hollow in a fallen tree.
• **DISTRIBUTION** S. Australia.
• **REMARK** Males are much larger than females.

DISTRIBUTION

disc-shaped lobe for display

FEMALE

tail lying in the water

Plumage Sexes differ	Habitat 〰️ 〰️	Migration Non-migrant

Family CATHARTIDAE	Species *Cathartes aura*	Length 70cm (28in)

TURKEY-VULTURE

A common vulture that is often seen soaring and circling in search of food, this species feeds mainly on carrion. Like other vultures of the Americas, it uses its acute sense of smell to locate a dead animal. Besides eating carrion, it sometimes kills small animals such as lizards, or steals eggs or nestlings of birds.
• **NEST** A platform of sticks, situated in a tree, cliff, or rocky place.
• **DISTRIBUTION** From S. Canada to S. South America and the Falklands.

JUVENILE

DISTRIBUTION

bird sunbathing with spread wings

Plumage Sexes alike	Habitat 〰️ 〰️ 〰️ ✈	Migration Partial migrant

Family CATHARTIDAE	Species *Gymnogyps californianus*	Length 115cm (45in)

CALIFORNIA CONDOR

In its natural state this large, carrion-eating bird lives by cruising over a wide area to find food. It cannot gain the required height without calm, warm weather and rising air currents on which to soar and circle upwards. On cold or very windy days the Condor has to remain on the ground. When not foraging, it spends long periods idling or preening its feathers at a roost site.

• **NEST** A single egg is laid on the ground, on a rock ledge, or in a cave.
• **DISTRIBUTION** W. USA (but now mainly found in captivity).
• **REMARK** The California Condor was considered a threat to livestock and birds were killed to the point where the species was in danger of extinction. Prospects of recovery were restricted by the slow breeding rate of the Condor, which reproduces every two years and takes five to seven years to mature. Numbers continued to fall, with only 17 left in 1984. The remaining population was taken into captivity in the middle 1980s. Since then they have increased with captive breeding, and a few birds are now being experimentally released into the wild.

DISTRIBUTION

bare head of a
• *scavenging bird*

inflated
throat
• *pouch*

• *bare neck*

JUVENILE

white wing
• *mark*

• *feet are very large, with long toes and claws, but are too weak for hunting live prey*

Plumage Sexes alike	Habitat	Migration Non-migrant

Family CATHARTIDAE	Species *Sarcoramphus papa*	Length 75cm (30in)

KING VULTURE

colourful, bare head

Living chiefly in rainforest, this vulture is recognized by pied plumage, a brightly-coloured head, broad wings, and a short tail. In calm weather it flies low over the treetops or descends to the forest floor to feed. On warm days it finds rising air currents (thermals) and circles to gain height. Foraging birds often leave the forest for tropical grassland, particularly in areas where cattle are ranched. Though not normally sociable, King Vultures sometimes gather at a large carcass. Here they take precedence over other species because of their greater size and strength. Within the forest, King Vultures are not easily observed, but are known to take stranded fish from sandbanks in rivers running through the forest. They are also thought to kill small reptiles and young mammals.

bulging crop stores recently eaten food

JUVENILE

• **NEST** Few data recorded; where observed, the single egg is placed in a hollow in the stump of a forest tree.
• **DISTRIBUTION** Mexico to N. Argentina.

large feet

DISTRIBUTION

Plumage Sexes alike	Habitat	Migration Non-migrant

Family PANDIONIDAE	Species *Pandion haliaetus*	L· 50cm (20in)/58cm (23in)

OSPREY

crest pushed up by the wind (normally lies flat)

Often soaring over lakes, rivers, and coasts, the Osprey is a fish-hawk, swooping down to take its prey from the water. It plunge-dives with feet first and wings raised, often submerging itself almost completely, to reappear with a fish and continue with its flight. The prey is usually carried head forwards, held in both feet, to be eaten on a tree branch or on the nest.

dark band through the eye and down to the nape

• **NEST** A mass of sticks, placed on a tree, a seashore, a crag, or an artificial nest platform.
• **DISTRIBUTION** Breeds in North America, Eurasia, Africa, and Australia. Winters in South America, Africa, and Asia.
• **REMARK** Females are larger than males.

long claws for holding fish

JUVENILE

DISTRIBUTION

Plumage Sexes alike	Habitat	Migration Migrant

Family ACCIPITRIDAE	Species *Pernis apivorus*	L. 50cm (20in)/58cm (23in)

WESTERN HONEY-BUZZARD

This unusual bird of prey obtains nine-tenths of its food by attacking the nests of wasps and wild bees. It watches and follows the insects, digs out their nests, and takes honey, young, and adult insects. Dense leg feathering and heavy leg scales protect the bird from stings. It also eats larger animals such as mice and frogs. After breeding, the birds form flocks in which they migrate to countries where their prey is active all year round.

DARK PHASE

• **NEST** A large, untidy cup nest made of sticks, high in a tree.
• **DISTRIBUTION** Breeds in much of Europe, W. Siberia, and C. Asia. Winters as far south as Central Africa.

PALE PHASE

• **REMARKS** Females are larger than males. Colour varies from dark to light through a series of phases (*see p. 13*). Variation is seen most clearly underneath the wing.

legs folded back

broad wings for soaring flight

DISTRIBUTION

Plumage Sexes alike	Habitat	Migration Migrant

Family ACCIPITRIDAE	Species *Milvus milvus*	L. 58cm (23in)/65cm (26in)

RED KITE

A slender bird of prey with a deeply forked tail, the Red Kite has a graceful look in the air. It flies with slow, deep wingbeats, glides for long periods, and performs quick, agile swoops to snatch small animals, from mouse to rabbit size.

pale head

• **NEST** A large, shallow structure, made of twigs, earth, and wool, and placed in a tree.
• **DISTRIBUTION** Much of Europe, N.W. Africa, and the Middle East.
• **REMARK** Females are larger than males.

long flank feathers

DISTRIBUTION

JUVENILE

Plumage Sexes alike	Habitat	Migration Partial migrant

Family ACCIPITRIDAE	Species *Haliaeetus vocifer*	L. 63cm (25in)/75cm (30in)

AFRICAN FISH-EAGLE

Most often seen singly or in pairs on high branches in its waterside territory, this is a specialist, fish-eating eagle. Watching from a perch more often than hunting in flight, it swoops to snatch fish from just beneath the surface, using a backward swing of the feet. It also eats stranded fish and other carrion, as well as killing waterbirds. The species is well-known for its yelping, four-note call.
• **NEST** A large pile of sticks with a central bowl, lined with grass and usually placed in a tree near water.
• **DISTRIBUTION** Africa south of the Sahara.
• **REMARK** Females are larger than males.

DISTRIBUTION

JUVENILE

bird launching itself into the air from a perch

Plumage Sexes alike	Habitat 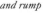	Migration Non-migrant

Family ACCIPITRIDAE	Species *Haliaeetus leucocephalus*	L. 75cm (30in)/110cm (43in)

BALD EAGLE

pure white head and neck

This large eagle gets its food from a wide range of sources. Most of its victims are caught live, including ducks, gulls, other seabirds, fish from lakes or the sea, and salmon from rivers. Bald Eagles challenge Ospreys (*see p. 88*), forcing them to abandon their catch. They also feed on dead and dying fish, as well as other carrion.
• **NEST** A large structure of sticks and twigs, situated in a tree close to water.
• **DISTRIBUTION** Breeds in much of North America. Northern populations winter in S. USA and parts of Mexico.
• **REMARK** Females larger than males.

strong, grasping feet

white tail and rump

DISTRIBUTION

JUVENILE

Plumage Sexes alike	Habitat	Migration Partial migrant

| Family ACCIPITRIDAE | Species *Haliaeetus albicilla* | L. 70cm (28in)/91cm (36in) |

WHITE-TAILED EAGLE

A large, heavy eagle of rocky coasts, islands, estuaries, and inland lakes, this species is recognized by its repeated, yelping calls. It is adept at snatching fish and birds from lakes and the sea, and seeks carrion along the shore. Pairs stay permanently in their territories in areas where winters are sufficiently mild.

• **NEST** A large structure of sticks, to which more material is added each year, with a hollow in the centre, lined with twigs and sometimes wool, placed on a cliff, rock ledge, or tree.

• **DISTRIBUTION** Breeds in Greenland and N. Eurasia. Some northern and northeastern populations migrate as far south as the Middle East and C. China.

• **REMARK** Females are larger than males.

prominent brow shields eye from sunlight

JUVENILE

white tail

DISTRIBUTION

| Plumage Sexes alike | Habitat 〰 🦆 〰 〰 | Migration Partial migrant |

| Family ACCIPITRIDAE | Species *Torgos tracheliotus* | Length 98cm (39in) |

LAPPET-FACED VULTURE

This large vulture takes first place at any animal carcass, dominating the smaller carrion-eating birds. Its heavy bill enables it to tear open the carcass, incidentally helping smaller species to feed, and to consume tougher parts such as skin and ligaments, for which there is less competition. The Lappet-face roosts solitarily or in pairs, and spends much of the day in soaring flight.

• **NEST** A platform of sticks with a central hollow, lined and placed on a flat-topped bush or tree.

• **DISTRIBUTION** Parts of Africa, Israel, S. and W. Arabian Peninsula.

bare head and neck of a scavenger

lappets (folds of bare skin)

broad wing for soaring flight

long legs for walking

JUVENILE

DISTRIBUTION

| Plumage Sexes alike | Habitat ⤏ ✈ | Migration Non-migrant |

| Family ACCIPITRIDAE | Species *Neophron percnopterus* | L. 63cm (25in)/70cm (28in) |

EGYPTIAN VULTURE

A small vulture with a bare face and shaggy neck feathering, this species occurs in open plains and semi-desert. It cannot compete with larger vultures at an animal carcass. On the other hand, being smaller, it is less dependent on rising currents of warm air to gain height, and starts flying soon after dawn, so reaching the carrion first. It raids nesting colonies of birds, seizing chicks and carrying away eggs in its bill. When attacking an Ostrich nest, it lifts stones with its bill and throws them about until one of the eggs is cracked.

bare face and throat

JUVENILE

• **NEST** A small platform made of sticks, lined with dung, hair, and skin, and placed on a rock ledge.
• **DISTRIBUTION** S. Europe, Middle East, Africa, W. Asia, and the Indian subcontinent.
• **REMARK** Females are larger than males.

DISTRIBUTION

long wings

| Plumage Sexes alike | Habitat | Migration Partial migrant |

| Family ACCIPITRIDAE | Species *Gypaetus barbatus* | L. 100cm (39in)/110cm (43in) |

LAMMERGEIER

A very large carrion-eating bird, thinly dispersed in its mountain habitat, the Lammergeier glides and soars for long periods on long, tapering wings and a wedge-shaped tail. It can eat parts of the carcass that other carrion-eaters cannot digest, including bones, which it smashes by dropping them on to rocks from the air.

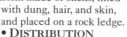

JUVENILE

• **NEST** A platform of twigs with a central hollow lined with grass, hair, skin, and bones, in a cave or on a cliff ledge.
• **DISTRIBUTION** Scattered areas in S. Europe, Africa, and through the Middle East to C. Asia.
• **REMARK** Females are larger than males.

tuft of bristly, black feathers

thick covering of feathers on upper leg

DISTRIBUTION

| Plumage Sexes alike | Habitat | Migration Non-migrant |

Family ACCIPITRIDAE	Species *Terathopius ecaudatus*	L. 55cm (22in)/70cm (28in)

BATELEUR

Beautifully adapted for prolonged and fast gliding
and for agility in the air, this small eagle inhabits scrub,
open woodland, and savanna (tropical and subtropical
grassland) with scattered trees. It roosts in trees and
is on the wing for most of the day, criss-crossing the
same area in very fast, gliding flight, as it searches for
prey. The shortness of the tail gives the Bateleur
an "all wings" appearance in flight, and causes the
gliding bird to swerve first to one side, then to the
other. The bird swoops on its prey, sometimes from
a great height, intercepting birds in flight, and taking
reptiles, small mammals, and large insects from the
ground. Pairs in courtship perform spectacular aerial
manoeuvres, from which the name Bateleur (French
for a juggler or acrobat) is derived.

• **NEST** A cup nest
made of twigs, lined
with leaves, and placed
in the canopy of a tree.
• **DISTRIBUTION**
Africa south of the Sahara.
• **REMARK** Females are
larger than males.

DISTRIBUTION

JUVENILE

very short • tail hidden by wings

Plumage Sexes alike	Habitat	Migration Non-migrant

Family ACCIPITRIDAE	Species *Melierax canorus*	L. 50cm (20in)/58cm (23in)

PALE CHANTING-GOSHAWK

This is a large hawk with long wings and tail,
inhabiting open landscapes such as arid thornbush
and semi-desert. It watches from a perch and swoops
in rapid flight to take a small animal such as a lizard,
bird, or mammal, or sometimes even a large insect.
The bird follows through with its flight, eventually
landing on a new perch or circling back to where it
began. Adults generally live in pairs, and each pair occupies
its own territory. Pale Chanting-Goshawks roost in trees by
night, and rest in shady foliage during midday heat.
• **NEST** A platform of sticks with a central hollow
which is lined with hair, dung, grass, and skin, placed
in the fork of a thorn tree just below the canopy.

prominent • brow

FEMALE

• **DISTRIBUTION**
Africa south of the Sahara.
• **REMARK** Females
are larger than males.

DISTRIBUTION

long legs

long, narrow wings

Plumage Sexes alike	Habitat	Migration Non-migrant

Family ACCIPITRIDAE	Species *Circus cyaneus*	L. 43cm (17in)/50cm (20in)

HEN HARRIER

This species is a typical harrier, hunting by
searching the ground in low, fast, gliding flight.
The wings are usually held in a shallow
"V" shape. This method enables the bird
to surprise small or disabled birds, small
rodents, and even large insects. The species
occurs in open landscapes such as moors,
marshes, steppe grassland, and sand dunes.
• **NEST** A mound of small twigs, grass, and
reeds, placed on the ground in dense cover.
• **DISTRIBUTION** Breeds in much of North
America and Eurasia. Winters as far south as
Central America, N. Africa, and S.E. Asia.
• **REMARK** Females larger than males.

• *disc of feathers around the face*

MALE

• *long wings*

long tail

DISTRIBUTION

Plumage Sexes differ	Habitat	Migration Migrant

Family ACCIPITRIDAE	Species *Accipiter nisus*	L. 28cm (11in)/38cm (15in)

EURASIAN SPARROWHAWK

Living in woodland and scrub, this is a small
species of hawk that specializes in catching
birds (often passerines) in flight. Usually flying
at a low height, it manoeuvres at speed
among trees and bushes, taking its victims off
their guard and seizing them after a short, fast chase.
• **NEST** A loose structure of twigs with a central
hollow, lined with finer twigs, placed in a tree.
• **DISTRIBUTION** Breeds in much of Eurasia
and N. Africa. Northern populations winter as
far south as N. Africa, N. India, and S. China.
• **REMARK** Females
larger than males.

female has a pale spot on the nape •

MALE

long, grasping toes •

DISTRIBUTION

Plumage Sexes differ	Habitat	Migration Partial migrant

Family ACCIPITRIDAE	Species *Accipiter striatus*	L· 27cm (10½in)/34cm (13½in)

SHARP-SHINNED HAWK

This small, bird-hunting hawk has broad wings
with narrow-tipped primary feathers that splay
out like fingers when the bird soars. Its tail
is long and broad. It is a woodland bird that
hunts by manoeuvring in low flight between
trees and bushes, taking songbirds by surprise
and capturing them in brief, sprinting
chases. In higher and more open flight, or on
migration, it seems to lack power and travels
slowly. As it passes, parties of small, fast-flying
birds such as Common Starlings or Swallows (*see
pp. 270, 375*) "mob" the Sharp-shinned Hawk,
flocking round it with mock attacks.
• **NEST** A platform of sticks and
twigs, lined with bark, smaller
twigs, and feathers, and built in a tree.
• **DISTRIBUTION** Breeds in North America
and Mexico. Northern and mountain populations
winter in southern parts of this range.
• **REMARKS** Females are larger than males.
Observations reveal that the two sexes reduce
competition by taking slightly different sizes
of prey, thus sharing the available food supply.

• *large,
keen eyes*

DISTRIBUTION

JUVENILE

• *long,
grasping
toes*

Plumage Sexes differ slightly	Habitat 🌳🌳🌳 🌿🌿 🏚️	Migration Partial migrant

Family ACCIPITRIDAE	Species *Accipiter gentilis*	L· 48cm (19in)/58cm (23in)

NORTHERN GOSHAWK

A large relative of the Eurasian Sparrowhawk, this
bird lives in mature, tall forest. It hunts in forests,
at the forest edge, and in adjoining areas of open
country, its main prey being birds in flight. The
Goshawk either flies low, taking a bird by surprise,
or it watches from a high perch in a tree and swoops
on its victim. Prey includes crows, jays, pigeons,
thrushes, grouse, pheasants, squirrels, and rabbits.
• **NEST** A platform of twigs and sticks, lined with
bark, smaller twigs, and feathers, built in a tree.
• **DISTRIBUTION** Breeds in North America, Eurasia,
and N. Africa. Northern populations migrate south.
• **REMARK** Females are larger than males.

• *pale,
prominent brow*

*broad, rounded
wing shape
revealed in
• flight*

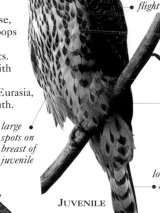

• *typical
hunched
resting
posture*

• *long
tail*

*large
spots on
breast of
juvenile*

JUVENILE

DISTRIBUTION

ADULT

Plumage Sexes differ slightly	Habitat 🌳🌳🌳 🏚️	Migration Partial migrant

| Family ACCIPITRIDAE | Species *Parabuteo unicinctus* | L. 45cm (17¹/₂in)/58cm (23in) |

HARRIS'S HAWK

This is a heavily built hawk of the tropics and subtropics, living in dry regions including semi-desert, semi-arid woodland, and scrub. It is a fast-flying hunter that swoops from a perch to pursue desert rabbits, rats, snakes, lizards, and birds. Unlike other hawks, this species has a strong pattern of cooperative behaviour, in which it is common for three birds to hunt together and share the kill. Larger family parties have been seen hunting in this way. Groups work together to catch prey that has gone into cover, one bird approaching directly to drive it out, the others hanging back, ready to give chase. Often a nesting female is fed by two or more males, and in some cases she mates with two males. The whole group cares for the young.

chestnut wing patch

• **NEST** A neat structure of twigs, roots, and stalks, lined with leaves, grass, and bark, in a tree or on top of a tall yucca or cactus.
• **DISTRIBUTION** From USA south through Central America to Chile and Argentina.
• **REMARK** Females are considerably larger than males.

DISTRIBUTION

JUVENILE

| Plumage Sexes alike | Habitat 〰️ 🛩️ 🌳 | Migration Partial migrant |

| Family ACCIPITRIDAE | Species *Buteo jamaicensis* | L. 48cm (19in)/63cm (25in) |

RED-TAILED HAWK

A typical open-country bird of prey, this species commonly seeks out rising air currents (thermals) on which it circles and soars while looking for prey. Alternatively, it often perches high in a tree to watch for its prey. Any animal that moves is taken, whether mammal, reptile, bird, or large insect. As well as occurring in open landscapes, the Red-tailed Hawk is found in mixed country with both fields and trees, and in semi-desert, especially where there are scattered trees.

large, broad wings

ADULT

• **NEST** A bulky platform made of sticks, with a cup-shaped hollow lined with finer twigs and stalks, sited in a tree.
• **DISTRIBUTION** North and Central America and the Caribbean. Some populations migrate within this range.
• **REMARKS** Females larger than males. Colour phases (*see p. 13*) are dark, rufous, and light. Subspecies include Harlan's Hawk, found in Alaska and W. Canada, which lacks the red tail.

powerful feet for holding prey

DISTRIBUTION

| Plumage Sexes alike | Habitat 〰️ 🌳 🛩️ | Migration Partial migrant |

| Family ACCIPITRIDAE | Species *Buteo buteo* | L. 50cm (20in)/55cm (22in) |

COMMON BUZZARD

This stoutly built bird of prey with broad, bluntly rounded wings and a wide tail is seen over fields, hills, forest clearings, and forest edges. It soars for hours, slowly searching for prey, or watches from a perch such as a tree or post, before swooping down to take any animal from beetle to rabbit size. Small carrion is also taken.
• **NEST** A bulky mass of twigs and roots, with a cup-shaped hollow, lined and sited on a tree or a cliff ledge.
• **DISTRIBUTION** Breeds in much of Eurasia. Winters as far south as South Africa, India, and S.E. Asia.
• **REMARKS** Females are larger than males. There are three colour phases (*p. 13*): pale, dark, and rufous.

rounded head

large eye

large, broad wings

DISTRIBUTION

RUFOUS PHASE

| Plumage Sexes alike | Habitat 🌳🌳 🏞️ | Migration Migrant |

| Family ACCIPITRIDAE | Species *Harpia harpyja* | L. 90cm (35in)/102cm (40in) |

HARPY EAGLE

A huge eagle with powerful feet and talons, this is the dominant bird of prey in the rainforests of Central and South America. It flies among trees and branches with agility, taking forest animals such as monkeys, sloths, possums, and snakes.
• **NEST** A large structure of thick sticks, with a cup-shaped hollow, high in the fork of a tall tree.
• **DISTRIBUTION** From Mexico to N. Argentina.
• **REMARK** Females are larger than males.

short, rounded wings

JUVENILE

deep bill

long tail

massive feet

DISTRIBUTION

| Plumage Sexes alike | Habitat 🌳🌳🌳 | Migration Non-migrant |

Family ACCIPITRIDAE	Species *Pithecophaga jefferyi*	L. 95cm (37in)/102cm (40in)

PHILIPPINE EAGLE

One of the largest of the world's birds of prey, this rainforest eagle has the typical shape of a forest-dwelling raptor. The wings are large with broad, rounded tips, and the tail is long. This combination provides speed and agility when the bird manoeuvres among the branches. At times the eagle is seen soaring over the rainforest, but its characteristic method of hunting is to move through the trees from one perch to another, waiting at each in turn to watch for prey. It takes forest animals such as monkeys, flying lemurs, and large birds up to hornbill size. The Philippine Eagle utters long, drawn-out whistles that seem rather weak for such a powerful bird. A single egg is laid, and the species probably nests only every second year.
• **NEST** A bulky structure of sticks and twigs, lined and placed in the fork of a large branch in a tree rising above the surrounding rainforest.
• **DISTRIBUTION** Philippine Islands.
• **REMARKS** Females are slightly larger than males. This species is rare and in danger of extinction, chiefly due to the felling of rainforests.

DISTRIBUTION

broad, rounded wings for manoeuvring among • branches of forest trees

large, strong • feet

• long tail

Plumage Sexes alike	Habitat 🌳🌳	Migration Non-migrant

Family ACCIPITRIDAE	Species *Aquila chrysaeto*s	L. 75cm (30in)/90cm (35in)

GOLDEN EAGLE

Adapted for hunting in open landscapes at high altitudes, this eagle is a strong and skilful flier, often seeming to plunge and dive in turbulent winds for sheer pleasure. Its typical hunting method is to fly fast and low, closing in on prey with a slanting dive. The eagle grips its prey with outstretched feet. Mammals, such as hares, are the main prey, but grouse and many birds, as well as carrion in winter, are also taken. The Golden Eagle is usually silent, but occasionally utters a yelping call.
• **NEST** A large nest made of sticks, lined with finer materials, and placed on a cliff or in a tree.
• **DISTRIBUTION** Breeds in much of North America, Eurasia, N. Africa, and the Middle East. Populations in N., C., and E. Eurasia migrate, wintering as far south as the Himalayas and China.
• **REMARK** Females are larger than the males.

golden-bronze • tint

DISTRIBUTION

JUVENILE

Plumage Sexes alike	Habitat ▲ 🦅 ⏐⏐⏐⏐	Migration Partial migrant

| Family ACCIPITRIDAE | Species *Hieraaetus morphnoides* | L. 47cm (18½in)/53cm (21in) |

LITTLE EAGLE

This is a small, compact eagle with a short crest and fully feathered legs. It hunts in partly wooded country, soaring and gliding to watch for prey on the ground below, or perching on a tree. Approaching in low flight, it takes young rabbits and other small mammals, birds, reptiles, and insects.
• **NEST** A large cup nest made of sticks, lined with green leaves and placed high in a tree.
• **DISTRIBUTION** Australia, New Guinea, and the Moluccan Islands in Indonesia.
• **REMARKS** Females are larger than males. There are two colour phases, light and dark (*see p. 13*).

lowered crest feathers

DISTRIBUTION

dark face

DARK PHASE

LIGHT PHASE

| Plumage Sexes alike | Habitat | Migration Non-migrant |

| Family ACCIPITRIDAE | Species *Polemaetus bellicosus* | L. 80cm (31in)/83cm (33in) |

MARTIAL EAGLE

A large eagle of open country, with a shaggy crest and feathered legs, this bird watches for prey by soaring and gliding, occasionally waiting on a perch. It takes a wide range of animal prey, attacking in a slanting dive and striking with wings and tail spread.
• **NEST** A large basin of thick twigs, with a small, cup-shaped hollow, lined and placed in the fork of a large tree.
• **DISTRIBUTION** Much of Africa south of the Sahara.
• **REMARK** Females are marginally larger than the males.

lowered crest

heavy, hooked bill

strong, feathered legs

DISTRIBUTION

JUVENILE

| Plumage Sexes alike | Habitat | Migration Non-migrant |

Family SAGITTARIIDAE	Species *Sagittarius serpentarius*	Length 150cm (59in)

SECRETARY BIRD

This large species, inhabiting grassland and open spaces, is an unusual type of bird of prey that has adapted itself so fully to a life of hunting on the ground that it rarely flies. This has resulted in its unusual appearance, with a tall, slender build, long legs, small feet, and long neck. The long wings and tail are useful mainly for keeping balance when the bird is walking, running, hunting, or engaged in territorial fights, which always take place on the ground. Flight is mainly restricted to visiting trees to roost and nest. The name of this species dates from pre-industrial times, when secretaries were court officials who carried quill pens tucked behind their ears. The Secretary Bird walks with a steady stride, nodding its head forwards with each step. It catches and kills prey on the ground, using its bill or stamping with its feet. When catching a snake, it holds out its wings to change its outline, which confuses the snake and prevents it from striking. Prey also includes insects, frogs, lizards, birds, and rodents.
• NEST A flat platform made of sticks and twigs, with a hollow in the centre, lined with grass, dung, and pellets of the undigested remains of prey, and placed on top of a bush or tree.
• DISTRIBUTION Africa south of the Sahara.
• REMARK This is the African counterpart of the Red-legged Seriema, a grassland bird of South America (*p. 129*).

FLYING ADULT

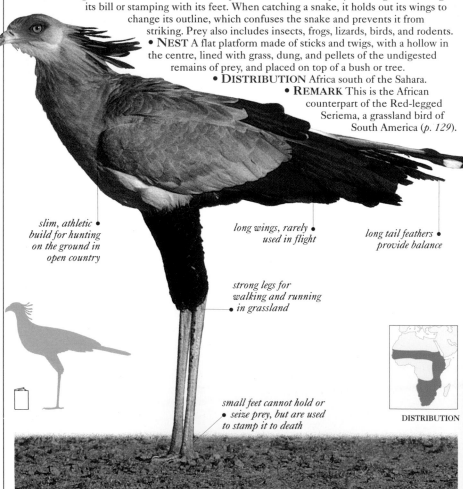

slim, athletic •
build for hunting
on the ground in
open country

long wings, rarely •
used in flight

long tail feathers •
provide balance

strong legs for
walking and running
• in grassland

small feet cannot hold or
• seize prey, but are used
to stamp it to death

DISTRIBUTION

Plumage Sexes alike	Habitat	Migration Non-migrant

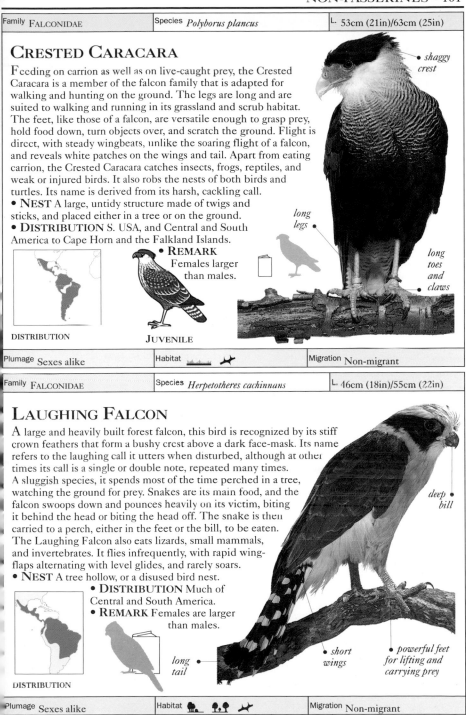

| Family FALCONIDAE | Species *Polyborus plancus* | L. 53cm (21in)/63cm (25in) |

CRESTED CARACARA

Feeding on carrion as well as on live-caught prey, the Crested
Caracara is a member of the falcon family that is adapted for
walking and hunting on the ground. The legs are long and are
suited to walking and running in its grassland and scrub habitat.
The feet, like those of a falcon, are versatile enough to grasp prey,
hold food down, turn objects over, and scratch the ground. Flight is
direct, with steady wingbeats, unlike the soaring flight of a falcon,
and reveals white patches on the wings and tail. Apart from eating
carrion, the Crested Caracara catches insects, frogs, reptiles, and
weak or injured birds. It also robs the nests of both birds and
turtles. Its name is derived from its harsh, cackling call.
• **NEST** A large, untidy structure made of twigs and
sticks, and placed either in a tree or on the ground.
• **DISTRIBUTION** S. USA, and Central and South
America to Cape Horn and the Falkland Islands.
• **REMARK**
Females larger
than males.

shaggy
crest

long
legs

long
toes
and
claws

DISTRIBUTION

JUVENILE

| Plumage Sexes alike | Habitat | Migration Non-migrant |

| Family FALCONIDAE | Species *Herpetotheres cachinnans* | L. 46cm (18in)/55cm (22in) |

LAUGHING FALCON

A large and heavily built forest falcon, this bird is recognized by its stiff
crown feathers that form a bushy crest above a dark face-mask. Its name
refers to the laughing call it utters when disturbed, although at other
times its call is a single or double note, repeated many times.
A sluggish species, it spends most of the time perched in a tree,
watching the ground for prey. Snakes are its main food, and the
falcon swoops down and pounces heavily on its victim, biting
it behind the head or biting the head off. The snake is then
carried to a perch, either in the feet or the bill, to be eaten.
The Laughing Falcon also eats lizards, small mammals,
and invertebrates. It flies infrequently, with rapid wingflaps alternating with level glides, and rarely soars.
• **NEST** A tree hollow, or a disused bird nest.
• **DISTRIBUTION** Much of
Central and South America.
• **REMARK** Females are larger
than males.

deep
bill

short
wings

powerful feet
for lifting and
carrying prey

long
tail

DISTRIBUTION

| Plumage Sexes alike | Habitat | Migration Non-migrant |

Family FALCONIDAE	Species *Falco sparverius*	L. 29cm (11½in)/32cm (12½in)

AMERICAN KESTREL

This small and beautifully patterned bird is one of the less powerful falcons, taking smaller and slower prey. It flies rapidly with quick downward wingbeats. When perched, it has a habit of wagging its tail up and down When hunting, it often hovers and drops on to prey, less commonly watching from a perch. In summer, it feeds chiefly on large insects, while in winter it more often takes mice and small birds. It utters a repeated "klee" or "killy" call.
• **NEST** A bare hollow in a natural cavity or crevice. Pairs occasionally make use of nest-boxes, or old nests of larger tree-nesting birds.
• **DISTRIBUTION** North, Central, and South America and Caribbean islands.
• **REMARK** Females are slightly larger than the males.

pale cheek patch

DISTRIBUTION

narrow wings

FEMALE

Plumage Sexes differ	Habitat	Migration Partial migrant

Family FALCONIDAE	Species *Falco tinnunculus*	L. 33cm (13in)/37cm (14½in)

COMMON KESTREL

A bird of open country that has adapted to the town environment, this species is often seen searching the ground in flight, hovering until it sees prey, and dropping gradually before the final pounce. Prey items include voles and mice, and smaller creatures such as grasshoppers or beetles. In towns and suburbs, sparrows are often taken. Prey is carried to a perch, plucked if necessary, and eaten. For a resting-place, the bird often selects a perch with a wide view. The Common Kestrel flies with small, rapid, downward wingbeats, interspersed with glides. At times it soars on rising air currents. It is often mobbed by flocks of Common Starlings (*see p. 375*) or martins (*see pp. 269–270*).
• **NEST** A natural hollow on a ledge of a cliff or a building, or a cavity in a tree trunk, or an old nest of a larger bird.
• **DISTRIBUTION** Eurasia and Africa. Northern and eastern populations winter as far south as South Africa, India, China, and Japan.
• **REMARK** Females are larger than males.

long, narrow wings

DISTRIBUTION

FEMALE

Plumage Sexes differ	Habitat	Migration Partial migrant

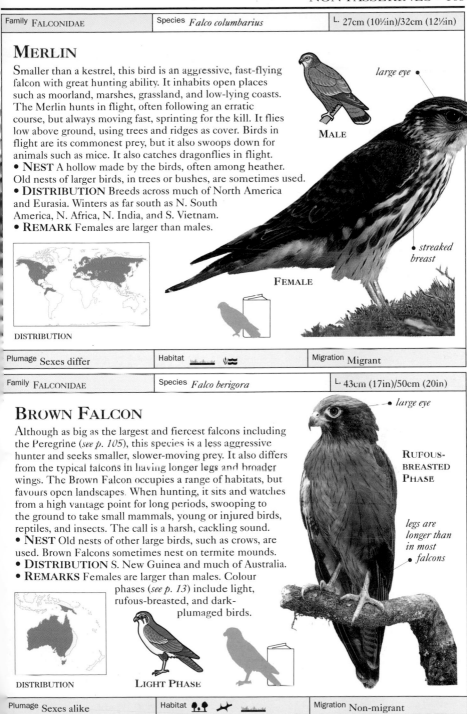

| Family FALCONIDAE | Species *Falco columbarius* | L. 27cm (10½in)/32cm (12½in) |

MERLIN

Smaller than a kestrel, this bird is an aggressive, fast-flying falcon with great hunting ability. It inhabits open places such as moorland, marshes, grassland, and low-lying coasts. The Merlin hunts in flight, often following an erratic course, but always moving fast, sprinting for the kill. It flies low above ground, using trees and ridges as cover. Birds in flight are its commonest prey, but it also swoops down for animals such as mice. It also catches dragonflies in flight.
• **NEST** A hollow made by the birds, often among heather. Old nests of larger birds, in trees or bushes, are sometimes used.
• **DISTRIBUTION** Breeds across much of North America and Eurasia. Winters as far south as N. South America, N. Africa, N. India, and S. Vietnam.
• **REMARK** Females are larger than males.

large eye

MALE

streaked breast

FEMALE

DISTRIBUTION

| Plumage Sexes differ | Habitat | Migration Migrant |

| Family FALCONIDAE | Species *Falco berigora* | L. 43cm (17in)/50cm (20in) |

BROWN FALCON

Although as big as the largest and fiercest falcons including the Peregrine (*see p. 105*), this species is a less aggressive hunter and seeks smaller, slower-moving prey. It also differs from the typical falcons in having longer legs and broader wings. The Brown Falcon occupies a range of habitats, but favours open landscapes. When hunting, it sits and watches from a high vantage point for long periods, swooping to the ground to take small mammals, young or injured birds, reptiles, and insects. The call is a harsh, cackling sound.
• **NEST** Old nests of other large birds, such as crows, are used. Brown Falcons sometimes nest on termite mounds.
• **DISTRIBUTION** S. New Guinea and much of Australia.
• **REMARKS** Females are larger than males. Colour phases (*see p. 13*) include light, rufous-breasted, and dark-plumaged birds.

RUFOUS-BREASTED PHASE

legs are longer than in most falcons

DISTRIBUTION

LIGHT PHASE

| Plumage Sexes alike | Habitat | Migration Non-migrant |

Family FALCONIDAE	Species *Falco subbuteo*	⌐ 30cm (12in)/37cm (14½in)

EURASIAN HOBBY

One of the small hunting falcons, the Eurasian Hobby is
built for speed, with narrow, tapering wings and a long tail.
It is fast enough to catch swallows (*see p. 270*) and swifts (*see
pp. 208–209*), moving very rapidly in level flight with bursts
of fast wingbeats. Its vision is keen enough for it to hunt bats
in poor light, and it also takes large insects, such as dragonflies.
These are often carried in the feet and eaten during flight.
• **NEST** An old nest of a large tree-nesting bird or a squirrel.
• **DISTRIBUTION** Breeds in much of Eurasia and in
N.W. Africa. Winters as far south as South Africa, India,
S. China, and S. Vietnam.
• **REMARK**
Females are larger
than males.

*bird in moult,
growing new
feathers* •

*chestnut
• thighs*

JUVENILE

*old tail •
feathers*

*narrow,
tapering
wings*

DISTRIBUTION

Plumage Sexes differ slightly	Habitat	Migration Migrant

Family FALCONIDAE	Species *Falco biarmicus*	⌐ 34cm (13½in)/50cm (20in)

LANNER FALCON

A robust hunting falcon, the Lanner occurs in
desert and savanna (tropical and subtropical
grassland) with occasional rocky crags on which
it perches and nests. The species also occurs
in open woodland. Lanners hunt either by
striking small birds in the air after a steep dive
(stoop), or by seizing ground prey, which they
approach in fast, low flight. Prey taken in flight
includes fruit bats and winged termites as
well as birds. Ground prey includes francolins
(*see pp. 111–112*), guineafowl (*see p. 117*), and small
bustards such as the Black Koorhaan (*see p. 130*).
When birds are scarce, rats and large burrowing desert
lizards are caught. Lanners are usually silent but nesting
pairs utter shrill, screaming and chattering calls.
• **NEST** A hollow on a ledge on a cliff or
building, or an old nest of a larger species.
• **DISTRIBUTION**
S.E. Europe, Middle East,
and much of Africa.
• **REMARK** Females are
larger than males.

DISTRIBUTION

*pale
under-
side of
adult
bird*

JUVENILE

*long,
tapering
wings*

Plumage Sexes differ slightly	Habitat	Migration Partial migrant/nomadic

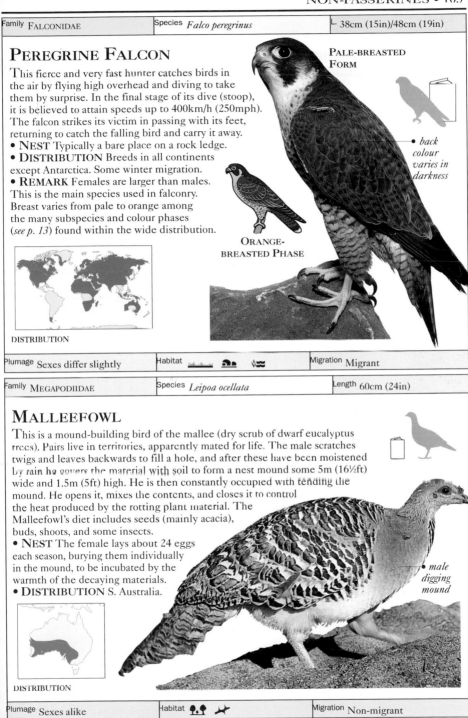

| Family FALCONIDAE | Species *Falco peregrinus* | L. 38cm (15in)/48cm (19in) |

PEREGRINE FALCON

PALE-BREASTED FORM

This fierce and very fast hunter catches birds in the air by flying high overhead and diving to take them by surprise. In the final stage of its dive (stoop), it is believed to attain speeds up to 400km/h (250mph). The falcon strikes its victim in passing with its feet, returning to catch the falling bird and carry it away.
• **NEST** Typically a bare place on a rock ledge.
• **DISTRIBUTION** Breeds in all continents except Antarctica. Some winter migration.
• **REMARK** Females are larger than males. This is the main species used in falconry. Breast varies from pale to orange among the many subspecies and colour phases (*see p. 13*) found within the wide distribution.

• *back colour varies in darkness*

ORANGE-BREASTED PHASE

DISTRIBUTION

| Plumage Sexes differ slightly | Habitat | Migration Migrant |

| Family MEGAPODIIDAE | Species *Leipoa ocellata* | Length 60cm (24in) |

MALLEEFOWL

This is a mound-building bird of the mallee (dry scrub of dwarf eucalyptus trees). Pairs live in territories, apparently mated for life. The male scratches twigs and leaves backwards to fill a hole, and after these have been moistened by rain he covers the material with soil to form a nest mound some 5m (16½ft) wide and 1.5m (5ft) high. He is then constantly occupied with tending the mound. He opens it, mixes the contents, and closes it to control the heat produced by the rotting plant material. The Malleefowl's diet includes seeds (mainly acacia), buds, shoots, and some insects.
• **NEST** The female lays about 24 eggs each season, burying them individually in the mound, to be incubated by the warmth of the decaying materials.
• **DISTRIBUTION** S. Australia.

• *male digging mound*

DISTRIBUTION

| Plumage Sexes alike | Habitat | Migration Non-migrant |

Family MEGAPODIIDAE	Species *Alectura lathami*	Length 70cm (28in)

AUSTRALIAN BRUSH-TURKEY

This species resembles a lanky gamebird with a long, bare neck, from which folds of wrinkled skin ("neck wattles") hang down. It is a forest dweller, feeding on insects, fruit, and seeds. The male scratches the ground, kicking leaf litter and mould behind him to form a nest mound that may be several times his height. This material rots and becomes warm, and he tests it with his bill, keeping the temperature constant by adding or removing material.

• **NEST** The female digs holes in the mound, laying an egg in each one, to be incubated by the heat of decay. The downy chicks hatch, dig their own way out, and fend for themselves.

• **DISTRIBUTION** N.E. and E. Australia.

bare skin on head and neck

flat-sided tail

CAPE YORK RACE

yellow wattle of typical race

DISTRIBUTION

Plumage Sexes alike	Habitat 🌳🌳 🌿 ✈	Migration Non-migrant

Family CRACIDAE	Species *Ortalis vetula*	Length 60cm (24in)

PLAIN CHACHALACA

Looking like a slender gamebird with long neck, legs, and tail, this species inhabits forest, scrub, and thickets, spending much of its time above ground. It usually occurs in small parties, walking along branches and feeding on fruit, buds, and leaves. The name is a version of the birds' harsh call, which is uttered in chorus, mostly at dusk and dawn. The whole flock roosts together in thickets, and small young clamber and flutter up to roost with their parents, each under a wing.

MALE

short wings

• **NEST** A small platform made of twigs, placed in dense tree foliage at medium height.

• **DISTRIBUTION** S.E. Texas to Nicaragua.

DISTRIBUTION

feet adapted for grasping twigs

Plumage Sexes differ slightly	Habitat 🌿 ✈	Migration Non-migrant

Family CRACIDAE	Species *Pipile pipile*	Length 68cm (27in)

COMMON PIPING-GUAN

A forest species resembling a gamebird, the Common Piping-Guan has a slender build, long legs, and strong feet, all of which are adaptations for walking along tree branches. It lives mostly in the upper and middle levels of the forest, where it walks, jumps, and flies among branches. The diet consists mainly of fruit, with some buds, leaves, and occasional small animals. Birds usually occur in groups, and often perch in open view on a high branch. As the name indicates, they utter high-pitched, whistling calls. Breeding birds perform a display flight from treetop to treetop, in which the flight feathers make a loud, whirring sound.
• **NEST** A scanty twig nest, placed high in the canopy.
• **DISTRIBUTION** South America, in the Amazon and Orinoco river basins.

slender • head with small crest

long, • slender neck

• throat wattle

feet are adapted for walking on • tree branches

• long, slender tail

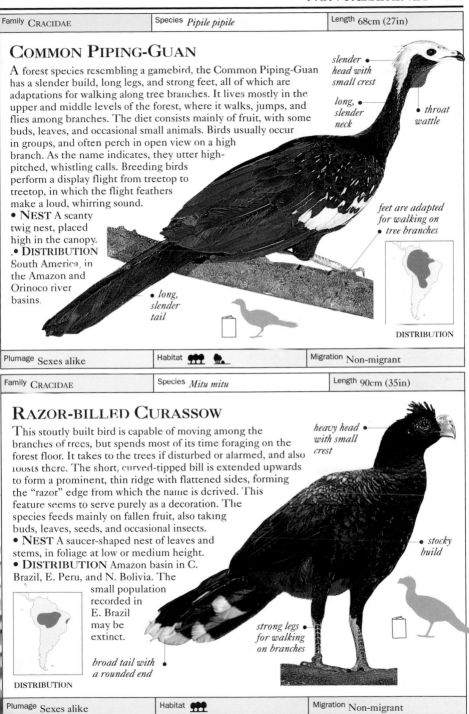

DISTRIBUTION

Plumage Sexes alike	Habitat	Migration Non-migrant

Family CRACIDAE	Species *Mitu mitu*	Length 90cm (35in)

RAZOR-BILLED CURASSOW

This stoutly built bird is capable of moving among the branches of trees, but spends most of its time foraging on the forest floor. It takes to the trees if disturbed or alarmed, and also roosts there. The short, curved-tipped bill is extended upwards to form a prominent, thin ridge with flattened sides, forming the "razor" edge from which the name is derived. This feature seems to serve purely as a decoration. The species feeds mainly on fallen fruit, also taking buds, leaves, seeds, and occasional insects.
• **NEST** A saucer-shaped nest of leaves and stems, in foliage at low or medium height.
• **DISTRIBUTION** Amazon basin in C. Brazil, E. Peru, and N. Bolivia. The small population recorded in E. Brazil may be extinct.

heavy head • with small crest

• stocky build

strong legs • for walking on branches

broad tail with • a rounded end

DISTRIBUTION

Plumage Sexes alike	Habitat	Migration Non-migrant

Family PHASIANIDAE	Species *Meleagris gallopavo*	L. 125cm (49in)/91cm (36in)

WILD TURKEY

In the wild, turkeys are cautious and evasive birds of forest edges and clearings. They feed on the ground, taking berries, seeds, nuts, other parts of plants, and invertebrates. In winter, Wild Turkeys often live in flocks. Some flocks are segregated, containing birds of only one sex. In spring, the breeding male displays with his tail spread, attracting a small flock of females that nest individually after mating.

fully fanned • tail

• **NEST** A shallow hollow in the ground, sparsely lined with leaves and stems, often in vegetation.

• **DISTRIBUTION** Patchily distributed in S. Canada, much of USA, and N. Mexico.

FEMALE

DISTRIBUTION

Plumage Sexes differ	Habitat 🌳🌱 🌿	Migration Non-migrant

Family PHASIANIDAE	Species *Tetrao tetrix*	55cm (22in)/43cm (17in)

BLACK GROUSE

A gamebird of forest edges and scrub, this species is seen perching, and sometimes roosting, in trees. It feeds mainly on tree buds, also eating insects in summer. In spring, males display competitively on a piece of ground known as the "lek". They leap in the air with whirring wings, and make excited, bubbling and sneezing calls. Females visit the lek, mate with a male, then nest alone.

elongated • undertail feathers

DISTRIBUTION

• upright display posture

• **NEST** A hollow in the ground, made by the birds and hidden among fairly tall vegetation.

• **DISTRIBUTION** Eurasia from British Isles to E. Siberia.

• tail feathers

• short, thick legs

FEMALE

Plumage Sexes differ	Habitat 🌿 ✈	Migration Non-migrant

| Family PHASIANIDAE | Species *Centrocercus urophasianus* | L. 80cm (31in)/55cm (22in) |

SAGE GROUSE

Dwelling in extensive scrub formed by sage bushes, this species alternates between the plains in winter, and the foothills in summer. It feeds on sage leaves and insects. In spring, groups of males advertise themselves to the females over a distance, spreading out their tails in a spiky fan, swelling out their necks, and repeatedly inflating the air sacs on their breasts. They utter deep, bubbling noises. Females select a mate and subsequently nest alone.

• **NEST** A hollow in the ground, often situated under a sage bush.

• **DISTRIBUTION** Interior of W. North America.

hair-like crest on the nape

spiky tail feathers

raised flight feathers

DISTRIBUTION

FEMALE

| Plumage Sexes differ | Habitat | Migration Non-migrant |

| Family PHASIANIDAE | Species *Callipepla californica* | L. 28cm (11in)/25cm (10in) |

CALIFORNIA QUAIL

both sexes have the forward-nodding crest

A small gamebird of open woodland, scrub, and farmland, the California Quail is often seen in flocks. Although it can fly well, it usually walks or runs. It perches and roosts (rests at night) in thick cover, on low branches. The diet consists of seeds, parts of green plants, and insects, taken from the ground.

• **NEST** A hollow in the ground, lined with plant stems plucked from close by, often sheltered by vegetation.

• **DISTRIBUTION** W. North America. Introduced in other countries, mainly for ornamental use in gardens and parks, with local populations of escaped birds.

streaked flank

FEMALE

DISTRIBUTION

| Plumage Sexes differ | Habitat | Migration Non-migrant |

Family PHASIANIDAE	Species *Colinus virginianus*	Length 25cm (10in)

NORTHERN BOBWHITE

For most of the year this small quail is fairly unobtrusive, but in spring it makes its presence known with its loud "bobwhite" call, given from a low perch such as a stone or a tree stump. It is common in thickets, in shrubby countryside, and in open woodland. In spring, the birds feed in pairs or family parties, gathering into small flocks later in the year. They are seen walking or running on the ground, often venturing into open fields. If disturbed, they first crouch among bushes, then fly low from one patch of cover to another on whirring wings. They roost huddled together on the ground, facing outwards so that all can take off and scatter if alarmed. They feed on seeds, shoots, leaves, and roots, with some insects and other small invertebrates.
• **NEST** A shallow hollow in the ground, lined with dead vegetation, often in a relatively open site, such as a meadow.
• **DISTRIBUTION** From E. USA south as far as Mexico. Introduced in other countries, mainly for ornamental use, with local populations of escaped birds.

DISTRIBUTION

• *upright calling posture*

white-flecked underside

FEMALE

Plumage Sexes differ	Habitat	Migration Non-migrant

Family PHASIANIDAE	Species *Cyrtonyx montezumae*	Length 22cm (8½in)

MONTEZUMA'S QUAIL

Characterized by a bolder head pattern than those of other quails, this is a bird of woodlands in drier mountain areas. It is found in canyons where oaks are interpersed with grass, and on hillsides with scattered conifers. Very much a ground-dweller, it tends to crouch and hide among grasses when alarmed. Both male and female look big-headed because of the way in which the crest curves back to enlarge the nape. The male's sandy-coloured crest may conceal the vivid pattern of black-and-white on the face when he crouches. The birds nest in pairs in the late summer, and gather in small flocks after breeding. They feed on seeds and some insects, and also scratch up the ground for tubers and bulbs.
• **NEST** A hollow in the ground, lined with grass, and situated in grass.
• **DISTRIBUTION** From S.W. USA to S. Mexico.

• *heavy crest on nape*

DISTRIBUTION

white spots on breast and flanks

jet black underside

strong, scratching feet

FEMALE

Plumage Sexes differ	Habitat	Migration Non-migrant

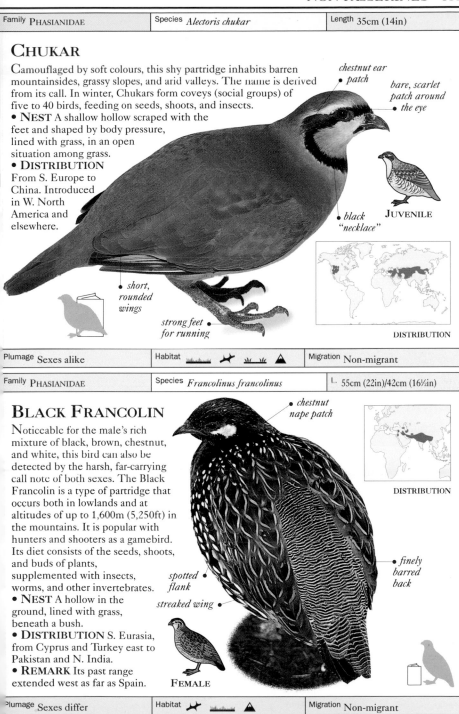

Family PHASIANIDAE	Species *Alectoris chukar*	Length 35cm (14in)

CHUKAR

Camouflaged by soft colours, this shy partridge inhabits barren mountainsides, grassy slopes, and arid valleys. The name is derived from its call. In winter, Chukars form coveys (social groups) of five to 40 birds, feeding on seeds, shoots, and insects.
• **NEST** A shallow hollow scraped with the feet and shaped by body pressure, lined with grass, in an open situation among grass.
• **DISTRIBUTION** From S. Europe to China. Introduced in W. North America and elsewhere.

chestnut ear patch

bare, scarlet patch around the eye

black "necklace"

JUVENILE

short, rounded wings

strong feet for running

DISTRIBUTION

Plumage Sexes alike	Habitat	Migration Non-migrant

Family PHASIANIDAE	Species *Francolinus francolinus*	L. 55cm (22in)/42cm (16½in)

BLACK FRANCOLIN

Noticeable for the male's rich mixture of black, brown, chestnut, and white, this bird can also be detected by the harsh, far-carrying call note of both sexes. The Black Francolin is a type of partridge that occurs both in lowlands and at altitudes of up to 1,600m (5,250ft) in the mountains. It is popular with hunters and shooters as a gamebird. Its diet consists of the seeds, shoots, and buds of plants, supplemented with insects, worms, and other invertebrates.
• **NEST** A hollow in the ground, lined with grass, beneath a bush.
• **DISTRIBUTION** S. Eurasia, from Cyprus and Turkey east to Pakistan and N. India.
• **REMARK** Its past range extended west as far as Spain.

chestnut nape patch

DISTRIBUTION

finely barred back

spotted flank

streaked wing

FEMALE

Plumage Sexes differ	Habitat	Migration Non-migrant

Family PHASIANIDAE	Species *Francolinus afer*	Length 38cm (15in)

RED-NECKED FRANCOLIN

Identified by its red face and throat, this bird is a type of partridge that lives in hot, dry countries. Throughout its wide range it is a bird of the lowlands, living in scrub, open woodland, and forest edge, and in wooded gorges. Red-necked Francolins live either in pairs or in family parties, and will sometimes allow francolins of other species to feed alongside them in their territories. Their diet consists mainly of seeds, shoots, leaves, and berries, but they also scratch the ground for roots and bulbs, and take insects and other invertebrates. They do not readily fly, preferring to escape danger by running.
• **NEST** A hollow formed by body pressure, lined with grass and roots, and surrounded by thick vegetation.
• **DISTRIBUTION** Africa from Gabon and Kenya south to the coastal strip of South Africa.

bare throat patch

bare skin around the eye

DISTRIBUTION

• *strong feet for running and scratching*

Plumage Sexes alike	Habitat	Migration Non-migrant

Family PHASIANIDAE	Species *Perdix perdix*	Length 32cm (12½in)

COMMON PARTRIDGE

This is one of the commonest gamebirds within its range, and its populations are artificially maintained for the benefit of hunters and shooters. Common Partridges usually live in pairs in spring, and form coveys (social groups) of up to 20 birds in autumn. The birds feed on the ground in farmland, taking seeds, insects, and grains. When alarmed, they crouch in the grass, passing for a clod of earth or a piece of dry turf. If a bird is approached directly, it bursts out of hiding in a rapid escape flight, low over the ground at first, making a sharply audible whistling sound with its wings.
• **NEST** A small hollow, often lined with dead plant materials, in an open situation in grass.
• **DISTRIBUTION** From Europe to W. China. Introduced in North America.

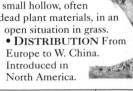

JUVENILE

alert posture typical of male bird

MALE

FEMALE

DISTRIBUTION

Plumage Sexes differ slightly	Habitat	Migration Non-migrant

Family PHASIANIDAE	Species *Coturnix coturnix*	Length 18cm (7in)

COMMON QUAIL

This species is one of the smaller gamebirds of the world. Its distinctive call, consisting of three liquid notes, can be heard both day and night. It conceals itself in dry grassland and growing crops. If threatened, it prefers to escape danger by running rather than flying, but will reluctantly make short, low flights. On its long-distance migratory journeys, however, it shows its ability to fly strongly.

streaked face pattern

"dead grass" camouflage pattern

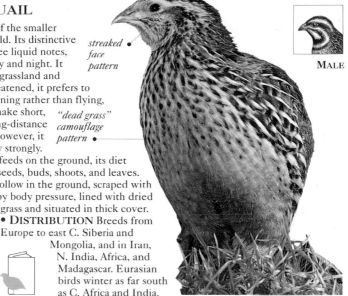

MALE

The Common Quail feeds on the ground, its diet consisting mainly of seeds, buds, shoots, and leaves.
• **NEST** A shallow hollow in the ground, scraped with the feet and shaped by body pressure, lined with dried grass and situated in thick cover.
• **DISTRIBUTION** Breeds from Europe to east C. Siberia and Mongolia, and in Iran, N. India, Africa, and Madagascar. Eurasian birds winter as far south as C. Africa and India.

DISTRIBUTION

Plumage Sexes differ	Habitat	Migration Migrant

Family PHASIANIDAE	Species *Tragopan temminckii*	Length 63cm (25in)

TEMMINCK'S TRAGOPAN

A bird of evergreen or mixed forest in mountains, Temminck's Tragopan occurs at altitudes up to 4,600m (15,000ft) and is normally solitary. Like other birds living in unpopulated regions, it is tame in human company. The diet consists of plant matter such as buds, shoots, and seeds, supplemented with insects. This species is remarkable for the male's coloured throat wattle which is inflated in display, expanding to cover his breast.
• **NEST** A platform made of twigs, gathered from the immediate surroundings, and placed in a bush or low tree.
• **DISTRIBUTION** Tibet, C. China, N.E. India, Burma, and N. Vietnam.

DISTRIBUTION

spotted plumage

FEMALE

Plumage Sexes differ	Habitat	Migration Non-migrant

| Family PHASIANIDAE | Species *Lophophorus impejanus* | L. 65cm (26in)/55cm (22in) |

IMPEYAN MONAL

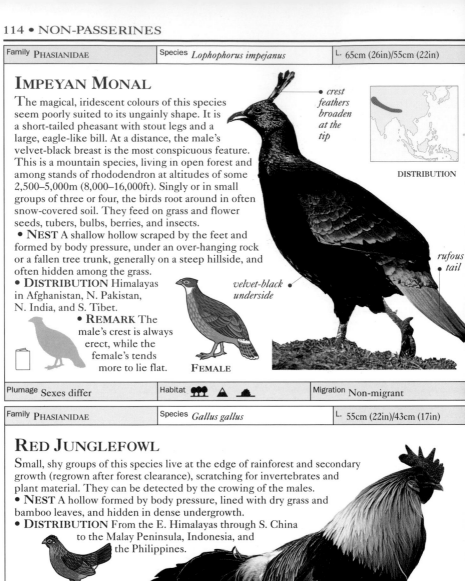

The magical, iridescent colours of this species seem poorly suited to its ungainly shape. It is a short-tailed pheasant with stout legs and a large, eagle-like bill. At a distance, the male's velvet-black breast is the most conspicuous feature. This is a mountain species, living in open forest and among stands of rhododendron at altitudes of some 2,500–5,000m (8,000–16,000ft). Singly or in small groups of three or four, the birds root around in often snow-covered soil. They feed on grass and flower seeds, tubers, bulbs, berries, and insects.
• **NEST** A shallow hollow scraped by the feet and formed by body pressure, under an over-hanging rock or a fallen tree trunk, generally on a steep hillside, and often hidden among the grass.
• **DISTRIBUTION** Himalayas in Afghanistan, N. Pakistan, N. India, and S. Tibet.
• **REMARK** The male's crest is always erect, while the female's tends more to lie flat.

crest feathers broaden at the tip

rufous tail

velvet-black underside

FEMALE

DISTRIBUTION

| Plumage Sexes differ | Habitat | Migration Non-migrant |

| Family PHASIANIDAE | Species *Gallus gallus* | L. 55cm (22in)/43cm (17in) |

RED JUNGLEFOWL

Small, shy groups of this species live at the edge of rainforest and secondary growth (regrown after forest clearance), scratching for invertebrates and plant material. They can be detected by the crowing of the males.
• **NEST** A hollow formed by body pressure, lined with dry grass and bamboo leaves, and hidden in dense undergrowth.
• **DISTRIBUTION** From the E. Himalayas through S. China to the Malay Peninsula, Indonesia, and the Philippines.

male bird closely resembles its domesticated relative, the farm cockerel

FEMALE

DISTRIBUTION

| Plumage Sexes differ | Habitat | Migration Non-migrant |

| Family PHASIANIDAE | Species *Phasianus colchicus* | L. 83cm (33in)/58cm (23in) |

COMMON PHEASANT

Although large and colourful, this is a secretive bird, creeping softly through shrubby copses, farmland, and marshes. In pairs during the breeding season and otherwise in small flocks, birds feed on weed seeds, grain, berries, earthworms, and insects.
• **NEST** A hollow formed by the birds, lined with grass, and situated underneath or within dense, low vegetation.
• **DISTRIBUTION** Europe, and in areas through Asia to China. Introduced in North America and in small areas in Australia and New Zealand.

DISTRIBUTION

male has a long, striped • tail

• **REMARK** Colours and markings vary with the many subspecies through the range. These include the Mongolian and Ring-necked Pheasants, which are commonly kept in aviaries as well as for sport.

FEMALE

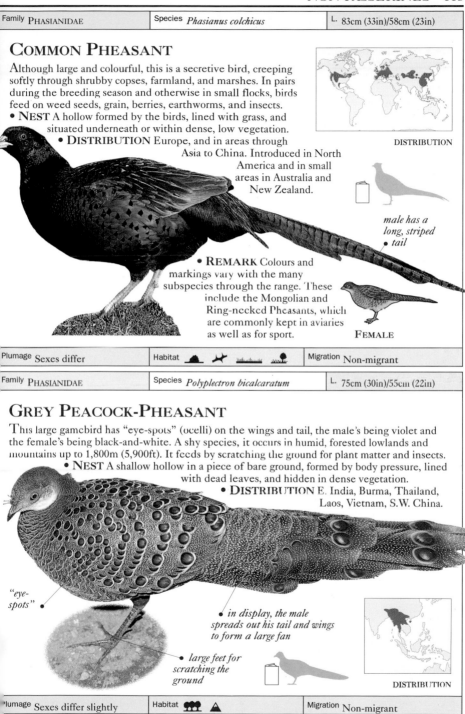

| Plumage Sexes differ | Habitat | Migration Non-migrant |

| Family PHASIANIDAE | Species *Polyplectron bicalcaratum* | L. 75cm (30in)/55cm (22in) |

GREY PEACOCK-PHEASANT

This large gamebird has "eye-spots" (ocelli) on the wings and tail, the male's being violet and the female's being black-and-white. A shy species, it occurs in humid, forested lowlands and mountains up to 1,800m (5,900ft). It feeds by scratching the ground for plant matter and insects.
• **NEST** A shallow hollow in a piece of bare ground, formed by body pressure, lined with dead leaves, and hidden in dense vegetation.
• **DISTRIBUTION** E. India, Burma, Thailand, Laos, Vietnam, S.W. China.

"eye-spots" •

• in display, the male spreads out his tail and wings to form a large fan

• large feet for scratching the ground

DISTRIBUTION

| Plumage Sexes differ slightly | Habitat | Migration Non-migrant |

Family PHASIANIDAE	Species *Pavo cristatus*	L. 213cm (84in)/85cm (34in)

BLUE PEAFOWL

As a wild bird, the Blue Peafowl (commonly known as the Peacock) lives in deciduous tropical forests and feeds in open places such as clearings or cultivated fields. Its diet consists of seeds, fruit, and other parts of plants, as well as small animals ranging from insects to mice. The male's long and colourful train is not the bird's tail but an ornament, composed of some 150 large feathers growing from his lower back. The real tail is short and dull-coloured, hidden underneath the train. The female lacks a train, as does the male in winter. Both sexes, and even the tiny young, possess little, fan-shaped crests on the crown of the head. In display, the male raises up his train in a symmetrical fan by lifting his tail. At the same time he lowers and shakes his chestnut-coloured wings, which he reveals when strutting and turning in front of the female. He also utters a loud, far-carrying call. A displaying male will soon attract, and then guard, a small flock of females. The flock remains with him for a few days, during which time he mates with each of them. Each female then departs to nest alone, without the help of the male. Both sexes are agile enough to fly up into the higher branches of trees to roost.

DISTRIBUTION

FEMALE

- **NEST** A shallow hollow made by the birds, bare or lined with sticks, leaves, and grass, and often concealed in thorny undergrowth.
- **DISTRIBUTION** Indian subcontinent including Sri Lanka.

vivid eye-spots

train feathers raised in a half circle

Plumage Sexes differ	Habitat	Migration Non-migrant

Family PHASIANIDAE	Species *Argusianus argus*	L. 185cm (73in)/70cm (28in)

GREAT ARGUS PHEASANT

A solitary-living pheasant of tropical rainforests, this species feeds on leaves, nuts, shoots, seeds, and invertebrates. Its courtship display is one of the most spectacular of all birds. After trampling clear a chosen area of the forest floor, the male begins to utter loud, ringing calls. He raises his tail and spreads his wings to form a vast fan, glittering with the many "eye-spots" on the vastly enlarged secondary flight feathers. Most females thus courted will nest unaided after mating, while the male displays to other females in turn.

• **NEST** A hollow formed by body pressure on the rainforest floor, lined with leaves and situated under overhanging foliage.

• **DISTRIBUTION** Malay Peninsula, Sumatra, and Borneo.

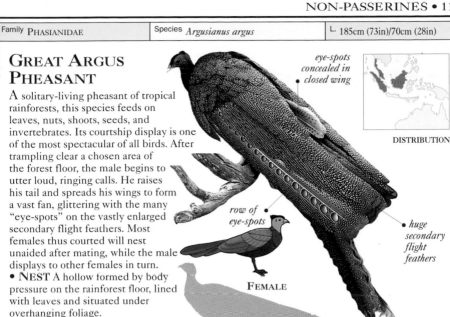

eye-spots concealed in closed wing

DISTRIBUTION

row of eye-spots

huge secondary flight feathers

FEMALE

Plumage Sexes differ	Habitat	Migration Non-migrant

Family PHASIANIDAE	Species *Acryllium vulturinum*	Length 60cm (24in)

VULTURINE GUINEAFOWL

This bird can be recognized by its bare head and neck, resembling those of a vulture. The small ruff of feathers on the nape, and the tapering, blue feathers of the breast, are also identification features. It prefers the denser scrub and thickets of forest edge, which provide open space for it at ground level, while sheltering it from aerial predators. When alarmed, it prefers to run, although it can fly well and roosts in trees. When not breeding, birds move around in small parties that feed and roost together, maintaining contact by short, harsh calls. Larger groups are seen at waterholes. The birds breed in scattered pairs. The diet consists of seeds, shoots, leaves, tubers, bulbs, and fallen fruit, together with insects, snails, and other small invertebrates. Birds scratch the ground with their long, strong legs to find food items beneath the soil.

• **NEST** A hollow formed by body pressure in the ground, thinly lined with plant stems, and hidden in low vegetation.

• **DISTRIBUTION** N.E. Africa in Somalia, Ethiopia, and Kenya.

• **REMARK** This is the largest species of guineafowl.

bare skin on neck and head

small ruff of dense brown feathers

DISTRIBUTION

long, tapering breast feathers

Plumage Sexes alike	Habitat	Migration Non-migrant

Family MESITORNITHIDAE	Species *Mesitornis unicolor*	Length 30cm (12in)

BROWN MESITE

This rare bird lives in tropical rainforest, where it feeds on the ground, taking seeds, fruit, and small insects. Superficially, it looks like a largish passerine with a small, rounded head and a pointed bill. The body is rather heavy and ends in a surprisingly broad tail. The wings are short and rounded, and the bird is virtually flightless. On the other hand this species has strong, agile legs, and it walks and runs easily on its lightly built feet. The Brown Mesite builds its nest in a tree, in a position that can be reached by walking up and down a sloping trunk or across branches.

• **NEST** A thin, concave platform made of twigs, sparsely lined with grass or leaves, and placed in a tree.

• **DISTRIBUTION** E. Madagascar.

large eye for finding food in poor light

short, round wings, hardly ever used in flight

large, broad tail

long legs of a ground-living bird

small, round head

lightly built feet

DISTRIBUTION

Plumage Sexes alike	Habitat 🌳	Migration Non-migrant

Family TURNICIDAE	Species *Turnix sylvatica*	Length 13cm (5in)

SMALL BUTTON-QUAIL

A soft, booming call may be the only indication of the presence of this small and secretive species. A ground-dwelling bird of open woodland, scrub, and grassland, it resembles a quail in behaviour and shape, but has a more slender bill. Females are a little larger and more brightly coloured than males, and take the dominant role in breeding, calling, and establishing territories. Males incubate the eggs, and care for the downy young.

• **NEST** A shallow hollow lined with fine grasses, situated in grass. Grass stems and leaves are pulled over the nest to hide it.

• **DISTRIBUTION** Extreme S Spain, parts of Africa, and from Pakistan and India to S.E. Asia including the Philippines.

staring, pale iris

DISTRIBUTION

"dried-grass" pattern for camouflage

strong feet, lacking a hind toe

Plumage Sexes differ slightly	Habitat ✈ ⛰ 🌿	Migration Non-migrant

Family PEDIONOMIDAE	Species *Pedionomus torquatus*	Length 17cm (6¾in)

PLAINS WANDERER

This is a small, ground-dwelling bird of dry, open grassland with a compact body, strong legs and feet, staring eyes, and a slender bill. In all these respects it is similar to the Small Button-Quail. However, it prefers more open habitats, moving cautiously and only occasionally standing on tiptoe to peer over the grass. It may be seen in fluttering, dipping flight, or perching on a fence post or mound. The diet consists of seeds and insects. The female is more brightly coloured than the male and is the dominant partner. She may mate with several males, which act as the main carers for the eggs and young.
• **NEST** A shallow hollow in the ground, lined with grass, and situated alongside a tussock or small shrub.
• **DISTRIBUTION** Interior of S.E. Australia.

patterned neck

brown breast patch

DISTRIBUTION

MALE

FEMALE

Plumage Sexes differ	Habitat	Migration Nomadic

Family GRUIDAE	Species *Grus canadensis*	Length 105cm (41in)

SANDHILL CRANE

This is one of the smaller species of crane, and is mostly grey apart from its red crown and white cheek. Some birds are, however, stained reddish with iron salts from water transferred to the plumage when the bird preens itself with a wet bill. A bird of open, marshy landscapes and grassland, the Sandhill Crane breeds in scattered pairs, but gathers in large and often noisy flocks for migration. It feeds on seeds including grain, and on buds, shoots, leaves, and small animals from insects to mice.
• **NEST** A heap of plant material, large if on a wet site, with a central hollow.
• **DISTRIBUTION** Breeds in N.E. Siberia and much of N. North America, also Florida. Winters in North America, as far south as Mexico.

bare, red display patch

slender build of a small crane

upper leg feathering

drooping feathers from the lower back (raised for display)

long stride of a grassland bird

DISTRIBUTION

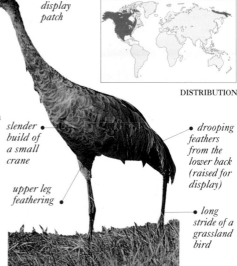

Plumage Sexes alike	Habitat	Migration Migrant

Family GRUIDAE	Species *Grus japonensis*	Length 140cm (55in)

JAPANESE CRANE

Of all the world's crane species, this rare and beautiful bird is among the tallest. It occurs in grassland in wide valleys with swampy areas, where its height is a natural advantage, giving a clear view of danger from a safe distance. The Japanese Crane walks with a deliberate, striding gait, pausing now and then to pick up food items, which may be relatively small. Mice, frogs, and large insects, and also seeds, buds, and leaves, form its diet. Flight is strong, with neck and legs extended, and with deliberate wingbeats, interspersed with gliding. Flocks usually fly in chevrons ("V shapes") or slanting lines. Migration to and from the winter feeding grounds tends to follow traditional routes. Pairs mate for life and the bond between them appears to be strengthened by mutual displays.

Displaying birds stand side by side with raised heads, uttering loud, trumpet-like calls. They then begin to perform a wild dance, very different from their usual, placid behaviour. Dancing birds wave their heads up and down, raise and flap their wings, and make clumsy-looking leaps into the air. They sometimes pick up sticks or pull up tufts of grass, and throw these into the air. Although each nesting pair normally has two eggs, one chick usually dies at an early age. The survivor is often seen walking behind the parents, which feed it with small insects, offered one at a time. The young bird migrates with its parents and stays with them until the following season.

• **NEST** A large mound of plant stalks and grasses, gathered at the nest site and piled together on the ground, with a hollow in the top.

• **DISTRIBUTION** Breeds in Japan, E. Siberia, and N. China. Winters in Korea, N.E. China, and S. Japan.

head raised in mutual trumpeting posture

drooping, decorative plumes, raised above the tail in display

snowy white plumage

wings partly raised from the body

long, slender toes

DISTRIBUTION

JUVENILE

Plumage Sexes alike	Habitat	Migration Migrant

Family GRUIDAE	Species *Grus grus*	Length 112cm (44in)

COMMON CRANE

For the most part a plain-looking crane of grassland and marshes, this bird's presence is given away by its bright head colour and far-carrying calls. The calls are used as part of the pairing display, and are also uttered in flight. The diet consists of insects, frogs, mice, seeds, and other parts of green plants. In winter, cranes visit drier habitats, such as farmland.

• **NEST** A mound of reeds, grass, and other vegetation, with a shallow hollow on top, often in a marsh and located near, or in, shallow water.

• **DISTRIBUTION** Breeds across Eurasia. Winters in S. Eurasia, N.W. and N.E. Africa, India, and China.

• **REMARK** Because it needs large, undisturbed areas of marshland, bogs, and grassland for breeding, the Common Crane has lost ground during the present century on account of the spread of human settlement. It occurs in areas where this type of habitat remains, also spreading in places into birch scrub or woodland.

• decorative patch of bare, red skin

DISTRIBUTION

• plumes droop from lower back (can be raised in display)

JUVENILE

Plumage Sexes alike	Habitat	Migration Migrant

Family GRUIDAE	Species *Balearica regulorum*	Length 105cm (41in)

GREY CROWNED-CRANE

spiky crest •

The large, white wing-patches on the grey plumage of this species are noticeable in flight and in display. This crane inhabits marshland, where it feeds on animals such as large insects, frogs, and toads, and on grain and other plant materials. It is seen in heavy flight, with neck and legs drooping slightly, or roosting in trees. Mated birds display to one another with a leaping dance and loud, two-note calls.

• **NEST** A large, flattened mound of reeds, rushes, and grass, screened by vegetation, in a marsh.

• **DISTRIBUTION** From Uganda and Kenya to South Africa.

• **REMARK** A closely related species, the Black Crowned-Crane, is found along the southern edge of the Sahara and in Sudan.

red • throat wattle

DISTRIBUTION

• long plumes on the neck and breast

white • wing patch

JUVENILE

Plumage Sexes alike	Habitat	Migration Non-migrant

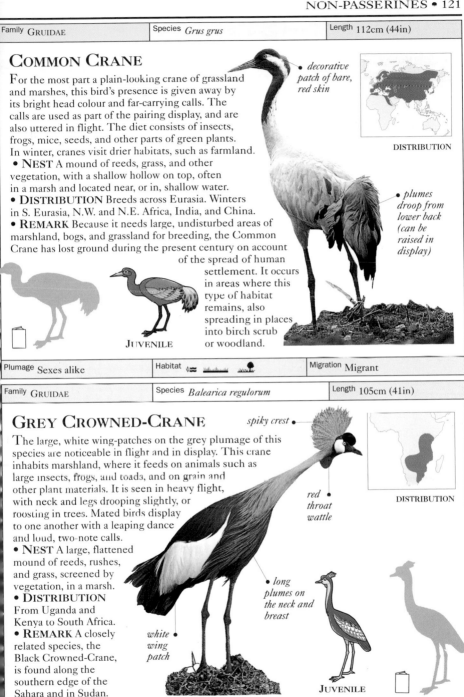

Family ARAMIDAE	Species *Aramus guarauna*	Length 65cm (26in)

LIMPKIN

The most noticeable characteristic of this marshland bird is the long, slender shape of its bill, neck, legs, and toes. The wings, however, are short and rounded in shape. Normally a wading bird of tropical and subtropical wooded swamps, it can swim well. It is solitary by day, becoming active at dusk and during the night when it utters loud calls that can sound like clucking, wailing, or screaming. The diet consists mainly of large water snails, and the Limpkin's vertically flattened bill is adapted for extracting these from their shells. Limpkins also feed on other molluscs, and other swamp creatures, from worms to crayfish and reptiles.

flat-sided bill for extracting snails

• **NEST** A large structure of sticks and rushes, built on the ground or, in wet areas, in trees at low or medium height.

• **DISTRIBUTION** From Florida and the Caribbean to Argentina.

DISTRIBUTION

Plumage Sexes alike	Habitat	Migration Non-migrant

Family PSOPHIIDAE	Species *Psophia viridis*	Length 50cm (20in)

DARK-WINGED TRUMPETER

hunched back

This bird gets its name from its loud, trumpeting threat call, uttered with outspread wings. In friendlier situations it utters low, booming notes. It is chiefly a ground-dweller and is normally seen walking, with a hump-backed posture. With its long, strong legs it can also run fast. The wings are rounded and weak-looking, and flight appears laborious. In spite of this, the birds always roost fairly high in trees. They feed on the ground, and are normally seen in small social groups. The diet consists mainly of fallen fruit and nuts. Trumpeters rely on other tree-dwelling animals, such as parrots and monkeys, to knock these down while feeding, and will also take berries and some insects. Little is known of their breeding behaviour.

• **NEST** A loose structure made of sticks and leaves and placed high in a tree, in a large tree hole, in an open cavity, or on a bare branch.

• **DISTRIBUTION** Middle and lower Amazon basin in C. Brazil.

strong, walking legs

DISTRIBUTION

Plumage Sexes alike	Habitat	Migration Non-migrant

Family RALLIDAE	Species *Rallus aquaticus*	Length 28cm (11in)

WATER RAIL

An extremely shy bird of swamps and fens, this species gives its presence away by loud, squealing calls. Once in the safety of its preferred surroundings, in or under growing vegetation, it ceases to be timid, but it is uneasy on open ground. Only at night, or in the evening, will it venture out into the open in search of food. The long, probing beak picks up aquatic insects, snails, frogs, and other small creatures; it can also be used like a pickaxe to break the skulls of small birds or mice. Water Rails run rapidly, with their heads lowered, and can swim well.

JUVENILE
white
undertail
coverts

• **NEST** A cup-shaped nest, woven out of grass, and placed at the base of a tussock of reeds, sedges, or grass.

• **DISTRIBUTION** Breeds in Eurasia, N. Africa, and the Middle East. Some populations migrate south to the Middle East and S.E. Asia.

bluish-grey
underside

DISTRIBUTION

Plumage Sexes alike	Habitat	Migration Partial migrant

Family RALLIDAE	Species *Gallirallus philippensis*	Length 30cm (12in)

BUFF-BANDED RAIL

Camouflaged against leaves and undergrowth by its speckled, banded plumage, this is a common waterside bird. It always occurs in places where plant cover borders on open water, whether this be the sea, a freshwater lake, a marsh, or a pool in wet grassland. This is always a wary bird, though it becomes less timid during its active periods at dusk and by night. By day it tends to stay within thick vegetation. If forced to move, it flies off awkwardly with dangling legs. Some populations fly long distances on migration, though others remain in one place all year. In general, the diet consists of insects and other invertebrates, small molluscs, seeds, and other parts of plants.

slender body
shape for ease of
movement among
• *plant stems*

DISTRIBUTION

upward
stretching
posture
(body is
more often
hunched)

• **NEST** A hollow in the ground, lined with grass and leaves, concealed in dense vegetation, often some distance from the waterside.
• **DISTRIBUTION** Philippines, Sulawesi, New Guinea, Australia, New Zealand, and the W. Pacific Islands.

Plumage Sexes alike	Habitat	Migration Partial migrant

| Family RALLIDAE | Species *Gallirallus australis* | Length 53cm (21in) |

WEKA

This stout, strong bird is flightless and lives in grassland, scrub, or forest edges, wherever undergrowth or thickets are plentiful. It is not timid, and is usually seen walking about in a deliberate manner, flicking its tail. If the need arises it can run fast, and it is a competent swimmer. The Weka feeds on the ground, taking a varied diet including earthworms, rats, small birds, bird's eggs, seeds, and grass shoots.

• **NEST** A shallow cup of sedges and grasses, hidden among herbage or fallen branches.

• **DISTRIBUTION** New Zealand.

• **REMARK** The Weka is one of a number of island-dwelling rail species that have become flightless. Like most of them, it also became larger.

• *small, slight wings, not capable of flight*

• *strong legs, set wide on the body*

DISTRIBUTION

| Plumage Sexes alike | Habitat | Migration Non-migrant |

| Family RALLIDAE | Species *Sarothrura lugens* | Length 15cm (6in) |

CHESTNUT-HEADED FLUFFTAIL

A difficult bird to see on account of its habit of skulking deep in dense vegetation, this rail is usually identified by its distinctive calls. Its nocturnal lifestyle makes it still harder to observe. The Chestnut-headed Flufftail lives in grassy forest clearings and in grassy marshes occurring in the African savanna (tropical grassland). It feeds on insects, including ants, and other invertebrates, as well as seeds. Its name is derived from the finely structured feathers of its tail, which have a curiously loose, soft texture.

FEMALE

DISTRIBUTION

• **NEST** Not scientifically recorded.

• **DISTRIBUTION** Separate areas in tropical Africa, from the Equator to N. Zimbabwe.

• **REMARK** This is one of nine species of flufftail, all of which live in Africa. They can be identified by their loud calls and sharp whistles, which differ in each species.

loose, soft feathering

| Plumage Sexes differ | Habitat | Migration Non-migrant |

Family RALLIDAE	Species *Crex crex*	Length 28cm (11in)

CORNCRAKE

At first sight, this species might be mistaken for a gamebird such as a partridge, but its bright, chestnut wings, which are conspicuous in flight, identify it for certain. It is a spring migrant to grassland, fallow land, and fields of growing crops, strongly favouring regions where farming is more traditional and hay is cut by hand. Males newly arrived from migration can be seen walking in the short grass, not yet high enough to hide them. They become still easier to see when they stand upright, raising their bills to utter rasping "crex-crex" calls to attract the females. The birds then nest in the fields. The diet consists of earthworms, insects, molluscs, frogs, seeds, and shoots.
• **NEST** A shallow cup nest lined with leaves and grasses, concealed in grass or in an isolated tussock.
• **DISTRIBUTION** Breeds in Europe and C. Asia. Winters in Mediterranean region and throughout Africa.
• **REMARK** Originally a bird of moist natural grassland, the Corncrake survived the spread of agriculture in past centuries by nesting in hay meadows. On modern farms, mechanized hay production destroys nests, eggs, and young of Corncrakes, so the bird has become rare.

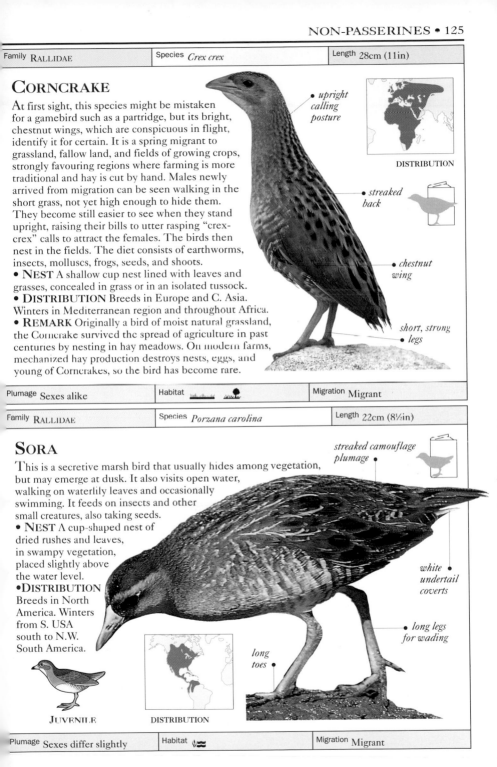

upright calling posture

DISTRIBUTION

streaked back

chestnut wing

short, strong legs

Plumage Sexes alike	Habitat	Migration Migrant

Family RALLIDAE	Species *Porzana carolina*	Length 22cm (8½in)

SORA

This is a secretive marsh bird that usually hides among vegetation, but may emerge at dusk. It also visits open water, walking on waterlily leaves and occasionally swimming. It feeds on insects and other small creatures, also taking seeds.
• **NEST** A cup-shaped nest of dried rushes and leaves, in swampy vegetation, placed slightly above the water level.
• **DISTRIBUTION** Breeds in North America. Winters from S. USA south to N.W. South America.

streaked camouflage plumage

white undertail coverts

long legs for wading

long toes

JUVENILE

DISTRIBUTION

Plumage Sexes differ slightly	Habitat	Migration Migrant

Family RALLIDAE	Species *Gallinula chloropus*	Length 33cm (13in)

COMMON MOORHEN

A cautious, sharp-voiced bird of the waterside, this species has managed to exploit most stretches of fresh water, however small, and is common and sometimes tame on village and town ponds. It walks on land, and swims with nodding head, feeding on insects and small water creatures, waterweeds, seeds, and berries.
• **NEST** A neat, bowl-shaped nest made of reeds and stems, concealed in growing plants at or above water level.
• **DISTRIBUTION** Parts of North and South America, Africa, Europe, Asia as far south as Java, and the W. Pacific.

DISTRIBUTION

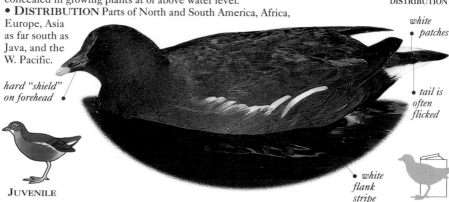

white patches

hard "shield" on forehead

tail is often flicked

white flank stripe

JUVENILE

Plumage Sexes alike	Habitat 〰〰 〰	Migration Partial migrant

Family RALLIDAE	Species *Porphyrio martinica*	Length 33cm (13in)

PURPLE GALLINULE

tough, blue "shield"

At first sight, this bird resembles the Common Moorhen, but is more brightly coloured, and has a more slender build, with longer neck and legs. In adults, the legs are bright yellow and the hard "shield" over the bill is bright blue. The Purple Gallinule occurs on lakes, pools, waterways, and wet marshes, where vegetation is tall and abundant, in regions where the climate is warm. It wades and walks easily over floating plants and waterlilies with its long-toed feet. Although it will venture onto open ground to feed, it does not stray far from cover. It walks with an upward jerking tail and on shorter flights the legs dangle. Birds often climb up reeds, rice plants, bushes, and trees in order to feed. The diet consists of invertebrates, frogs, waterplants, seeds, and berries.
• **NEST** A bulky cup nest made of fresh or dead stems and leaves of rushes and cat-tails, built in marshland and situated in plants in or near water, or in bushes above water level.
• **DISTRIBUTION** S.E. USA, Central America, West Indies, and South America to N. Argentina.

DISTRIBUTION

JUVENILE

long toes

Plumage Sexes alike	Habitat 〰〰 〰	Migration Migrant

Family RALLIDAE	Species *Porphyrio mantelli*	Length 63cm (25in)

TAKAHE

A heavy, flightless bird with a capacious bill and stout legs, the Takahe feeds on tussock grass. It consumes the seeds and the fleshy bases of the stems. To eat the stem bases, it holds down a tuft of grass with one foot and shears through it with its bill, removing the inedible upper stalks. The Takahe's small population lives in a few high-altitude valleys in mountains. In cold weather, the birds retreat into beech forests on lower slopes.
• **NEST** A hollow in the ground, lined with grass and leaves, and hidden between grass tussocks.
• **DISTRIBUTION** New Zealand on South Island.
• **REMARK** This species evolved after becoming isolated in New Zealand where predators were absent. It became flightless and, no longer needing to be light, grew large and heavy. Man brought in predators such as cats, and grazing competitors such as deer. The Takahe was thought to be extinct until a relict population was discovered in 1948. Conservationists are trying to save this by breeding it in captivity and releasing birds in safer areas.

massive bill for shearing grass

DISTRIBUTION

solid, heavy build

Plumage Sexes alike	Habitat ▲ ⬛ 🌳	Migration Non-migrant

Family RALLIDAE	Species *Fulica americana*	Length 39cm (15½in)

AMERICAN COOT

This is a bird of larger areas of open water. It is seen on lakes, large rivers, and flooded swamps, and winter flocks sometimes settle on sheltered salt water areas such as estuaries. Coots feed on buds, leaves, and stems of water plants, as well as on seeds, insects, and other small creatures. They feed by foraging on the ground at the waterside or by diving in open water, taking waterweed from the bottom. They cannot take off easily and need to run along the surface to get airborne. Breeding pairs defend territories aggressively, both birds fighting intruders.
• **NEST** A bulky cup nest made of dead leaves and stems, placed among vegetation in or beside the water, or on low or submerged branches.
• **DISTRIBUTION** Breeds in North and Central America, the Caribbean region, and in the Andes of Colombia. North American populations winter as far south as Colombia.

very small "shield"

uniform, dark grey plumage

DISTRIBUTION

short tail

lobed toes

Plumage Sexes alike	Habitat 〰️ 〰️〰️	Migration Partial migrant

Family HELIORNITHIDAE	Species *Podica senegalensis*	L. 58cm (23in)/50cm (20in)

AFRICAN FINFOOT

With its streamlined body, the African Finfoot is able to swim well, either fully on the surface, or with its body submerged and the neck and head out of the water. The feet, with their wide, fleshy lobes, make very effective "paddles". The bill is slender and streamlined.

This is a secretive bird that lives where trees and bushes overhang a river or lake. It spends as much of its time on land as on the water, feeding on insects and small aquatic life.

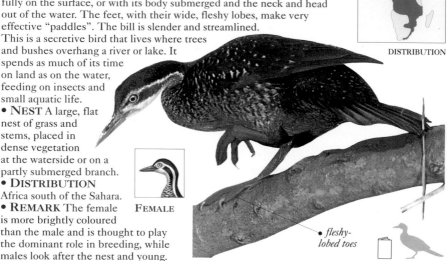

DISTRIBUTION

• **NEST** A large, flat nest of grass and stems, placed in dense vegetation at the waterside or on a partly submerged branch.
• **DISTRIBUTION** Africa south of the Sahara.
• **REMARK** The female is more brightly coloured than the male and is thought to play the dominant role in breeding, while males look after the nest and young.

FEMALE

• *fleshy-lobed toes*

Plumage Sexes differ	Habitat 〰〰	Migration Non-migrant

Family RHYNOCHETIDAE	Species *Rhynochetos jubatus*	Length 55cm (22in)

KAGU

The squat body shape, strong legs, and powerful bill of the Kagu are adaptations to a ground-dwelling life. It inhabits forested mountainsides with undergrowth and small streams. The Kagu is virtually flightless, but can glide down hill slopes. It normally walks, tapping the ground to detect the earthworms and other small creatures on which it feeds. In display, it erects its shaggy crest into a tall, vertical fan and sometimes spreads its wings, showing the black, chestnut, and white barring on the flight feathers. It feeds in loose flocks but breeding birds live in pairs. Kagus utter noisy, rattling calls, and pairs maintain contact with melodious notes, heard especially before dawn.

DISTRIBUTION

• *weak, little-used wings*

RAISED CREST

• **NEST** A loose structure of sticks and leaves, placed on the ground.
• **DISTRIBUTION** New Caledonia in the S.W. Pacific.

Plumage Sexes alike	Habitat ▲ 🌳 ✈	Migration Non-migrant

Family EURYPYGIDAE	Species *Eurypyga helias*	Length 48cm (19in)

SUNBITTERN

Living alongside shady forest streams, the Sunbittern is a slender bird with a sedate, deliberate walk. Single birds or pairs forage along the water's edge for insects, spiders, crustaceans, and small fish. Sunbitterns hunt silently with tilted bodies, ready to seize prey with a quick jab of the bill. When disturbed, they fly up into the trees. In flight, they reveal a large, dark "eye-spot" on each wing.

slender bill for picking up animal prey

• **NEST** A rounded heap of moss, other plant material, and mud, with a nest hollow on top, lined with leaves, and built on a horizontal tree branch.
• **DISTRIBUTION** From C. Mexico south through Central America to the Amazon basin.
• **REMARK** The eyespots are an important feature in display behaviour, in which the bird holds out its opened wings and fans its tail.

long, wading legs

DISTRIBUTION

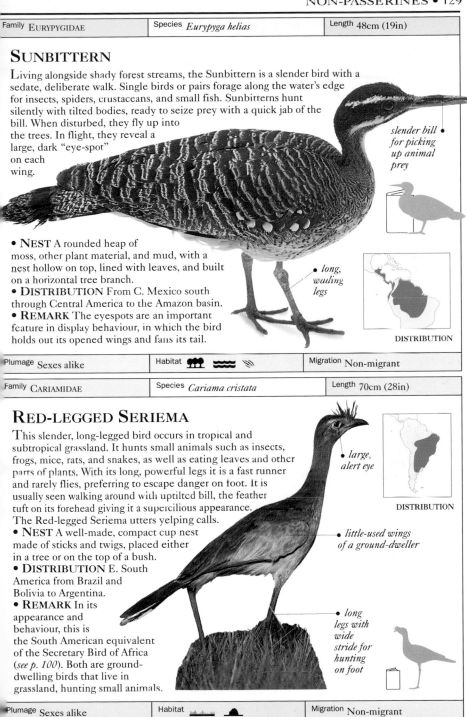

Plumage Sexes alike	Habitat 🌳 〰️ 〰️	Migration Non-migrant

Family CARIAMIDAE	Species *Cariama cristata*	Length 70cm (28in)

RED-LEGGED SERIEMA

This slender, long-legged bird occurs in tropical and subtropical grassland. It hunts small animals such as insects, frogs, mice, rats, and snakes, as well as eating leaves and other parts of plants. With its long, powerful legs it is a fast runner and rarely flies, preferring to escape danger on foot. It is usually seen walking around with uptilted bill, the feather tuft on its forehead giving it a supercilious appearance. The Red-legged Seriema utters yelping calls.

large, alert eye

DISTRIBUTION

• **NEST** A well-made, compact cup nest made of sticks and twigs, placed either in a tree or on the top of a bush.
• **DISTRIBUTION** E. South America from Brazil and Bolivia to Argentina.
• **REMARK** In its appearance and behaviour, this is the South American equivalent of the Secretary Bird of Africa (*see p. 100*). Both are ground-dwelling birds that live in grassland, hunting small animals.

little-used wings of a ground-dweller

long legs with wide stride for hunting on foot

Plumage Sexes alike	Habitat	Migration Non-migrant

Family OTIDIDAE	Species *Otis tarda*	L. 100cm (39in)/80cm (31in)

GREAT BUSTARD

The long neck and legs of the Great Bustard give it an unobstructed view in its open grassland habitat. Here it moves with a slow, deliberate walk, flying infrequently. In spring the males display to the females in a group, on a specially reserved display ground. Females then nest and raise the young unaided. The diet consists of plants, insects, and other small animals.
• **NEST** A hollow in the ground, often hidden in crops or high grass.
• **DISTRIBUTION** Breeds in parts of Spain, Morocco, E. Europe, C. and E. Asia. Winters in the south of this range.

inflated throat pouch

wing twisted in display

MALE IN FULL DISPLAY

DISTRIBUTION

FEMALE

Plumage Sexes differ	Habitat	Migration Non-migrant

Family OTIDIDAE	Species *Eupodotis afra*	Length 53cm (21in)

BLACK KORHAAN

This is a sturdily built bird of grassland and other open landscapes. Both sexes have camouflaged upper-parts to prevent detection by predators overhead. Males have a black neck and underside which are conspicuous to other birds at ground level. Black Korhaans live in pairs, each pair holding its own territory. The male utters a harsh, repetitive "cracker" call, either from a raised perch or in a display flight. Displaying males rise in flapping flight, then drop slowly with fluttering wings and dangling legs. The birds feed on the ground, pairs sometimes walking together with sedate steps and heads held high. They feed mainly on growing plants, also taking insects.
• **NEST** A slight hollow in the ground, scraped by body pressure, among tufts of grass.
• **DISTRIBUTION** Parts of southern Africa.

camouflage pattern on the back

bold, black-and-white underside

DISTRIBUTION

long legs for constant walking

FEMALE

Plumage Sexes differ	Habitat	Migration Non-migrant

Family JACANIDAE	Species *Hydrophasianus chirurgus*	Length 55cm (22in)

PHEASANT-TAILED JACANA

This bird lives on lakes and swamps, its chief adaptations being long legs, toes, and claws. These enable it to spread its weight, so that it can walk on the floating leaves of water plants. It feeds on invertebrates, frogs, and fish. A female may mate with up to ten males, each of these incubating a clutch and raising his own brood.

WINTER

narrow, drooping tail •

• *both sexes have long tails during the breeding season*

• *black wing tips*

• *white wings*

long toes and • *claws*

• **NEST** A thin layer of dried water weeds and other plants, placed on floating leaves.
• **DISTRIBUTION** Indian subcontinent, and from C. China through S.E. Asia as far as Java and the Philippines.
• **REMARK** Females are slightly larger than males, with similar but brighter colours.

DISTRIBUTION

Plumage Sexes differ slightly	Habitat 〰〰 〰	Migration Partial migrant

Family JACANIDAE	Species *Jacana spinosa*	Length 24cm (9½in)

NORTHERN JACANA

• *soft, fleshy wattle*

Long legs, toes, and claws enable this bird to walk on floating water plants. It can swim, but does so reluctantly, and will occasionally fly, usually slowly with dangling legs. In more sustained flight, the legs are extended backwards, with the long toes projecting. Both sexes display to one another by raising their wings to reveal vivid yellow patches underneath. They also hold the wings up after landing. The female is bigger than the male and, when breeding, holds a large territory that encompasses up to four male territories. Each male has his own nest, in which he incubates a clutch of her eggs and rears and feeds the young.

JUVENILE

long toes and claws •

• **NEST** A loose layer of dried water weeds, on floating leaves.
• **DISTRIBUTION** Central America and the larger islands of the Caribbean.

DISTRIBUTION

Plumage Sexes alike	Habitat 〰〰 〰	Migration Non-migrant

Family ROSTRATULIDAE	Species *Rostratula benghalensis*	L. 25cm (10in)/28cm (11in)

GREATER PAINTED-SNIPE

A bird of shallow swamps, the Greater
Painted-Snipe hides among low
vegetation or reeds during the
day, where it is inconspicuous
despite its patterned plumage. Birds
are active from dusk till dawn, probing
the mud with their bills. They feed
on earthworms, crustaceans, insects,
and some plant seeds. Early in the
breeding season, the female performs a
display flight over her territory with soft,
hooting calls. She may pair with several
males and each of these will incubate a
clutch of eggs and also rear the young.

large eyes for night feeding

female has a darker, stronger pattern

long, wading legs

MALE

FEMALE

• **NEST** A layer of
plant materials that
forms a raised site amid
marsh vegetation.
• **DISTRIBUTION**
Scattered areas in Africa,
Asia, and N. and E. Australia.
• **REMARK** Females are larger
and more colourful than the males.

DISTRIBUTION

Plumage Sexes differ	Habitat 〰	Migration Non-migrant

Family DROMADIDAE	Species *Dromas ardeola*	Length 40cm (16in)

CRAB PLOVER

long legs extend beyond tail

Occurring on sandy seashores or tidal flats,
this species feeds like a plover, running
and making sudden jabs to catch prey
on the ground. It eats crabs, cracking
their shells with its powerful
bill. Crab Plovers are seen in
low, slow flight. They
often feed in groups, and roost in
large flocks on the shore.
• **NEST** A burrow in sand, 1.5m
(5ft 11in) or more in length. Nests are
packed closely together in colonies,
located on sandy islands or dunes.
• **DISTRIBUTION** Coastline of Indian Ocean,
Red Sea, and Persian
Gulf. Some birds winter
as far south as Madagascar
and Malay Peninsula.
• **REMARK** Of all the
shorebirds (220 species),
this is the only one that
nests in a burrow.

DISTRIBUTION

JUVENILE

Plumage Sexes alike	Habitat 〰	Migration Partial migrant

Family HAEMATOPODIDAE	Species *Haematopus ostralegus*	Length 43cm (17in)

EURASIAN OYSTERCATCHER

Bold, black-and-white plumage, a bright orange bill, and a piping
"kleep" call make this a well-known bird of shores and mudflats. In
flight it reveals a large, white wingstripe and white rump. Winter
flocks feed on open shores or estuaries. The blade-like bill-
tip is useful for smashing open shellfish and detaching
limpets from rocks. The diet consists of shellfish,
worms, and small fish. In display, males run
side by side with
lowered bills, trilling
noisily, and also
perform a flight with
slowly flapping wings.
• **NEST** A hollow scraped by
body pressure, in shingle, sand, or grass.
• **DISTRIBUTION** Breeds
in N. Europe, C. Asia, and
N.E. Asia. Winters to the south,
as far as Africa, India, and S. China.

*bill-tip
is vertically
flattened, like
a knife blade*

*white
wing stripe,
revealed in
flight*

JUVENILE

DISTRIBUTION

Plumage Sexes alike	Habitat	Migration Migrant

Family RECURVIROSTRIDAE	Species *Himantopus mexicanus*	Length 35cm (14in)

BLACK-NECKED STILT

This distinctive shorebird has an elegant
appearance with its very long legs, upright
stance, and neatly proportioned bill. It is
adapted for wading through the water, where it picks
items of food from the surface or catches them by swinging
its bill from side to side. The bill is also used to probe into
the mud in search of food. The diet consists mainly of
aquatic insects, together with other small invertebrates. In
flight, the Black-necked Stilt reveals its long, tapering wings,
which are black both above and below. This bird is usually
seen in groups, and sometimes joins mixed- species flocks of
shorebirds. Needing shallow water, which may be either fresh or
salt, it occurs around water margins and in marshes. Habitats of this
type dry up rapidly and are often only temporarily suitable for nesting,
so birds sometimes travel about nomadically, seeking new sites.
• **NEST** A hollow scraped with the feet and shaped by body pressure,
on an open, dry site or in low vegetation, lined with a few stems; or a
substantial cup nest of stems and leaves, on a tussock, where it can
be built up rapidly if the water level rises.
• **DISTRIBUTION** Breeds from the Canadian
border through parts of the USA as far south as
S. Brazil. Northern birds migrate south within this range.

*black
extends
up the
neck*

DISTRIBUTION

*tapering
wings*

Plumage Sexes alike	Habitat	Migration Migrant/nomadic

Family RECURVIROSTRIDAE	Species *Recurvirostra avosetta*	Length 43cm (17in)

PIED AVOCET

A long-legged shorebird, known for its slender, upcurved bill, this species is also unusual for having webbed feet. It is found in estuaries, coastal lagoons, and saltwater lakes, and feeds mainly in shallow water, preferably salt or brackish (partly salt and partly fresh water). Its most characteristic method of feeding is to stand in the water and swing its head and neck from side to side, sweeping its bill to and fro in the water in search of small aquatic animals. Pied Avocets can also target their prey and seize it without sweeping, and sometimes feed by swimming and up-ending like ducks. Nesting colonies are located on open ground beside water.

• **NEST** A hollow in the ground, bare or with a lining of stems, grass, or pebbles, collected from within reach.

• **DISTRIBUTION** Breeds in Eurasia from British Isles east to Far East. Winters as far south as Africa, Pakistan, and China.

slender, upcurved bill

long, tapering wings

JUVENILE

webbed feet – unusual for a shorebird

DISTRIBUTION

Plumage Sexes alike	Habitat	Migration Migrant

Family BURHINIDAE	Species *Burhinus oedicnemus*	Length 40cm (16in)

STONE CURLEW

This unusual shorebird is always found in an open landscape, whether this be a tract of semi-desert, a stony heath in the subtropics, or a stretch of arable farmland. It lies hiding on the ground by day, and, if alarmed, runs rather than flies. It can fly strongly, and at night it may travel some distance to feed. The Stone Curlew is active at dusk and after dark, hunting insects and other invertebrates. Individuals meet by night for noisy calling and display. The wailing, whistling, curlew-like calls can be heard from far off.

• **NEST** A hollow, scraped with the feet and shaped by body pressure; either bare or lined with small stones.

• **DISTRIBUTION** Breeds in W. Europe and C. Asia. Winters as far south as Africa, India, and parts of S.E. Asia.

streaked plumage for camouflage

large eye for night feeding

white wing stripe

strong legs for foraging on dry ground

DISTRIBUTION

Plumage Sexes alike	Habitat	Migration Migrant

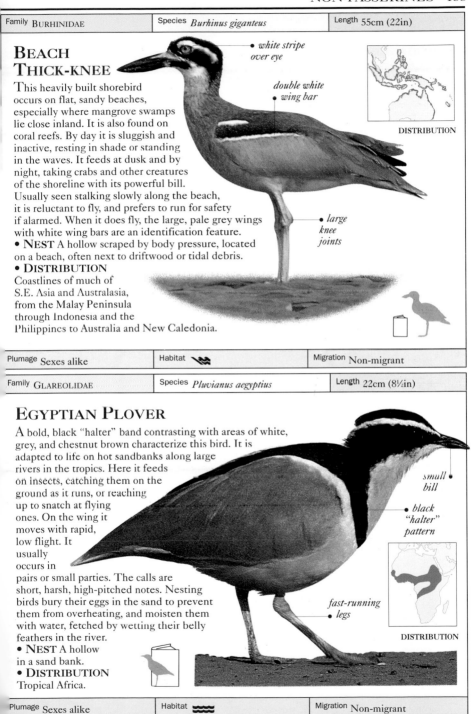

Family BURHINIDAE	Species *Burhinus giganteus*	Length 55cm (22in)

BEACH THICK-KNEE

This heavily built shorebird occurs on flat, sandy beaches, especially where mangrove swamps lie close inland. It is also found on coral reefs. By day it is sluggish and inactive, resting in shade or standing in the waves. It feeds at dusk and by night, taking crabs and other creatures of the shoreline with its powerful bill. Usually seen stalking slowly along the beach, it is reluctant to fly, and prefers to run for safety if alarmed. When it does fly, the large, pale grey wings with white wing bars are an identification feature.
• **NEST** A hollow scraped by body pressure, located on a beach, often next to driftwood or tidal debris.
• **DISTRIBUTION** Coastlines of much of S.E. Asia and Australasia, from the Malay Peninsula through Indonesia and the Philippines to Australia and New Caledonia.

• white stripe over eye

double white • wing bar

DISTRIBUTION

• large knee joints

Plumage Sexes alike	Habitat	Migration Non-migrant

Family GLAREOLIDAE	Species *Pluvianus aegyptius*	Length 22cm (8¼in)

EGYPTIAN PLOVER

A bold, black "halter" band contrasting with areas of white, grey, and chestnut brown characterize this bird. It is adapted to life on hot sandbanks along large rivers in the tropics. Here it feeds on insects, catching them on the ground as it runs, or reaching up to snatch at flying ones. On the wing it moves with rapid, low flight. It usually occurs in pairs or small parties. The calls are short, harsh, high-pitched notes. Nesting birds bury their eggs in the sand to prevent them from overheating, and moisten them with water, fetched by wetting their belly feathers in the river.
• **NEST** A hollow in a sand bank.
• **DISTRIBUTION** Tropical Africa.

small • bill

• black "halter" pattern

DISTRIBUTION

fast-running • legs

Plumage Sexes alike	Habitat	Migration Non-migrant

| Family GLAREOLIDAE | Species *Cursorius temminckii* | Length 20cm (8in) |

TEMMINCK'S COURSER

A slenderly built bird with long legs, Temminck's Courser inhabits dry, open country. Here it travels in rapid sprints, or stands upright and on the alert, showing a chestnut-and-black pattern on the belly. In flight, it can be recognized by its quick, jerky wingbeats. This species favours habitats with plenty of bare ground across which it can run easily. It is normally found in short grassland and scrub, and has a preference for areas that have been burned in bush and grass fires. Temminck's Coursers feed by catching insects and other invertebrates on the ground with their thin, curved bills, sometimes also taking seeds. Breeding in scattered pairs on open stretches of ground, they feed the nestlings in the first few days. The young then begin to learn to find their food, though parents often continue partially feeding them until they fly.
• **NEST** Simply bare ground, or, in places where sand or soil is soft, a shallow hollow scraped with the feet and shaped by body pressure.
• **DISTRIBUTION** Open areas of Africa south of the Sahara.
• **REMARK** A number of shorebirds, including all coursers, pratincoles, thick-knees, oystercatchers, woodcocks, and snipes, feed their young for the first few days. Most others do not feed their young – nestlings run and feed themselves within hours of hatching.

stripes meeting at the nape

DISTRIBUTION

slender body

long, fast-running legs

| Plumage Sexes alike | Habitat | Migration Non-migrant |

| Family GLAREOLIDAE | Species *Stiltia isabella* | Length 23cm (9in) |

AUSTRALIAN PRATINCOLE

A long-winged shorebird resembling a swallow, this species feeds both in the air and on the ground. In the air, it flies with stiff, strong wingbeats, patrolling for insects in flight. On the ground it runs across open spaces to feed, tilting to snatch insects from the surface, or darting up at flying ones. It chooses bare, open habitats including beaches or lake shores, but sometimes occurs as far as 2km (1¼ miles) from water.
• **NEST** A hollow scraped with the feet and shaped by body pressure, sometimes ringed with tiny stones.
DISTRIBUTION Breeds in Australia. Winters in N. Australia, New Guinea, Sulawesi, S.E. Borneo, and islands from Timor to Java.

JUVENILE

dark belly pattern

short tail

long wings

DISTRIBUTION

| Plumage Sexes alike | Habitat | Migration Migrant |

Family GLAREOLIDAE	Species *Glareola nordmanni*	Length 25cm (10in)

BLACK-WINGED PRATINCOLE

This species is a typical pratincole, a shore-dwelling bird that has become adapted to feeding in the air like a swallow, catching insects. It has large eyes, a broad-based bill, long, narrow wings, and a forked tail. Equipped with fairly long legs, this bird will also chase insects on the ground. The black underwings become visible in flight, which is distinctively agile and rapid. The species is highly sociable, feeding in flocks, and is particularly active at dusk and dawn. In the breeding season it flocks on the margins of steppe lakes and marshes with short vegetation or bare mud. It rests, and nests, on the ground, where its coloration makes it inconspicuous on mud or soil.

• **NEST** A shallow, bare depression, in sparse vegetation or on bare ground.

• **DISTRIBUTION** Breeds in C. Asia. Winters in Africa south of the Sahara.

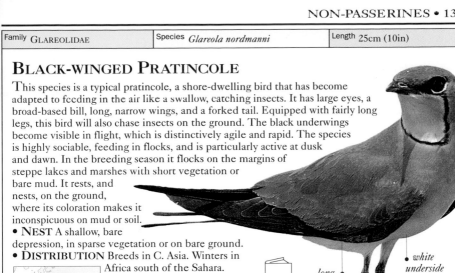

long, slender wings

white underside

DISTRIBUTION

WINTER PLUMAGE

Plumage Sexes alike	Habitat	Migration Migrant

Family CHARADRIIDAE	Species *Vanellus vanellus*	Length 30cm (12in)

NORTHERN LAPWING

A conspicuous bird of farmland and grazing marshes, the Lapwing is most noticeable in spring when the male performs a tumbling display flight over the nest territory, uttering wild "peewit" calls. The species prefers to feed in short, grazed grass and hunts by sight, making short runs and sudden, forward-tilting pecks at the ground. The diet consists of earthworms, insects, and other small invertebrates. After nesting the birds begin forming into flocks. These migrate to moister, milder wintering areas, most often in the west.

slender, black crest

female's throat and face are whiter than the male's in summer

SUMMER MALE

DISTRIBUTION

SUMMER FEMALE

• **NEST** A hollow, scraped with the feet and shaped by body pressure, on open ground or in grass, lined with plant stems and grass from within reach.

• **DISTRIBUTION** Breeds across Eurasia. Winters as far south as N. Africa and N.W. India but mainly in Europe.

WINTER (BOTH SEXES)

Plumage Sexes alike	Habitat	Migration Migrant

| Family CHARADRIIDAE | Species *Anitibyx armatus* | Length 30cm (12in) |

BLACKSMITH PLOVER

A conspicuous but wary bird, the
Blacksmith Plover gets its name from its
loud, clinking alarm note. This is its most
frequently heard call, although it is usually
silent unless disturbed. It lives in open
landscapes with moist, short grass or sparse
bushes, close to lakes or large rivers. Most
of the time birds are seen singly or in pairs,
although they sometimes form flocks,
particularly when not breeding. In flight,
conspicuous features are broad wings, a
flapping wingbeat, white underwings, and
a white tail with a black tip. This assertive
species has a sharp spur on the front angle
of the wing, which is used when
fighting. The diet consists of insects,
worms, and molluscs.
• **NEST** A hollow scraped with the feet
and shaped by body pressure in open soil,
sparsely lined with small pebbles, dry
fragments of dung, or plant stems.
• **DISTRIBUTION** Open country
areas in Africa south of the Equator.

white nape patch

red eye

black frontal patch

fighting spur concealed in plumage

DISTRIBUTION

white belly

very long legs for a plover

JUVENILE

| Plumage Sexes alike | Habitat | Migration Non-migrant |

| Family CHARADRIIDAE | Species *Pluvialis dominica* | Length 25cm (10in) |

AMERICAN GOLDEN PLOVER

The combination of a gold-spangled back, a black
underside, and a black face surrounded by a white
border, make this a spectacular plover. The back is
camouflaged against tundra vegetation for safety
from birds of prey, but the black underside is
visible to other birds at ground level,
especially in the display flight. This
species breeds on drier areas of the
Arctic tundra and winters on
coasts, marshes, and
sometimes grassland.
It feeds in the typical
manner of a plover,
running rapidly and
snatching prey from the ground, taking worms,
insects, and other invertebrates. A long-distance
migrant, it flies strongly on tapering wings.
• **NEST** A thinly lined hollow in the ground, in
an exposed site with a wide view for safety.
• **DISTRIBUTION** Breeds in
N. North America. Winters in
S. Brazil, N. Argentina, Uruguay.

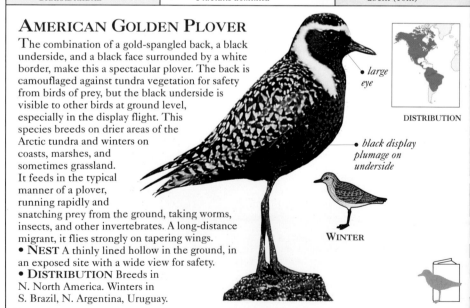

large eye

DISTRIBUTION

black display plumage on underside

WINTER

| Plumage Sexes alike | Habitat | Migration Migrant |

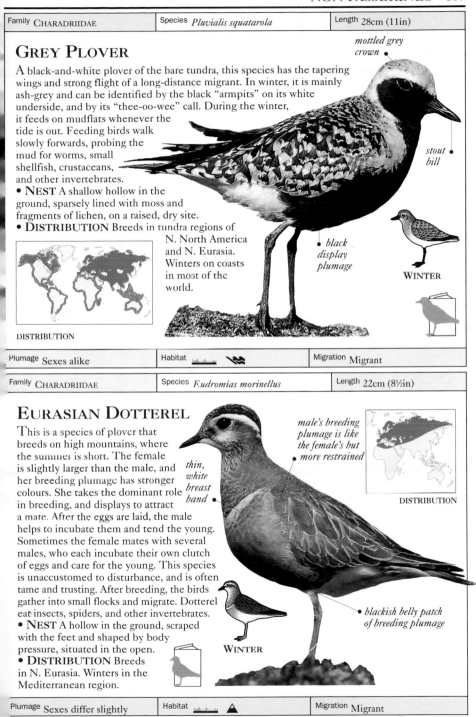

Family CHARADRIIDAE	Species *Pluvialis squatarola*	Length 28cm (11in)

GREY PLOVER

A black-and-white plover of the bare tundra, this species has the tapering wings and strong flight of a long-distance migrant. In winter, it is mainly ash-grey and can be identified by the black "armpits" on its white underside, and by its "thee-oo-wee" call. During the winter, it feeds on mudflats whenever the tide is out. Feeding birds walk slowly forwards, probing the mud for worms, small shellfish, crustaceans, and other invertebrates.

• NEST A shallow hollow in the ground, sparsely lined with moss and fragments of lichen, on a raised, dry site.

• DISTRIBUTION Breeds in tundra regions of N. North America and N. Eurasia. Winters on coasts in most of the world.

mottled grey crown

stout bill

black display plumage

WINTER

DISTRIBUTION

Plumage Sexes alike	Habitat	Migration Migrant

Family CHARADRIIDAE	Species *Eudromias morinellus*	Length 22cm (8½in)

EURASIAN DOTTEREL

This is a species of plover that breeds on high mountains, where the summer is short. The female is slightly larger than the male, and her breeding plumage has stronger colours. She takes the dominant role in breeding, and displays to attract a mate. After the eggs are laid, the male helps to incubate them and tend the young. Sometimes the female mates with several males, who each incubate their own clutch of eggs and care for the young. This species is unaccustomed to disturbance, and is often tame and trusting. After breeding, the birds gather into small flocks and migrate. Dotterel eat insects, spiders, and other invertebrates.

• NEST A hollow in the ground, scraped with the feet and shaped by body pressure, situated in the open.

• DISTRIBUTION Breeds in N. Eurasia. Winters in the Mediterranean region.

male's breeding plumage is like the female's but more restrained

DISTRIBUTION

thin, white breast band

blackish belly patch of breeding plumage

WINTER

Plumage Sexes differ slightly	Habitat	Migration Migrant

Family CHARADRIIDAE	Species *Charadrius hiaticula*	Length 19cm (7½in)

RINGED PLOVER

With its black-and-white markings this bird is camouflaged against a background of pebbles. In flight it shows a white wing stripe. It occurs on coasts, mudflats, and beaches, and sometimes beside inland waters. The diet consists of small insects and invertebrates.
• **NEST** A shallow hollow in sand or pebbles, situated on a beach.
• **DISTRIBUTION** Breeds on Arctic coasts from N.E. Canada to E. Siberia. Winters in Africa.

DISTRIBUTION

• *white neck ring*

• *white underside*

• *long legs for running*

Plumage Sexes alike	Habitat	Migration Migrant

Family CHARADRIIDAE	Species *Charadrius vociferus*	Length 27cm (10½in)

KILLDEER

Like the Northern Lapwing in Europe, this large plover occurs on farmland, although with its tapering wings and white wing stripe it is more like the Ringed Plover. It feeds in grassland, marshes, and river estuaries, and is often seen near houses. A noisy species, it utters shrill "kill-dee" calls. The diet consists of insects, worms, and other invertebrates.
• **NEST** A shallow hollow in the ground, sometimes lined with a few pebbles. Birds occasionally nest on flat roofs.
• **DISTRIBUTION** Breeds in North, Central, South America. Northern birds migrate south.

DISTRIBUTION

• *double black band*

orange-rufous • *rump*

long tail •

long, tapering wings

Plumage Sexes alike	Habitat	Migration Migrant

Family CHARADRIIDAE	Species *Anarhynchus frontalis*	Length 20cm (8in)

WRYBILL

The sideways-curving bill of this bird is used for reaching under pebbles when feeding in stony riverbeds. The Wrybill eats aquatic insects and invertebrates, and possibly also fish eggs. It nests on shingle banks by rivers, and winters in flocks on inlets by the coast.
• **NEST** A shallow hollow formed by the birds, among pebbles.
• **DISTRIBUTION** New Zealand.
• **REMARK** The only bird in the world with a bill that curves sideways.

forked • *eyestripes*

DISTRIBUTION

• *black breast band*

• *white underside*

Plumage Sexes alike	Habitat	Migration Migrant

Family SCOLOPACIDAE	Species *Limosa haemastica*	Length 39cm (15½in)

HUDSONIAN GODWIT

Long legs and a long, slightly upcurved
bill equip this large shorebird to
walk and feed in tall grass
as well as mud. It also
wades belly-deep in water, submerging its
head and neck to feed. Prey includes insects,
worms, and other invertebrates. This species
nests on marshland near open water, and on
estuaries. In spring, the males perform a display
flight, showing the undersides of their wings.
These are white, with the forward half
black. In winter, the body plumage
becomes duller, but the wings and tail
keep their black-and-white pattern.
• **NEST** A shallow
depression, lined
with moss or leaves.
• **DISTRIBUTION**
Breeds in Alaska and
Arctic Canada.
Winters in
S.E. South
America.

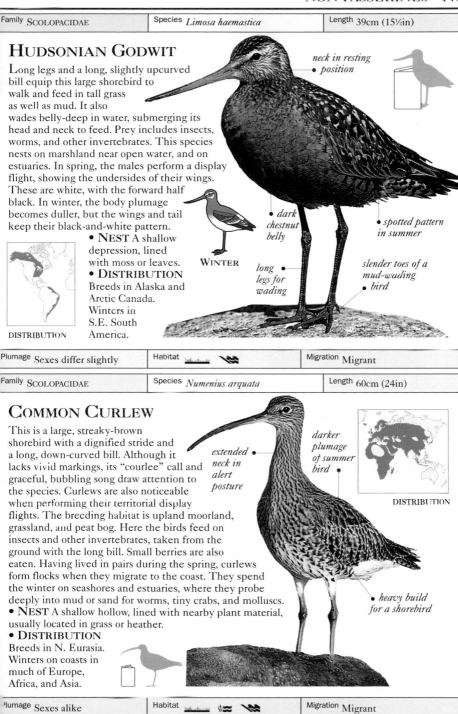

*neck in resting
position*

*dark
chestnut
belly*

*spotted pattern
in summer*

WINTER

*long
legs for
wading*

*slender toes of a
mud-wading
bird*

DISTRIBUTION

Plumage Sexes differ slightly	Habitat	Migration Migrant

Family SCOLOPACIDAE	Species *Numenius arquata*	Length 60cm (24in)

COMMON CURLEW

This is a large, streaky-brown
shorebird with a dignified stride and
a long, down-curved bill. Although it
lacks vivid markings, its "courlee" call and
graceful, bubbling song draw attention to
the species. Curlews are also noticeable
when performing their territorial display
flights. The breeding habitat is upland moorland,
grassland, and peat bog. Here the birds feed on
insects and other invertebrates, taken from the
ground with the long bill. Small berries are also
eaten. Having lived in pairs during the spring, curlews
form flocks when they migrate to the coast. They spend
the winter on seashores and estuaries, where they probe
deeply into mud or sand for worms, tiny crabs, and molluscs.
• **NEST** A shallow hollow, lined with nearby plant material,
usually located in grass or heather.
• **DISTRIBUTION**
Breeds in N. Eurasia.
Winters on coasts in
much of Europe,
Africa, and Asia.

*extended
neck in
alert
posture*

*darker
plumage
of summer
bird*

DISTRIBUTION

*heavy build
for a shorebird*

Plumage Sexes alike	Habitat	Migration Migrant

Family SCOLOPACIDAE	Species *Tringa totanus*	Length 28cm (11in)

COMMON REDSHANK

Standing erect on its long legs, with head held high, this alert shorebird quickly notices any intruder in its surroundings. It utters piping alarm calls, which often alert all the other birds in the area. Apart from its red legs and bill, it is inconspicuous on the ground with its brown plumage. In flight, the white rump and hind edges of the wings help to identify the species. In spring it lives in meadows, wet grasslands, and marshes. Here it raises its young, feeding on insects and other invertebrates, which it takes from vegetation, the ground surface, or from the marsh. It feeds with a nervous, jerky manner. In winter the Common Redshank is found on estuaries and mudflats, where it feeds on tiny shellfish, crustaceans, and other small creatures. These it either picks from the mud surface or finds by probing with its long, pointed bill.
• **NEST** A hollow scraped with the feet and shaped by body pressure, lined, and hidden in tall grass and plants.
• **DISTRIBUTION** Breeds in Iceland and across Eurasia from the British Isles to E. Asia. Winters on coastlines of much of Eurasia, Africa, India, and S.E. Asia.

slender • build

DISTRIBUTION

• white hind edge of wing revealed in flight

Plumage Sexes alike	Habitat	Migration Migrant

Family SCOLOPACIDAE	Species *Tringa melanoleuca*	Length 35cm (14in)

GREATER YELLOWLEGS

Typically seen wading in shallow water, this active shorebird can be recognized by its piping calls. In spring it lives in swamps and the edges of coniferous forests, and its plumage is black-and-white above and heavily spotted below. The Greater Yellowlegs winters on lake shores and coastal mudflats, moulting into a greyer and paler plumage. It feeds by probing shallow water and mud for invertebrates.
• **NEST** A shallow hollow in moss or dry peat, with a scanty lining of plant materials, built in an open site, usually near water.
• **DISTRIBUTION** Breeds in North America. Winters from S. USA to S. South America.

long, slender bill

• barred tail

pale colours of • winter plumage

long, thin legs for wading in • shallow water

DISTRIBUTION

Plumage Sexes alike	Habitat	Migration Migrant

Family SCOLOPACIDAE	Species *Arenaria interpres*	Length 24cm (9½in)

RUDDY TURNSTONE

A stout and busily active shorebird, the Ruddy Turnstone thrusts its bill under stones or fronds of seaweed, flipping them over to get at the small animals hidden underneath. In flight, white patterns on the wings and back help to identify this species.

WINTER

• **NEST** A shallow hollow in the ground.

• **DISTRIBUTION** Breeds in the high Arctic. Winters on coasts throughout the world.

• *striped crown*

DISTRIBUTION

Plumage Sexes differ slightly	Habitat	Migration Migrant

Family SCOLOPACIDAE	Species *Phalaropus lobatus*	Length 20cm (8in)

RED-NECKED PHALAROPE

This dainty shorebird is a long-distance migrant. It feeds on aquatic life in tundra pools in spring, and on sea plankton in winter.
• **NEST** A hollow lined with grass, hidden in grass.
• **DISTRIBUTION** Breeds in the high Arctic. Winters mid-ocean.

WINTER

pale, straw-coloured stripes •

female is more brightly coloured than male •

FEMALE

DISTRIBUTION

Plumage Sexes differ slightly	Habitat	Migration Migrant

Family SCOLOPACIDAE	Species *Calidris canutus*	Length 27cm (10½in)

RED KNOT

rich pattern of summer • plumage

In summer, when few people see this bird, its plumage is a blend of chestnut, black, and white. In winter it is pale grey, and flocks are seen on mudflats, feeding on invertebrates.
• **NEST** A shallow hollow in the ground, lined with lichens.
• **DISTRIBUTION** Breeds on tundra in the high Arctic. Winters on coastal sands and mudflats throughout much of the world.

DISTRIBUTION

WINTER

Plumage Sexes alike	Habitat	Migration Migrant

Family SCOLOPACIDAE	Species *Scolopax rusticola*	Length 34cm (13½in)

EURASIAN WOODCOCK

The main habitat of this species, in winter and summer alike, is woodland. Active mainly after dark, it walks and probes for food in moist and marshy areas. Its long bill has a flexible, touch-sensitive tip that is useful for probing into mud or soft soil to locate invertebrates. In their display behaviour, known as "roding", males fly slowly at treetop level over their territories, uttering piping and croaking calls, at dusk and dawn.

very stout body

large eyes, set high on the head

• **NEST** A hollow in mossy ground, lined with a layer of dead leaves.
• **DISTRIBUTION** Breeds across much of Eurasia. Winters as far south as N. Africa, India, and S.E. Asia, moving west as well as south.

DISTRIBUTION

Plumage Sexes alike	Habitat	Migration Migrant

Family SCOLOPACIDAE	Species *Gallinago gallinago*	Length 27cm (10½in)

COMMON SNIPE

The straight bill of the Common Snipe is the longest, in proportion to its body, of all the shorebirds. The tip of the bill is flexible, enabling the bird to probe into soft mud, sensing and feeding on worms, small molluscs, and other creatures. The eyes are set high on either side of the head allowing it to remain vigilant when resting and feeding. It rests in low marsh vegetation or grass, camouflaged by the striped plumage, rising in twisting flight when alarmed. Newly hatched chicks only have short bills and have to be fed worms by the parents. The Common Snipe performs a "roller-coaster" display flight, in which the outer tail feathers produce a sound like bleating as the bird dives steeply.

streaked camouflage pattern

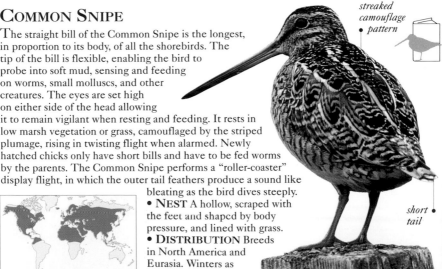

• **NEST** A hollow, scraped with the feet and shaped by body pressure, and lined with grass.
• **DISTRIBUTION** Breeds in North America and Eurasia. Winters as far south as N. South America, and C. Africa.

short tail

DISTRIBUTION

Plumage Sexes alike	Habitat	Migration Migrant

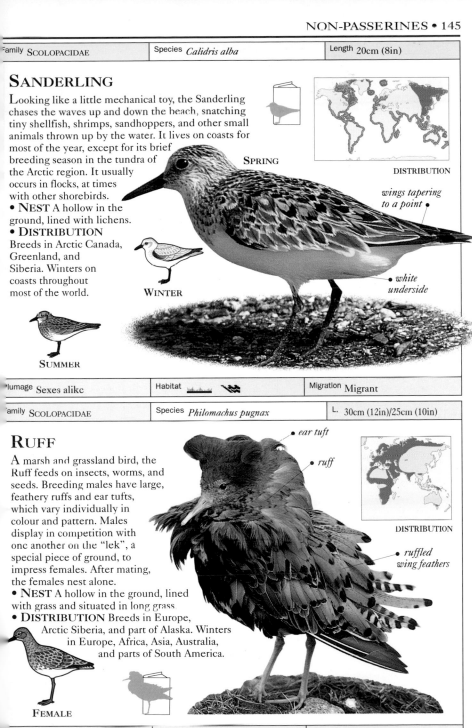

Family SCOLOPACIDAE	Species *Calidris alba*	Length 20cm (8in)

SANDERLING

Looking like a little mechanical toy, the Sanderling chases the waves up and down the beach, snatching tiny shellfish, shrimps, sandhoppers, and other small animals thrown up by the water. It lives on coasts for most of the year, except for its brief breeding season in the tundra of the Arctic region. It usually occurs in flocks, at times with other shorebirds.
• **NEST** A hollow in the ground, lined with lichens.
• **DISTRIBUTION** Breeds in Arctic Canada, Greenland, and Siberia. Winters on coasts throughout most of the world.

DISTRIBUTION

SPRING

wings tapering to a point

white underside

WINTER

SUMMER

Plumage Sexes alike	Habitat	Migration Migrant

Family SCOLOPACIDAE	Species *Philomachus pugnax*	L. 30cm (12in)/25cm (10in)

RUFF

A marsh and grassland bird, the Ruff feeds on insects, worms, and seeds. Breeding males have large, feathery ruffs and ear tufts, which vary individually in colour and pattern. Males display in competition with one another on the "lek", a special piece of ground, to impress females. After mating, the females nest alone.
• **NEST** A hollow in the ground, lined with grass and situated in long grass.
• **DISTRIBUTION** Breeds in Europe, Arctic Siberia, and part of Alaska. Winters in Europe, Africa, Asia, Australia, and parts of South America.

ear tuft

ruff

DISTRIBUTION

ruffled wing feathers

FEMALE

Plumage Sexes differ	Habitat	Migration Migrant

Family THINOCORIDAE	Species *Thinocorus orbignyianus*	Length 22cm (8½in)

GREY-BREASTED SEEDSNIPE

This hardy species lives on the high plateau of the southern Andes, only moving to lower altitudes during severe weather. It is a ground-dwelling bird with a round body and short legs, using its short, stubby bill to feed on seeds, berries, and other parts of plants. It walks and runs rapidly but, if alarmed, crouches and relies on camouflage. When forced to flee, it escapes in zig-zag flight, usually returning to cover after a short distance. Both sexes utter brief alarm or contact calls. Birds also perform a repetitive, cooing song, either from the top of a rock or in a low display flight.

short, stout, plant-eating bill

FEMALE

camouflaged plumage on back

plump body

• **NEST** A depression in an open site or among low vegetation, sparsely lined with plant fragments.

• **DISTRIBUTION** Southern Andes, and extreme south of South America.

• **REMARK** This bird evolved from the shorebirds, but in its ground-dwelling lifestyle and behaviour it is more like a gamebird, such as a partridge.

short legs

DISTRIBUTION

Plumage Sexes differ	Habitat ▲	Migration Non-migrant

Family CHIONIDIDAE	Species *Chionis alba*	Length 39cm (15½in)

SNOWY SHEATHBILL

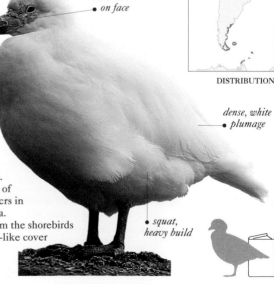

This is a scavenging bird of rocky South Atlantic coasts, where it visits colonies of seals, penguins, cormorants, and other seabirds. It feeds on eggs and any kind of carrion. Despite its squat shape it is a fast and agile runner. On short flights it looks ungainly in the air, with its legs dangling, but it flies more strongly, with feet tucked up, when crossing open water.

bare skin on face

DISTRIBUTION

dense, white plumage

• **NEST** An untidy construction of shells, pebbles, and stones, placed in a crevice in a cliff or rocky outcrop.

• **DISTRIBUTION** Breeds on coast of Antarctica and offshore islands. Winters in the Falkland Islands and S. Argentina.

• **REMARK** This species evolved from the shorebirds and became a scavenger. The sheath-like cover on its bill, and the bare skin on its face, enable it to eat messy food without harming the bill or feathers.

squat, heavy build

Plumage Sexes alike	Habitat 〰 ⌂	Migration Migrant

Family STERCORARIIDAE	Species *Catharacta skua*	Length 58cm (23in)

GREAT SKUA

Resembling a large, brown gull, this species is a powerful, predatory seabird that dominates others within its range. It feeds by catching fish, taking eggs and nestlings of seabirds, and killing adult birds including gulls, ducks, and shorebirds. Although its flight is normally powerful and slow, it can chase birds with speed and agility. It forces them to disgorge fish that they have swallowed. When nesting, it shows off a large, white patch on each wing in "raised wing" displays, and fiercely attacks all intruders.
• **NEST** A depression on the ground, lined with grass, moss, or heather. Birds nest in colonies at a few locations on islands in the ocean.
• **DISTRIBUTION** Breeds in N. Atlantic. Winters at sea, some birds reaching equatorial waters.

powerful, stocky build

DISTRIBUTION

short, blunt tail

strong legs

webbed feet

Plumage Sexes alike	Habitat	Migration Migrant

Family STERCORARIIDAE	Species *Stercorarius longicaudus*	Length 55cm (22in)

LONG-TAILED SKUA

This small, lightly built seabird has long, narrow wings and, when fully grown, long central tail feathers. It flies with great agility, soaring upwards, or hovering over the water looking for food. It picks fish from the sea surface, follows boats for discarded fish, and attacks gulls or terns to make them disgorge fish that they have caught and swallowed. On its Arctic breeding grounds it hunts lemmings and other small animals, as well as eating berries.
• **NEST** A depression lined with mosses, lichens, or grass.
• **DISTRIBUTION** Breeds in N. Eurasia and N. North America. Winters in Southern Pacific and Atlantic oceans.

long, narrow wing

light, slender build

DISTRIBUTION

JUVENILE

Plumage Sexes alike	Habitat	Migration Migrant

Family LARIDAE	Species *Larus pacificus*	Length 63cm (25in)

PACIFIC GULL

This large gull with black back and wings has the largest bill of all the gull family. It patrols the shoreline, foraging for food, and makes shallow dives after fish, squid, crabs, and other marine creatures. Large shellfish are cracked open by dropping them onto rocks. Also included in its diet are the eggs and young of nesting seabirds, and even adults of smaller bird species. The Pacific Gull occurs in small, loose colonies or in scattered pairs on the coast, and is only occasionally seen inland.
• **NEST** A loose structure of grass and plants, under a bush or rock.
• **DISTRIBUTION** Restricted to coastal areas of W. and S. Australia.

massive head and bill

JUVENILE

powerful, sturdy build

long, powerful wings

black back

DISTRIBUTION

Plumage Sexes alike	Habitat	Migration Non-migrant

Family LARIDAE	Species *Larus delawarensis*	Length 45cm (17½in)

RING-BILLED GULL

This gull has a pearl-grey back and a black band towards the tip of its bill. It nests in noisy colonies, usually beside a lake or reservoir, but in winter it is more often seen on the coast. It looks for food wherever the opportunity arises, catching fish, hunting invertebrates on the ground, or seeking out carrion.
• **NEST** An untidy nest, made of vegetation, situated on the ground.
• **DISTRIBUTION** Breeds N. North America. Winters in North and Central America, and in Bahamas and N. Caribbean.

JUVENILE

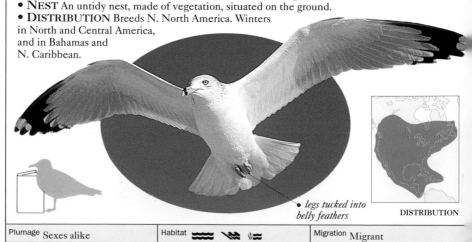

legs tucked into belly feathers

DISTRIBUTION

Plumage Sexes alike	Habitat	Migration Migrant

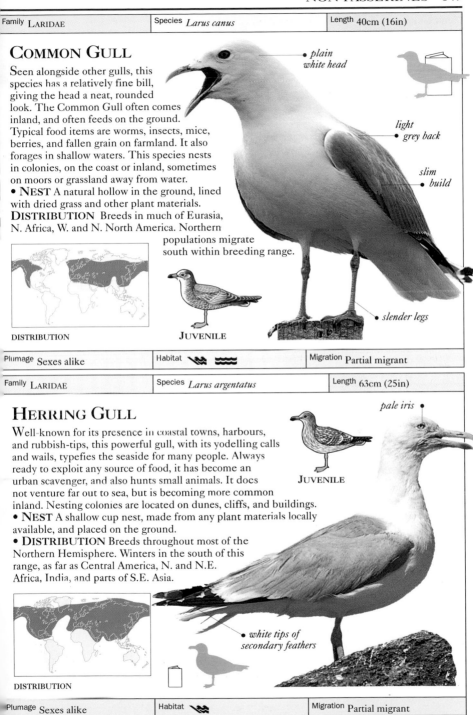

| Family LARIDAE | Species *Larus canus* | Length 40cm (16in) |

COMMON GULL

Seen alongside other gulls, this species has a relatively fine bill, giving the head a neat, rounded look. The Common Gull often comes inland, and often feeds on the ground. Typical food items are worms, insects, mice, berries, and fallen grain on farmland. It also forages in shallow waters. This species nests in colonies, on the coast or inland, sometimes on moors or grassland away from water.
• **NEST** A natural hollow in the ground, lined with dried grass and other plant materials.
DISTRIBUTION Breeds in much of Eurasia, N. Africa, W. and N. North America. Northern populations migrate south within breeding range.

• *plain white head*

light • grey back

slim • build

• *slender legs*

DISTRIBUTION

JUVENILE

| Plumage Sexes alike | Habitat | Migration Partial migrant |

| Family LARIDAE | Species *Larus argentatus* | Length 63cm (25in) |

HERRING GULL

pale iris •

Well-known for its presence in coastal towns, harbours, and rubbish-tips, this powerful gull, with its yodelling calls and wails, typifies the seaside for many people. Always ready to exploit any source of food, it has become an urban scavenger, and also hunts small animals. It does not venture far out to sea, but is becoming more common inland. Nesting colonies are located on dunes, cliffs, and buildings.
• **NEST** A shallow cup nest, made from any plant materials locally available, and placed on the ground.
• **DISTRIBUTION** Breeds throughout most of the Northern Hemisphere. Winters in the south of this range, as far as Central America, N. and N.E. Africa, India, and parts of S.E. Asia.

JUVENILE

• *white tips of secondary feathers*

DISTRIBUTION

| Plumage Sexes alike | Habitat | Migration Partial migrant |

Family LARIDAE	Species *Larus atricilla*	Length 42cm (16½in)

LAUGHING GULL

Common in coastal areas of North America in summer, this gull is recognized by its very dark "hood". It is boldly inquisitive, feeding wherever the opportunity occurs: it follows the plough to pick worms from the soil; scavenges for whatever is washed up on the shoreline; and follows ships for refuse and food scraps. Breeding colonies are located in marshes, by seashores, and on offshore islands.
• **NEST** A cup nest made of plant material, located among tall plants or bushes.
• **DISTRIBUTION** Breeds in E. and S. USA and the Caribbean. Migrates as far south as Peru in winter.

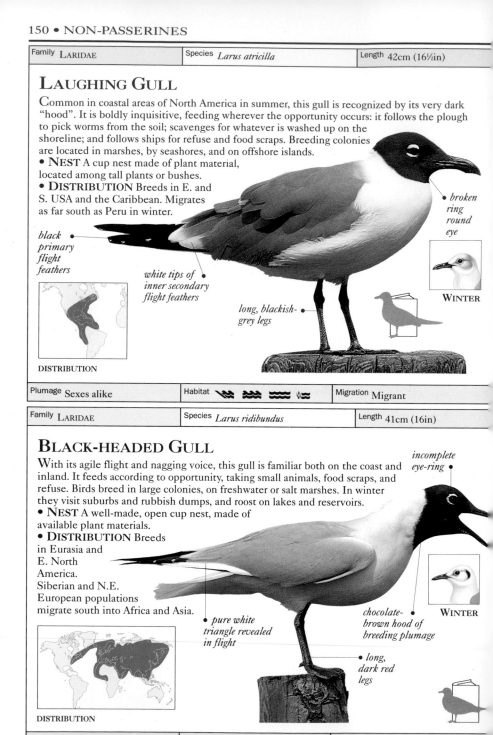

black primary flight feathers

white tips of inner secondary flight feathers

broken ring round eye

WINTER

long, blackish-grey legs

DISTRIBUTION

Plumage Sexes alike	Habitat	Migration Migrant

Family LARIDAE	Species *Larus ridibundus*	Length 41cm (16in)

BLACK-HEADED GULL

With its agile flight and nagging voice, this gull is familiar both on the coast and inland. It feeds according to opportunity, taking small animals, food scraps, and refuse. Birds breed in large colonies, on freshwater or salt marshes. In winter they visit suburbs and rubbish dumps, and roost on lakes and reservoirs.
• **NEST** A well-made, open cup nest, made of available plant materials.
• **DISTRIBUTION** Breeds in Eurasia and E. North America. Siberian and N.E. European populations migrate south into Africa and Asia.

incomplete eye-ring

pure white triangle revealed in flight

chocolate-brown hood of breeding plumage

WINTER

long, dark red legs

DISTRIBUTION

Plumage Sexes alike	Habitat	Migration Migrant

Family LARIDAE	Species *Rhodostethia rosea*	Length 34cm (13½in)

ROSS'S GULL

This small, neat gull is an inhabitant of the high Arctic. It nests in small colonies on the coast, dispersing along the shore and out to islands, and winters at sea at the edge of the pack ice. When seen in the air, it can be identified by the grey undersides of its wings, and by the tapering shape of the tail. Ross's Gull feeds by swooping to take food from the surface or makes very shallow surface-dives after small fish or crustaceans, and sometimes walks on mudflats to pick up small invertebrates.
• **NEST** A cup nest of dry grass and leaves, on the ground.
• **DISTRIBUTION** Breeds in N. Alaska, N. Canada, Greenland, and N. Siberia. Winters on Arctic, N. Atlantic, and N. Pacific Oceans.

WINTER

thin, black neck ring

pale pink flush on underside

short legs

tail ends in a bluntly tapering wedge shape, unlike most other gulls

DISTRIBUTION

Plumage Sexes alike	Habitat 〰〰 〰〰	Migration Migrant

Family LARIDAE	Species *Rissa tridactyla*	Length 43cm (17in)

BLACK-LEGGED KITTIWAKE

A small gull with short legs and a notched tail, this species lives on the open sea for much of the year, coming ashore to breed on cliffs and on the walls of caves. It feeds on small crustaceans and fish.
• **NEST** A tightly trampled, drum-shaped nest of mud, grass, and seaweed, placed on a small projection or ledge.
• **DISTRIBUTION** Breeds on coasts of Arctic, N. Atlantic, and N. Pacific Oceans. Winters at sea as far south as the tropics.

plain black wing tips

JUVENILE

plain grey back and wings

bill marked with floating oil while feeding at the sea surface

DISTRIBUTION

Plumage Sexes alike	Habitat 〰〰 〰〰 🗻	Migration Migrant

Family STERNIDAE	Species *Chlidonias niger*	Length 25cm (10in)

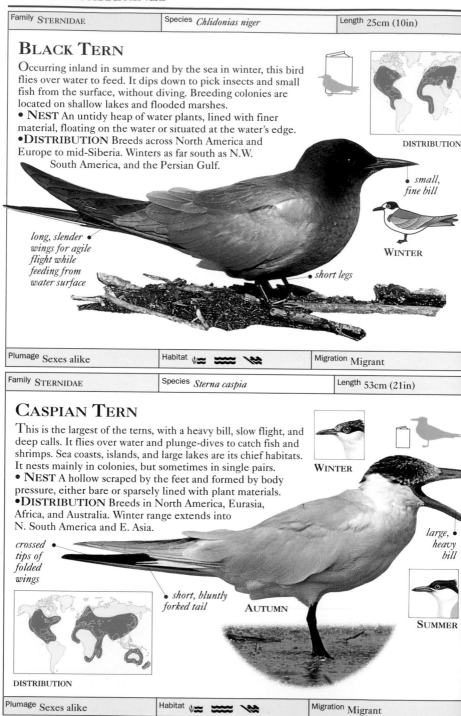

BLACK TERN

Occurring inland in summer and by the sea in winter, this bird flies over water to feed. It dips down to pick insects and small fish from the surface, without diving. Breeding colonies are located on shallow lakes and flooded marshes.
• **NEST** An untidy heap of water plants, lined with finer material, floating on the water or situated at the water's edge.
•**DISTRIBUTION** Breeds across North America and Europe to mid-Siberia. Winters as far south as N.W. South America, and the Persian Gulf.

DISTRIBUTION

• *small, fine bill*

WINTER

long, slender • wings for agile flight while feeding from water surface

short legs

Plumage Sexes alike	Habitat	Migration Migrant

Family STERNIDAE	Species *Sterna caspia*	Length 53cm (21in)

CASPIAN TERN

This is the largest of the terns, with a heavy bill, slow flight, and deep calls. It flies over water and plunge-dives to catch fish and shrimps. Sea coasts, islands, and large lakes are its chief habitats. It nests mainly in colonies, but sometimes in single pairs.
• **NEST** A hollow scraped by the feet and formed by body pressure, either bare or sparsely lined with plant materials.
•**DISTRIBUTION** Breeds in North America, Eurasia, Africa, and Australia. Winter range extends into N. South America and E. Asia.

WINTER

large, • heavy bill

crossed • tips of folded wings

short, bluntly • forked tail

AUTUMN

SUMMER

DISTRIBUTION

Plumage Sexes alike	Habitat	Migration Migrant

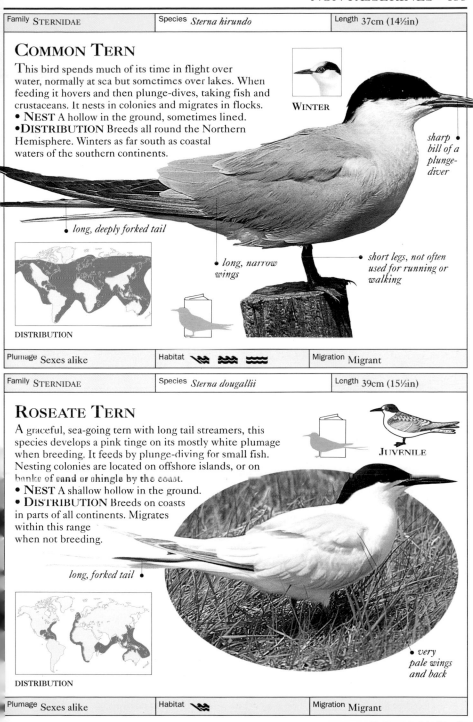

| Family STERNIDAE | Species *Sterna hirundo* | Length 37cm (14½in) |

COMMON TERN

This bird spends much of its time in flight over water, normally at sea but sometimes over lakes. When feeding it hovers and then plunge-dives, taking fish and crustaceans. It nests in colonies and migrates in flocks.
• **NEST** A hollow in the ground, sometimes lined.
• **DISTRIBUTION** Breeds all round the Northern Hemisphere. Winters as far south as coastal waters of the southern continents.

WINTER

sharp bill of a plunge-diver

long, deeply forked tail

long, narrow wings

short legs, not often used for running or walking

DISTRIBUTION

| Plumage Sexes alike | Habitat | Migration Migrant |

| Family STERNIDAE | Species *Sterna dougallii* | Length 39cm (15½in) |

ROSEATE TERN

A graceful, sea-going tern with long tail streamers, this species develops a pink tinge on its mostly white plumage when breeding. It feeds by plunge-diving for small fish. Nesting colonies are located on offshore islands, or on banks of sand or shingle by the coast.
• **NEST** A shallow hollow in the ground.
• **DISTRIBUTION** Breeds on coasts in parts of all continents. Migrates within this range when not breeding.

JUVENILE

long, forked tail

very pale wings and back

DISTRIBUTION

| Plumage Sexes alike | Habitat | Migration Migrant |

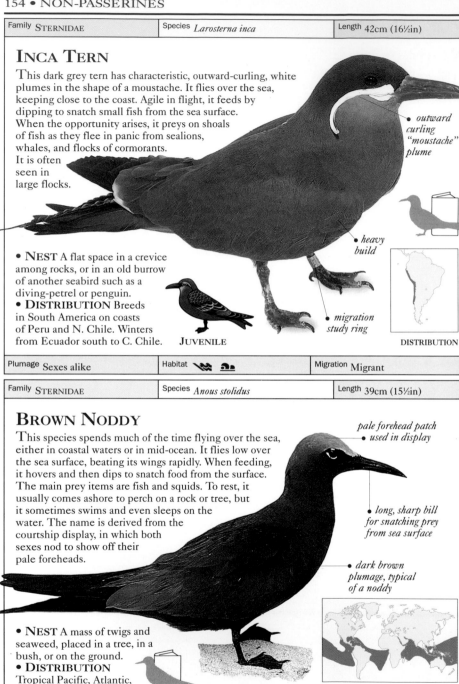

Family STERNIDAE	Species *Larosterna inca*	Length 42cm (16½in)

INCA TERN

This dark grey tern has characteristic, outward-curling, white
plumes in the shape of a moustache. It flies over the sea,
keeping close to the coast. Agile in flight, it feeds by
dipping to snatch small fish from the sea surface.
When the opportunity arises, it preys on shoals
of fish as they flee in panic from sealions,
whales, and flocks of cormorants.
It is often
seen in
large flocks.

• outward
curling
"moustache"
plume

• heavy
build

• **NEST** A flat space in a crevice
among rocks, or in an old burrow
of another seabird such as a
diving-petrel or penguin.
• **DISTRIBUTION** Breeds
in South America on coasts
of Peru and N. Chile. Winters
from Ecuador south to C. Chile.

• migration
study ring

JUVENILE

DISTRIBUTION

Plumage Sexes alike	Habitat	Migration Migrant

Family STERNIDAE	Species *Anous stolidus*	Length 39cm (15½in)

BROWN NODDY

This species spends much of the time flying over the sea,
either in coastal waters or in mid-ocean. It flies low over
the sea surface, beating its wings rapidly. When feeding,
it hovers and then dips to snatch food from the surface.
The main prey items are fish and squids. To rest, it
usually comes ashore to perch on a rock or tree, but
it sometimes swims and even sleeps on the
water. The name is derived from the
courtship display, in which both
sexes nod to show off their
pale foreheads.

pale forehead patch
• used in display

• long, sharp bill
for snatching prey
from sea surface

• dark brown
plumage, typical
of a noddy

• **NEST** A mass of twigs and
seaweed, placed in a tree, in a
bush, or on the ground.
• **DISTRIBUTION**
Tropical Pacific, Atlantic,
and Indian Oceans.

DISTRIBUTION

Plumage Sexes alike	Habitat	Migration Partial migrant

Family STERNIDAE	Species *Gygis alba*	Length 32cm (12½in)

WHITE TERN

This is an elegant sea tern of tropical oceans, with a gentle, delicate appearance. In behaviour it is unusually tame and will allow an observer to approach. It has a forked tail and a slender bill that appears to be tilted slightly upwards. This is the only tern species that has all-white plumage. It spends much of the time flying over the sea, either in coastal waters or in mid-ocean. Its flight is light and buoyant, combining agility with graceful movement. The wings are broader and more rounded in flight than those of other terns. When feeding at sea, it follows a rising, then falling flight path, dipping to snatch fish and small squids from the surface. It also catches fish as they leap. The large eyes appear to be an adaptation for night feeding, its prey normally rising to surface waters after dark.
• **NEST** No nest is made, but the female lays her egg and balances it throughout incubation on a small space on a tree branch, in the fork of a twig, on a palm frond, or on a rock ledge.
• **DISTRIBUTION** Pacific, Atlantic, and Indian Oceans.

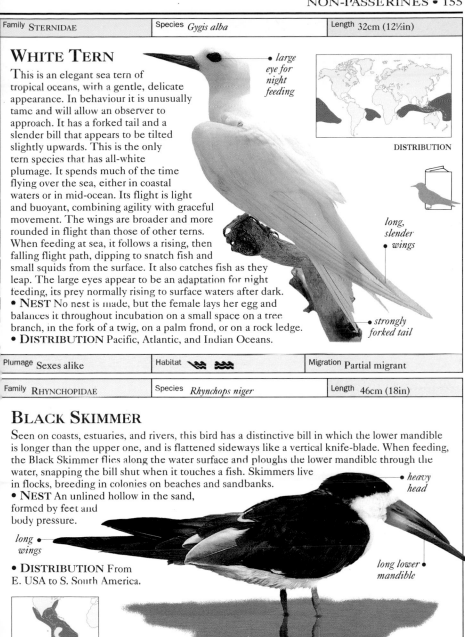

large eye for night feeding

DISTRIBUTION

long, slender wings

strongly forked tail

Plumage Sexes alike	Habitat 〰️ 〰️	Migration Partial migrant

Family RHYNCHOPIDAE	Species *Rhynchops niger*	Length 46cm (18in)

BLACK SKIMMER

Seen on coasts, estuaries, and rivers, this bird has a distinctive bill in which the lower mandible is longer than the upper one, and is flattened sideways like a vertical knife-blade. When feeding, the Black Skimmer flies along the water surface and ploughs the lower mandible through the water, snapping the bill shut when it touches a fish. Skimmers live in flocks, breeding in colonies on beaches and sandbanks.
• **NEST** An unlined hollow in the sand, formed by feet and body pressure.

long wings

• **DISTRIBUTION** From E. USA to S. South America.

heavy head

long lower mandible

DISTRIBUTION

Plumage Sexes alike	Habitat 〰️ 〰️	Migration Partial migrant

Family ALCIDAE	Species *Alle alle*	Length 22cm (8½in)

LITTLE AUK

This black-and-white seabird has a dumpy outline and narrow wings, which give it its characteristic, whirring flight. It feeds at sea, diving from the surface to swim underwater, using its wings as flippers, and taking animal plankton (tiny, drifting marine life). Little Auks breed in swarming colonies on rocky screes in the far north, wintering on the open sea, and sometimes driven inland by storms.
• **NEST** Eggs are layed in an unlined rock crevice, or in a burrow.
• **DISTRIBUTION** Breeds on coasts of the Arctic Ocean. Winters at sea in N. Atlantic Ocean.

WINTER

small white mark over eye

throat pouch swollen with food

weak legs

DISTRIBUTION

Plumage Sexes alike	Habitat 〰️ 🐚 〰️	Migration Migrant

Family ALCIDAE	Species *Alca torda*	Length 43cm (17in)

RAZORBILL

A knife-shaped, black bill, decorated with white lines, identifies this cliff-nesting auk. The legs are set well back and propel the bird when swimming on the sea surface, although they are not strong when used for walking. The wings are used as flippers when the Razorbill swims underwater. The diet consists almost entirely of fish.
• **NEST** A single egg is laid in a recess at the back of a rock ledge, in a rock crevice, or under a boulder.
• **DISTRIBUTION** Breeds on N. American and European coasts of N. Atlantic Ocean. Winters at sea on N. Atlantic Ocean.

bird steadying itself on landing

DISTRIBUTION

strong wings

small, pointed tail

weak legs

WINTER

Plumage Sexes alike	Habitat 〰️ 🐚 〰️	Migration Partial migrant

Family ALCIDAE	Species *Fratercula cirrhata*	Length 38cm (15in)

TUFTED PUFFIN

This is a heavily built auk with head tufts that can
be swept back and do not impede underwater fishing.
Bill and head decorations are used only for display.
With its muscular body, the bird cannot take off
from the water without a wing-flapping run.
The birds breed in colonies on rocky islands,
and spend the winter out in mid-ocean.
• **NEST** A burrow, or a hollow in a rock
crevice, lined with grass and feathers.
• **DISTRIBUTION** Breeds
on W. and E. coasts of
N. Pacific Ocean.
Winters at sea
in N. Pacific.

WINTER

• *display tuft*

• *sheath lost in winter*

short tail

DISTRIBUTION

Plumage Sexes alike	Habitat	Migration Migrant

Family ALCIDAE	Species *Fratercula arctica*	Length 32cm (12½in)

ATLANTIC PUFFIN

A stout bird with a large head and a short
tail, the Atlantic Puffin has a comical
appearance, with its masked eyes
and massive bill. In breeding
birds, the bill is covered with a
red sheath, with yellow stripes
and a grey triangle at the base.
Pairs perform face-to-face bill-
rapping displays in spring. The
Atlantic Puffin flies strongly on fast-
beating wings and swims underwater,
chasing fish, particularly sand-eels. It packs
these cross-wise in its bill to carry them to its
young. Breeding colonies are located on cliff-tops
on coasts and islands. In winter, birds stay out at sea.
• **NEST** A shallow hollow in an underground
burrow, lined with grass and feathers.
• **DISTRIBUTION**
Breeds on W. and E.
coasts of N. Atlantic
Ocean. Winters on
N. Atlantic Ocean.

orange display wattle (lost in winter)

WINTER

DISTRIBUTION

• *upright posture*

short tail

Plumage Sexes alike	Habitat	Migration Migrant

Family PTEROCLIDAE	Species *Pterocles lichtensteinii*	Length 25cm (10in)

LICHTENSTEIN'S SANDGROUSE

A semi-desert species, this sandgrouse prefers rocky and hilly country where some bushes occur. It feeds chiefly on seeds and other parts of plants including acacia trees and shrubs. During the hot midday hours it rests in the shade and is reluctant to move. It flies to drink daily, late at dusk or before dawn, uttering soft, two-note calls. The nest is often up to 30km (19 miles) from a water source, and the male brings water for the young, carried in his belly feathers.
• **NEST** A slight hollow on bare ground, without a lining.
• **DISTRIBUTION** Scattered areas from Morocco through Africa to Arabia and Pakistan.

FEMALE

long, tapering wings

short tail

short, feathered legs

narrow, black breast bands

DISTRIBUTION

Plumage Sexes differ	Habitat	Migration Non-migrant

Family PTEROCLIDAE	Species *Pterocles alchata*	Length 28cm (11in)

PIN-TAILED SANDGROUSE

This is a sandgrouse of flat, dry country. Its fine pattern of colours camouflages it against sand, pebbles, and sparse vegetation. This species normally occurs in flocks and sometimes breeds in loose colonies. Birds are seen creeping or running on their rather short legs, and feeding on seeds, shoots, and leaves. They fly considerable distances to water, and when drinking sometimes float on the surface. Males carry water for the young in their soft breast feathers.
• **NEST** A slight, unlined hollow on bare ground.
• **DISTRIBUTION** Breeds in Portugal, Spain, S. France, N. Africa, Middle East, and C. Asia. C. Asian populations winter as far south as Pakistan and N.W. India.

thin, black eyestripe

chestnut breast band, edged in grey

DISTRIBUTION

FEMALE

Plumage Sexes differ	Habitat	Migration Partial migrant

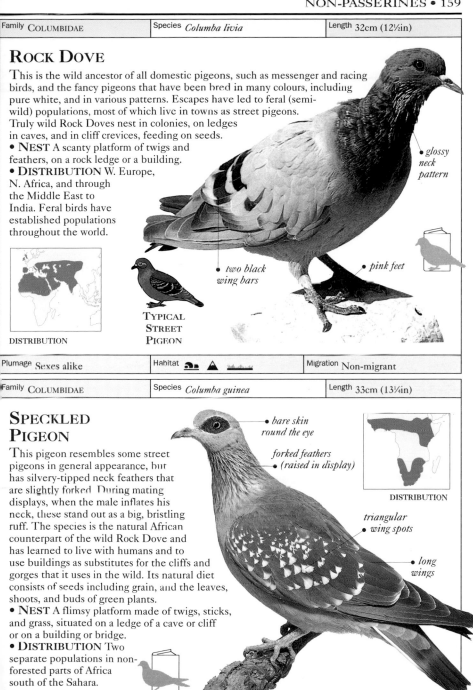

Family COLUMBIDAE	Species *Columba livia*	Length 32cm (12½in)

ROCK DOVE

This is the wild ancestor of all domestic pigeons, such as messenger and racing birds, and the fancy pigeons that have been bred in many colours, including pure white, and in various patterns. Escapes have led to feral (semi-wild) populations, most of which live in towns as street pigeons. Truly wild Rock Doves nest in colonies, on ledges in caves, and in cliff crevices, feeding on seeds.

• **NEST** A scanty platform of twigs and feathers, on a rock ledge or a building.

• **DISTRIBUTION** W. Europe, N. Africa, and through the Middle East to India. Feral birds have established populations throughout the world.

glossy neck pattern

two black wing bars

pink feet

TYPICAL STREET PIGEON

DISTRIBUTION

Plumage Sexes alike	Habitat	Migration Non-migrant

Family COLUMBIDAE	Species *Columba guinea*	Length 33cm (13¼in)

SPECKLED PIGEON

This pigeon resembles some street pigeons in general appearance, but has silvery-tipped neck feathers that are slightly forked. During mating displays, when the male inflates his neck, these stand out as a big, bristling ruff. The species is the natural African counterpart of the wild Rock Dove and has learned to live with humans and to use buildings as substitutes for the cliffs and gorges that it uses in the wild. Its natural diet consists of seeds including grain, and the leaves, shoots, and buds of green plants.

• **NEST** A flimsy platform made of twigs, sticks, and grass, situated on a ledge of a cave or cliff or on a building or bridge.

• **DISTRIBUTION** Two separate populations in non-forested parts of Africa south of the Sahara.

bare skin round the eye

forked feathers (raised in display)

DISTRIBUTION

triangular wing spots

long wings

Plumage Sexes alike	Habitat	Migration Non-migrant

Family COLUMBIDAE	Species *Columba palumbus*	Length 42cm (16½in)

COMMON WOOD-PIGEON

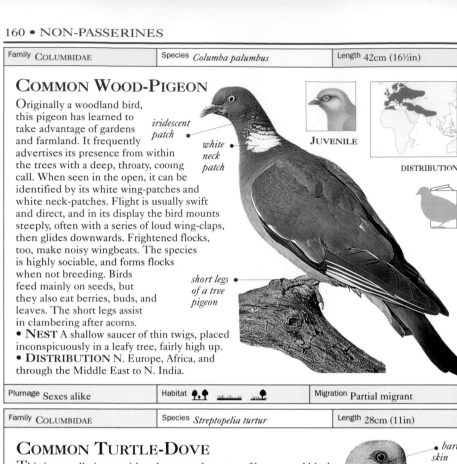

Originally a woodland bird, this pigeon has learned to take advantage of gardens and farmland. It frequently advertises its presence from within the trees with a deep, throaty, cooing call. When seen in the open, it can be identified by its white wing-patches and white neck-patches. Flight is usually swift and direct, and in its display the bird mounts steeply, often with a series of loud wing-claps, then glides downwards. Frightened flocks, too, make noisy wingbeats. The species is highly sociable, and forms flocks when not breeding. Birds feed mainly on seeds, but they also eat berries, buds, and leaves. The short legs assist in clambering after acorns.

iridescent patch

white neck patch

JUVENILE

DISTRIBUTION

short legs of a tree pigeon

• **NEST** A shallow saucer of thin twigs, placed inconspicuously in a leafy tree, fairly high up.
• **DISTRIBUTION** N. Europe, Africa, and through the Middle East to N. India.

Plumage Sexes alike	Habitat	Migration Partial migrant

Family COLUMBIDAE	Species *Streptopelia turtur*	Length 28cm (11in)

COMMON TURTLE-DOVE

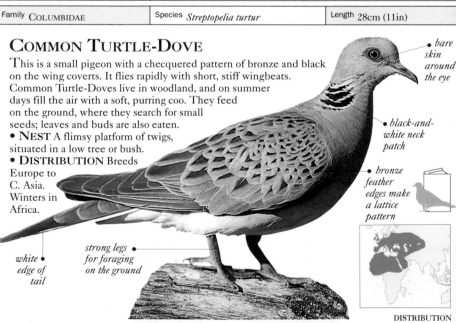

This is a small pigeon with a chequered pattern of bronze and black on the wing coverts. It flies rapidly with short, stiff wingbeats. Common Turtle-Doves live in woodland, and on summer days fill the air with a soft, purring coo. They feed on the ground, where they search for small seeds; leaves and buds are also eaten.
• **NEST** A flimsy platform of twigs, situated in a low tree or bush.
• **DISTRIBUTION** Breeds Europe to C. Asia. Winters in Africa.

bare skin around the eye

black-and-white neck patch

bronze feather edges make a lattice pattern

white edge of tail

strong legs for foraging on the ground

DISTRIBUTION

Plumage Sexes alike	Habitat	Migration Migrant

Family COLUMBIDAE	Species *Streptopelia decaocto*	Length 30cm (12in)

COLLARED DOVE

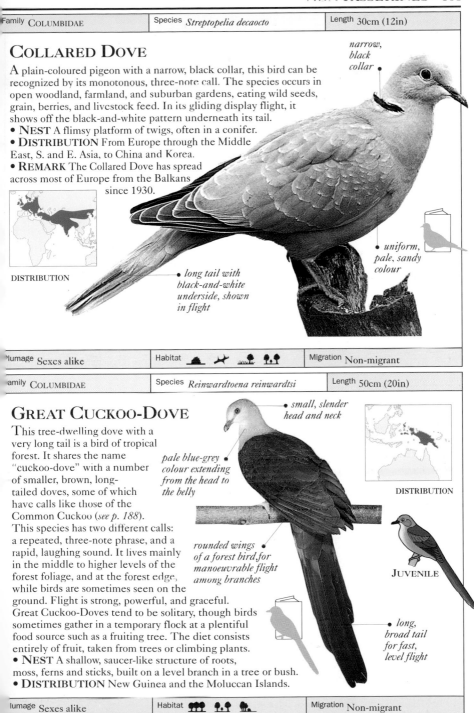

A plain-coloured pigeon with a narrow, black collar, this bird can be recognized by its monotonous, three-note call. The species occurs in open woodland, farmland, and suburban gardens, eating wild seeds, grain, berries, and livestock feed. In its gliding display flight, it shows off the black-and-white pattern underneath its tail.
• **NEST** A flimsy platform of twigs, often in a conifer.
• **DISTRIBUTION** From Europe through the Middle East, S. and E. Asia, to China and Korea.
• **REMARK** The Collared Dove has spread across most of Europe from the Balkans since 1930.

narrow, black collar

uniform, pale, sandy colour

DISTRIBUTION

long tail with black-and-white underside, shown in flight

Plumage Sexes alike	Habitat	Migration Non-migrant

Family COLUMBIDAE	Species *Reinwardtoena reinwardtsi*	Length 50cm (20in)

GREAT CUCKOO-DOVE

This tree-dwelling dove with a very long tail is a bird of tropical forest. It shares the name "cuckoo-dove" with a number of smaller, brown, long-tailed doves, some of which have calls like those of the Common Cuckoo (*see p. 188*). (*see p. 188*) This species has two different calls: a repeated, three-note phrase, and a rapid, laughing sound. It lives mainly in the middle to higher levels of the forest foliage, and at the forest edge, while birds are sometimes seen on the ground. Flight is strong, powerful, and graceful. Great Cuckoo-Doves tend to be solitary, though birds sometimes gather in a temporary flock at a plentiful food source such as a fruiting tree. The diet consists entirely of fruit, taken from trees or climbing plants.
• **NEST** A shallow, saucer-like structure of roots, moss, ferns and sticks, built on a level branch in a tree or bush.
• **DISTRIBUTION** New Guinea and the Moluccan Islands.

small, slender head and neck

pale blue-grey colour extending from the head to the belly

DISTRIBUTION

JUVENILE

rounded wings of a forest bird for manoeuvrable flight among branches

long, broad tail for fast, level flight

Plumage Sexes alike	Habitat	Migration Non-migrant

Family COLUMBIDAE	Species *Oena capensis*	Length 25cm (10in)

NAMAQUA DOVE

A tiny, ground-feeding dove with a long, tapering tail, this bird is similar in size, shape, and lifestyle to the Budgerigar (*see p.177*). Only the male has a black face-mask and bright bill. Both sexes have chestnut-orange on the wing
• *black face and throat* feathers, revealed in flight. Namaqua Doves fly rapidly, with quick, irregular wingbeats. They occur in dry, open country, scrub, and farmland, and are seen singly, in pairs, or
• *glossy, dark wing spots* in parties. They feed on the ground, taking small seeds. In more arid regions they travel about nomadically, and soon colonize places where food and water have become available.
• **NEST** A small, flimsy, saucer-shaped nest fashioned out of rootlets, fine twigs, and grass stems, situated in a low bush.
• **DISTRIBUTION** Africa south of the Sahara, and parts of the Middle East and Arabian Peninsula.

DISTRIBUTION

FEMALE

Plumage Sexes differ	Habitat	Migration Partial migrant/nomadic

Family COLUMBIDAE	Species *Phaps elegans*	Length 29cm (11½in)

BRUSH BRONZEWING

This stoutly built pigeon favours areas of low, thick vegetation that conceal its colours, including the double bar of iridescent plumage on its wings. These sparkle in a range of colours from purple to bronze, giving the bird its name. It usually occurs in pairs, living unobtrusively among dense bushes and low trees, particularly in coastal heathland, or in the undergrowth of open woodland. The birds feed on the ground, mainly taking seeds, and sometimes venture into fields adjoining their normal habitat to take grain. They are cautious when visiting water, coming to drink quietly after dusk and before dawn. Their call is a subdued, mournful cooing.
• **NEST** A substantial platform of twigs and stems, located in a small tree, thick shrub, or occasionally on the ground in a sheltered site.
• **DISTRIBUTION** S.W. and S.E. Australia, including Tasmania.

chestnut head • *stripe*

DISTRIBUTION

• *bluntly tapering tail*

FEMALE

• *bright, iridescent wing bars*

Plumage Sexes differ	Habitat	Migration Non-migrant

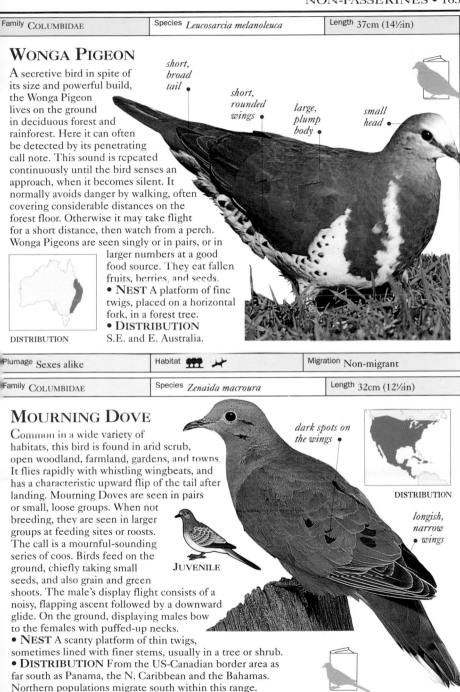

| Family COLUMBIDAE | Species *Leucosarcia melanoleuca* | Length 37cm (14½in) |

WONGA PIGEON

A secretive bird in spite of its size and powerful build, the Wonga Pigeon lives on the ground in deciduous forest and rainforest. Here it can often be detected by its penetrating call note. This sound is repeated continuously until the bird senses an approach, when it becomes silent. It normally avoids danger by walking, often covering considerable distances on the forest floor. Otherwise it may take flight for a short distance, then watch from a perch. Wonga Pigeons are seen singly or in pairs, or in larger numbers at a good food source. They eat fallen fruits, berries, and seeds.
• **NEST** A platform of fine twigs, placed on a horizontal fork, in a forest tree.
• **DISTRIBUTION** S.E. and E. Australia.

short, broad tail

short, rounded wings

large, plump body

small head

DISTRIBUTION

| Plumage Sexes alike | Habitat | Migration Non-migrant |

| Family COLUMBIDAE | Species *Zenaida macroura* | Length 32cm (12½in) |

MOURNING DOVE

Common in a wide variety of habitats, this bird is found in arid scrub, open woodland, farmland, gardens, and towns. It flies rapidly with whistling wingbeats, and has a characteristic upward flip of the tail after landing. Mourning Doves are seen in pairs or small, loose groups. When not breeding, they are seen in larger groups at feeding sites or roosts. The call is a mournful-sounding series of coos. Birds feed on the ground, chiefly taking small seeds, and also grain and green shoots. The male's display flight consists of a noisy, flapping ascent followed by a downward glide. On the ground, displaying males bow to the females with puffed-up necks.
• **NEST** A scanty platform of thin twigs, sometimes lined with finer stems, usually in a tree or shrub.
• **DISTRIBUTION** From the US-Canadian border area as far south as Panama, the N. Caribbean and the Bahamas. Northern populations migrate south within this range.

dark spots on the wings

DISTRIBUTION

longish, narrow wings

JUVENILE

| Plumage Sexes alike | Habitat | Migration Partial migrant |

| Family COLUMBIDAE | Species *Geophaps plumifera* | Length 22cm (8½in) |

SPINIFEX PIGEON

With its upright posture, short wings and tail, cinnamon-brown plumage, and thin, erect crest, this pigeon is readily recognizable. It lives among clumps of prickly spinifex grass in semi-desert and desert areas, within reach of water. Its diet consists of seeds, with occasional insects.

bare skin around the eye

• **NEST** A slight hollow formed by body pressure, sometimes lined with twigs, often under a clump of spinifex grass.
• **DISTRIBUTION** Drier areas of Australia north of the Tropic of Capricorn.

DISTRIBUTION

| Plumage Sexes alike | Habitat | Migration Non-migrant |

| Family COLUMBIDAE | Species *Geopelia cuneata* | Length 20cm (8in) |

DIAMOND DOVE

A tiny dove with a long, white-edged tail, this species occurs in scrub and bushes. Usually seen in pairs or small flocks, it feeds on the ground, eating small seeds, and also taking leaves and buds. In flight, a chestnut-orange patch on the wings is revealed. Birds often visit waterholes in the late afternoon to drink. The call is a high-pitched, plaintive coo.

• **NEST** A small platform made of very fine twigs and plant stems, placed in a tree.
• **DISTRIBUTION** Semi-arid and desert areas of N., W., and interior Australia.

DISTRIBUTION

JUVENILE

| Plumage Sexes alike | Habitat | Migration Non-migrant |

| Family COLUMBIDAE | Species *Columbina passerina* | Length 17cm (6¾in) |

COMMON GROUND-DOVE

This stocky species is often seen in pairs or small groups, walking on the ground and feeding on fallen seeds. In flight, a chestnut colour in the wings is revealed.

scaly pattern on the breast
short tail
short wings

• **NEST** A loose platform of twigs, either on the ground or in a tree.
• **DISTRIBUTION** From S. North America to N. South America.

DISTRIBUTION

FEMALE

| Plumage Sexes differ | Habitat | Migration Non-migrant |

Family COLUMBIDAE	Species *Caloenas nicobarica*	Length 33cm (13in)

NICOBAR PIGEON

An island-dwelling pigeon, this odd-looking species has a thin head and neck, an upright wattle on the bill, and long, spiky neck feathers that can be raised in a ruff. The tail is short and white. Nicobar Pigeons feed in the forest undergrowth, taking fruit and seeds. The birds fly nomadically from island to island in search of feeding sites. Nesting colonies are close-packed and sometimes very large.
• **NEST** An untidy structure made of twigs, either in a bush or a tree.
• **DISTRIBUTION** From the Nicobar Islands (in the Indian Ocean off Burma) through S.E. Asia to Indonesia, New Guinea, and the Solomon Islands.

ruff of elongated feathers

irregular wattle on the bill

large, strong feet

ring of an aviary bird

DISTRIBUTION

JUVENILE

Plumage Sexes alike	Habitat 🌳 ✈	Migration Nomadic

Family COLUMBIDAE	Species *Gallicolumba luzonica*	Length 29cm (11½in)

LUZON BLEEDING HEART

The blood-like breast markings of this species vary from one bird to another, and must serve as recognition marks by which individuals can identify each other. This is necessary because they live in the permanent semi-darkness of the rainforest floor. Here they move quietly among low, shrubby vegetation in search of seeds and berries, and also taking grubs, snails, and other invertebrates.
• **NEST** A scanty nest of twigs, placed in a shrub or low tree.
• **DISTRIBUTION** N. Philippine Islands.

bright breast mark

DISTRIBUTION

Plumage Sexes alike	Habitat 🌳	Migration Non-migrant

Family COLUMBIDAE	Species *Goura victoria*	Length 75cm (30in)

VICTORIA CROWNED PIGEON

The lacy crest of this enormous pigeon is made up of fan-shaped tufts and is permanently raised over the head. Displaying males utter soft, booming calls as they show off their crests and tails to the females. Both sexes perform threat or defence displays in which they wag their tails and hold out one or both wings, like banners. This is a ground-feeding species that lives on the rainforest floor, walking around slowly and taking fallen fruits, seeds, and berries. It flies heavily, either to escape danger or to ascend into the branches of the trees, where it also roosts and nests.
• **NEST** A large, solid platform-like mass of stems and twigs, in a tree.
• **DISTRIBUTION** N. New Guinea.

DISTRIBUTION

pale wing bar

scaly legs

Plumage Sexes alike	Habitat 🌳	Migration Non-migrant

Family COLUMBIDAE	Species *Treron bicincta*	Length 29cm (11½in)

ORANGE-BREASTED GREEN-PIGEON

Strong legs and feet, useful for clambering in trees, and a stout bill for eating soft fruits, make this species a typical example of the fruit-pigeons. Flocks are usually seen in the lower branches of trees or in bushes, feeding on figs, wild dates, berries, and other fruits. Birds rarely visit the ground and when they do, for instance to drink, they walk clumsily, with their tails raised.
• **NEST** A flimsy platform of twigs in a small tree, close to open space.
• **DISTRIBUTION** India and parts of S.E. Asia.

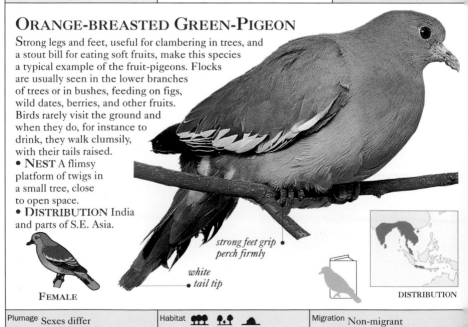

FEMALE

strong feet grip perch firmly

white tail tip

DISTRIBUTION

Plumage Sexes differ	Habitat 🌳 🌳 🔺	Migration Non-migrant

Family COLUMBIDAE	Species *Ptilinopus superbus*	Length 22cm (8½in)

SUPERB FRUIT-DOVE

The vivid plumage of this species provides surprisingly good camouflage among the fruit and foliage of sun-dappled forests. It feeds in forest trees that produce small, oil-rich fruits. Birds live in pairs or alone, although large groups sometimes gather temporarily at a plentiful food source.

• **NEST** A platform of twigs, in a tree or vine-tangle.
• **DISTRIBUTION** Australasian region from Sulawesi through New Guinea to the Solomon Islands, and in N.E. and E. Australia.

DISTRIBUTION

• *white belly and undertail coverts*

• *green back with dark spots*

FEMALE

Plumage Sexes differ	Habitat	Migration Partial migrant

Family COLUMBIDAE	Species *Ducula pacifica*	Length 35cm (14in)

PACIFIC IMPERIAL PIGEON

This is a large and subtly coloured fruit dove that inhabits small, wooded islands and atolls. Flocks wander between islands in search of fruit. They are capable of long sea crossings. The Pacific Imperial Pigeon is an agile bird, clambering, hanging, and reaching for food among the higher foliage, taking fruit and berries. The call is a single, growling note from high in the tree canopy.
• **NEST** A platform made of bare twigs and placed high up in a large tree.
• **DISTRIBUTION** From islands of N.E. New Guinea through Tonga, Fiji, and New Caledonia to islands of S.W. Pacific.

• *fleshy wattle on the bill*

long wings for distance flight •

DISTRIBUTION

Plumage Sexes alike	Habitat	Migration Partial migrant

Family COLUMBIDAE	Species *Lopholaimus antarcticus*	Length 43cm (17¼in)

TOPKNOT PIGEON

long, drooping crest •

A large, grey, long-tailed pigeon, this tree-dwelling species has a swept-back, double crest that runs from forehead to nape. It is a sociable and nomadic bird that roams the treetops of rainforests in flocks, feeding on a wide variety of fruit. The short legs and strong feet are typical of a fruit-pigeon and enable the birds to cling acrobatically to the twigs when feeding, often hanging upside down with flapping wings to keep in place. Topknot Pigeons rarely come down to the ground even to drink, normally obtaining water from tree hollows or wet leaves, or by hanging from a low twig over a stream or freshwater pool.
• **NEST** A flat platform made of twigs, and usually placed high in a tree.
• **DISTRIBUTION** E. Australia.

• blue-grey plumage

long • wings

DISTRIBUTION

short legs and strong feet of a tree-living fruit-pigeon

JUVENILE

Plumage Sexes alike	Habitat 🌳🌳 🌲	Migration Nomadic

Family COLUMBIDAE	Species *Hemiphaga novaeseelandiae*	Length 51cm (20in)

NEW ZEALAND PIGEON

The dull colours of this stout fruit-pigeon are broken up by sparkling green and purple sheens. These help to provide camouflage among foliage, but the bird can often be detected by the loud flapping of its wings as it steadies itself while clambering about in search of fruit. This species lives in forests, sometimes venturing into nearby gardens and farmland with trees. The diet includes fruit, berries, buds, flowers, and leaves from trees and shrubs. Birds also come down to the ground to feed from small plants. They are seen in pairs or small parties. The male's display flight consists of a rapid ascent followed by a downward glide with spread wings and tail.
• **NEST** A flimsy structure of twigs, built on the branch of a tree.
• **DISTRIBUTION** New Zealand.

• dark plumage with a dull, green gloss

DISTRIBUTION

Plumage Sexes alike	Habitat 🌲 🌿 🌳	Migration Non-migrant

Family PSITTACIDAE	Species *Chalcopsitta duivenbodei*	Length 32cm (12½in)

DUYVENBODE'S LORY

One of the more soberly coloured lories, this parrot feeds mainly on the flowers of forest trees. It visits large heads of tree blossoms, from which it laps nectar with its thin tongue. On the tip of the tongue there are special projections that gather up pollen. The pollen is important to the birds as it provides protein in an otherwise sugary diet. Duyvenbode's Lories are usually seen in pairs, or in parties of six to eight birds, in the treetops of lowland rainforest, and are fairly common within their normal range. They utter shrill screeches and short, harsh contact calls as they move through the trees in search of food. When feeding, the birds sometimes join company with other blossom-feeding species, such as Rainbow Lorikeets.
• **NEST** Not scientifically recorded, but birds have been seen investigating holes high in trees during the breeding season, which suggests cavity nesting.
• **DISTRIBUTION** Lowlands in N. New Guinea.

• crest ruffled in excitement

DISTRIBUTION

yellow wing patch

short legs and strong feet of a tree-dweller

Plumage Sexes alike	Habitat 🌳🌳 🏞️	Migration Non-migrant

Family PSITTACIDAE	Species *Trichoglossus haematodus*	Length 26cm (10½in)

RAINBOW LORIKEET

A vividly coloured and noisy bird, this species is often seen in chattering and screeching flocks, feeding in flowering trees. It is common in lowland forests and also in open woodland and parkland. Birds feed on pollen and nectar, also eating blossoms, some seeds and fruit, and occasional insects.
• **NEST** In a cavity in a hollow limb or treetrunk.
• **DISTRIBUTION** Parts of E. Indonesia; New Guinea; S.W. Pacific islands to New Caledonia; N., E., and S. Australia.
• **REMARK** Plumage varies over the range; some island forms lack the blue and red colouring.

DISTRIBUTION

RED-COLLARED FORM

• yellow underwing patches

Plumage Sexes alike	Habitat 🌳🌳 🌲🌲 🏞️	Migration Non-migrant

Family PSITTACIDAE	Species *Vini peruviana*	Length 18cm (7in)

TAHITIAN LORIKEET

This rarely seen parrot has deep blue plumage all over, except for a white triangle on the lower face and throat. The bill and feet are bright red. This simple arrangement makes the bird unusual among lorikeets, which are generally vivid birds with complex patterns. The Tahitian Lorikeet lives on remote tropical islands, where its main food is probably the nectar and pollen of the flowers of coconut palms.
• **NEST** A hollow in a tree or a broken-off coconut stump.
• **DISTRIBUTION** S. Pacific Ocean: in the Society Islands (but no longer occurring in Tahiti), and introduced in the Cook Islands.
• **REMARK** Endangered as a result of the raiding of nests by an introduced predator, the Black Rat.

DISTRIBUTION

• *uniform, deep blue plumage*

• *short legs and strong feet of a tree-dwelling bird*

• *short, tapering tail*

Plumage Sexes alike	Habitat	Migration Non-migrant

Family PSITTACIDAE	Species *Charmosyna papou*	Length 42cm (16½in)

PAPUAN LORIKEET

Living in tropical forests on mountainsides, this colourful parrot feeds in the trees on the flowers of epiphytes (independent plants that grow on the branches). It drinks the nectar and also eats pollen and the blossoms of the epiphytes, as well as taking berries and seeds. Its long, curving tail is an encumbrance as it hops jerkily through the twigs. Papuan Lorikeets occur in pairs or small parties and are seen in the upper branches of the forest. Their flight is direct but not fast, with the tail trailing behind. Birds fly among the branches rather than over the top of the canopy. Their calls are soft and subdued.
• **NEST** Not scientifically recorded.
• **DISTRIBUTION** Mountains of New Guinea.
• **REMARK** There is also a black phase (*see p. 13*) of this species, in which much of the red is replaced by black.

blue-and-black nape pattern •

• *red underside*

DISTRIBUTION

BLACK PHASE

• *two long central tail feathers*

Plumage Sexes alike	Habitat	Migration Non-migrant

Family PSITTACIDAE	Species *Calyptorhynchus funereus*	Length 68cm (27in)

YELLOW-TAILED BLACK COCKATOO

This large, forest-dwelling cockatoo has a massive bill that can destroy any unprotected wooden structure, whether it be a live tree or part of an aviary containing a captive specimen. In the forest, the cockatoo tears open branches to take out the large, wood-boring grubs of moths and beetles that form the greater part of its diet. It also eats seeds, nuts, berries, and blossoms. Yellow-tailed Black Cockatoos live mainly up in the trees, roosting and feeding in the branches. They descend to drink at dawn and in the late afternoons. In spite of their size, their slow, flapping flight is light and bouncy. The birds fly low over the trees in search of good feeding sites, maintaining contact with loud calls. Adults utter a drawn-out, high-pitched yell, and juveniles a growling note. The yellow cheek and tail patches are conspicuous in flight.
• **NEST** A spacious hollow limb or a large cavity in the trunk of a tree, without any lining.
• **DISTRIBUTION** E. and S. Australia from S. Queensland as far as Eyre Peninsula and Tasmania.

yellow face patch

massive bill

long tail with yellow side panels

DISTRIBUTION

Plumage Sexes alike	Habitat	Migration Non-migrant

Family PSITTACIDAE	Species *Cacatua galerita*	Length 35cm (14in)

SULPHUR-CRESTED COCKATOO

The snowy plumage of this beautiful cockatoo is often soiled, as the bird feeds on the ground in open locations, such as farmers' fields. Large flocks utter screeching calls as they feed on seeds, buds, leaves, and fruits of plants, also digging up roots, tubers, and bulbs with their bills. They visit trees to roost by night, and to rest in the midday heat.
• **NEST** An unlined hollow in a tree.
• **DISTRIBUTION** Parts of New Guinea and N., E., and S. Australia.

erect crest

powerful bill

pure white plumage

short legs with strong feet

short, rounded tail

DISTRIBUTION

Plumage Sexes alike	Habitat	Migration Non-migrant

Family PSITTACIDAE	Species *Eolophus roseicapillus*	Length 35cm (14in)

GALAH

A grey and pink cockatoo with a folding crest, the Galah is the commonest species of parrot in Australia. Large flocks manoeuvre in the air over open country, or feed on the ground, uttering screeching contact calls. Their habitats also include thinly wooded areas, and lines of woodland alongside rivers. The Galah feeds on grain and other seeds, leaf buds, and insects. It also digs up roots, tubers, and invertebrates with its bill. The species thrives on cereal fields, and its numbers increased enormously with the spread of wheat growing in Australia. It has long since come to be considered an agricultural pest. Galah pairs stay together for life, and share the tasks of caring for the young. Fledgling Galahs live together in flocks in the treetops, and juveniles spend their first two or three years in large flocks that roam about the country.
• **NEST** A hollow in a branch or trunk of a tree, lined with a layer of eucalyptus leaves.
•**DISTRIBUTION** Australia, except for wetter coastal areas.

eastern form has a slightly pinker crest

WESTERN FORM

pink plumage extends through underside to the belly

DISTRIBUTION

Plumage Sexes alike	Habitat	Migration Non-migrant

Family PSITTACIDAE	Species *Nymphicus hollandicus*	Length 32cm (12½in)

COCKATIEL

A strong-flying parrot of arid country, this species looks like a cockatoo but is more agile and active in its behaviour. The Cockatiel occurs on open plains, sometimes with light woodland. Pairs or small flocks are seen feeding on the ground, camouflaged by their colours. They pick up fallen seeds of grasses, weeds, shrubs, and trees, as well as eating berries and visiting harvested fields to feed on leftovers of grain. If alarmed while feeding, the birds fly up, often settling in a dead tree, where they make themselves inconspicuous by perching lengthwise on larger branches. Flight is fast and direct, with strong, regular wingbeats, in which the large, white wing-patches are conspicuous. Birds maintain contact during flight with a loud, warbled, double note. In some parts of its range the Cockatiel leads a nomadic life, travelling about in any direction in search of areas where food is available. Other populations migrate between summer and winter ranges.
• **NEST** A hollow in a tree, often near or standing in water.
•**DISTRIBUTION** Australia, except for wetter coastal areas.

raised crest

light red cheek patch

DISTRIBUTION

white wing patch

Plumage Sexes differ	Habitat	Migration Migrant/nomadic

Family PSITTACIDAE	Species *Eclectus roratus*	Length 35cm (14in)

ECLECTUS PARROT

There is a startling difference in colour between the sexes in this stoutly built parrot species. It is seen mainly in lowland forest, also occurring in more open country where groups of tall trees are found. Birds occur in pairs and small parties, in which males are more in evidence than females. Flocks gather to feed where fruit is ripe, and larger flocks are seen roosting in trees. The diet consists mainly of fruit, but nuts, seeds, buds, blossom, and nectar are also eaten. The flight is strong but rather slow, with deliberate, downward wingbeats and frequent, short glides. During longer journeys the Eclectus Parrot often flies high above the tree canopy. The call is a raucous, screeching sound.

FEMALE

MALE

• **NEST** A hole in the trunk of a tall tree, often situated close to the forest edge.
• **DISTRIBUTION** Islands of E. Indonesia, New Guinea, the Solomon Islands, and extreme N.E. tip of Australia.

DISTRIBUTION

Plumage Sexes differ	Habitat	Migration Non-migrant

Family PSITTACIDAE	Species *Psittrichas fulgidus*	Length 46cm (18in)

PESQUET'S PARROT

Bald-headedness in birds is usually associated with eating messy foods, and this parrot has a bare face that may possibly be connected with its mainly fruit diet. It eats softer fruits, particularly figs, and also blossoms and probably nectar. Living in mountain forest, it sits for long periods on high, bare branches that project above the forest foliage. It tends to jump from twig to twig with a quick wing-flick rather than using the bill to climb about. Birds screech noisily during flight. They fly strongly but slowly, with rapid, shallow wingbeats and the occasional glide.

bare face

red underside

• **NEST** Not scientifically recorded.
• **DISTRIBUTION** Highland forests of New Guinea.

very broad tail •

DISTRIBUTION

Plumage Sexes alike	Habitat	Migration Non-migrant

Family PSITTACIDAE	Species *Polytelis alexandrae*	Length 45cm (17½in)

ALEXANDRA'S PARROT

FEMALE

The slender build of this parrot, and the long, narrow wings and tapering tail, are probably adaptations to its nomadic life in the deserts of Australia. Its flight is undulating, with irregular wingbeats, as it moves between the scattered trees of its arid habitat, or follows the lines of eucalyptus trees that mark the presence of a creek. It is also seen in acacia scrub. Most of the day is spent at ground level searching for the small seeds of grasses and other plants which form its diet. Alexandra's Parrot also eats tree blossoms and mistletoe berries. A quiet bird, it has a soft twitter of alarm and a harsher, rattling call. When alarmed, it flies up and perches lengthwise along a branch, thus making its outline less conspicuous.
• **NEST** An unlined cavity, either in a hollow branch or in the trunk of a tree.
• **DISTRIBUTION** Interior of W. and C. Australia.

slender build

long wings

MALE

tail feathers are graduated in length

long tail for distant flight

DISTRIBUTION

Plumage Sexes differ	Habitat	Migration Nomadic

Family PSITTACIDAE	Species *Platycercus eximius*	Length 30cm (12in)

EASTERN ROSELLA

With its bright plumage in the primary colours, and scale-like black markings on the back, this parrot is a well-known inhabitant of the farmland and gardens within its range. Pairs or small groups search for a variety of food, including fruit, blossoms, nectar from trees, berries from shrubs, and seeds from the ground. Since it takes fruit from orchards it is considered to be an agricultural pest. It also feeds on spilled grain in harvested fields. The Eastern Rosella's calls include loud metallic notes, screeches, and chattering. Its flight is undulating, usually close to the ground, with a final upward swoop to a perch. The male performs a swaggering display in which he walks on the ground, wagging his tail from side to side.
• **NEST** An unlined hollow in a living or dead tree.
• **DISTRIBUTION** S.E. Australia.

tail feathers are graduated in length

DISTRIBUTION

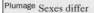

Plumage Sexes differ	Habitat	Migration Non-migrant

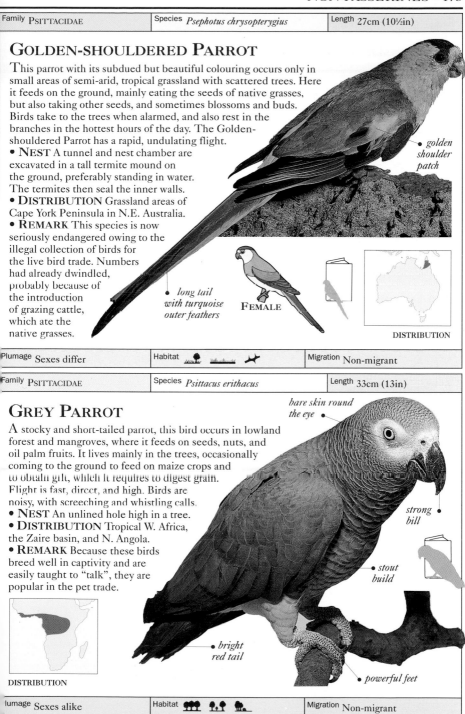

Family PSITTACIDAE	Species *Psephotus chrysopterygius*	Length 27cm (10½in)

GOLDEN-SHOULDERED PARROT

This parrot with its subdued but beautiful colouring occurs only in small areas of semi-arid, tropical grassland with scattered trees. Here it feeds on the ground, mainly eating the seeds of native grasses, but also taking other seeds, and sometimes blossoms and buds. Birds take to the trees when alarmed, and also rest in the branches in the hottest hours of the day. The Golden-shouldered Parrot has a rapid, undulating flight.

- **NEST** A tunnel and nest chamber are excavated in a tall termite mound on the ground, preferably standing in water. The termites then seal the inner walls.
- **DISTRIBUTION** Grassland areas of Cape York Peninsula in N.E. Australia.
- **REMARK** This species is now seriously endangered owing to the illegal collection of birds for the live bird trade. Numbers had already dwindled, probably because of the introduction of grazing cattle, which ate the native grasses.

golden shoulder patch

long tail with turquoise outer feathers

FEMALE

DISTRIBUTION

Plumage Sexes differ	Habitat	Migration Non-migrant

Family PSITTACIDAE	Species *Psittacus erithacus*	Length 33cm (13in)

GREY PARROT

A stocky and short-tailed parrot, this bird occurs in lowland forest and mangroves, where it feeds on seeds, nuts, and oil palm fruits. It lives mainly in the trees, occasionally coming to the ground to feed on maize crops and to obtain grit, which it requires to digest grain. Flight is fast, direct, and high. Birds are noisy, with screeching and whistling calls.

- **NEST** An unlined hole high in a tree.
- **DISTRIBUTION** Tropical W. Africa, the Zaire basin, and N. Angola.
- **REMARK** Because these birds breed well in captivity and are easily taught to "talk", they are popular in the pet trade.

bare skin round the eye

strong bill

stout build

bright red tail

powerful feet

DISTRIBUTION

Plumage Sexes alike	Habitat	Migration Non-migrant

Family PSITTACIDAE	Species *Cyclopsitta diophthalma*	Length 14cm (5½in)

DOUBLE-EYED FIG-PARROT

In spite of its bright plumage this little parrot
is easily overlooked as it feeds quietly among the
foliage of the rainforest canopy. It forages in pairs
or small flocks, searching for fruit such as figs and
berries, as well as seeds, nectar, and the grubs
of wood-boring insects.
The flight is fast and direct,
with short, shrill calls.
• **NEST** A hole bored by
the birds in a rotten tree.
• **DISTRIBUTION** New
Guinea and E. Australia.

• *bright
face pattern
of male*

FEMALE

DISTRIBUTION

Plumage Sexes differ	Habitat	Migration Non-migrant

Family PSITTACIDAE	Species *Neophema bourkii*	Length 19cm (7½in)

BOURKE'S PARROT

This delicately coloured parrot is rarely
seen in the wild. Pairs or small groups
forage nomadically through dry acacia scrub,
feeding on the seeds of grasses and herbaceous
plants. Bourke's Parrot has large eyes that
are adapted to poor light. It drinks at
waterholes after sunset or before dawn, when it is cooler
and there is less danger from predators. The male shows
off his blue underwings and flanks in a raised-wing display.
• **NEST** An unlined hole in a treetrunk.
• **DISTRIBUTION** Interior of Australia.
• **REMARK** This species breeds well in
captivity, and colour varieties have been produced.

DISTRIBUTION

• *scaly pattern
on the wings*

FEMALE

Plumage Sexes alike	Habitat	Migration Non-migrant/nomadic

Family PSITTACIDAE	Species *Neophema pulchella*	Length 20cm (8in)

TURQUOISE PARROT

Small flocks of this beautiful species feed
quietly on the ground in grassy areas bordering
dry woodland, taking small seeds, buds, and
leaves. When alarmed they fly into trees or
bushes. The birds fly swiftly but erratically,
uttering soft, two-note,
whistling calls.
• **NEST** A hollow
in a tree stump,
fence post, or log
on the ground.
•**DISTRIBUTION**
E. Australia.

FEMALE

• *male
displaying to
the female*

DISTRIBUTION

Plumage Sexes differ	Habitat	Migration Non-migrant

| Family PSITTACIDAE | Species *Melopsittacus undulatus* | Length 18cm (7in) |

BUDGERIGAR

In the wild this familiar small parrot lives in nomadic flocks, which search for seeding grasses and other vegetation in their arid habitat. Flight is strong and rapid. Flocks rarely stay long in one place, but the birds settle and breed in holes available during the brief period of plant growth that follows rain.
• **NEST** An unlined hole or hollow in a treetrunk, a rotten stump, or a fence post.
• **DISTRIBUTION** Australia.
• **REMARK** Many colour variations have been bred in captivity, but the wild bird is always green and yellow.

DISTRIBUTION

| Plumage Sexes alike | Habitat | Migration Partial migrant/Nomadic |

| Family PSITTACIDAE | Species *Poicephalus rueppellii* | Length 23cm (9in) |

RUEPPELL'S PARROT

Uncommon and inconspicuous, this species betrays its presence with a short, sharp call note. Found in the large trees of dry forest, particularly along watercourses, it feeds at all levels. In addition to prizing insect grubs from rotten wood, it also feeds on berries, green shoots, seeds, and the pods of melon and acacia.
• **NEST** An unlined hole in a tree.
• **DISTRIBUTION** S.W. Africa.

• *orange iris of female*

• *blue flank patch of female*

DISTRIBUTION

MALE

| Plumage Sexes differ | Habitat | Migration Non-migrant |

| Family PSITTACIDAE | Species *Agapornis personatus* | Length 14.5cm (5¾in) |

MASKED LOVEBIRD

This short-tailed little parrot is usually seen in small flocks. It inhabits seasonally arid grassland with scattered trees and shrubs. Here it feeds mainly on seeds, which it extracts while clinging to plant stems, also taking berries, green buds, and leaves. Flight is fast and direct. Breeding in loose colonies, pairs form a strong bond, perching close together and preening each other (hence the species' name).
• **NEST** A bulky, domed nest of thin twigs and bark strips, in a hole in a tree or building.
• **DISTRIBUTION** Tanzanian Highlands. Introduced in coastal Tanzania and S. Kenya.

DISTRIBUTION

• *blackish head with white eye-ring*

• *short, rounded wings*

| Plumage Sexes alike | Habitat | Migration Non-migrant |

| Family PSITTACIDAE | Species *Loriculus galgulus* | Length 12cm (4¾in) |

BLUE-CROWNED HANGING PARROT

This tiny parrot of open woodland occurs in small, fast-flying flocks. It uses its brush-tipped tongue to gather nectar, and also eats flowers, fruit, and seeds, sometimes (though rarely) hanging upside down. Hanging parrots, like some lovebird species, carry nesting material tucked into their rump feathers.
• **NEST** Tree hole lined with leaves.
• **DISTRIBUTION** Malay Peninsula, Sumatra, Borneo.

FEMALE

female lacks red throat patch

DISTRIBUTION

| Plumage Sexes differ | Habitat | Migration Non-migrant |

| Family PSITTACIDAE | Species *Forpus coelestis* | Length 12cm (4¾in) |

PACIFIC PARROTLET

blue stripe

Not easily seen among the foliage, this tiny, green-faced parrot inhabits secondary forest (regrown after felling) and scrub. Here it feeds mainly on small seeds taken from grasses and other low plants, and on berries from bushes. It usually occurs in flocks or family parties, uttering noisy, chattering calls. The flight is fast and erratic.
• **NEST** An unlined hole in a branch, treetrunk, or post.
• **DISTRIBUTION** W. Ecuador and N.W. Peru.

FEMALE

short tail

DISTRIBUTION

| Plumage Sexes differ | Habitat | Migration Non-migrant |

| Family PSITTACIDAE | Species *Brotogeris chiriri* | Length 22cm (8½in) |

YELLOW-CHEVRONED PARAKEET

yellow chevron is conspicuous in flight

This small parrot is hard to detect when resting in foliage. It is more easily noticeable when it moves about and calls shrilly in its forest habitat. It eats seeds, fruits, flowers, and shoots. At times it forms large flocks, but pairs scatter to breed.
• **NEST** A hole in a treetrunk, hollow branch, or tree-termite nest.
• **DISTRIBUTION** From C. Brazil to N. Argentina and Paraguay.

DISTRIBUTION

tapering tail

outer toe turns backwards

| Plumage Sexes alike | Habitat | Migration Non-migrant |

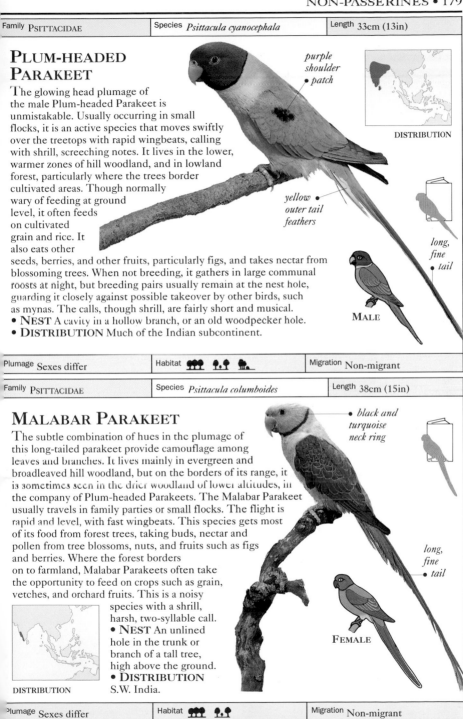

| Family PSITTACIDAE | Species *Psittacula cyanocephala* | Length 33cm (13in) |

PLUM-HEADED PARAKEET

The glowing head plumage of the male Plum-headed Parakeet is unmistakable. Usually occurring in small flocks, it is an active species that moves swiftly over the treetops with rapid wingbeats, calling with shrill, screeching notes. It lives in the lower, warmer zones of hill woodland, and in lowland forest, particularly where the trees border cultivated areas. Though normally wary of feeding at ground level, it often feeds on cultivated grain and rice. It also eats other seeds, berries, and other fruits, particularly figs, and takes nectar from blossoming trees. When not breeding, it gathers in large communal roosts at night, but breeding pairs usually remain at the nest hole, guarding it closely against possible takeover by other birds, such as mynas. The calls, though shrill, are fairly short and musical.
• **NEST** A cavity in a hollow branch, or an old woodpecker hole.
• **DISTRIBUTION** Much of the Indian subcontinent.

purple shoulder patch

DISTRIBUTION

yellow outer tail feathers

long, fine tail

MALE

| Plumage Sexes differ | Habitat | Migration Non-migrant |

| Family PSITTACIDAE | Species *Psittacula columboides* | Length 38cm (15in) |

MALABAR PARAKEET

The subtle combination of hues in the plumage of this long-tailed parakeet provide camouflage among leaves and branches. It lives mainly in evergreen and broadleaved hill woodland, but on the borders of its range, it is sometimes seen in the drier woodland of lower altitudes, in the company of Plum-headed Parakeets. The Malabar Parakeet usually travels in family parties or small flocks. The flight is rapid and level, with fast wingbeats. This species gets most of its food from forest trees, taking buds, nectar and pollen from tree blossoms, nuts, and fruits such as figs and berries. Where the forest borders on to farmland, Malabar Parakeets often take the opportunity to feed on crops such as grain, vetches, and orchard fruits. This is a noisy species with a shrill, harsh, two-syllable call.
• **NEST** An unlined hole in the trunk or branch of a tall tree, high above the ground.
• **DISTRIBUTION** S.W. India.

black and turquoise neck ring

long, fine tail

FEMALE

DISTRIBUTION

| Plumage Sexes differ | Habitat | Migration Non-migrant |

Family PSITTACIDAE	Species *Anodorhynchus hyacinthinus*	Length 100cm (39in)

HYACINTH MACAW

Deep blue plumage offset by the yellow chin and eye-patches, and large size, with a long tail and long, narrow wings identify this species, which is the largest of all the parrots. It almost always occurs in pairs which fly closely together. Groups of pairs or small family parties form small flocks. Hyacinth Macaws are often seen in palm groves. They are also seen in more open areas and swamps with some tall trees, and in forests along watercourses. The diet includes palm nuts and other nuts, seeds, and fruits. Birds call loudly in flight, with a harsh screech, and if alarmed take refuge in the highest branches of trees.
• **NEST** A large, unlined cavity in a treetrunk.
• **DISTRIBUTION** Bolivia and Brazil.
• **REMARK** This species is threatened in the wild owing to trapping for the pet trade, although it is still locally common in some areas.

yellow eye-patch

uniform blue plumage

massive bill

short legs with strong feet

DISTRIBUTION

long, tapering tail

Plumage Sexes alike	Habitat	Migration Non-migrant

Family PSITTACIDAE	Species *Ara macao*	Length 85cm (34in)

SCARLET MACAW

The brilliant colours of the Scarlet Macaw, and its daily flights between roosting and feeding areas make it a highly conspicuous species. It occurs widely in broken woodland, in the trees of the forest edge, and in open country with scattered groups of tall trees. Pairs keep together and flocks are composed of pairs or small parties. The diet consists of a variety of fruits, nuts, and seeds. In areas of human settlement the Scarlet Macaw has become scarce because of trapping. The birds are usually silent when feeding, but utter harsh calls in flight and screech when alarmed.
• **NEST** A cavity in the trunk of a forest tree.
• **DISTRIBUTION** Mexico to Brazil and Bolivia.

bare face patch

yellow wing patch

DISTRIBUTION

long, tapering tail

Plumage Sexes alike	Habitat	Migration Non-migrant

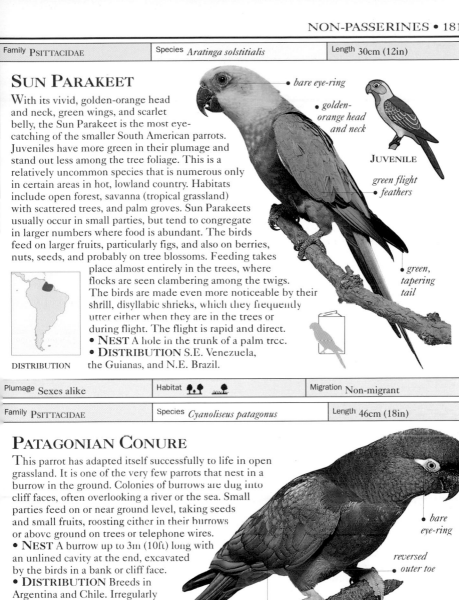

Family PSITTACIDAE	Species *Aratinga solstitialis*	Length 30cm (12in)

SUN PARAKEET

With its vivid, golden-orange head and neck, green wings, and scarlet belly, the Sun Parakeet is the most eye-catching of the smaller South American parrots. Juveniles have more green in their plumage and stand out less among the tree foliage. This is a relatively uncommon species that is numerous only in certain areas in hot, lowland country. Habitats include open forest, savanna (tropical grassland) with scattered trees, and palm groves. Sun Parakeets usually occur in small parties, but tend to congregate in larger numbers where food is abundant. The birds feed on larger fruits, particularly figs, and also on berries, nuts, seeds, and probably on tree blossoms. Feeding takes place almost entirely in the trees, where flocks are seen clambering among the twigs. The birds are made even more noticeable by their shrill, disyllabic shrieks, which they frequently utter either when they are in the trees or during flight. The flight is rapid and direct.
• **NEST** A hole in the trunk of a palm tree.
• **DISTRIBUTION** S.E. Venezuela, the Guianas, and N.E. Brazil.

bare eye-ring

golden-orange head and neck

JUVENILE

green flight feathers

green, tapering tail

DISTRIBUTION

Plumage Sexes alike	Habitat	Migration Non-migrant

Family PSITTACIDAE	Species *Cyanoliseus patagonus*	Length 46cm (18in)

PATAGONIAN CONURE

This parrot has adapted itself successfully to life in open grassland. It is one of the very few parrots that nest in a burrow in the ground. Colonies of burrows are dug into cliff faces, often overlooking a river or the sea. Small parties feed on or near ground level, taking seeds and small fruits, roosting either in their burrows or above ground on trees or telephone wires.
• **NEST** A burrow up to 3m (10ft) long with an unlined cavity at the end, excavated by the birds in a bank or cliff face.
• **DISTRIBUTION** Breeds in Argentina and Chile. Irregularly winters as far north as N. Argentina and possibly Uruguay.

bare eye-ring

reversed outer toe

bronze sheen on the wings

DISTRIBUTION

Plumage Sexes alike	Habitat	Migration Partial migrant

Family PSITTACIDAE	Species *Myiopsitta monachus*	Length 22cm (8½in)

MONK PARAKEET

A stout little parrot living in a colony in open woodland, the Monk Parakeet is conspicuous for its lively, noisy behaviour. Besides breeding in their colony, the birds use it as a communal roosting place, which makes it the permanent centre for all their activity. From here they disperse daily to feed, usually on open ground near to trees. They eat seeds, nuts, fruit, buds, and blossoms, and raid citrus orchards. Activity is accompanied by constant, short shrieks and chattering.
• **NEST** An unlined, domed nest made of twigs, preferably thorny, with a low, upward-slanting entrance. Each pair builds its nest up against the next, forming a large colony in a tree.
• **DISTRIBUTION** S.W. and S. Brazil, and through Paraguay to N. Argentina and Uruguay. Introduced in E. North America, the Bahamas, and Puerto Rico.

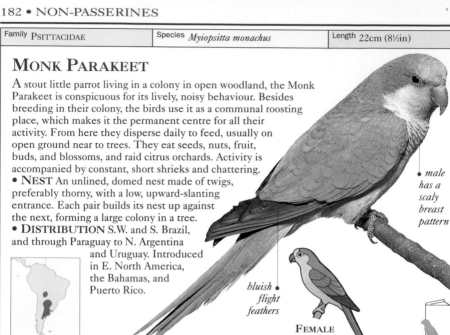

• *male has a scaly breast pattern*

bluish flight feathers

FEMALE

DISTRIBUTION

Plumage Sexes alike	Habitat	Migration Non-migrant

Family PSITTACIDAE	Species *Pionus menstruus*	Length 28cm (11in)

BLUE-HEADED PARROT

Large-headed, short-tailed, and solidly built, this is a parrot of heavily forested areas, living mainly in the treetops. It forms flocks when not breeding, and roosts in large numbers in the trees. Birds often fly for some distance daily to and from their roosting places, usually travelling in strong, fast flight high above the trees. In flight, they are noisy, with loud, harsh, screams and high-pitched, screeching calls. After settling to feed in the trees, they become silent. The diet consists of fruit, seeds, and blossoms, mostly taken from trees, but birds sometimes visit farmland to take crops such as maize or bananas.
• **NEST** A bare, natural hollow, extended by the birds, in a dead or living tree, often high above ground level.
• **DISTRIBUTION** From Costa Rica south as far as Bolivia and S.E. Brazil.

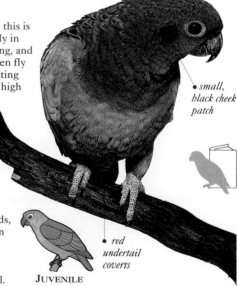

• *small, black cheek patch*

• *red undertail coverts*

JUVENILE

DISTRIBUTION

Plumage Sexes alike	Habitat	Migration Non-migrant

Family PSITTACIDAE	Species *Amazona oratrix*	Length 35cm (14in)

YELLOW-HEADED PARROT

Recognizable by the all-yellow head of the adult
bird, this is the northernmost species in a series of
yellow-crowned parrots of the Amazon group. Pairs
or small parties are seen in mature trees, both in
ADULT
forest and in more open places. The species is not
highly gregarious, though roosting flocks are sometimes seen.
Flight is strong and steady, often accompanied with loud,
screeching calls. When feeding, the birds are rather silent,
and seem reluctant to fly, preferring to clamber and walk
among branches. They take fruit, seeds, nuts, and
blossoms, either from trees or from bushes. This
species uses its foot to hold food up to its bill.
• **NEST** An unlined hollow in a tree or stump,
sometimes excavated by the nesting pair.
• **DISTRIBUTION** Coastal regions of Mexico,
Belize, and extreme
N.W. Honduras.

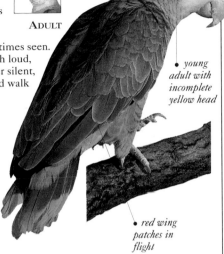

• *young
adult with
incomplete
yellow head*

• *red wing
patches in
flight*

DISTRIBUTION

Plumage Sexes alike	Habitat	Migration Non-migrant

Family PSITTACIDAE	Species *Amazona aestiva*	Length 37cm (14½in)

BLUE-FRONTED PARROT

As in most of the large Amazon parrots,
adults of this species have a bright patch
of colour on the head. The "blue front"
is a pale blue stripe above the base of
the bill, in front of the yellow crown.
The head pattern helps birds to find and
recognize members of their own species,
among the many similar-looking birds that share
their habitat. In the forest, Blue-fronted Parrots
feed quietly in the upper branches of trees
where most of their food is found. Their
diet includes fruits, seeds, nuts, blossoms,
and buds. In areas of mixed forest and
farmland they sometimes venture
out of the trees and raid crops.
• **NEST** A hollow in a large treetrunk.
• **DISTRIBUTION** Forested areas
of interior E. and S. Brazil, Bolivia,
Paraguay, and N.E. Argentina.
• **REMARK** This species is often kept as a
pet and is sometimes bred in aviaries. It has
a reputation as a good mimic of human speech.

• *yellow
shoulder
patch*

ADULT

DISTRIBUTION

Plumage Sexes differ	Habitat	Migration Non-migrant

| Family MUSOPHAGIDAE | Species *Corythaeola cristata* | Length 75cm (30in) |

GREAT BLUE TURACO

• *broad, upright crest is permanently raised*

DISTRIBUTION

A large turaco with blue upperparts, a red and yellow underside, and a broad crest, this species lives in tropical rainforest. Here it feeds principally on forest fruits. In the trees the bird is agile and active, hopping and running along branches. Its flight consists of little more than downward glides and swoops, and it usually gains height by leaping between branches. Habitats include lowland forest edges, river valley forest, mountain forest, and isolated woodland in savanna (tropical grassland). This shy bird is not easily seen among the foliage, but small groups often gather and can be detected by their habit of calling in chorus, sometimes for several minutes. The chorus begins with plaintive cries, followed by a series of short "kok-kok" notes, and dies down with deeper, vibrating calls.

• **NEST** A thin platform of dry twigs with a shallow central hollow, lined with finer twigs, and placed high in a tree.
• **DISTRIBUTION** Tropical forest in W. and C. Africa.
• **REMARK** This is the largest species of turaco.

| Plumage Sexes alike | Habitat ⛲ 🌳 🌿 ⛰ | Migration Non-migrant |

| Family MUSOPHAGIDAE | Species *Criniferoides leucogaster* | Length 50cm (20in) |

WHITE-BELLIED GO-AWAY-BIRD

raised crest •

Soberly coloured in grey, black, and white, with an upright crest, this is a turaco of dry, open scrub and woodland. Here it tends to perch conspicuously on high branches, and is seen in flocks that cross open spaces one after another in flapping flight. Flying birds reveal prominent white bars on the wings and tail. As each lands, it raises its long tail and tall crest. The name derives from the nasal, complaining "go-wayeerr" call, although a loud, barking note is also uttered. Single birds, pairs, or small parties forage among trees and bushes for fruit, flowers, and green pods of seeds.

• **NEST** An untidy, shallow nest made of twigs, usually in a dense thorn tree.
• **DISTRIBUTION** E. Africa, from Ethiopia as far south as Tanzania.

DISTRIBUTION

• *strong, hooked bill*

• *long, narrow tail*

black-edged • *wing feathers*

| Plumage Sexes alike | Habitat 🌿 ✈ | Migration Non-migrant |

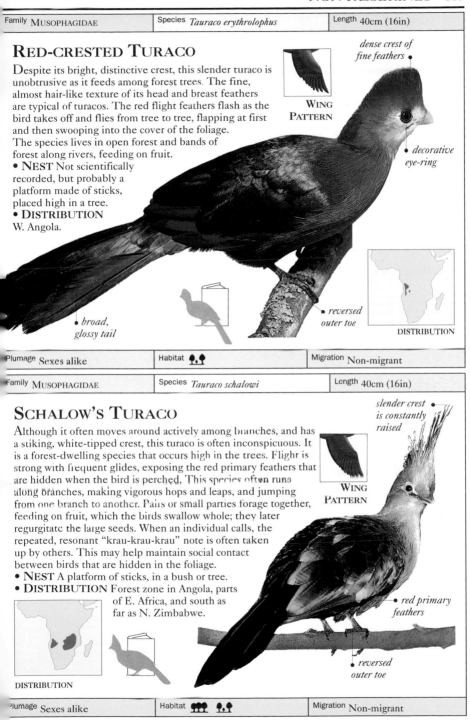

Family MUSOPHAGIDAE	Species *Tauraco erythrolophus*	Length 40cm (16in)

RED-CRESTED TURACO

Despite its bright, distinctive crest, this slender turaco is unobtrusive as it feeds among forest trees. The fine, almost hair-like texture of its head and breast feathers are typical of turacos. The red flight feathers flash as the bird takes off and flies from tree to tree, flapping at first and then swooping into the cover of the foliage. The species lives in open forest and bands of forest along rivers, feeding on fruit.

• **NEST** Not scientifically recorded, but probably a platform made of sticks, placed high in a tree.

• **DISTRIBUTION** W. Angola.

dense crest of fine feathers •

WING PATTERN

• decorative eye-ring

• *reversed outer toe*

• *broad, glossy tail*

DISTRIBUTION

Plumage Sexes alike	Habitat	Migration Non-migrant

Family MUSOPHAGIDAE	Species *Tauraco schalowi*	Length 40cm (16in)

SCHALOW'S TURACO

Although it often moves around actively among branches, and has a stiking, white-tipped crest, this turaco is often inconspicuous. It is a forest-dwelling species that occurs high in the trees. Flight is strong with frequent glides, exposing the red primary feathers that are hidden when the bird is perched. This species often runs along branches, making vigorous hops and leaps, and jumping from one branch to another. Pairs or small parties forage together, feeding on fruit, which the birds swallow whole; they later regurgitate the large seeds. When an individual calls, the repeated, resonant "krau-krau-krau" note is often taken up by others. This may help maintain social contact between birds that are hidden in the foliage.

• **NEST** A platform of sticks, in a bush or tree.

• **DISTRIBUTION** Forest zone in Angola, parts of E. Africa, and south as far as N. Zimbabwe.

slender crest • is constantly raised

WING PATTERN

• *red primary feathers*

• *reversed outer toe*

DISTRIBUTION

Plumage Sexes alike	Habitat	Migration Non-migrant

Family CUCULIDAE	Species *Clamator glandarius*	Length 38cm (15in)

GREAT SPOTTED CUCKOO

Hunting in trees and bushes for its prey, this cuckoo eats the hairy caterpillars that most other birds find distasteful. It also takes other insects, particularly grasshoppers and locusts, and other small creatures. Usually silent, it becomes noisy when breeding, with a song that is partly a harsh chatter and partly a gobbling sound. After hatching, the young cuckoo imitates the calls of the nestlings of the host species, begging for food from the parent. Before long it outgrows the other young birds, though it does not eject them from the nest.
• **NEST** This bird is a nest parasite. A single egg is laid in the nest of a magpie, crow, or (in South Africa) one of several species of starling.
• **DISTRIBUTION** Two populations: one breeds in S. Europe and winters in W. Africa; the other breeds in South Africa and winters in tropical Africa.

ADULT

• *black head of juvenile*

chestnut wing patch of juvenile

• *spotted plumage retained by adult birds*

• *long tail with tapering tip*

DISTRIBUTION

Plumage Sexes alike	Habitat	Migration Migrant

Family CUCULIDAE	Species *Cuculus canorus*	Length 33cm (13in)

COMMON CUCKOO

The loud "cuckoo" call of the male gives this species, and the family, its name. It feeds on large, hairy caterpillars, and other small invertebrates. The female watches a pair of small birds building their nest; then at an opportune moment she visits it, removes and often eats an egg, and lays one of her own in its place.
• **NEST** This bird is a nest parasite. A single egg is laid in the nest of an insect-eating bird which rears the young cuckoo.
• **DISTRIBUTION** Breeds in Eurasia, east to E. Siberia and south to N. Africa. Winters in South Africa and Asia.

JUVENILE

• *small feet*

broad tail with white spots •

DISTRIBUTION

Plumage Sexes alike	Habitat	Migration Migrant

Family CUCULIDAE	Species *Chrysococcyx caprius*	Length 18cm (7in)

DIDRIC CUCKOO

Common in a variety of habitats from open forest to savanna, this small, glossy green-and-white cuckoo feeds mainly on caterpillars. Its name refers to the plaintive "deea-deea-deedaric" call used by males when breeding. The male displays with shivering wings and spread tail, calling continuously.
• **NEST** A nest parasite; the female lays
a single egg in the nest of a passerine bird,
preferring those of weaver and sparrow
species. The young cuckoo sometimes
pushes the chicks of the host
bird out of the nest.
• **DISTRIBUTION** Africa
south of the Sahara;
S.W. Arabian
peninsula.

• *orange eye-ring*

• *broken white stripe across the eye*

• *glossy bronze-green plumage*

• *white bars on outer tail feathers revealed when spread*

FEMALE

• *barred flanks*

DISTRIBUTION

Plumage Sexes alike	Habitat 🌿🌳 ⬛	Migration Migrant

Family CUCULIDAE	Species *Scythrops novaehollandiae*	Length 65cm (26in)

CHANNEL-BILLED CUCKOO

With its huge, powerful bill, long wings, and long tail, in flight this cuckoo resembles a hornbill (*see pp. 230–231*) or a toucan (*see pp. 236–237*). It is most active at dusk and dawn and sometimes flies at night. Loud, raucous calls are uttered in flight. Birds feed mainly in the treetops, taking fruit such as figs, as well as insects, and sometimes eggs and nestlings.
• **NEST** Parasitizes nests of currawongs, butcherbirds, crows, and Australasian Magpies (*see pp. 383–384*).
• **DISTRIBUTION** Breeds in N. and E. Australia.
Winters in New Guinea
and the island of
Sulawesi in
Indonesia.

JUVENILE

DISTRIBUTION

• *dark-tipped wing feathers*

• *mottled pattern of sunlight and shadow from the foliage*

• *white tail tip*

Plumage Sexes alike	Habitat 🌳🌿	Migration Migrant

Family CUCULIDAE	Species *Coccyzus erythropthalmus*	Length 30cm (12in)

BLACK-BILLED CUCKOO

This is one of the many cuckoos that do not parasitize other species'
nests. Instead pairs build their own nest and rear their own
young, with both parents sharing the task of feeding the
nestlings. A bird of tree foliage and streamside
thickets, it runs and leaps easily among the
branches. Caterpillars are an important part of
the diet for both adults and young.
• **NEST** A cup nest of twigs and
stems, lined with grasses and leaves,
placed low in a bush or tree.
• **DISTRIBUTION** E. USA
and S. Canada. Winters in
South America.

• *red
eye-
ring*

JUVENILE

• *short
legs*

• *long
wings*

DISTRIBUTION

Plumage Sexes alike	Habitat	Migration Migrant

Family CUCULIDAE	Species *Ceuthmochares aereus*	Length 35cm (14in)

YELLOW-BILL

Agile and active, this slender, long-tailed cuckoo hides in dense, leafy thickets
and lives in forest and clusters of scrubby vegetation in grassland. Often occurring
in pairs, it takes small animals such as insects,
slugs, and tree-frogs. It sometimes joins
hunting flocks of mixed passerines.
Although it is evasive and rarely
seen it can be detected by its
harsh, low-pitched "chaaa".
• **NEST** This cuckoo does
not parasitize nests of other
species. A saucer of sticks
is built, in a tree fork.
• **DISTRIBUTION**
Africa south of the Sahara.

DISTRIBUTION

Plumage Sexes alike	Habitat	Migration Non-migrant

Family CUCULIDAE	Species *Crotophaga ani*	Length 37cm (14½in)

SMOOTH-BILLED ANI

With a short, squat body and heavy head, this
dishevelled-looking bird does not resemble other
cuckoos. It has a deep, blunt bill and a long, wedge-shaped
tail that droops and wags as though loosely
attached. Despite its ungainly appearance it
walks and runs well, but its flight is poorly
developed, consisting of a few rapid flaps
interspersed with short glides. Feeding mainly
on the ground, it takes grasshoppers and other
insects, and follows cattle to catch the insects they
disturb. The bird may also settle on the back of an animal
and pick ticks off its skin. The species is highly sociable and
feeds in small groups, communicating with a long, whining
note. When resting, either on the ground or in bushes and small
trees, the birds huddle together, sometimes preening each other.
Breeding is loosely communal. Several pairs cooperate to build
a nest, several females lay their eggs in it, and the whole group
shares in incubation and in rearing the nestlings The young
often stay with the group and help to rear subsequent broods.
• **NEST** This bird does not parasitize the nests of other species.
A cup nest of coarse twigs is made, with a lining, in a thorny tree.
• **DISTRIBUTION** From S. USA (C. Florida) south through Central and South
America to W. Ecuador and N. Argentina. Also in the West Indies.

DISTRIBUTION

Plumage Sexes alike	Habitat	Migration Non-migrant

Family CUCULIDAE	Species *Guira guira*	Length 37cm (14½in)

GUIRA CUCKOO

Almost always encountered in small groups of 8-10 individuals, this is a highly
sociable species. It lives in dry, grassy plains with widely scattered trees. At
night it roosts in flocks that perch closely together on the branch of a tree.
Resting in daytime in a similar fashion, the birds huddle in a
tight knot, occasionally preening each other. Flight consists
of a laboured series of flaps and swoops on short, rounded
wings, with a pronounced, dipping swoop when landing.
Birds are seen flying one after another from bush to bush.
Most of the food is taken on the ground, but occasionally
groups of birds forage in trees. A variety of prey is taken,
including worms, insects, small lizards, and
mice, as well as eggs and nestlings. The
Guira Cuckoo nests communally, with a
number of pairs building the
nest, and several females laying
their eggs in it. The group
cooperates to incubate and rear the young.
• **NEST** This bird does not parasitize
the nests of other species. A primitive
structure of twigs is built in a tree.
• **DISTRIBUTION** South America in
Bolivia, Paraguay, Brazil, and Argentina.

DISTRIBUTION

• birds
sun-
bathing
with
back
feathers
fluffed

• loose,
untidy
plumage

long
• tail

Plumage Sexes alike	Habitat	Migration Non-migrant

Family CUCULIDAE	Species *Geococcyx californianus*	Length 58cm (23in)

GREATER ROADRUNNER

With its long legs and narrow tail, this ground-dwelling cuckoo is famous for its ability to run swiftly. It lives in arid, sparsely vegetated country and is often seen hurrying across open spaces, with head and tail extended horizontally, either to snatch up prey or avoid enemies. Although it can fly, it crouches or relies on its speed when alarmed. Prey items include insects, lizards, scorpions, and young snakes. Pairs hold permanent territories, calling with a series of cooing notes.
• **NEST** Not a nest parasite; a cup nest is made, lined with debris, and placed in a cactus or thorn bush.
• **DISTRIBUTION** From S.W. USA to C. Mexico.

• *shaggy crest*

• *bare blue stripe behind the eye*

• *long, narrow tail provides balance when running and manoeuvring rapidly on the ground*

short, rounded, little-used wings •

• *long legs for fast running*

DISTRIBUTION

Plumage Sexes alike	Habitat	Migration Non-migrant

Family CUCULIDAE	Species *Carpococcyx renauldi*	Length 68cm (27in)

CORAL-BILLED GROUND-CUCKOO

This long-legged, long-tailed bird, with its compact build, is adapted for ground-dwelling in forest conditions. It lives in warm, moist forest, secondary forest (areas where the trees have regrown after forest clearance), and scrub, in lowlands and hills.

Within these habitats it prefers areas of thick vegetation, running fast to escape when danger threatens. An evasive bird, it is difficult to observe, and is thinly distributed across its range. It eats a wide range of small creatures. Calls are used to maintain contact between individuals; pairs are heard "duetting" with a harsh, deep, whistling note.
• **NEST** Not a nest parasite; a cup nest of twigs and leaves is made, in a tree or occasionally on the ground.
• **DISTRIBUTION** From N.W. Thailand to S. Vietnam.

• *long legs of a ground-dweller*

DISTRIBUTION

Plumage Sexes alike	Habitat	Migration Non-migrant

Family CUCULIDAE	Species *Centropus superciliosus*	Length 40cm (16in)

WHITE-BROWED COUCAL

Slenderly built, with a long, broad tail and strong legs, this ground-dwelling cuckoo is a bird of undergrowth. It walks and runs rapidly, pushing its way through grass and herbage, and also jumping and clambering among low branches. Although capable of flight it prefers to hide in dense vegetation. The wings are short and rounded, and flight is low, laboured, and clumsy. The White-browed Coucal lives in grassy areas with bushes, overgrown marshland vegetation, and undergrowth, usually near water. It eats a wide range of insects and small animals. The call is a distinctive bubbling sound, rising and falling in pitch.
• **NEST** A large, untidy, dome with a side entrance, made of grass, placed low above ground or water, in reeds or in a bush.
• **DISTRIBUTION** From the Nile Valley in Sudan, south through E. Africa, Angola, and Zimbabwe to South Africa.
• **REMARK** Southern subspecies lacks the white "eyebrow" and back markings.

• *rounded wings*

long, broad • tail

DISTRIBUTION

SOUTHERN SUBSPECIES

Plumage Sexes alike	Habitat	Migration Non-migrant

Family OPISTHOCOMIDAE	Species *Opisthocomus hoazin*	Length 65cm (26in)

HOATZIN

With its large, heavy body and small head, the Hoatzin is unlike the cuckoos, to which it is now thought to be closely related. It inhabits swampy forest edges bordering rivers and lakes, nesting above the water. Parties and small flocks feed on green leaves. The Hoatzin eats large quantities of these, which it stores in its crop to digest. The full crop swells up and appears to weigh the bird down, making movement awkward and flight laborious. Nestlings, if threatened, will drop into the water below the nest, in which they are able to swim; they then climb back, with the help of a claw on the forward edge of each wing.
• **NEST** A frail platform of sticks in a tree above water.
• **DISTRIBUTION** From Venezuela to Bolivia and Brazil.

spiky crest •

• *broad tail*

• *crop bulging with recently eaten leaves*

dead palm leaf •

DISTRIBUTION

Plumage Sexes alike	Habitat	Migration Non-migrant

Family TYTONIDAE	Species *Tyto alba*	Length 40cm (16in)

BARN OWL

This bird can be recognized by the "heart shape" formed by the pair of facial discs around its eyes. It has an easy, drifting style of flight, and hunts by flying low over open ground, or by watching from a perch before swooping on silent wings to seize prey. The species can hunt in total darkness, locating prey by sound. Mice, rats, and any small animals that move are eaten. The best known call is a long, quavering screech, uttered in flight, but nesting birds also make snoring, hissing calls.
• **NEST** An unlined scrape or cavity in a tree hole, or in a barn or other building.
• **DISTRIBUTION** Much of North and South America, Europe, Africa, and through S. and S.E. Asia to Australia.
• **REMARK** Colour phases (*see p. 13*) range from light to dark.

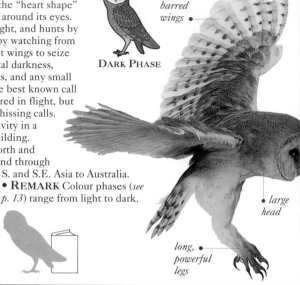

finely barred wings

DARK PHASE

large head

long, powerful legs

DISTRIBUTION

Plumage Sexes alike	Habitat	Migration Non-migrant

Family TYTONIDAE	Species *Phodilus badius*	Length 30cm (12in)

ORIENTAL BAY-OWL

A bird of thick forest, the Oriental Bay-Owl has a distinctive oval face but is difficult to observe as it hunts at night among dense branches and foliage. The facial discs are narrow, and the inner side of each disc projects forward from the head at the top. This results in two blunt projections of feathers at the upper end of the forehead, equivalent to the ear tufts of some "typical" owls (*see pp. 195–203*). The Oriental Bay-Owl occurs in dense forest and secondary forest (areas where trees have regrown after forest clearance). By day it roosts in a hole in a tree, becoming active at night, when it often relies on its hearing to hunt in complete darkness. The short, rounded wings and square tail enable it to manoeuvre through close-set young trees, and it uses its strong claws to cling to vertical stems, one foot gripping high above the other. A variety of prey is taken, including large insects, frogs, lizards, small birds, and mammals. The call is a rising phrase of musical whistles.
• **NEST** A cavity in the trunk or branch of a tree.
• **DISTRIBUTION** N. India, Sri Lanka, and through Asia to China, Borneo, and Java.

narrow facial disc

foot holds prey

DISTRIBUTION

Plumage Sexes alike	Habitat	Migration Non-migrant

Family STRIGIDAE	Species *Otus scops*	Length 20cm (8in)

EURASIAN SCOPS OWL

The streaked plumage of this tiny owl provides
camouflage as the bird roosts by day. If alarmed,
the bird stands motionless and erects its ear tufts
vertically, relying on its ability to blend into tree
bark for protection. A bird of warm, dry climates,
it hunts in open spaces, and rests in scattered trees
during the day. Flight is rapid and level, with
regular wingbeats. When hunting, the
Scops Owl swoops down from its perch
to seize prey with its feet, sometimes
landing beside it first, taking insects,
earthworms, amphibians, lizards, and
small birds. Sometimes it catches moths in
mid-air. This species is predominantly a night
hunter, but males also hunt during the day when
the females are incubating eggs or tending the young.
The call is a penetrating "tyu" note, the female's
note being a little higher in pitch than the male's.
• **NEST** An unlined hole or cavity in a tree.
• **DISTRIBUTION** S. Europe east to Russia and
W. China. Winters in N. and C. Africa, and N. India.
• **REMARK** In this species there are two distinct
colour phases (*see p. 13*): grey and rufous brown.

DISTRIBUTION

**RUFOUS
PHASE**

• *upright alarm
posture, with feathers
sleeked down*

Plumage Sexes alike	Habitat	Migration Migrant

Family STRIGIDAE	Species *Otus leucotis*	Length 28cm (11in)

WHITE-FACED SCOPS OWL

This small owl can be identified by its white face
with grey ear tufts, and large, fiery-orange eyes.
The plumage is mottled, providing camouflage
against tree bark when the bird roosts. When
alarmed it freezes into an upright posture with sleeked-down
feathers and erect ear tufts, resembling a broken-ended
branch. If provoked into a reaction it opens its eyes wide
and snaps aggressively with its bill. The White-
faced Scops Owl is a bird of savanna (tropical
and subtropical grassland) and thorn scrub, also
inhabiting open forest. It is a nocturnal hunter,
taking large insects, small rodents, and small
birds caught while roosting. The male utters a
two-note hoot, the female has a quavering trill.
• **NEST** An unlined hole in a tree, or an
old nest of various birds such as a turacos
(*see pp. 186–187*), some sparrowhawks
(*see p. 94*), or crows
(*see pp. 394–395*). Some
pairs nest on the ground.
• **DISTRIBUTION**
Africa south of the Sahara.

*ear tufts •
not fully
raised*

*large eyes with •
orange irises*

DISTRIBUTION

Plumage Sexes alike	Habitat	Migration Non-migrant

Family STRIGIDAE	Species *Otus asio*	Length 22cm (8½in)

EASTERN SCREECH-OWL

This small woodland owl roosts in tree cavities or thick foliage, and hunts such prey as insects, birds, and squirrels. Its calls are a descending series of quavering whistles, or the wailing sounds to which the name refers, or a long, sharp trill.
• **NEST** An unlined cavity in a tree.
• **DISTRIBUTION** From S. Canada through E., C., and S. USA to N.E. Mexico.
• **REMARKS** This species has two distinct colour phases (*see p. 13*): rufous and grey. This is one of the many owls that possess ear-like tufts, which can be raised or lowered; they express a bird's mood, e.g. whether excited or at rest.

• lowered ear tufts

GREY PHASE

Plumage Sexes alike	Habitat	Migration Non-migrant

Family STRIGIDAE	Species *Pulsatrix perspicillata*	Length 46cm (18in)

SPECTACLED OWL

A large and round-headed forest owl, this species has an unmistakable face pattern that accounts for its name. Even more striking is the white-bodied juvenile bird, with its black face-mask. The species lives in such habitats as thick rainforest, open woodland, and riverside bands of trees, but is nocturnal and rarely seen. Its most typical call is a series of rapid, low-pitched hoots. The Spectacled Owl roosts by day on a branch and hunts at night, being more active on moonlit nights. Prey includes insects, tree-frogs, birds, mammals, and, in mangrove forest, crabs.
• **NEST** A large hole or cavity in a tree.
• **DISTRIBUTION** From Mexico south as far as N. Argentina, Paraguay, and S. Brazil.

JUVENILE

feet arranged with • two toes forward, two toes back

Plumage Sexes alike	Habitat	Migration Non-migrant

| Family STRIGIDAE | Species *Bubo virginianus* | Length 55cm (22in) |

GREAT HORNED OWL

Largest and fiercest of the American owls, with large ear tufts and a finely barred breast, this species occurs in a range of habitats from rocky desert to broadleaved and coniferous forest. Usually hunting by night, it watches from a perch before swooping silently on its prey. It takes any prey from insect size to hares, geese, and turkeys. Its call is a series of deep, soft hoots.
• **NEST** An old nest of a large bird of prey, in a tree or on a cliff.
• **DISTRIBUTION** The Americas.
• **REMARK** Colour phases (*p. 13*) from dark to pale.

powerful feet hold prey

DISTRIBUTION   **PALE PHASE**

| Plumage Sexes alike | Habitat | Migration Non-migrant |

| Family STRIGIDAE | Species *Bubo bubo* | Length 70cm (28in) |

EURASIAN EAGLE-OWL

This powerfully built bird is the largest of the world's owls. It has prominent ear tufts and a boldly-streaked breast. Most of the rest of the plumage, too, is mottled, giving camouflage when resting. The Eurasian Eagle-Owl is found in most types of country, although it favours rocky outcrops and forests. In parts of its range it is active by day as well as night. It relies on sharp sight when hunting, taking a range of prey from insects to hares, foxes, ducks, and large gamebirds. The call is a deep hoot.
• **NEST** A hollow on a rock ledge or in a cave, or an old nest of an eagle or buzzard (*see pp. 97–99*).
• **DISTRIBUTION** Much of Europe, east to Siberia and south to India and China.
• **REMARK** There is considerable variety of colour, with phases and local subspecies (*see p. 13*), ranging from dark to light.

pupils reduced in daylight

mottled plumage

GREY SUBSPECIES

DISTRIBUTION

| Plumage Sexes alike | Habitat | Migration Non-migrant |

Family STRIGIDAE	Species *Ketupa ketupa*	Length 42cm (16½in)

BUFFY FISH-OWL

Looking like an eagle-owl (*see p. 197*) in its general appearance, this is one of the fish-owls, in which a number of features are suited to their specialized diet. The legs are bare, the soles of the feet have sharp-edged, spiky scales, and the claws are long and curved for snatching fish from water. Fish-owls lack the silent flight of other owls, whose feathers have a fine surface layer of downy strands and a downy edge, which muffle the sound of the flying bird. The wings of fish-owls make a slight noise in flight, presumably without impairing fishing ability. The Buffy Fish-Owl occurs in pairs alongside rivers, roosting in the thick foliage of trees beside water. Hunting at night, it watches from a bare branch and swoops to snatch fish from the water surface, also taking crabs, crayfish, amphibians, reptiles, birds, and some large insects. It has a soft, musical, two-note hooting call.

bare legs of a fish • catcher

• **NEST** An unlined cavity in a large tree, or an old nest of another large, tree-nesting bird.
• **DISTRIBUTION** S.E. Asia from Burma and Borneo to Java.

DISTRIBUTION

• long claws

Plumage Sexes alike	Habitat	Migration Non-migrant

Family STRIGIDAE	Species *Nyctea scandiaca*	Length 58cm (23in)

SNOWY OWL

With thick, white plumage that extends to the toes, the Snowy Owl is insulated against cold and camouflaged against snow. Living and nesting on Arctic tundra, it hunts by day as well as night. It feeds on lemmings for most of the time, occasionally taking larger prey such as hares, gulls, and ducks. The usual call is a single hoot, while barking, cackling calls are used at the nest site.
• **NEST** A shallow hollow in the ground, on a slightly raised site in open tundra.
• **DISTRIBUTION** Breeds in N. North America, Greenland, and N. Eurasia. Migrates to the southern limits of this range in years of food shortage.

insulating plumage covers • nostrils

FEMALE

DISTRIBUTION

Plumage Sexes alike	Habitat	Migration Partial migrant

Family STRIGIDAE	Species *Strix aluco*	Length 38cm (15in)

TAWNY OWL

A bird of woodland and open areas with large trees, this stout, round-headed owl roosts inconspicuously among branches or hidden in a hole. It has two calls: one is an advertisement call consisting of a short and a long hoot, while a sharp "ke-wick" call is also uttered for contact purposes. These are the sounds represented by the popular "to-whit to-whoo" imitation of an owl. The Tawny Owl is nocturnal and is able to hunt in complete darkness, using only its hearing to locate prey. The main foods are mice and voles.
• **NEST** A hollow in a tree or rock.
• **DISTRIBUTION** From Europe and N.W. Africa east to China and Korea.
• **REMARK** Three colour phases (*see p. 13*): grey, rufous brown, and dark brown.

rich, rufous plumage

downy covering on legs and feet

GREY PHASE

DISTRIBUTION

Plumage Sexes alike	Habitat	Migration Non-migrant

Family STRIGIDAE	Species *Strix varia*	Length 53cm (21in)

BARRED OWL

The large, dark eyes of this species adapt to the darkness and make use of the slightest amount of light. It is a typical owl of forest habitats, both coniferous and broadleaved, though it also hunts in more open country. It frequently occurs near water. By day it roosts in thick foliage. Like other owls, it is able to hunt in total darkness, provided the prey moves. This is made possible by the asymmetrical positioning of the owl's ear openings on either side of its head. One opening is set a little higher than the other, enabling the bird to pinpoint the source of a sound accurately, and to pounce on it. Hunting in this way, the owl catches a wide variety of prey – mainly mice and voles, though other animals, from lizards and frogs to squirrels and hares, are taken. In swampy places, it catches crayfish and fish. The species advertises its presence with a rhythmic series of four or five deep hoots.
• **NEST** The eggs are laid in an unlined cavity in a tree.
• **DISTRIBUTION** North America, mostly east of the Rockies, and the Central Plateau of Mexico to Veracruz and Oaxaca.

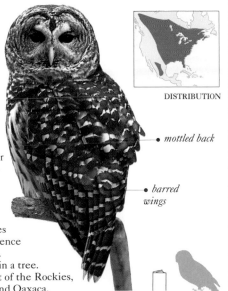

DISTRIBUTION

mottled back

barred wings

Plumage Sexes alike	Habitat	Migration Non-migrant

Family STRIGIDAE	Species *Strix nebulosa*	Length 68cm (27in)

GREAT GREY OWL

small, yellow eyes

This owl inhabits the cold forests and birch scrub of the far north. It has a round head with very large feather discs on each side of its face. The tops of these stand like bold, questioning eyebrows over the small eyes. The Great Grey Owl looks sturdy but is in fact moderately sized and slender, its large appearance being created by a deep, dense layer of feathers extending to the toes and insulating it against cold weather. This species hunts both by day and by night, watching from a perch and swooping silently to seize prey. Sometimes it plunges through deep snow in pursuit of prey. It roosts in trees, perching close to the trunk. The diet consists mainly of small voles and mice, and also of shrews and small birds.

large facial disc

dense, soft plumage

large wings

• **NEST** An old nest of another large bird in a tree, particularly a conifer; or a hollow in a large, broken tree stump.

• **DISTRIBUTION** Much of N. North America and across N. Eurasia. Some populations move south irregularly in winter.

DISTRIBUTION

Plumage Sexes alike	Habitat	Migration Partial migrant/nomadic

Family STRIGIDAE	Species *Surnia ulula*	Length 38cm (15in)

NORTHERN HAWK-OWL

With long, tapering wings, a long tail, and a low-crowned head, in outline this species resembles a hawk or a falcon. It is an active daytime hunter, and often leans forward on a conspicuous perch to watch for prey. Flight is steady and direct, with short bursts of wingbeats alternating with glides, and quick turns of agility when catching small birds in the air. The Northern Hawk-Owl usually hunts from a perch, though it will sometimes patrol slowly overhead, hover, and then drop down on to prey. Voles are its main prey, but it also takes some larger mammals. Birds are taken, more importantly in winter when other food is scarce, and are sometimes seized in flight. This species utters a deep, rolling hoot and sharp, yelping calls.

JUVENILE

typical look-out posture

long tail

• **NEST** A hole in a tree, or the old nest of another bird.

• **DISTRIBUTION** Much of N. North America and across N. Eurasia. Some birds move south in winter within this range.

DISTRIBUTION

Plumage Sexes alike	Habitat	Migration Partial migrant/nomadic

Family STRIGIDAE	Species *Athene noctua*	Length 22cm (8½in)

LITTLE OWL

This small, compact owl has a broad head, round wings, a short tail, and feathered legs. The small, wide-set facial discs combined with the low forehead give the bird a scowling expression. An occupant of open places with some cover, it is found in a variety of habitats including farmland, parks, and stony waste. It is active by day as well as by night, and is able to walk, run, and hop well. Alternating bursts of wingbeats and brief glides produce a distinctly undulating style of flight. The Little Owl hunts by sight, taking insects, small mammals including rats, and small birds.
• **NEST** A hole in a tree or rock face; a cranny in a barn or outbuilding; or a hollow in a rabbit burrow.
• **DISTRIBUTION** From Europe east to China and south into Africa.
• **REMARK** Colour phases range from dark to light

PALE DESERT FORM

small facial discs •

feathered • legs and feet

DISTRIBUTION

Plumage Sexes alike	Habitat	Migration Non-migrant

Family STRIGIDAE	Species *Speotyto cunicularia*	Length 24cm (9½in)

BURROWING OWL

Small but long-legged, this is a ground-dwelling owl of open, grassy plains. The facial discs are wide-set, and the forehead is low, imparting a permanent frown. At all times of the year, this species frequents a burrow in the ground, which is used for breeding in the season, and as a refuge at other times. Being mainly a night-time hunter, it is seen only in the vicinity of the burrow during the day, disappearing inside if alarmed. Flight is low and undulating, a series of rapid wingbeats alternating with brief glides. The Burrowing Owl hunts by swooping from a perch or from the air, or it may hover first, to drop down on to prey. It feeds mainly on insects, particularly grasshoppers and beetles, and sometimes takes lizards, snakes, mice, rats, and birds. It utters a cooing hoot and a clucking alarm note.
• **NEST** A chamber in the old burrow of a ground squirrel or other mammal, or a burrow dug by the pair, lined with stems or dry dung.
• **DISTRIBUTION** From S.W. Canada, W. USA, Florida, and Central America to S. South America.

DISTRIBUTION

• short, rounded wings

long legs for running and • walking

• short tail

Plumage Sexes alike	Habitat	Migration Partial migrant

| Family STRIGIDAE | Species *Aegolius funereus* | Length 25cm (10in) |

TENGMALM'S OWL

This small, tree-dwelling owl has large, high facial discs and close-set eyes, which combine to give it a surprised expression. It is always found in pine forest, both in densely grown tracts and in more openly spaced fringes and clearings. Its flight is level with rapid wingbeats and straight glides, manoeuvring with great skill between trees and branches. Tengmalm's Owl roosts by day in thick foliage in trees and is active at night; it also hunts by day when it has nestlings to feed. The diet consists mainly of voles and some mice, shrews, and small birds. The call is a rapid series of musical, cooing notes.

JUVENILE

- **NEST** An unlined hole in a tree, or a nest-box.
- **DISTRIBUTION** Breeds across N. Eurasia and in N. North America, and from Wyoming to New Mexico. Some birds migrate south.

DISTRIBUTION

• *short wings and tail*

| Plumage Sexes alike | Habitat | Migration Partial migrant |

| Family STRIGIDAE | Species *Ninox novaeseelandiae* | Length 35cm (14in) |

SOUTHERN BOOBOOK

With a rounded head, prominent bill, and poorly defined facial discs, this species is typical of Australasian hawk-owls. Birds live in pairs but roost singly in thick foliage. Like most nocturnal owls it is mobbed by songbirds if they find it by day. Living in any areas with trees, including suburbs and even towns, it feeds at night, eating mainly insects, and also mice, small birds, and other creatures. Its name is derived from its "boobook" call.

• *large eyes*

- **NEST** In a hole in a tree.
- **DISTRIBUTION** Timor, S. New Guinea, Australia, and New Zealand.

GREY PHASE

downcovered legs and feet •

DISTRIBUTION

| Plumage Sexes alike | Habitat | Migration Non-migrant |

Family STRIGIDAE	Species *Asio flammeus*	Length 38cm (15in)

SHORT-EARED OWL

small • ear tufts

Long-winged and with short ear tufts, this is an owl of open places, grassy plains, marshland, and dunes. In these treeless habitats it rests on the ground or perches on small mounds or posts, and roosts in sheltered hollows. On the wing it flies easily, with regular, deliberate, deep wingbeats and slow glides, the wings forming a shallow "V". It hunts in flight, often hovering briefly when it has sighted a victim. The owl seizes the prey in its feet and carries it elsewhere to be eaten. Mice and voles are the main food, but like most owls this species will take any animals, from insects to moorhens and hedgehogs.
• **NEST** A shallow hollow in the ground, made by the birds, either in the open, or in low cover such as heather.
• **DISTRIBUTION** Breeds in much of Eurasia, North America, and South America. Northern populations migrate as far south as Mexico, Africa, and India.

• long wings

• long tail

DISTRIBUTION

Plumage Sexes alike	Habitat	Migration Partial migrant

Family STEATORNITHIDAE	Species *Steatornis caripensis*	Length 48cm (19in)

OILBIRD

Adapted for feeding on the wing at night, the Oilbird has large eyes, a strong, hooked bill surrounded by sensitive bristles, long, narrow wings, and a long tail. The legs are short and weak. By day it hides in colonies on ledges in dark caves, emerging at night to snatch **FEMALE** fruit from trees such as palms. On returning to the colony, birds regurgitate the seeds, so that these cover the ledges and the cave floor. Loud, screaming and snarling calls can be heard from the hundreds of birds in the cave. Inside, the birds emit clicks, and use the echoes to find their way in the dark.
• **NEST** A mound of regurgitated seeds on a cave ledge.
• **DISTRIBUTION** From E. Panama south to Bolivia and east to Venezuela and Trinidad.

DISTRIBUTION

Plumage Sexes differ slightly	Habitat	Migration Non-migrant

Family PODARGIDAE	Species *Podargus papuensis*	Length 50cm (20in)

PAPUAN FROGMOUTH

This is one of several nocturnal birds that hide during the day by imitating the appearance of a broken-ended branch. It has finely mottled plumage, and rests on a tree branch or projecting snag with eyes closed and bill uptilted. Tail, body, head, and bill form a stiff, slanting shape like a piece of wood, and the ragged tuft on the forehead helps to break up the bird outline. The frogmouth sits motionless all day among forest foliage or on a more open perch, singly or in groups of up to four. At dusk it opens its large eyes and surveys the ground for prey. It swoops down and, instead of taking prey with its feet, opens its bill and mouth in a wide gape and scoops it from the ground. Insects are the main food, but frogs, lizards, mice, and birds are also eaten.

- **NEST** A small, flat nest made of twigs, and placed either in a tree fork or in a cavity on a large branch.
- **DISTRIBUTION** New Guinea and extreme N.E. Australia.
- **REMARK** This species has two distinct colour phases, rufous and grey.

DISTRIBUTION

typical upright posture

small legs

camouflage plumage

GREY PHASE

Plumage Sexes differ	Habitat 🌳🌳🌳	Migration Non-migrant

Family NYCTIBIIDAE	Species *Nyctibius jamaicensis*	Length 40cm (16in)

COMMON POTOO

A nocturnal, forest-dwelling bird with camouflage plumage, this is one of the species that hides during the day by imitating the appearance of a broken-ended branch. Usually solitary, it perches upright on a sloping branch or the upper end of a vertical, broken branch. It sits with head raised, eyes closed, and bill tilted upwards, looking like an extension of the branch. The bill is short and slender with a downcurved tip, but when it is opened a gaping mouth is revealed which stretches across the width of the head. The Potoo becomes active at night. Opening its large eyes, it watches intently from its perch and darts out to catch insects in the air, before returning to the perch. Its calls are a guttural "ho-wow", and a hoarse "waark-cucu". When breeding, the Common Potoo incubates its egg in a similar upright posture to that used during its normal daytime rests.

- **NEST** A single egg is laid in a bare depression or knot-hole on a branch, at the top end of a broken branch, or on a broken stump.
- **DISTRIBUTION** Jamaica, Hispaniola; from Mexico to Costa Rica.

DISTRIBUTION

upright resting posture

Plumage Sexes alike	Habitat 🌳🌳🌳 🌿🌳	Migration Non-migrant

Family AEGOTHELIDAE	Species *Aegotheles insignis*	Length 30cm (12in)

FELINE OWLET-NIGHTJAR

The long, bristling whiskers on the face of this bird resemble those of a cat, giving the species its name. A nocturnal bird of mountain forest, it roosts in tangles of vines or in tree cavities. It is thought to snatch insects from where they rest, in the foliage or branches.
• **NEST** Probably in a cavity in a tree.
• **DISTRIBUTION** New Guinea Highlands.

long, touch-sensitive bristles

BROWN PHASE

DISTRIBUTION

Plumage Sexes alike	Habitat ▲ 🏞 🌳	Migration Non-migrant

Family CAPRIMULGIDAE	Species *Chordeiles minor*	Length 24cm (9½in)

COMMON NIGHTHAWK

Grey plumage, long, tapering wings with a white patch, and a white throat band help to identify this nightjar. During the day it rests on the ground, on a post, or perched along a branch, but it begins to hunt flying insects in the late afternoon, continuing after dark. Males perform a display flight in which their vibrating wings make a roaring noise. The call is a low, nasal note.
• **NEST** Any bare, flat surface.
• **DISTRIBUTION** Breeds in North and Central America. Winters in South America to N. Argentina.

JUVENILE

small legs and feet

DISTRIBUTION

Plumage Sexes alike	Habitat ▬ 🌳	Migration Migrant

Family CAPRIMULGIDAE	Species *Eurostopodus argus*	Length 30cm (12in)

SPOTTED EARED-NIGHTJAR

The plumage of this species provides camouflage among dead leaves. It rests on the ground by day in open places, dry woodland, and scrub. At night it hunts in low flight, taking moths, beetles, and other insects. The call is a rising series of whistles.
• **NEST** A hollow in the ground.
• **DISTRIBUTION** Australia. Winters as far north as Aru Islands off New Guinea.

JUVENILE

tip of left wing

bird resting with wing tips crossed

right wing

DISTRIBUTION

Plumage Sexes alike	Habitat 🌳 ✈ ▬	Migration Migrant

Family CAPRIMULGIDAE	Species *Nyctidromus albicollis*	Length 28cm (11in)

PAURAQUE

This species lives in forest edges, secondary growth (regrown after clearance), and open scrub, nesting in more open areas. By day it rests on the ground or on a low branch where, in typical nightjar fashion, it perches lengthwise, crouching so that its tapering outline looks like a projection on the branch. It hunts by night, in low, patrolling flight or by darting out from a perch, to seize flying insects such as beetles, moths, and fireflies. In flight a white patch is revealed on each blunt-tipped wing. The Pauraque often rests on roads at night. The name

of this bird imitates its "pur-wheee" call.
- **NEST** A shallow, natural hollow in the ground, close to low-growing plants.
- **DISTRIBUTION** From S. Texas and Mexico south to Bolivia, Brazil, and N.E. Argentina.

MALE TAIL   **FEMALE TAIL**

camouflage against dead leaves

white tail stripe of male

DISTRIBUTION

Plumage Sexes differ	Habitat 🌳🌱 🏞️ ✈️	Migration Non-migrant

Family CAPRIMULGIDAE	Species *Phalaenoptilus nuttallii*	Length 20cm (8in)

COMMON POORWILL

This small nightjar has a dumpy look, being short and rounded in both wings and tail. A two-syllable whistled "poor-will" call, with a barely audible third note, gives the bird its name. Being nocturnal, the Common Poorwill is more often heard than seen. By day it rests on the ground, in desert sage brush, dry scrub, or open pinewood. At night it hunts flying insects, either cruising low above the ground or perching on the ground, on a rock, or a low branch, to watch and fly out to intercept its prey. When nesting it relies on camouflage for protection.
- **NEST** A slight depression on the ground.
- **DISTRIBUTION** Breeds in W. Canada and USA. Winters as far south as C. Mexico.
- **REMARK** One bird was found, in several successive years, apparently hibernating in a rock crevice in S.W. USA.

camouflage plumage

DISTRIBUTION

Plumage Sexes differ	Habitat ⌇ ✈️	Migration Partial migrant

Family CAPRIMULGIDAE	Species *Caprimulgus europaeus*	Length 28cm (11in)

EURASIAN NIGHTJAR

Rarely seen except when startled from its daytime resting
place, this well-camouflaged bird is best known for the
prolonged, churring note, on
a rising or falling trend, that
the breeding male utters by
night. This sound is difficult
to locate. The bird rests by
day, on the ground or lying
along a branch. By night
it chases insects silently
in quick, erratic flight.
The species favours open
sites close to trees, where the
ground is covered with leaves and twigs.
• **NEST** A piece of open ground,
usually close to trees or bushes.
• **DISTRIBUTION** Eurasia and
N. Africa, east to China. Winters
as far as South
Africa.

• *white wing
patch of male*

FEMALE

Plumage Sexes differ	Habitat	Migration Migrant

Family CAPRIMULGIDAE	Species *Macrodipteryx longipennis*	Length 23cm (9in)

STANDARD-WINGED NIGHTJAR

The breeding male of this species has one of the most startling
forms of display plumage of all birds. Having evolved to fly
in poor light at dusk and dawn, nightjars generally tend
to display by flying erratically or by showing unusual
white patches or shapes. In this case, a huge feather
grows from the middle of each wing. Seen in flight, these
appear as two long, slender shafts, each supporting a big,
flag-like vane at the tip. In display, the male circles above
the female with vibrating wingbeats, raising his two large
feathers. These feathers are lost after the breeding season.
The Standard-winged Nightjar occurs in dry, stony
country with scattered bushes. By day it rests on the
ground, where it lies unnoticed unless disturbed.
At night it catches insects on the wing. It advertises
its presence to females and rival
males with a shrill, churring call.
• **NEST** A slight, natural hollow
in a bare piece of open ground.
• **DISTRIBUTION** Africa south
of the Sahara, from Senegal east
to Ethiopia; isolated population
in Uganda and W. Kenya.

FEMALE

• *feather
vane*

Plumage Sexes differ	Habitat	Migration Migrant

Family APODIDAE	Species *Tachymarptis melba*	Length 22cm (8½in)

ALPINE SWIFT

This very large swift is recognizable in the air, where size comparisons are difficult, by its white belly. A powerful flier, it frequents mountain crags, large rock outcrops, and tall buildings, which provide sites for nesting colonies. Unlike the Common Swift, it often roosts at the nest site. The call is a long, trilling scream. The diet consists entirely of insects caught in flight.

• **NEST** A cup nest of plant debris and feathers, glued with saliva, on a ledge or in a crevice.

• **DISTRIBUTION** Breeds in S. Europe and through E. Africa to the Cape. Northern birds winter in India and Africa.

DISTRIBUTION

JUVENILE

• *distinctive white belly patch*

Plumage Sexes alike	Habitat	Migration Migrant

Family APODIDAE	Species *Apus apus*	Length 17cm (6¾in)

COMMON SWIFT

Often seen circling in fast flight around its breeding colonies, this species never comes down to rest except when nesting. Among the most permanently airborne of birds, it even mates and sleeps on the wing. The natural nest site is a hole among rocks or in a cliff, but the species has very largely taken to nesting in the roof space of houses or in holes in walls. To feed, the swift flies along with its small bill open, revealing a very wide, gaping mouth, in which insects are caught in the air. Prey caught for the young is stored in a pouch below the tongue. The Common Swift even drinks in flight, skimming low over lakes and rivers to scoop up water in its bill.

• **NEST** A shallow cup nest of plant debris, and feathers caught drifting in the air, stuck together with saliva, and placed on a ledge or in a hole.

• **DISTRIBUTION** Much of Europe east to North India, Mongolia and China. Winters in tropical and southern Africa.

DISTRIBUTION

• *long, tapering wings for sustained flight*

long, slender body

tail is forked when not spread out

Plumage Sexes alike	Habitat	Migration Migrant

Family APODIDAE	Species *Hirundapus caudacutus*	Length 20cm (8in)

WHITE-THROATED NEEDLETAIL

A squarely built swift with long, slender, curving wings and a short body, the White-throated Needletail has projecting spiny tips on the short tail feathers, to which its name refers. In flight it reveals its white throat and a curved white mark at the rear of the belly. It occurs singly or in small parties, catching insects on the wing and uttering screaming calls.
• **NEST** A shallow half-cup in a crevice or a hollow treetrunk.
• **DISTRIBUTION** Breeds in Asia and the Himalayas. Winters as far south as New Zealand.

DISTRIBUTION

JUVENILE

Plumage Sexes alike	Habitat	Migration Migrant

Family APODIDAE	Species *Chaetura pelagica*	Length 13cm (5in)

CHIMNEY SWIFT

This small swift has long wings and a short, square tail. It lives and nests in flocks. Birds roost by clinging inside chimneys or hollow trees, where they also nest. They are extremely agile in flight, uttering short, twittering calls. At the nesting colonies, extra adults often help to feed the young.
• **NEST** A half-cup made of twig fragments, glued together with saliva, inside a chimney or hollow tree.
• **DISTRIBUTION** Breeds in E. Canada and USA. Winters as far south as N.E. Peru.

long, slender
• wings

• short, square tail

DISTRIBUTION

• nest twigs glued with saliva

Plumage Sexes alike	Habitat	Migration Migrant

Family HEMIPROCNIDAE	Species *Hemiprocne longipennis*	Length 23cm (9in)

GREY-RUMPED TREE-SWIFT

Unlike most swifts, this tree-swift perches on twigs in treetops to rest. It hunts insects, either in darting sallies from a perch, or in cruising flight. It often occurs in small flocks but nesting pairs defend their territory aggressively. Flight consists of bursts of rapid wingbeats and glides on slightly lowered wings.
• **NEST** A tiny cup for the single egg, placed alongside a twig on which the bird sits to incubate it.
• **DISTRIBUTION** Malay Peninsula, and Sumatra, Borneo, Java, Bali, and Sulawesi in Indonesia.

typical upright
• posture

DISTRIBUTION

long, forked tail •

JUVENILE

Plumage Sexes alike	Habitat	Migration Non-migrant

Family TROCHILIDAE	Species *Phaethornis guy*	Length 13cm (5in)

GREEN HERMIT

This small hummingbird is called a hermit because it usually occurs singly and inconspicuously, on low perches in damp forest undergrowth. It visits a series of feeding places, sometimes quite far off, to take nectar from flowers, and also eats small insects.
• **NEST** A long cup nest of plant fibres, tapering to a tail, and bound with spiders' webs to the inner tip of a leaf or palm frond.
• **DISTRIBUTION** From Costa Rica south as far as Peru. Also occurs on the island of Trinidad.

• slender, curved bill

• shaggy chin feathers

• glossy green plumage

DISTRIBUTION

• tapering tail feathers

Plumage Sexes differ	Habitat	Migration Non-migrant

Family TROCHILIDAE	Species *Eutoxeres aquila*	Length 12cm (4¾in)

WHITE-TIPPED SICKLEBILL

The down-curving, strong bill of this small hummingbird is designed for probing deep into the curved, tubular flowers of plants such as Heliconias. The shape of the bill makes hovering awkward, so instead the bird clambers over the flowerheads on strong feet. White-tipped Sicklebills occur in rainforest shrubs or at the forest edge.
• **NEST** A long, tapering cup nest of palm fibres, bound to the tip of a leaf with spiders' webs, often over water.
• **DISTRIBUTION** Forest zone from Costa Rica to N. Peru.

DISTRIBUTION

• typical short leg of a hummingbird

Plumage Sexes alike	Habitat	Migration Non-migrant

Family TROCHILIDAE	Species *Colibri coruscans*	Length 12cm (4¾in)

SPARKLING VIOLET-EAR

Occurring in open places with trees, this active bird protects a territory around flowering plants and trees, chasing away competitors with a rapid, buzzing attack. It takes nectar from flowers and catches tiny insects in the air. Sitting on a high, bare twig, it repeats a quick "tsip" note. The display flight is a steep climb and a swoop back to the perch.
• **NEST** A small, open cup nest of down and moss, bound with spiders' webs and fixed to a horizontal twig, not far above the ground.
• **DISTRIBUTION** From Venezuela to Argentina.

tiny • feet

glossy green • plumage

DISTRIBUTION

Plumage Sexes alike	Habitat	Migration Non-migrant

Family TROCHILIDAE	Species *Stephanoxis lalandi*	Length 9cm (3½in)

BLACK-BREASTED PLOVERCREST

The male of this species has a long, wispy crest that is barely apparent at a distance. This is an undergrowth-dwelling bird, feeding on nectar and insects. Males display in groups of scattered individuals, each singing from his own perch in a bush.
• **NEST** A tiny cup nest made of plant fibres and spider's webs, attached to a horizontal twig close to the ground.
• **DISTRIBUTION** S.E. Brazil to N.E. Argentina.

DISTRIBUTION

• *horizontal wingbeat of hovering bird*

FEMALE

Plumage Sexes alike	Habitat 🌳🌳🌳 🌿 🌿🌿 🏞	Migration Non-migrant

Family TROCHILIDAE	Species *Discosura longicauda*	L. 9.5cm (3¾in)/7.5cm (3in)

RACQUET-TAILED COQUETTE

The two elongated tail feathers of the male make this tiny bird appear slightly larger. Living in lowland rainforest, it is rarely seen as it feeds on small, open flowers high in the foliage canopy, taking nectar with its short bill. Males show off their distinctive tail feathers in display flights.
• **NEST** A tiny cup nest, bound with spider's webs, in a twig fork at the forest edge.
• **DISTRIBUTION** Two populations; one in S. Venezuela and the Guianas, one in E. Brazil.

long, bare shafts of outer tail feathers

DISTRIBUTION

decorative discs of feather vane

FEMALE

Plumage Sexes differ	Habitat 🌳🌳🌳 🌿	Migration Non-migrant

Family TROCHILIDAE	Species *Thalurania furcata*	Length 9.5cm (3¾in)

FORK-TAILED WOODNYMPH

A solitary and territorially aggressive hummingbird, this species lives in undergrowth, in tropical forest and at the forest edge. It feeds on low-growing flowers and also on insects, taken from plants or caught in the air. The broad, forked tail is conspicuous in flight.
• **NEST** A little cup nest made of plant down and spider's webs, saddling a small fork or twig, situated low in a bush.
• **DISTRIBUTION** From Venezuela to Brazil and Argentina.

glistening green breast

FEMALE

DISTRIBUTION

• *bird resting on one foot*

Plumage Sexes differ	Habitat 🌳🌳🌳 🌿 🏞	Migration Non-migrant

Family TROCHILIDAE	Species *Trochilus polytmus*	L. 25cm (10in)/11cm (4¼in)

STREAMERTAIL

With its black cap, tapering, pointed
crest and long tail streamers, the male of this
species is highly distinctive. The Streamertail
feeds on nectar and small insects. As a bird
of gardens and sunlit forest clearings, it has
benefited from forest clearance, which has
created more of its habitat. It has a loud,
repetitive "tee-tee-tee" call and often
performs a sideways-dancing display flight.
• **NEST** A cup nest of plant fibres and plant
down, on a level branch, usually in a shrub.
• **DISTRIBUTION** Jamaica.

• *low, tapering crest*

wavy outer tail • feathers

FEMALE

DISTRIBUTION

Plumage Sexes differ	Habitat	Migration Non-migrant

Family TROCHILIDAE	Species *Topaza pella*	L. 19cm (7½in)/15cm (6in)

CRIMSON TOPAZ

A vividly coloured bird occurring alongside streams
in seasonally flooded rainforest, the Crimson Topaz is
rare within its range. It feeds in middle and upper levels
of the forest, taking nectar from a variety of
flowers and also catching small insects. The
glistening plumage is shown
off in a frontal display.
• **NEST** A cup nest,
on a branch over a stream.
• **DISTRIBUTION**
Two populations: one from
S.E. Venezuela to N. Brazil,
the other in E. Ecuador.

FEMALE

• *bright colour under the wing*

glossy underside displayed when the bird hovers

DISTRIBUTION

Plumage Sexes differ	Habitat	Migration Non-migrant

Family TROCHILIDAE	Species *Polytmus guainumbi*	Length 10cm (4in)

WHITE-TAILED GOLDENTHROAT

This is a bird of open, grassy places, including marshy grassland
and areas with scattered shrubs. One of the less vividly coloured
hummingbirds, it feeds in low foliage, hovering to take nectar
from flowers or to pick insects from leaves. It sings a high,
three-note phrase from the top of a bush.
• **NEST** A tapering, cone-shaped
cup nest made of fine plant
material, placed low
in a bush or in grass
and weeds, often
over water.
• **DISTRIBUTION**
Venezuela to S. Brazil.

feathers ruffled during • preening

• pink rump

white tail- • tip

FEMALE

DISTRIBUTION

Plumage Sexes differ	Habitat	Migration Non-migrant

Family TROCHILIDAE	Species *Oreotrochilus estella*	Length 14cm (5½in)

ANDEAN HILLSTAR

A bird of high mountains, this species lives in the sparse vegetation and grassland of the Puna Plateau in the Andes. It becomes torpid (inactive, maintaining a reduced body temperature) to conserve energy and survive during cold nights, reviving and becoming active in warm sunlight. In open, windy places it uses its strong feet to cling to branches instead of hovering to feed. It takes nectar from flowers, also catching insects. Andean Hillstars are unusual for their territorial behaviour. The females hold permanent territories, where nesting takes place, and after nesting the males move out and live elsewhere, usually at higher altitude.

• **NEST** A thick-walled cup nest of moss, plant down, and lichens, suspended under a cliff overhang, in a cave, or under house eaves.

• **DISTRIBUTION** Andes from Peru to Argentina and Chile.

DISTRIBUTION

iridescent throat patch looks black or green depending on angle of view

dark belly

FEMALE

Plumage Sexes differ	Habitat ▲	Migration Non-migrant

Family TROCHILIDAE	Species *Patagonia gigas*	Length 23cm (9in)

GIANT HUMMINGBIRD

When seen in flight, this dull-coloured hummingbird looks more like a martin or a swift with a long bill. Its wingbeats are slower, and more visible, than those of other hummingbirds as it hovers, bat-like, in front of a flower to take nectar. It often perches to feed. This is an aggressive bird that will chase other species away from its feeding sites. Like other hummingbird species, it also eats small insects. A bird of semi-open scrub in the more arid parts of the Andes, at altitudes where the climate is temperate, it also frequents cultivated areas. Its size helps it to withstand the low temperatures in the mountains; having less surface area relative to body size than the smaller hummingbirds, it is better able to conserve its body heat. In some parts of their range, Giant Hummingbirds move down to lower altitudes during cold weather.

• **NEST** A small cup nest made of moss and lichens, placed on top of a level branch, or sometimes on a cactus stem. The nest appears too small for a bird of this size.

• **DISTRIBUTION** Andes from Ecuador to Chile, and in lowlands in W. Argentina.

• **REMARK** The largest hummingbird

pale rump

tiny feet

DISTRIBUTION

Plumage Sexes differ	Habitat	Migration Non-migrant

Family TROCHILIDAE	Species *Ensifera ensifera*	Length 25cm (10in)

SWORD-BILLED HUMMINGBIRD

The long, slender bill of this species doubles its total length, and when the bird perches to rest it tilts back its head and slants the bill steeply upwards, the more easily to support its weight. This is also the typical angle at which the bill is inserted into the large, hanging, trumpet-shaped flowers of *Datura* and similar plant species. These plants provide the bird with nectar and pollen for food, and are pollinated in return. The bird also manages to catch insects in its bill in flight.

iridescent breast and belly •

tiny feet extended for landing •

• *iridescent patch under the wing*

iridescent underside of • *tail feathers*

• *tail spread for landing*

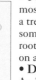

• **NEST** A small cup nest of moss, usually set on a twig in a tree at the forest edge, or sometimes suspended in root fibres exposed on a steep slope.

• **DISTRIBUTION** Andes from Venezuela south to Bolivia.

DISTRIBUTION

Plumage Sexes differ	Habitat ▲ 🌳 🏔	Migration Non-migrant

Family TROCHILIDAE	Species *Ocreatus underwoodii*	L. 12cm (4¾in)/7.5cm (3in)

BOOTED RACQUET-TAIL

The thick, fluffy feathers around the legs of this bird become conspicuous in flight. Although both sexes have these feathers only the male has the long tail ending in small, rounded "racquets". The birds are seen weaving in and out of the foliage in fast, bee-like flight. They stop to hover before a flower, the fast-beating wings producing a deep hum. With their short bills, Booted Racquet-tails prefer tree flowers that lack petal tubes. In these flowers, nectar and pollen are within easy reach at the surface. Birds sometimes cling to flowers to feed. While feeding, they utter soft, twittering calls. The species occurs in the more open types of forest environment, including the forest edge, feeding from shrub height up to the canopy.

fluffy leg • *feathering ("boots")*

FEMALE

bare shafts of outer • *tail feathers*

rounded feather • *vanes*

DISTRIBUTION

• **NEST** A tiny cup nest of plant down and spider's webs, placed on top of a level twig.
• **DISTRIBUTION** Andes from Venezuela south to Bolivia.

Plumage Sexes differ	Habitat 🌳 🏔 ⛰	Migration Non-migrant

Family TROCHILIDAE	Species *Sappho sparganura*	L. 19cm (7½in)/13cm (5in)

RED-TAILED COMET

This is a bird of the arid scrub and open woodland at the upper limits of forest on the Andes. Both sexes have long, forked tails with black-tipped, red feathers.

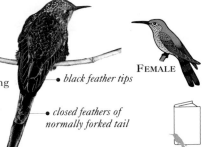

The Comet hovers to feed, preferring red flowers. It often fans and waves its tail up and down while perching.
• **NEST** A cup nest of plant fibres and moss, on a sheltered ledge or niche of a rock face, wall, or tree.
• **DISTRIBUTION** Andes from Bolivia to N.W. Argentina.

FEMALE

• *black feather tips*

• *closed feathers of normally forked tail*

• *black feather tips*

DISTRIBUTION

Plumage Sexes differ	Habitat	Migration Non-migrant

Family TROCHILIDAE	Species *Ramphomicron microrhynchum*	Length 8cm (3¼in)

PURPLE-BACKED THORNBILL

An unusually short bill for a hummingbird, and the male's shining, purple back, help to identify this diminutive bird. It lives at the forest edge and in open, grassy areas with scattered trees, and is a sociable feeder, visiting flowering trees to take nectar and pollen alongside other individuals and other hummingbird species. Normally hovering to feed, it occasionally also clings to flowers. Insects are caught by gleaning through foliage, or hunted on the wing.
• **NEST** A cup nest of plant down, on a twig.
• **DISTRIBUTION** Andes from Venezuela and Colombia as far south as Bolivia.

tiny, short bill

DISTRIBUTION

rounded tail

FEMALE

Plumage Sexes differ	Habitat	Migration Non-migrant

Family TROCHILIDAE	Species *Heliomaster squamosus*	Length 10cm (4in)

STRIPE-BREASTED STARTHROAT

Green and violet iridescence on the crown and throat, and a dark breast illuminated by a vertical white stripe, feature in the Starthroat's hovering, frontal display. It is a bird of woodland edges, scrub, and tall grass with scattered trees. Usually solitary, it is seen resting towards the tip of an exposed dead twig in a tree. Besides nectar, it takes insects in flight.
• **NEST** A shallow cup nest, made of plant material and spider's webs, placed on the top of a twig.
• **DISTRIBUTION** E. Brazil.

horizontally beating wings as bird lands

DISTRIBUTION

spread tail

Plumage Sexes differ	Habitat	Migration Non-migrant

| Family TROCHILIDAE | Species *Archilochus colubris* | Length 9cm (3½in) |

RUBY-THROATED HUMMINGBIRD

This migrant species visits birdfeeders
and garden flowers in summer. Besides its
main diet of nectar, it takes insects and spiders.
• **NEST** A small cup nest made of plant down,
bound with spider's webs
and covered with lichen.
• **DISTRIBUTION** Breeds in
E. North America.
Winters in
S. Florida,
Central
America.

iridescent throat patch

bird holds position accurately in hovering flight

DISTRIBUTION

FEMALE

| Plumage Sexes differ | Habitat | Migration Migrant |

| Family TROCHILIDAE | Species *Calypte anna* | Length 9.5cm (3¾in) |

ANNA'S HUMMINGBIRD

Living in woodlands, gardens, and scrub,
this bird feeds on nectar and insects. Males
have a red head, females a red-flecked throat.
• **NEST** A cup nest of
stems, plant down, and
feathers, bound with spiders'
webs, and placed on
a level twig.
• **DISTRIBUTION**
Breeds in W. USA.
Winters as far south as Mexico.

iridescent ear patch

iridescent throat patch

inner flight feathers curve forwards as bird hovers

DISTRIBUTION

FEMALE

| Plumage Sexes alike | Habitat | Migration Non-migrant |

| Family TROCHILIDAE | Species *Stellula calliope* | Length 8cm (3¼in) |

CALLIOPE HUMMINGBIRD

This is North America's smallest bird,
occurring by streams in canyons, upland
meadows, and conifer forest. It takes nectar,
mainly from red flowers.
• **NEST** A small, lichen-covered
cup on a twig in a bush or low tree.
• **DISTRIBUTION**
Breeds in W. USA.
Winters as far
south as
Mexico.

light green crown and back

elongated, iridescent feathers

feet held under the belly in flight

DISTRIBUTION

FEMALE

| Plumage Sexes differ | Habitat | Migration Migrant |

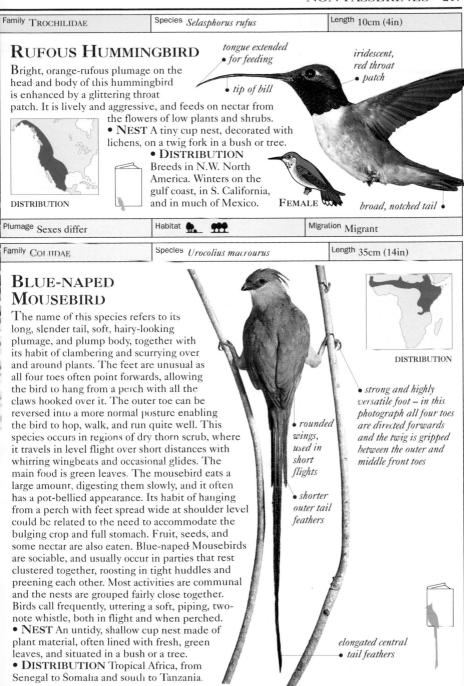

| Family TROCHILIDAE | Species *Selasphorus rufus* | Length 10cm (4in) |

RUFOUS HUMMINGBIRD

tongue extended • for feeding

tip of bill

iridescent, red throat • patch

Bright, orange-rufous plumage on the head and body of this hummingbird is enhanced by a glittering throat patch. It is lively and aggressive, and feeds on nectar from the flowers of low plants and shrubs.

• **NEST** A tiny cup nest, decorated with lichens, on a twig fork in a bush or tree.

• **DISTRIBUTION** Breeds in N.W. North America. Winters on the gulf coast, in S. California, and in much of Mexico.

DISTRIBUTION

FEMALE

broad, notched tail •

| Plumage Sexes differ | Habitat | Migration Migrant |

| Family COLIIDAE | Species *Urocolius macrourus* | Length 35cm (14in) |

BLUE-NAPED MOUSEBIRD

DISTRIBUTION

The name of this species refers to its long, slender tail, soft, hairy-looking plumage, and plump body, together with its habit of clambering and scurrying over and around plants. The feet are unusual as all four toes often point forwards, allowing the bird to hang from a perch with all the claws hooked over it. The outer toe can be reversed into a more normal posture enabling the bird to hop, walk, and run quite well. This species occurs in regions of dry thorn scrub, where it travels in level flight over short distances with whirring wingbeats and occasional glides. The main food is green leaves. The mousebird eats a large amount, digesting them slowly, and it often has a pot-bellied appearance. Its habit of hanging from a perch with feet spread wide at shoulder level could be related to the need to accommodate the bulging crop and full stomach. Fruit, seeds, and some nectar are also eaten. Blue-naped Mousebirds are sociable, and usually occur in parties that rest clustered together, roosting in tight huddles and preening each other. Most activities are communal and the nests are grouped fairly close together. Birds call frequently, uttering a soft, piping, two-note whistle, both in flight and when perched.

• strong and highly versatile foot – in this photograph all four toes are directed forwards and the twig is gripped between the outer and middle front toes

• rounded wings, used in short flights

• shorter outer tail feathers

• **NEST** An untidy, shallow cup nest made of plant material, often lined with fresh, green leaves, and situated in a bush or a tree.

• **DISTRIBUTION** Tropical Africa, from Senegal to Somalia and south to Tanzania.

elongated central • tail feathers

| Plumage Sexes alike | Habitat | Migration Non-migrant |

Family TROGONIDAE	Species *Trogon curucui*	Length 24cm (9½in)

BLUE-CROWNED TROGON

In spite of its bright plumage, this is an inconspicuous, forest-dwelling bird with soft, dense plumage, a stout bill, small, weak feet, and an upright, watchful posture. It is uncommon, living in lowland rainforest, and tall secondary growth (areas where the trees have regrown after forest clearance). Perching in the middle or lower levels of forest vegetation, it sits quietly for long periods. The diet consists of fruit and insects. The bird watches for an insect from a perch, then swoops out, hovers momentarily with a flutter of wings, snatches the insect, and takes it back to the perch. The song is a series of "kyou" notes, accelerating and then stopping abruptly. There is also a low, purring call.
• **NEST** A cavity in a tree, or a woodpecker hole, or a hole excavated by the bird in rotten wood or a tree-termite nest.
• **DISTRIBUTION** From Colombia and N.W. Brazil as far south as Peru, Bolivia, Paraguay, and N.E. Argentina.

DISTRIBUTION

barred outer tail feathers covering dark
• *inner feathers*

FEMALE

Plumage Sexes differ	Habitat 🌳🌳	Migration Non-migrant

Family TROGONIDAE	Species *Apaloderma narina*	Length 32cm (12½in)

NARINA TROGON

Sitting motionless for long periods on an open branch, this quiet bird is inconspicuous in the upper levels of forest. It is mainly a solitary bird although pairs sometimes perch near each other. The diet consists of insects, particularly caterpillars. The bird flies out to seize an insect from foliage or a twig while hovering, afterwards returning to its perch. Insects are also sometimes chased and caught in mid-air, and at times the bird creeps along branches in search of prey. Usually the flight is direct and heavy but the bird is capable of fast, twisting movements when chasing insects in flight. The Narina Trogon sometimes joins the mixed-species flocks of birds that hunt insects through the forest. The male bird utters a soft, rapidly repeated, dove-like "coo", while flexing his tail up and down.
• **NEST** An unlined, natural cavity in a treetrunk, branch, or dead stump.
• **DISTRIBUTION** Forested regions of Africa south of the Sahara.

pale markings on the face

• *mottled grey wings*

FEMALE

• *white outer tail feathers*

DISTRIBUTION

Plumage Sexes differ	Habitat 🌳🌳 🌿	Migration Non-migrant

Family TROGONIDAE	Species *Harpactes diardii*	Length 30cm (12in)

DIARD'S TROGON

A quiet and inconspicuous bird, Diard's Trogon is widely distributed but nowhere common in the forested lowlands where it lives. It has the rounded wings and long tail with square-tipped feathers that are typical of the trogons but, as in other Asiatic species, its back is rufous-brown instead of green. Usually occurring in pairs, it perches on bare branches in the middle and lower levels of forest foliage. Here it sits upright and motionless for long periods, except for slight, watchful movements of the head. When pursuing small insects such as beetles and moths, it moves in rapid and agile flight among branches and vines. The prey is grabbed with a quick movement and a loud flutter of wings, before the bird returns to the perch. Diard's Trogon also snatches insects from leaves or twigs while it flies.

short, very • broad bill

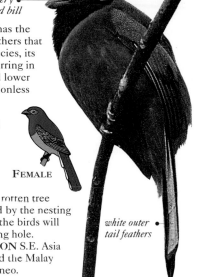

FEMALE

white outer • tail feathers

• **NEST** An unlined hole in a rotten tree stump, excavated by the nesting pair. Sometimes the birds will enlarge an existing hole.
• **DISTRIBUTION** S.E. Asia from Sumatra and the Malay Peninsula to Borneo.

DISTRIBUTION

Plumage Sexes differ	Habitat 🌳	Migration Non-migrant

Family ALCEDINIDAE	Species *Megaceryle alcyon*	Length 33cm (13in)

BELTED KINGFISHER

short, shaggy crest •

A big, shaggy-headed kingfisher with mainly blue-grey and white plumage, this is a conspicuous bird of rivers, ponds, and streams. It is seen in unsteady-looking flight along streams, or pausing to sit on a prominent perch. From here it watches the water below and when a fish or other moving creature is sighted, the bird plunge-dives to seize it, often first hovering briefly. Fish are carried to the perch, slapped against it, then swallowed head first.
• **NEST** An upward-slanting burrow in a bank beside water, up to 5m (16½ft) long.
• **DISTRIBUTION** Breeds in North America. Winters as far south as N. South America.

• grey breast band

barred • outer tail feathers

• white spots on tips of covert feathers

• chestnut flanks of female

DISTRIBUTION

MALE

Plumage Sexes differ	Habitat 〰️	Migration Migrant

Family ALCEDINIDAE	Species *Ceryle rudis*	Length 28cm (11in)

PIED KINGFISHER

Boldly patterned in black and white, with a short, shaggy crest, this conspicuous plunge-diving bird frequents waters of many kinds, from coasts and rivers to inland marshes. It usually hunts in flight, pausing and hovering, with body almost vertical and head looking down, before plunging to catch a fish, crustacean, or large insect. This bird is noisy, with high-pitched, squeaky calls.

• **NEST** A burrow in a sandy bank, with a layer of regurgitated fish scales and bones.

• **DISTRIBUTION** Much of Africa, Middle East, India, and S.E. Asia.

shaggy crest in partly raised position

long, tapering bill of a plunge-diver •

• incomplete breast band of male

FEMALE

• uptilted tail

• long wing used in hovering flight

DISTRIBUTION

Plumage Sexes differ	Habitat 〰〰 〰〰	Migration Non-migrant

Family ALCEDINIDAE	Species *Dacelo novaeguineae*	Length 45cm (17½in)

LAUGHING KOOKABURRA

Largest of the kingfishers, this bird occurs in dry country, well away from water. It lives in open forest and woodland, where it swoops down from its perch to snatch insects, lizards, snakes, rodents, and small birds. Young birds stay with their parents for several years as "nest helpers". Pairs and their helpers utter cackling calls, with heads stretched up and tails raised, to advertise possession of their territory. The bird's name is an imitation of these calls.

• **NEST** An unlined cavity in a trunk or branch.

• **DISTRIBUTION** E. and S.W. Australia.

blunt, heavy • bill

• dark eyestripe

• blue-tipped wing coverts

MALE

white tips of outer tail feathers •

• small feet used mainly for perching

FEMALE

DISTRIBUTION

Plumage Sexes differ	Habitat 🌳🌳 ✈	Migration Non-migrant

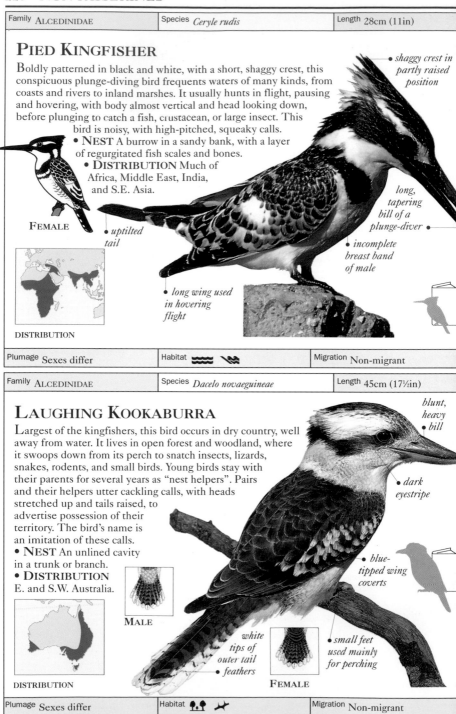

Family ALCEDINIDAE	Species *Dacelo tyro*	Length 33cm (13in)

SPANGLED KOOKABURRA

This is a large, thicket-dwelling kingfisher
with spectacular plumage. It is common within
its range, occurring in monsoon forest, at the fringes
of swamps, and in thickets in savanna (tropical
grassland). Usually it perches low in a bush
or tree, scanning the ground for food. It feeds
on a variety of invertebrates, including beetles,
ants, and stick insects. This bird is sometimes
seen in small flocks and it is possible
that, like its Australian relatives,
the Spangled Kookaburra has a complex
social system that includes "helpers"
at the nest. The call is a gurgling
noise, followed by a rattling, even-pitched
laugh. Birds also utter a single, loud "kurk" note.

• **NEST** A hole in the
side of a tree-termite
nest, often as much as 5m
(16½ft) above the ground.
• **DISTRIBUTION**
Lowlands in S. New
Guinea and the Aru Islands
(off S.W. New Guinea).

DISTRIBUTION

spangled
pattern made
by white
• feather tips

bright blue
wing
• coverts

• short
legs, used
mainly for
perching

Plumage Sexes alike	Habitat	Migration Non-migrant

Family ALCEDINIDAE	Species *Halcyon malimbica*	Length 28cm (11in)

BLUE-BREASTED KINGFISHER

Typical of thicket-dwelling kingfishers, this bird is stoutly
built, with a shorter and blunter bill than those of plunge-
diving species. It lives in forests bordering open country,
also occurring in mature secondary forest (where trees
have regrown after forest clearance) and in mangrove
swamps. Watching from a perch, it swoops down
to take insects and other small creatures. It will
occasionally dive for fish. The usual call is
a far-carrying series of 7–10 slow, plaintive
whistling notes, falling in pitch and volume.
• **NEST** An unlined cavity, bored in the
side of a tree-termite nest.
• **DISTRIBUTION**
Tropical W. Africa.

bright blue
wing patch •

DISTRIBUTION

stout bill •
with upwardly
curved lower
mandible

• two toes are partly
joined, giving a broader
base for perching

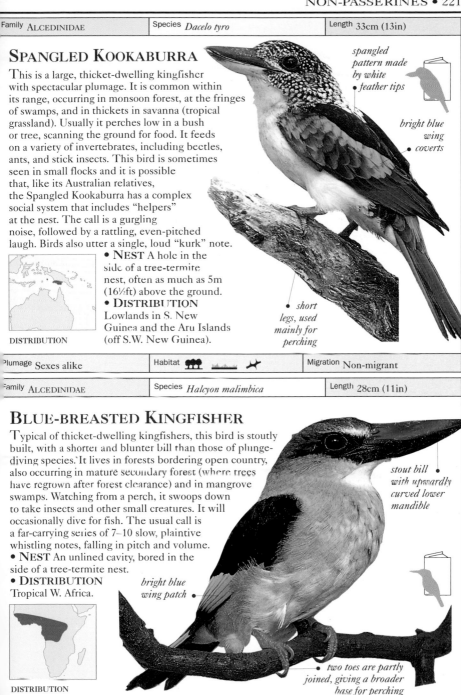

Plumage Sexes differ	Habitat	Migration Non-migrant

Family ALCEDINIDAE	Species *Alcedo atthis*	Length 16cm (6¼in)

COMMON KINGFISHER

Small and active, this kingfisher hunts
along streams and on the banks of
rivers and lakes. It moves in fast,
direct flight, revealing a bright
blue rump patch. Watching
from a perch, it plunges into
the water to take small fish or crustaceans, returning
to the perch to swallow them. It has a short, shrill call.
• **NEST** An upward-sloping tunnel in a bank near water.
• **DISTRIBUTION** Eurasia and N. Africa east to
Japan and south to Indonesia and S.W. Pacific;
northern birds migrate south within this range.

• white ear tuft

DISTRIBUTION

Plumage Sexes alike	Habitat 〰️ 🌿	Migration Partial migrant

Family ALCEDINIDAE	Species *Ceyx rufidorsa*	Length 14cm (5½in)

RUFOUS-BACKED KINGFISHER

This vivid little kingfisher lives
in lowland rainforests, where it is
often concealed in the undergrowth. It occurs beside
streams, pools, and puddles that lie half-hidden by
foliage. In flight, the lilac rump patch is conspicuous.
The bird flies low and rapidly along streams, or through
vegetation, alighting on any convenient perch over water.
It plunges into water after small fish, crustaceans, or aquatic
insects, or seizes insects and other invertebrates on land.
• **NEST** A deep tunnel in a bank near water, in forest.
• **DISTRIBUTION** Malaysia, Indonesia, Philippines.

DISTRIBUTION

lilac rump • patch

Plumage Sexes alike	Habitat 🌳 〰️ 🌲	Migration Non-migrant

Family ALCEDINIDAE	Species *Todirhamphus chloris*	Length 28cm (11in)

WHITE-COLLARED KINGFISHER

With a wide distribution in the
tropics, this adaptable kingfisher lives in
a number of habitats including inland open
woodland and farmland, rainforest, and mangrove
swamps. Its flight is fast and direct. When feeding, it
swoops from a perch to take prey on land or in water,
taking any small animals from fish and crabs to frogs
and lizards. The call is a loud, repetitive "ke-kik".
• **NEST** A burrow in a bank, or a hole in a tree or termite nest.
• **DISTRIBUTION** Isolated areas from E. Africa to W. India; much of
S.E. Asia and New Guinea; N. and E. Australia and islands in S.W. Pacific.

• black eyestripe

• white neck band

DISTRIBUTION

Plumage Sexes alike	Habitat 🏞️ 🌿 〰️ 🌿	Migration Partial migrant

Family TODIDAE	Species *Todus todus*	Length 9cm (3½in)

JAMAICAN TODY

Small and rounded, with a plump body but
small feet, this is a hunter that sits and waits for
prey. It watches from an exposed perch and darts
out to catch passing insects or snatch them from
the undersides of overhanging leaves. The call is
a short "cherek". Todies live singly or in pairs,
and defend territories
on wooded hillsides.
• **NEST** A small burrow up to
30cm (12in) into a low bank.
• **DISTRIBUTION**
Occurs only in Jamaica.

large head

DISTRIBUTION

typical tody posture with uptilted bill

JUVENILE

Plumage Sexes alike	Habitat	Migration Non-migrant

Family MOMOTIDAE	Species *Baryphthengus martii*	Length 46cm (18in)

RUFOUS MOTMOT

A sluggish bird of tropical forest, the Rufous
Motmot has the small legs and feet and
large bill of a bird that sits and waits for
prey to appear in its vicinity. It lives in
lowland and hill forest, and in mature
secondary forest
(where trees have
regrown after
clearance). Most of the
time it sits high in the trees on
a branch, flying out to seize an
insect from a leaf or a branch in a
sudden, abrupt movement. Occasionally it
drops to the ground to capture a small creature,
and at times it follows columns of army ants to seize
insects and other small animals as they try to escape
from the ants. Prey items include many kinds of insect
or invertebrate, and small animals such as mice or
lizards. The downcurved bill has serrated edges which
ensure a firm grip on the prey. Larger creatures are
carried back and beaten against the perch, to kill them
before they are swallowed. The birds also feed on small
fruits, which are plucked in hovering flight. Rufous
Motmots live singly or in pairs. Their calls are often
heard from high in the trees at dawn, when birds make
contact with other individuals, amid considerable noise.
Each utters a soft, owl-like hooting sound which echoes
through the trees, making the bird hard to locate.
• **NEST** An unlined chamber at the end of a burrow dug
by the breeding pair in a bank or in the side of a gully.
• **DISTRIBUTION** Two populations: one from Nicaragua
south to W. Ecuador, and one in the western Amazon Basin.
• **REMARK** This is the largest species of motmot.

DISTRIBUTION

blue edges of flight feathers

two central tail feathers are elongated. Some closely related motmots have "racquet-tipped" tails

worn tail-tip (usually square-ended)

Plumage Sexes differ	Habitat	Migration Non-migrant

Family MEROPIDAE	Species *Nyctyornis amictus*	Length 32cm (12½in)

RED-BEARDED BEE-EATER

This forest-dwelling bee-eater has a downcurved bill, rounded wings, and loose, shaggy-looking, red feathers on its throat and forehead. It occurs singly or in pairs in the upper and middle foliage of forest and at the forest edge. Here it hunts insects from a perch. It has a chuckling call.

• **NEST** A burrow in a sand or earth bank beside a forest stream.

• **DISTRIBUTION** S. Thailand, Malay Peninsula, Sumatra, and Borneo.

• large head

JUVENILE

short, rounded • wings

DISTRIBUTION

square- • tipped tail

Plumage Sexes alike	Habitat	Migration Non-migrant

Family MEROPIDAE	Species *Merops albicollis*	Length 23cm (9in)

WHITE-THROATED BEE-EATER

A typical bee-eater of open country, this species has a thin, downcurved bill, long, narrow wings, and two thin tail streamers which are made up of the elongated central tail feathers. A useful identification feature is the combination of a white brow, a white throat, and a pale breast below a black neck band. This is a migrant species, alternating between two habitats. It breeds in dry, very open country with some thorn scrub, and winters in moister savanna (tropical grassland) and forest borders and clearings. Flight is light and fast, with frequent glides, either straight or in circling patterns. The bee-eater usually hunts from a low perch, taking flying insects, particularly bees and wasps. It recognizes ones that are venomous and holds them carefully in the tip of its bill, rubbing the sting of the insect against a perch or the ground to discharge the poison, after which the prey can be swallowed safely. Flying termites are taken avidly when they swarm. Insects are also captured on open ground, as well as spiders and small lizards. This bird is highly sociable and often occurs in parties and flocks. In cooler weather and when roosting, birds are seen huddling together in tightly packed rows on perches. When breeding, however, birds roost in their nest burrows. Breeding usually takes place in large colonies. The flock selects a site and then all the pairs excavate their nest burrows simultaneously, apparently stimulated by the activity of the group as a whole. The pairs show few signs of territorial behaviour and limit themselves to guarding a small area around the entrances to their burrows. In this species, a majority of pairs at a colony are likely to have at least one additional individual helping in nesting tasks, and up to six "helpers" have been recorded at a single nest.

black-and-white striped head • and throat

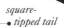

JUVENILE

long, narrow • wings

• **NEST** A tunnel dug in flat or sloping sand, ending in an unlined nest chamber.

two elongated central tail feathers •

• **DISTRIBUTION** Breeds in a narrow band south of the Sahara. Winters further south in W. and C. Africa.

DISTRIBUTION

Plumage Sexes alike	Habitat	Migration Migrant

Family MEROPIDAE	Species *Merops apiaster*	Length 27cm (10½in)

EUROPEAN BEE-EATER

This bee-eater has an unmistakable pattern, being blue underneath and bronze above, with a yellow throat. However, because the bird is usually seen in flight, the whole pattern is not always visible. A vigorous, liquid "quilp" call is often the first thing to draw attention to the bird. The European Bee-eater favours open habitats with scattered trees and bushes. It spends much of its time hunting in the air, but also perches on high, bare twigs and telephone wires. The diet consists of insects, mainly bees and wasps, caught in the air. Sociable at all times of the year, birds are almost always seen in parties or flocks. Nesting colonies are located in earth banks and cliffs.
• **NEST** An unlined chamber at the end of a burrow up to 1.5m (3ft) long.
• **DISTRIBUTION** Breeds from S. Europe and N.W. Africa to N. India, and in South Africa. Winters in much of tropical Africa, and in W. India.

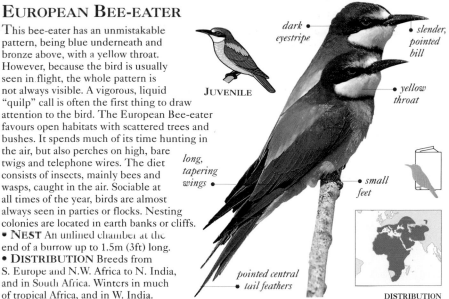

JUVENILE

dark eyestripe

slender, pointed bill

yellow throat

long, tapering wings

small feet

pointed central tail feathers

DISTRIBUTION

Plumage Sexes alike	Habitat	Migration Migrant

Family MEROPIDAE	Species *Merops nubicoides*	Length 38cm (15in)

SOUTHERN CARMINE BEE-EATER

A vividly coloured scarlet bird with a turquoise head and rump, this species occurs in very large flocks. The two central tail feathers are extended in the form of narrow tail streamers. The species lives in open, semi-arid savanna (tropical and subtropical grassland) and grassy river plains. Here it hunts low in a graceful flight with frequent glides, uttering a soft, two-note call. It also hunts from an open perch and sometimes rests on the backs of grazing animals and on ostriches (*see p. 39*) or large bustards (*see p. 130*), swooping out to catch the insects they disturb. In addition it takes insects fleeing from grass fires, and searches out swarms of locusts and flying termites. Nesting colonies are located on steep cliffs beside rivers. Colonies consist of tens of thousands of pairs, each with a separate burrow.
• **NEST** An unlined chamber at the end of a burrow.
• **DISTRIBUTION** N. Angola north to Rwanda, east to Tanzania, and south to E. South Africa.

blue crown

pink throat

thin, slightly downcurved bill

blue undertail coverts

blue rump

square-tipped outer tail feathers

elongated central tail feathers

DISTRIBUTION

Plumage Sexes alike	Habitat	Migration Partial migrant

Family CORACIIDAE	Species *Coracias garrulus*	Length 30cm (12in)

EUROPEAN ROLLER

A heavily built, blue bird with a chestnut back, this roller is usually
seen hunched on a commanding look-out perch in a tree, or on a post
or a telephone wire. It watches for large insects on the ground, suddenly
exposing its long, broad wings as it swoops to seize them, then returns
to the perch. Passing insects are also caught in mid-air. In the
breeding season the displaying male flies high in the air and
performs steep ascents followed by wild, twisting dives which
show off his wing colours. The display is accompanied
by croaking and rattling calls. This species defends
a territory, but flocks form before migration.
• **NEST** An unlined cavity in a tree,
or exceptionally in a bank or cliff.
• **DISTRIBUTION** Breeds in parts of
Europe and N. Africa. Winters
as far south as South Africa.

*vivid blue
wing patch
shows in
flight*

*square-tipped
blue tail*

JUVENILE

DISTRIBUTION

Plumage Sexes alike	Habitat	Migration Migrant

Family CORACIIDAE	Species *Coracias caudata*	Length 40cm (16in)

LILAC-BREASTED ROLLER

Identified by its lilac-coloured breast and forked, swallow-like tail,
this roller lives in dry, open places ranging from open grassland with
a few bushes and trees to thornbush savanna (grassland) and dry,
open woodland. It watches from an exposed perch, then swoops
down with its large, blue wings to seize prey from the ground,
taking large insects, spiders, and sometimes small reptiles and
birds. During the midday heat it abandons its exposed perch
and seeks shade. It is aggressive and noisy, with loud,
squawking calls. Similar wild, raucous calling is heard
during the male's aerial display, which apparently serves
to advertise the pair's presence as well as impress
the female. The displaying male repeatedly climbs
steeply then dives in rolling and twisting flight.
• **NEST** A cavity in a dead tree or termite mound,
some 3–5m (10–16½ft)
above the ground.
• **DISTRIBUTION**
From Ethiopia
through E. Africa
and Angola into
N. South
Africa.

*white
streaks on
the throat*

*vivid blue
wing patch*

*two
elongated
outer tail
feathers form the
point*

JUVENILE

DISTRIBUTION

Plumage Sexes alike	Habitat	Migration Partial migrant

Family CORACIIDAE	Species *Coracias spatulata*	Length 40cm (16in)

RACQUET-TAILED ROLLER

The tail of this roller has a lengthened pair of outer feathers ending in expanded tips which give this species its name. A subtly coloured bird of open woodland, it is sparsely distributed within its range. It occurs singly or in pairs or family parties, individuals feeding separately but within sight of each other. Swooping from a perch, it takes prey mainly from the ground but also from the air. It eats insects such as flying ants and termites, as well as grasshoppers, crickets, centipedes, and scorpions.

• **NEST** An unlined cavity in a branch or treetrunk.
• **DISTRIBUTION** S. Angola, S.E. Zaire, and through Zimbabwe to N.E. South Africa.

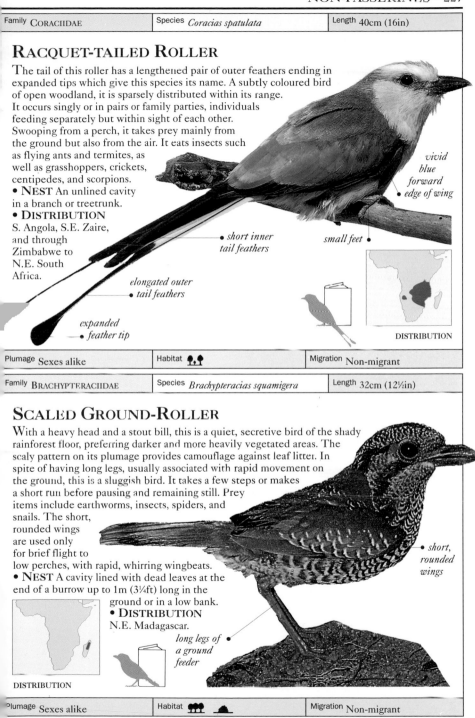

vivid blue forward edge of wing

short inner tail feathers

small feet

elongated outer tail feathers

expanded feather tip

DISTRIBUTION

Plumage Sexes alike	Habitat 🌳🌳	Migration Non-migrant

Family BRACHYPTERACIIDAE	Species *Brachypteracias squamigera*	Length 32cm (12½in)

SCALED GROUND-ROLLER

With a heavy head and a stout bill, this is a quiet, secretive bird of the shady rainforest floor, preferring darker and more heavily vegetated areas. The scaly pattern on its plumage provides camouflage against leaf litter. In spite of having long legs, usually associated with rapid movement on the ground, this is a sluggish bird. It takes a few steps or makes a short run before pausing and remaining still. Prey items include earthworms, insects, spiders, and snails. The short, rounded wings are used only for brief flight to low perches, with rapid, whirring wingbeats.

• **NEST** A cavity lined with dead leaves at the end of a burrow up to 1m (3¼ft) long in the ground or in a low bank.
• **DISTRIBUTION** N.E. Madagascar.

short, rounded wings

long legs of a ground feeder

DISTRIBUTION

Plumage Sexes alike	Habitat 🌳🌳 🌿	Migration Non-migrant

Family LEPTOSOMATIDAE	Species *Leptosomus discolor*	Length 50cm (20in)

CUCKOO-ROLLER

This species has the short legs, heavy bill, and large head of a roller (*see pp. 226–227*), but with its long wings and tail it has a slight resemblance to a cuckoo (*see pp. 188–191*). A bird of tropical forest and open woodland, it feeds on insects, particularly hairy caterpillars, and also takes chameleons. Liquid, whistling notes are uttered from a perch, or in circling flight over the territory.
• **NEST** A hole in a tree.
• **DISTRIBUTION** Madagascar.

feathers ruffled and raised as bird turns its head •

MALE

DISTRIBUTION

pale, spotted • underside of female bird

Plumage Sexes differ	Habitat	Migration Non-migrant

Family UPUPIDAE	Species *Upupa epops*	Length 29cm (11½in)

HOOPOE

Unmistakable with its bold colouring and crest, the Hoopoe has stripes that, like those of a zebra, merge into the background when seen at a distance. It feeds mostly on the ground, probing for insects and small lizards. The call is a soft, repeated "hoop" sound.
• **NEST** A hole in a tree, termite mound, or wall.
• **DISTRIBUTION** Eurasia, Africa, and Madagascar. Northern populations winter in tropical Africa, India, and S.E. Asia.
• **REMARK** Hoopoes breeding south of the Sahara are sometimes regarded as a separate species.

• almost lowered crest

slender bill for probing

SPREAD WING

• barred wing pattern

DISTRIBUTION

• black tail with white band revealed in flight

Plumage Sexes alike	Habitat	Migration Partial migrant

Family PHOENICULIDAE	Species *Phoeniculus purpureus*	Length 40cm (16in)

GREEN WOOD-HOOPOE

Adapted for clambering on treetrunks and branches, this species has short, strong legs and sharp claws for gripping bark firmly. The long, graduated tail with a white bar near the feather tips is used, either closed or spread, as a support. In flight a white wing bar is revealed. This bird occurs wherever there are large trees except in thick rainforest, individuals following each other in single file in short flights from one tree to another. Green Wood-Hoopoes probe into crevices and holes with their long, slender, and slightly curved bills, feeding on insects and other invertebrates, together with some fruit such as berries. This species is sociable, and lives in small parties of up to 16 individuals, which are noisy with loud, cackling calls. These are frequently used in social display in which several birds perform a rapid, exaggerated bowing movement, vigorously flexing the tail up and down. Other members of the party help a dominant pair by feeding the incubating female and the nestlings when hatched.
• NEST A natural cavity in a tree, or an old woodpecker hole, up to 22m (72ft) above the ground.
• DISTRIBUTION Africa south of the Sahara.

JUVENILE

DISTRIBUTION

• *white wing patch*

• *white bars on outer tail feathers*

long, tapering • *tail*

Plumage Sexes alike	Habitat	Migration Non-migrant

Family PHOENICULIDAE	Species *Rhinopomastus cyanomelas*	Length 28cm (11in)

COMMON SCIMITARBILL

A slender bird, the Scimitarbill is adapted for foraging and clambering among trees. The legs are short and the feet strong, with sharp claws for maintaining a strong grip on the bark. It is agile and acrobatic, and often feeds while hanging upside down. The plumage is dark, glossed with violet-blue in the male. Scimitarbills probe holes and crevices with their long, slender, curved bills, in search of beetles and spiders, and also catch large insects such as preying mantises. They use their long tails to support themselves while feeding. They have rounded wings, and this species has a white wingbar which is revealed in flight. It lives in trees in woodland and dry, open scrub, usually occurring singly or in pairs, and nesting in isolated pairs. However, it often joins parties of mixed bird species feeding in woodland. The call is a series of plaintive whistles.
• NEST A narrow hollow in a treetrunk.
• DISTRIBUTION From Somalia and Kenya through E. Africa to Angola and southern Africa.

• *thin, curved bill for probing*

DISTRIBUTION

FEMALE

• *long, tapering tail*

Plumage Sexes alike	Habitat	Migration Non-migrant

Family BUCEROTIDAE	Species *Tockus erythrorhynchus*	Length 45cm (17½in)

RED-BILLED HORNBILL

This is a small, slender hornbill with a narrow, downcurved bill. Usually occurring in pairs or small parties, it gathers into flocks at an abundant food source. Red-billed Hornbills feed by hopping on the ground, searching the surface, and probing holes for insects. They frequent the paths of game animals in order to hunt for dung beetles.

JUVENILE

• **NEST** A hole in a tree, sparsely lined with plants. The female inside the nest, helped by the male outside, plasters the entrance with mud and droppings leaving only a narrow slit. The male brings food which is passed through the slit, and droppings are squirted out. The female leaves when the young are half-grown, and they reseal the nest until ready to leave.

• **DISTRIBUTION** From the S. Sahara through E. Africa to South Africa.

bare skin around the eye

white underside

long tail

DISTRIBUTION

Plumage Sexes alike	Habitat	Migration Non-migrant

Family BUCEROTIDAE	Species *Ceratogymna bucinator*	Length 65cm (26in)

TRUMPETER HORNBILL

large casque, following the curve of the bill

A heavily built hornbill of forest and woodland, this species has a long, curved casque on the top of its bill. It feeds mainly on fruit and insects found in the trees, and normally occurs in small flocks.

JUVENILE

• **NEST** A natural hole in a tree. The female seals herself in by plastering the entrance with a mixture of mud and droppings, leaving only a narrow, vertical slit. The male brings all the food for the female and the young. All birds leave the nest at the same time.

• **DISTRIBUTION** E. and C. Africa.

bare skin around the eye

DISTRIBUTION

Plumage Sexes differ	Habitat	Migration Non-migrant

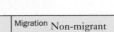

Family BUCEROTIDAE	Species *Buceros rhinoceros*	L. 125cm (49in)/90cm (35in)

RHINOCEROS HORNBILL

• *massive casque*

DISTRIBUTION

*broad,
rounded
• wings*

One of the larger hornbills, this species has
a huge casque extending along most of
the bill and curving upwards at the end.
A bird of lowland and foothill forest, it
prefers the tops of high trees in areas
of mature growth. In spite of its size it moves
easily among the branches with large, springy
hops. It flies strongly above the
trees with noisy, flapping wingbeats,
frequently uttering its resonant,
trumpeting call. The wings are
broad and black, and in flight the
white rump and white tail with a
black band are revealed. Usually
occurring singly or in pairs, it gathers in small
parties where fruiting trees offer an abundant
food source. Although fruit forms the main
part of its diet, small birds and nestlings are
sometimes taken, and also other small creatures.
• **NEST** A hole in a tree, the entrance plastered
over to leave only a narrow slit for feeding.
• **DISTRIBUTION** S.E. Asia in Malay
Peninsula, Sumatra, Borneo, and Java.

*white
tail* •

Plumage Sexes differ	Habitat 🌳	Migration Non-migrant

Family BUCORVIDAE	Species *Bucorvus cafer*	Length 107cm (42in)

SOUTHERN GROUND-HORNBILL

A large, dark hornbill, this bird
walks and forages on the ground
for most of the time, although it
roosts in trees. It lives in groups of
up to eight birds, which share and defend a
territory. Groups patrol their territories probing,
pecking, and digging at the ground, and eating
small animals including insects, snakes, tortoises,
and rodents. Some members of the group act as
"helpers" for the dominant pair when they nest.
• **NEST** A hole in a tree, lined with dry leaves.
• **DISTRIBUTION** Parts of Africa south of the Sahara.
  • **REMARK** This is the largest
   species of hornbill.

*red •
throat wattle*

JUVENILE   FEMALE

• *white wing patch
revealed in flight*

DISTRIBUTION

Plumage Sexes differ	Habitat 🌳	Migration Non-migrant

Family GALBULIDAE	Species *Galbula ruficauda*	Length 20cm (8in)

RUFOUS-TAILED JACAMAR

Slenderly built with a long, thin bill, a long tail, and short, weak legs, this is one of the birds that sits and waits to snatch its prey. It occurs at forest edges, in clearings, and in areas where trees have begun to regrow after clearance, and along streams. Alert and nervously active rather than sluggish, it sits on an open perch with bill uptilted, moving its head frequently. It flies out to catch passing insects before returning to the same perch, or to one nearby. Food is swallowed whole, but big butterflies are first beaten against the perch to remove the wings. Other prey includes dragonflies, bees, wasps, and flying beetles. This species lives in pairs, and the two birds frequently perch and hunt close to one another. They utter frequent, sharp, high-pitched calls which merge into a trill at times of agitation.
• **NEST** An unlined burrow up to 50cm (20in) long, in a bank, an upturned tree root, or a chamber in a termite nest.
• **DISTRIBUTION** Two populations; one from Mexico to N. Brazil, the other from C. Brazil south to N.E. Argentina.

FEMALE

DISTRIBUTION

• *two toes forward, two back (outer toes are reversed)*

• *tail is glossy green above, with pale orange outer feathers below*

Plumage Sexes differ	Habitat 🌳 🌿 ✈	Migration Non-migrant

Family BUCCONIDAE	Species *Bucco macrodactylus*	Length 14cm (5½in)

CHESTNUT-CAPPED PUFFBIRD

A squat bird with a large head, this species has lax, fluffy-looking plumage from which its name is derived. The bill is stout, with bristles surrounding the base to help in trapping insects, and the legs and feet are small and weak. The species is found in forest, along river banks within forest, and in low woodland that grows up in clearings. It sits on a low perch that may be either exposed or partly hidden in foliage, and makes short flights to take insects from nearby vegetation. Usually quiet, it utters a rising sequence of short notes, dying away to a twitter.
• **NEST** A burrow excavated in the ground, or cut into a tree-termite nest.
• **DISTRIBUTION** From Colombia and Venezuela south to Bolivia and W. Brazil.

DISTRIBUTION

• *short, rounded wings*

• *loose, fluffy plumage*

• *squat, heavy posture*

Plumage Sexes alike	Habitat 🌿 🌳 〰	Migration Non-migrant

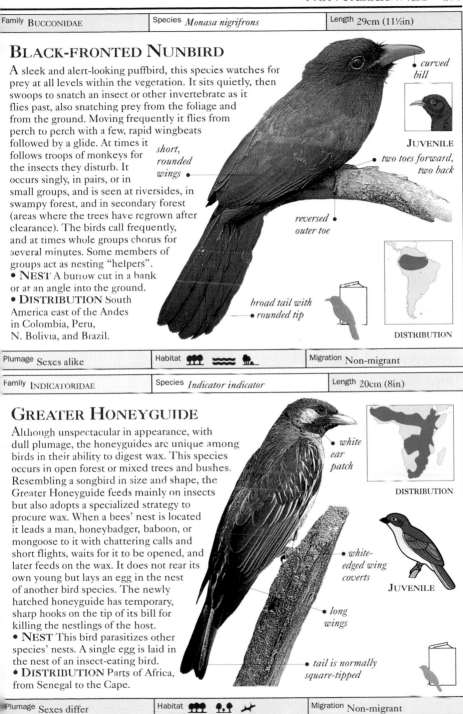

Family BUCCONIDAE	Species *Monasa nigrifrons*	Length 29cm (11½in)

BLACK-FRONTED NUNBIRD

A sleek and alert-looking puffbird, this species watches for prey at all levels within the vegetation. It sits quietly, then swoops to snatch an insect or other invertebrate as it flies past, also snatching prey from the foliage and from the ground. Moving frequently it flies from perch to perch with a few, rapid wingbeats followed by a glide. At times it follows troops of monkeys for the insects they disturb. It occurs singly, in pairs, or in small groups, and is seen at riversides, in swampy forest, and in secondary forest (areas where the trees have regrown after clearance). The birds call frequently, and at times whole groups chorus for several minutes. Some members of groups act as nesting "helpers".
• NEST A burrow cut in a bank or at an angle into the ground.
• DISTRIBUTION South America east of the Andes in Colombia, Peru, N. Bolivia, and Brazil.

curved bill

JUVENILE

two toes forward, two back

short, rounded wings

reversed outer toe

broad tail with rounded tip

DISTRIBUTION

Plumage Sexes alike	Habitat	Migration Non-migrant

Family INDICATORIDAE	Species *Indicator indicator*	Length 20cm (8in)

GREATER HONEYGUIDE

Although unspectacular in appearance, with dull plumage, the honeyguides are unique among birds in their ability to digest wax. This species occurs in open forest or mixed trees and bushes. Resembling a songbird in size and shape, the Greater Honeyguide feeds mainly on insects but also adopts a specialized strategy to procure wax. When a bees' nest is located it leads a man, honeybadger, baboon, or mongoose to it with chattering calls and short flights, waits for it to be opened, and later feeds on the wax. It does not rear its own young but lays an egg in the nest of another bird species. The newly hatched honeyguide has temporary, sharp hooks on the tip of its bill for killing the nestlings of the host.
• NEST This bird parasitizes other species' nests. A single egg is laid in the nest of an insect-eating bird.
• DISTRIBUTION Parts of Africa, from Senegal to the Cape.

white ear patch

DISTRIBUTION

white-edged wing coverts

JUVENILE

long wings

tail is normally square-tipped

Plumage Sexes differ	Habitat	Migration Non-migrant

Family RAMPHASTIDAE	Species *Pteroglossus castanotis*	Length 37cm (14½in)

CHESTNUT-EARED ARACARI

The long, slim, gently curved bill of this species, with its distinctly serrated edges, is typical of the aracaris. Living in forest and forest edge, this slenderly built bird is active and sociable. It usually occurs in small parties that hunt together, moving in single file in short flights through the trees, and roosting huddled in a cavity such as an old woodpecker's hole. The diet consists of fruit such as figs, tree catkins, insects, and a variety of small animals.

• **NEST** An unlined cavity in a tree or an old woodpecker hole.

• **DISTRIBUTION** From E. Colombia and Ecuador south to Bolivia and N.E. Argentina.

bare blue skin around the eye •

DISTRIBUTION

dull chestnut ear patch revealed at certain angles to the light

red band • across the belly

serrated • edges on both mandibles

• long tail, tapering at the tip

slender • tongue

Plumage Sexes alike	Habitat	Migration Non-migrant

Family RAMPHASTIDAE	Species *Andigena laminirostris*	Length 50cm (20in)

PLATE-BILLED MOUNTAIN-TOUCAN

The most obvious feature of toucans is the brightly coloured and massive bill. In this species there is an additional bright yellow horny plate on the outside of the upper mandible, the purpose of which is unknown. The long bill is used to help the bird to reach for food, which consists mainly of fruit, with some insects and other small creatures. This species has the typical colouring of a mountain-toucan, with dark upperparts and mainly blue-grey underside, and the plumage is fine, with a hairy texture. It is a bird of mountain forest, occurring in pairs or small groups. At times these groups join flocks of mixed species to move through the forest looking for fruit and eating the insects that they disturb in the process. The usual call is a rising series of querulous, whining notes, uttered while the bird is hidden in foliage. The species also has a loud, rattling call.

• **NEST** A natural hole in a tree.

• **DISTRIBUTION** W. Andes in S.W. Colombia and W. Ecuador.

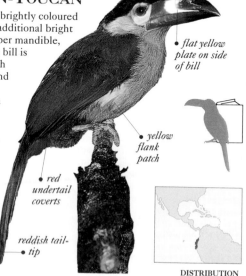

• flat yellow plate on side of bill

• yellow flank patch

• red undertail coverts

reddish tail- • tip

DISTRIBUTION

Plumage Sexes alike	Habitat	Migration Non-migrant

| Family RAMPHASTIDAE | Species *Ramphastos tucanus* | Length 53cm (21in) |

RED-BILLED TOUCAN

This large toucan inhabits tall rainforest and forest edges, usually staying in the higher branches and foliage canopy of mature trees. Like other toucans, it roosts by squatting with its head turned backwards, resting its bill on its back, with the tail turned forwards and resting on the bill. Usually occurring singly or in pairs, at times it may gather in larger groups since five birds have been reported roosting huddled together on a branch. Seen in flight it appears top-heavy with its large bill; it makes a few, quick wingflaps, then glides along on set wings. Red-billed Toucans feed on fruit, tree catkins, insects, spiders, other animals such as lizards, snakes, and eggs and nestlings of small birds. The call is a loud series of rhythmic yelps, often accompanied by upward jerks of the bill and tail.
• **NEST** A natural cavity in a tree, sometimes lined unintentionally with regurgitated fruit stones.
• **DISTRIBUTION** N. Amazonia from E. Colombia and E. Venezuela to the Guianas and N. Brazil.

bare blue skin around eye

DISTRIBUTION

short wings

yellow rump

red undertail coverts

square tipped tail

| Plumage Sexes alike | Habitat 🌳 🏞 〰 | Migration Non-migrant |

| Family RAMPHASTIDAE | Species *Ramphastos toco* | Length 60cm (24in) |

TOCO TOUCAN

The huge, unwieldy bill of this toucan gives the bird an unbalanced look, but the bill is light and hollow in structure. It is very conspicuous when the bird is seen in flight, which is undulating, with alternating flaps and glides. The white rump and red undertail coverts are also noticeable in flight. The Toco Toucan lives in woodland, secondary forest (areas where the trees have regrown after forest clearance), and coconut and other palm plantations. It is seen moving along branches with heavy, bounding hops, taking mainly fruit and insects, but also other small creatures, and the eggs and nestlings of small birds. The large bill enables the bird to reach food on the end of thin twigs which cannot support its weight. Food is seized in the bill-tip and the head is tossed back, opening the bill. This throws the food to the back of the throat where the long, bristly tongue may help to catch it. Toco Toucans utter deep, croaking calls in a deliberate manner, often from a high twig.
• **NEST** A hollow in a dead or living tree.
• **DISTRIBUTION** From Venezuela south through Brazil to N.W. Argentina.

bare yellow skin around eye

white throat

red undertail coverts

DISTRIBUTION

| Plumage Sexes alike | Habitat 🌳 🌳 | Migration Non-migrant |

| Family PICIDAE | Species *Jynx torquilla* | Length 16cm (6¼in) |

EURASIAN WRYNECK

This bird's name refers to its neck-stretching and head-twisting movements, used to threaten an enemy. It feeds on ants, extending its sticky tongue into their burrows to extract them.
• **NEST** A hole in a tree, wall, or bank.
• **DISTRIBUTION** Eurasia and N.W. Africa. Winters in Africa, India, and S.E. Asia.

small, thin bill

DISTRIBUTION

finely patterned plumage for camouflage

JUVENILE

| Plumage Sexes alike | Habitat | Migration Migrant |

| Family PICIDAE | Species *Sasia abnormis* | Length 10cm (4in) |

RUFOUS PICULET

Tiny and active, this woodpecker sometimes looks more like a small passerine when seen feeding and foraging. It lives in undergrowth in forests, clambering and hopping among branches, leaves, and twigs, and searching the ground-litter, taking ants and other small insects. When feeding in bamboo and small trees, it taps the surface and probes the bark in more usual woodpecker fashion.
• **NEST** A hole excavated in a branch.
• **DISTRIBUTION** S.E. Asia in Malay Peninsula, Sumatra, Java, and Borneo.

FEMALE

strong feet with a wide grasp for clambering

very short tail

DISTRIBUTION

| Plumage Sexes differ | Habitat | Migration Non-migrant |

| Family PICIDAE | Species *Melanerpes formicivorus* | Length 23cm (9in) |

ACORN WOODPECKER

staring eye

This sociable woodpecker has a close association with oak trees. It lives in groups of up to 12 birds that defend a shared territory and nest communally. In late summer the birds bore rows of holes into trees, fences, and wooden buildings, fixing an acorn in each hole to be stored as a future food supply for the group. Insects are also eaten in the summer, and some other nuts and fruits in winter. The call is a raucous double note.
• **NEST** A hole cut in a trunk.
• **DISTRIBUTION** From W. North America to Colombia.

white facial markings

FEMALE

streaked breast pattern

DISTRIBUTION

| Plumage Sexes differ | Habitat | Migration Non-migrant |

| Family PICIDAE | Species *Melanerpes candidus* | Length 24cm (9½in) |

WHITE WOODPECKER

The vividly pied plumage of this species, combined with the fact that it is often seen in open country, make the bird very conspicuous. Its habitats range from semi-open forest and forest edges to cultivated clearings and open grassland with sparsely scattered trees. For a woodpecker, it has unusually direct, strong flight (*see p. 16*). When crossing open country, it tends to pause and rest periodically on the tops of dead trees. White Woodpeckers usually occur in small parties, but it is not known whether these are purely family parties or include some unrelated birds. The birds are often seen climbing up trees, tapping and searching for insects, but their main food is fruit, and the species has become a pest at orange groves. White Woodpeckers also eat seeds, such as grain. Captive specimens show a fondness for honey, which suggests that wild birds may take nectar from flowers.
• **NEST** A hole excavated in a tree.
• **DISTRIBUTION** E. South America from Surinam south through Brazil to N. Argentina.

bare eye-ring

pure white underside

DISTRIBUTION

hind toe

outer front toe turned backwards

tail used as a prop

| Plumage Sexes differ | Habitat 🌳🌳 🌿 | Migration Non-migrant |

| Family PICIDAE | Species *Melanerpes flavifrons* | Length 22cm (8½in) |

YELLOW-FRONTED WOODPECKER

This species is a fruit-eating woodpecker which occurs in forest, open woodland, and even in places where forests have been cleared, leaving only a few scattered trees. Although observations in the wild have been limited, the bird is fairly common within its range and is thought to be very sociable in its behaviour. It forages in the trees in small parties, searching for fruit, staying mainly in the branches but sometimes descending to feed on berries from tall herbaceous plants. The behaviour of aviary-kept specimens suggests that Yellow-fronted Woodpeckers also eat insects, and their liking for nectar-solution indicates that wild birds may probe flowers for nectar. Courtship and defensive displays involve raising, lowering, and turning the head. These movements show off the vivid yellow eye-rings and throat and the bright scarlet cap.
• **NEST** Not scientifically recorded; probably a cavity excavated in a tree.
• **DISTRIBUTION** E. South America in S.E. Brazil, Paraguay, and N.E. Argentina.

bare eye-ring

FEMALE

bright yellow throat

white streak down the back

white barring on the tail feathers

spiny-tipped tail feathers for support

DISTRIBUTION

| Plumage Sexes differ | Habitat 🌳🌳 🌿🌿 🌿 ✈ | Migration Non-migrant |

Family PICIDAE	Species *Melanerpes carolinus*	Length 24cm (9½in)

RED-BELLIED WOODPECKER

This species is one of the "ladder-backed" woodpeckers, which have black-and-white barring across the back. It has a large area of red on the head and nape, which is an easier identification mark than the more limited red flush on the belly. In flight, a white rump and a short, white wingbar are revealed. The species is widespread in open woodland, and also occurs in parks and suburbs. It is usually seen in pairs, but family groups remain together for a short period after breeding. The diet consists of insects, obtained by hacking at dead and dying wood, and birds visit garden birdfeeders in winter. Feeding in this way, birds make good use of the tail, with its stiffened feather shafts, as a support. The splayed, sharp-clawed feet help the birds to cling firmly to where they feed. The call is a rolling "churr".
• **NEST** An unlined hole, excavated in a tree.
• **DISTRIBUTION** E. North America. Northern populations winter south within this range.

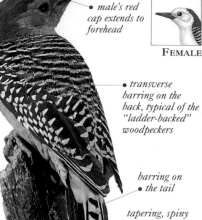

• *male's red cap extends to forehead*

FEMALE

• *transverse barring on the back, typical of the "ladder-backed" woodpeckers*

• *barring on the tail*

• *tapering, spiny feather tips*

DISTRIBUTION

Plumage Sexes differ	Habitat ♠♠,♠	Migration Partial migrant

Family PICIDAE	Species *Sphyrapicus varius*	Length 22cm (8½in)

YELLOW-BELLIED SAPSUCKER

Tapping into a tree produces more than just burrowing insects, and this species of woodpecker makes holes in the bark in order to feed on the sugary sap. The bird drills grid-like rows of holes into any suitable tree, and renews them each year. Broadleaved trees such as maples, fruit-trees, birches, and poplars are used, but other tree species are also tested, including conifers. A series of small holes is chiselled into the tree and after a short while the bird returns to drink the oozing sap. The sapsucker also eats many of the insects attracted by the sap. Other animals also take the opportunity to drink the sap, including squirrels, warblers, and hummingbirds. This bird is mainly silent but has a mewing call note, and advertises possession of its territory in spring by a rapid drumming on a resonant, dead branch. Possibly because it must rely on sap rising in spring, this is a migrant species.
• **NEST** An unlined hole, which is excavated by the bird, in a tree.
• **DISTRIBUTION** Breeds in Canada and N. and E. USA. Winters in S. USA south to C. Panama, and the Caribbean.

striped face pattern

black upper breast patch

FEMALE

DISTRIBUTION

Plumage Sexes differ	Habitat 🌳🌳 ♠♠,♠	Migration Migrant

Family PICIDAE	Species *Dendrocopos major*	Length 23cm (9in)

GREAT SPOTTED WOODPECKER

FEMALE

- black "bridle" on face
- white shoulder patch

The commonest and most widespread of the pied woodpeckers of Eurasia and Africa, this species is identified by a white shoulder patch, and by its separated cheek and neck patches. It is a successful species, occurring in most areas with trees. It feeds mainly over the surfaces of treetrunks and branches, moving in typical woodpecker fashion with head up, tail-tip pressed against the bark as a support, and with the feet spread. The strong bill is used to lever up bark, and holes are probed using the sticky tongue. The bird also hacks deeply into rotten wood for insect grubs. It has a loud "chik" call and drums on branches in spring.
- **NEST** An unlined hole excavated in a tree.

- **DISTRIBUTION** From Europe east to Japan and south to N. Africa, N.E. India, and China.

DISTRIBUTION

Plumage Sexes differ	Habitat 🌳 🌲 ✈	Migration Non-migrant

Family PICIDAE	Species *Picoides villosus*	Length 24cm (9½in)

HAIRY WOODPECKER

MALE

black face stripe

Identified by the white band stretching down the middle of the back and the pure white outer tail feathers, this is a widespread woodpecker of North American woodland. Its habitats range from dense coniferous or broadleaved forests to open woodland, but it does not venture readily into farmland and suburbs. Climbing treetrunks and larger branches, it explores the bark of trees, levering up the bark or hacking into rotten wood in search of insects and wood-boring grubs, which it extracts with its very long, barb-tipped tongue. It utters a loud "peek" note and also a slurred, whinnying call.
- **NEST** A hole excavated by the birds, in a dead or decaying tree.

- **DISTRIBUTION** From Alaska and Canada to Panama.

- outer front toe turned backwards
- hind toe

DISTRIBUTION

Plumage Sexes differ	Habitat 🌳 🌲	Migration Non-migrant

Family PICIDAE	Species *Colaptes auratus*	Length 32cm (12½in)

NORTHERN FLICKER

Adapted to feeding mainly on the ground, this woodpecker spends most of its time on a level surface, in a posture more like that of a passerine, although its undulating flight is typical of a woodpecker (*see p. 16*). In flight a vivid colour is revealed on the underside of the wings: this is yellow in eastern birds and red in western birds; also revealed is the white rump. The Northern Flicker feeds mainly on ants, crouching and probing into the ground with its long, sticky tongue. The calls include loud, repeated "wick", or "wick-ker" notes.
• **NEST** A cavity excavated in a dead tree or branch.
• **DISTRIBUTION** North America, the West Indies, and Central America as far south as Nicaragua. Northern populations winter south within this range.

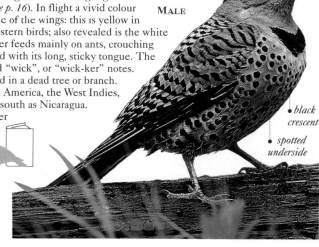

MALE

• *red patch on nape*

• *black crescent*

• *spotted underside*

DISTRIBUTION

Plumage Sexes differ	Habitat	Migration Partial migrant

Family PICIDAE	Species *Celeus flavus*	Length 28cm (11in)

CREAM-COLOURED WOODPECKER

This species is unmistakable for its pale, creamy-yellow colour and its short, tapering, bushy crest, which is permanently raised and makes the bird seem large-headed. It is rather uncommon, and is usually found in moister forests such as those that are seasonally flooded, swampy forest, and wet secondary forest (where trees have regrown after clearance), and riverside forest in grassland regions. It specializes in feeding on tree ants, breaking open the thin, papery nests that they make, and leaving the hard, mud nests of tree-termites. Feeding mainly in the middle levels of forest vegetation, it also takes other insects from trees and branches, and some fruit. Several birds call in a group, uttering a loud "wheyah" call, usually repeated several times. There is also a "pueer" call which is repeated four times, the final two notes being shorter, and falling in pitch.
• **NEST** Not scientifically recorded; probably a hole in a tree, excavated by the birds.
• **DISTRIBUTION** South America east of the Andes, from Columbia and the Guianas south to Peru, Bolivia and E. Brazil.

FEMALE

• *male's dark eye-ring*

tail used as a support •

DISTRIBUTION

Plumage Sexes differ	Habitat	Migration Non-migrant

Family PICIDAE	Species *Dryocopus pileatus*	Length 42cm (16½in)

PILEATED WOODPECKER

The combination of black plumage, white neck stripes, and a scarlet crest make this bird highly distinctive. Its flight is strong and direct. The species occurs mainly in forest, but is found in parkland and woodlots (small stands of woodland for timber use). A liking for insects that bore into dead wood, such as carpenter ants that excavate from the ground upwards, often attracts a Pileated Woodpecker down to the foot of a tree or a dead trunk. The hammering sound made by the feeding birds is a noticeable sound in quiet woodland. Birds also take some nuts, acorns, and small wild fruits. The call is a repeated "wuck-a-wuck-a", rising and falling in pitch. In spring, the male also advertises his territory by rapid drumming on a branch.

prominent red crest is always raised

striped neck

FEMALE

• **NEST** A hole excavated in a treetrunk (often in a close stand of trees) or in a dead tree stump or a telephone pole.
• **DISTRIBUTION** Much of Canada and parts of USA, especially in the east.
• **REMARK** Since the extinction of the Ivory-billed Woodpecker in the middle decades of the 20th century, this is now the largest species of woodpecker occurring in North America.

DISTRIBUTION

Plumage Sexes differ	Habitat	Migration Non-migrant

Family PICIDAE	Species *Picus viridis*	Length 32cm (12½in)

EUROPEAN GREEN WOODPECKER

red crown

A ground-feeding woodpecker that often forages in grassy places, this species is well-camouflaged with its green plumage. Its habitats include open woodland, woodland edge, shrubby growth, and open areas with scattered trees. In flight, a yellow rump is revealed. This species displays the typical flight pattern of woodpeckers, rising with a few, quick wingbeats, then making a short, downward swoop with wings closed, repeating these movements to create an undulating flight path (*see p. 16*). Because of its camouflage plumage the species is difficult to spot, and is best known for its ringing call, a rapidly repeated "plui-plui-plui" that falls away in pitch and volume. When feeding, it crouches and probes for ants' nests, extending its very long, sticky tongue into their burrows, often working for long periods. In winter it digs deep into snow to locate the large nest heaps made by wood ants.

FEMALE

• **NEST** A hole excavated in the trunk of a free-standing tree, sometimes as low as 1m (3¼ft) above the ground.
• **DISTRIBUTION** Europe from Britain to Russia, and parts of S.W. Asia to N. Iran.

DISTRIBUTION

Plumage Sexes differ	Habitat 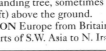	Migration Non-migrant

PASSERINES

T HE 74 PASSERINE FAMILIES contain more than half the world's bird species. The precise meaning of the word passerine is "sparrow-like", and a common, though possibly misleading, alternative is "perching birds" (many non-passerines perch). A third name, not always deserved, is "songbirds". Most passerines are relatively small and there is a basic similarity of shape throughout the group. Identification may depend on minor details. Legs vary according to lifestyle, for instance whether the bird forages on the ground, or perches in foliage. Bill shapes vary with the food eaten – most commonly insects, fruit, or seeds. The shape of body, wings, and tail help too, and song can often be decisive in identifying a passerine species.

Family EURYLAIMIDAE	Species *Psarisomus dalhousiae*	Length 28cm (11in)

LONG-TAILED BROADBILL

A big-headed bird with a short, heavy bill, this species is found in mountain rainforests, subtropical forests, and bamboo thickets. It also occurs in secondary forests (where trees have regrown after clearance). Small flocks feed in the middle height of the trees, taking insects in flight or probing for them on mossy branches and creepers.
• **NEST** A pear-shaped structure with a porched entrance-hole at the side, hanging from a branch.
• **DISTRIBUTION** N. India and S. China to Sumatra and Borneo.

broad-based bill

short legs

long tail is unique to this species of broadbill

JUVENILE

DISTRIBUTION

Plumage Sexes alike	Habitat	Migration Non-migrant

Family EURYLAIMIDAE	Species *Calyptomena viridis*	Length 19cm (7½in)

GREEN BROADBILL

The wide mouth and bill of this small broadbill are concealed under the feathers of its oversized-looking head. Small groups feed in the lower branches on soft fruit, buds, and occasionally insects.
• **NEST** A pear-shaped structure with a porched entrance hole at the side, hanging from a branch.
• **DISTRIBUTION** Malay Peninsula, Sumatra (including small islands), and Borneo.

crest on the front of the face

bill hidden under the crest

typical broadbill tail

DISTRIBUTION

Plumage Sexes alike	Habitat	Migration Non-migrant

| Family DENDROCOLAPTIDAE | Species *Xiphocolaptes promeropirhynchus* | Length 30cm (12in) |

STRONG-BILLED WOODCREEPER

This stoutly built bird, resembling a woodpecker, lives in tropical and mountain forests. Often solitary, it is usually seen climbing up treetrunks and larger branches. It feeds by probing for insects in crevices on treetrunks and branches, as well as hunting them in the foliage. Strong-billed Woodcreepers also feed near the rainforest floor, watching army ant swarms from a perch and swooping to the ground to prey on the insects disturbed by the ants.
• **NEST** Details have not been recorded scientifically.
• **DISTRIBUTION** From Mexico through Central America to South America. From Colombia east to Guyana, and south through the Andes as far as Bolivia.

thick bill probes into moss and leaves

feet with a wide grasp

stout, heavy body

stiff tail can be bent under body for support

DISTRIBUTION

| Plumage Sexes alike | Habitat | Migration Non-migrant |

| Family DENDROCOLAPTIDAE | Species *Campylorhamphus trochilirostris* | Length 27cm (10½in) |

RED-BILLED SCYTHEBILL

A slender, woodpecker-like bird with a long, downward-curving bill, this species climbs the trunks and larger branches of trees, probing under bark and into crevices and inside the flowers of bromeliads for insects. It occurs either in rainforests or in sections of swampy woodland that are surrounded by open country. The Red-billed Scythebill is a sociable bird, often seen among flocks of mixed insect-eating species, each one feeding in its own fashion.
• **NEST** A cup nest, made of plant materials, usually built in the hollow of a broken-open stump.
• **DISTRIBUTION** From Panama through lowland South America to N. Argentina and Paraguay.
• **REMARK** The five species of scythebill all belong to the woodcreeper family, most of whose members have long, sickle-like bills for probing into crevices and pulling out prey. Scythebills have the advantage of a very long reach to search deep inside large flowers and capture insects that hide there.

scythe-shaped bill for long reach

strongly built feet for climbing up treetrunks

DISTRIBUTION

stiff tail used as a support

| Plumage Sexes alike | Habitat | Migration Non-migrant |

Family FURNARIIDAE	Species *Furnarius rufus*	Length 18cm (7in)

RUFOUS HORNERO

Slim and long-legged, this bird is adapted
to living on the ground in open grassland.
It is frequently seen probing the
surface litter for invertebrates.
• **NEST** A domed mud
nest on top of a branch
or pole, resembling a
bread oven – hence
the Spanish name *el
hornero* – "the baker".
• **DISTRIBUTION** Open lowland
in southern half of South America.

*long,
ground-
probing
bill*

DISTRIBUTION

NEST

*long, springy
legs for foraging*

Plumage Sexes alike	Habitat	Migration Non-migrant

Family FURNARIIDAE	Species *Aphrastura spinicauda*	Length 15cm (6in)

THORN-TAILED RAYADITO

A small, active bird with distinctive
stripes on the head and wings, this
bird gets its name from the tough
spines that strengthen its longish
tail. Flocks are seen in forest and scrub
at all altitudes from lowland to mountains.
The birds feed on insects which they hunt in
vegetation, on treetrunks, and on branches.
• **NEST** A cup nest of plant materials built
behind loose bark or in a tree hole.
• **DISTRIBUTION** Lower Andean
slopes and low-lying forests
from C. Chile southwards.

head stripe

DISTRIBUTION

*spines give
support when
climbing trees*

Plumage Sexes alike	Habitat	Migration Non-migrant

Family FURNARIIDAE	Species *Cinclodes antarcticus*	Length 20cm (8in)

BLACKISH CINCLODES

This squat bird is found on rocky
beaches and in coastal tussock grass,
usually on small islands. It is the only
dark, ground-dwelling, smallish bird in
these habitats. The Blackish Cinclodes
is inquisitive and tame, feeding on
insects and other invertebrates.
• **NEST** A shallow cup nest
made of dry grass, placed
in a crevice among rocks.
• **DISTRIBUTION**
Falkland Islands, S. Tierra
del Fuego, offshore islands.

*thin, probing
bill*

*stout body
shape*

DISTRIBUTION

Plumage Sexes alike	Habitat	Migration Non-migrant

Family FURNARIIDAE	Species *Margarornis squamiger*	Length 16cm (6¼in)

PEARLED TREERUNNER

This upland bird is usually seen high in
the trees, in forests and along forest edges,
at altitudes where the climate is either subtropical or temperate. It characteristically climbs trunks
and branches, often hitching itself under a branch or
spiralling along towards a branch tip; otherwise, it may
be seen feeding among the foliage. The diet consists almost
entirely of insects and spiders. Small groups are often found
among mixed-species flocks, hunting invertebrates.
• **NEST** A ball-shaped structure with a side entrance,
made of moss and hidden at the base of the branch of a tree.
• **DISTRIBUTION** Andes from Venezuela to Bolivia.

pearl-like spots •

DISTRIBUTION

spine-tipped tail for
• support

Plumage Sexes alike	Habitat 🌳 🌲	Migration Non-migrant

Family FURNARIIDAE	Species *Philydor amaurotis*	Length 16cm (6¼in)

WHITE-BROWED FOLIAGE-GLEANER

A small, unobtrusive bird, this
species inhabits forests at altitudes
where the climate is subtropical. It frequents
thick vegetation in the lower and middle
forest storeys, hopping along branches and
clambering about actively. Often joining
mixed-species flocks to feed, it searches
tangles of dead leaves for invertebrates.
• **NEST** Not scientifically recorded.
• **DISTRIBUTION** Coastal range of
hills in S.E. Brazil and N.E. Argentina.

small, stout bill •

DISTRIBUTION

• bright rufous-red tail

stiff spines •

Plumage Sexes alike	Habitat 🌳	Migration Non-migrant

Family FURNARIIDAE	Species *Automolus rubiginosus*	Length 19cm (7½in)

RUDDY FOLIAGE-GLEANER

A furtive and retiring species,
this bird occurs in rainforest and at
forest edges, in lowlands and foothills.
It clambers about in thick vegetation
near the ground, feeding on insects
and small invertebrates. This bird does
not normally join the mixed flocks
that hunt insects in the undergrowth.
• **NEST** Probably of twigs and plant
fibres, the nest is at the end of a long
burrow, which the bird digs in a bank.
• **DISTRIBUTION** From Mexico
to Bolivia, and through the Guianas.

• pale throat

plain brown
• plumage

DISTRIBUTION

long tail for balance

Plumage Sexes alike	Habitat 🌳 🌲	Migration Non-migrant

Family FORMICARIIDAE	Species *Cymbilaimus lineatus*	Length 17cm (6¾in)

FASCIATED ANTSHRIKE

A heavy bird with a sluggish appearance, the Fasciated Antshrike hunts insects in vine tangles at the rainforest edge.
• **NEST** A cup nest situated in a bush or a tree fork.
• **DISTRIBUTION** From Honduras through Colombia as far south as N.W. Ecuador. On east side of Andes, from Colombia to N. Bolivia and Brazil.

• *large head*

• *stout, hooked bill*

DISTRIBUTION

FEMALE

Plumage Sexes differ	Habitat	Migration Non-migrant

Family FORMICARIIDAE	Species *Taraba major*	Length 20cm (8in)

GREAT ANTSHRIKE

Living in the undergrowth of secondary forests (regrown after forest clearance), this species usually moves about in pairs, hopping through thickets and pausing to peer after their insect prey.
• **NEST** An open cup nest made of grass and leaves, suspended by its outer rim from a twig in a low bush or thicket.
• **DISTRIBUTION** From S. Mexico to Brazil and N. Argentina.

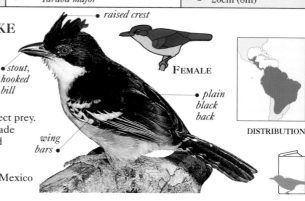

• *raised crest*

FEMALE

• *stout, hooked bill*

• *plain black back*

wing bars •

DISTRIBUTION

Plumage Sexes differ	Habitat	Migration Non-migrant

Family FORMICARIIDAE	Species *Thamnophilus palliatus*	Length 15cm (6in)

LINED ANTSHRIKE

This thickset bird hops about in the dense undergrowth of forest edges, or sometimes in clearings with bushes. It snatches insects and spiders with its stout, hooked bill.
• **NEST** A cup nest of grass and leaves, built into a branch fork, and hidden in the undergrowth.
• **DISTRIBUTION** Much of Brazil, and neighbouring countries north to Colombia and south to Bolivia.

FEMALE

• *stout, hooked bill*

• *white lines from which the bird gets its name*

• *tough feet for a secure grip on perch*

DISTRIBUTION

Plumage Sexes differ	Habitat	Migration Non-migrant

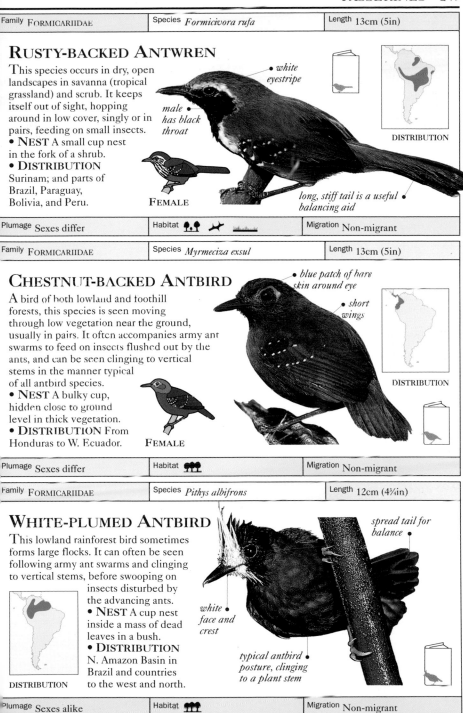

Family FORMICARIIDAE	Species *Formicivora rufa*	Length 13cm (5in)

RUSTY-BACKED ANTWREN

This species occurs in dry, open landscapes in savanna (tropical grassland) and scrub. It keeps itself out of sight, hopping around in low cover, singly or in pairs, feeding on small insects.
• **NEST** A small cup nest in the fork of a shrub.
• **DISTRIBUTION** Surinam; and parts of Brazil, Paraguay, Bolivia, and Peru.

white eyestripe

male has black throat

FEMALE

long, stiff tail is a useful balancing aid

DISTRIBUTION

Plumage Sexes differ	Habitat	Migration Non-migrant

Family FORMICARIIDAE	Species *Myrmeciza exsul*	Length 13cm (5in)

CHESTNUT-BACKED ANTBIRD

A bird of both lowland and foothill forests, this species is seen moving through low vegetation near the ground, usually in pairs. It often accompanies army ant swarms to feed on insects flushed out by the ants, and can be seen clinging to vertical stems in the manner typical of all antbird species.
• **NEST** A bulky cup, hidden close to ground level in thick vegetation.
• **DISTRIBUTION** From Honduras to W. Ecuador.

blue patch of bare skin around eye

short wings

FEMALE

DISTRIBUTION

Plumage Sexes differ	Habitat	Migration Non-migrant

Family FORMICARIIDAE	Species *Pithys albifrons*	Length 12cm (4¾in)

WHITE-PLUMED ANTBIRD

This lowland rainforest bird sometimes forms large flocks. It can often be seen following army ant swarms and clinging to vertical stems, before swooping on insects disturbed by the advancing ants.
• **NEST** A cup nest inside a mass of dead leaves in a bush.
• **DISTRIBUTION** N. Amazon Basin in Brazil and countries to the west and north.

spread tail for balance

white face and crest

typical antbird posture, clinging to a plant stem

DISTRIBUTION

Plumage Sexes alike	Habitat	Migration Non-migrant

Family FORMICARIIDAE	Species *Phlegopsis nigromaculata*	Length 18cm (7in)

BLACK-SPOTTED BARE-EYE

This large antbird inhabits rainforest undergrowth, moving about in flocks. It regularly follows army ant swarms to prey on other insects fleeing from the ants.
• **NEST** An unlined cup nest, usually in the hollow top of a palm stump.
• **DISTRIBUTION** Amazon basin.
• **REMARK** Several antbird species have bare skin around the eye.

• *each feather carries a spot*

bare eye-patch

large feet

short tail •

DISTRIBUTION

Plumage Sexes alike	Habitat	Migration Non-migrant

Family FORMICARIIDAE	Species *Phaenostictus mcleannani*	Length 19cm (7½in)

OCELLATED ANTBIRD

Strikingly marked with "eye-spots" (ocellated), this is a large antbird of lowland rainforest. Like other birds of the antbird family it characteristically feeds by watching the ground for army ant swarms, and pouncing on insects flushed out of their hiding places by the ants. It dominates the smaller antbirds, claiming the lowest perches so as to have first choice of the insects as they make their escape from the ants.
• **NEST** Not scientifically recorded.
• **DISTRIBUTION** Central and South America from Honduras to W. Ecuador.

• *each "eye-spot" is a dark feather with a light edge*

bare eye-patch •

DISTRIBUTION

Plumage Sexes alike	Habitat	Migration Non-migrant

Family FORMICARIIDAE	Species *Pittasoma rufopileatum*	Length 16.5cm (6½in)

RUFOUS-CROWNED ANTPITTA

This bird lives in tropical rainforest also occurring in mature secondary forest (regrown after rainforest clearance). It feeds mainly by bounding along on the forest floor, catching insects as it goes; it also watches over army ant swarms to prey on insects flushed from cover by the ants.
• **NEST** Not scientifically recorded.
• **DISTRIBUTION** Lowlands and foothills west of the Andes in Colombia and Ecuador.

• *large head with rufous crown*

orange throat

• *powerful, springy legs*

FEMALE

DISTRIBUTION

Plumage Sexes differ	Habitat	Migration Non-migrant

Family CONOPOPHAGIDAE	Species *Conopophaga melanops*	Length 11.5cm (4½in)

BLACK-CHEEKED GNATEATER

Adapted for life in the undergrowth of rainforests, this bird is also found in mature secondary forest (regrown after rainforest clearance). It is usually solitary and stays near the ground, creeping through the vegetation or making brief flights to take insects from the ground and from foliage.
• **NEST** Details not scientifically recorded.
• **DISTRIBUTION** Coastal lowlands of E. Brazil.

short wings

short tail

DISTRIBUTION

FEMALE

Plumage Sexes differ	Habitat	Migration Non-migrant

Family RHINOCRYPTIDAE	Species *Liosceles thoracicus*	Length 20cm (8in)

RUSTY-BELTED TAPACULO

A ground-dwelling inhabitant of lowland rainforest, this species hops about on the forest floor or in low vegetation, seeking its insect prey.
• **NEST** Not scientifically recorded.
• **DISTRIBUTION** Amazonian rainforest in W. Brazil and adjoining areas of Colombia, Ecuador, and Peru.
• **REMARK** *Tapaculo* is Spanish for "cover your rear end" in a joking reference to the cocked tail.

DISTRIBUTION

typical up-tilted tail

pointed bill

slender, agile legs

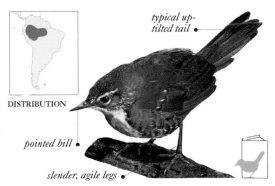

Plumage Sexes alike	Habitat	Migration Non-migrant

Family TYRANNIDAE	Species *Suiriri suiriri*	Length 15cm (6in)

SUIRIRI FLYCATCHER

This slenderly built tyrant flycatcher is a bird of open woodland, thinly scattered trees, and scrubby growth. It feeds by gleaning insects from among the foliage, and often joins mixed-species flocks of insect-hunting birds.
• **NEST** A simple cup nest of plant fibres in the fork of a twig.
• **DISTRIBUTION** From N.E. Brazil southwards as far as C. Argentina; and from N. Brazil across the border into Surinam.

raised crest

bristles

short legs

spotted plumage denotes a juvenile bird

DISTRIBUTION

long wings for rapid flight

Plumage Sexes alike	Habitat	Migration Non-migrant

Family TYRANNIDAE	Species *Stigmatura budytoides*	Length 15cm (6in)

GREATER WAGTAIL-TYRANT

Like the Old World wagtails, this is a
slender bird with a long tail, which it
bobs up and down and does not "wag"
from side to side. This species normally
holds its tail cocked, and frequents trees
rather than water. It is usually seen in pairs,
gleaning insects in open woodland and scrub.
• **NEST** A shallow cup, close to the ground.
• **DISTRIBUTION** S. Bolivia, part of
Argentina, and E. Brazil.

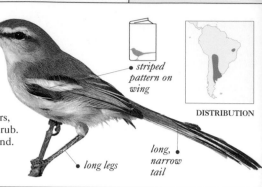

• striped pattern on wing

DISTRIBUTION

long, narrow tail

• long legs

Plumage Sexes alike	Habitat 🌳 ✈	Migration Non-migrant

Family TYRANNIDAE	Species *Pseudotriccus ruficeps*	Length 11cm (4¼in)

RUFOUS-HEADED PYGMY-TYRANT

This is a plump, wren-sized bird
with a tiny bill, occurring on forested
mountain slopes, at altitudes where
the climate is either subtropical or
temperate. Inconspicuous and often
solitary, it creeps about hunting insects in the
undergrowth. It occasionally makes short, abrupt
flights, accompanied by an audible whirr of wings.
• **NEST** Not scientifically recorded.
• **DISTRIBUTION** The Andes in a series of
areas in Colombia, Ecuador, Peru, and Bolivia.

thin bill

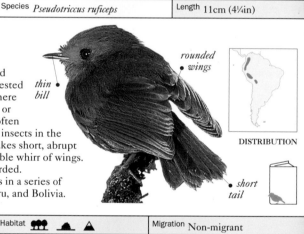

rounded wings

DISTRIBUTION

short tail

Plumage Sexes alike	Habitat 🌳 🏔 ▲	Migration Non-migrant

Family TYRANNIDAE	Species *Onychorhynchus coronatus*	Length 17cm (6¾in)

ROYAL FLYCATCHER

A slender tyrant flycatcher, this
species inhabits the lower levels
of rainforest and subtropical open
forest. Its typical way of feeding
is to watch from a perch and fly out, either
to seize an insect in the air or to take it
from the foliage. The vivid, transverse crest is
normally folded away and sometimes protrudes
behind the head, resulting in a "hammerhead"
look. The male's crest is red, the female's yellow.
• **NEST** A slender bag up to 2m (6½ft) long,
suspended from a branch, often over a stream.
• **DISTRIBUTION** Mexico to Bolivia and S.E. Brazil.

hook-tipped bill

MALE

DISTRIBUTION

short legs

Plumage Sexes differ slightly	Habitat 🌳	Migration Non-migrant

Family TYRANNIDAE	Species *Contopus sordidulus*	Length 16.5cm (6½in)

WESTERN WOOD-PEWEE

This medium-sized tyrant flycatcher of open forest or forest edge is often seen perching on an open branch or bare snag, from which it flies out to catch insects in mid-air.
• **NEST** An open cup nest fixed on a horizontal branch, often high.
• **DISTRIBUTION** Breeds in forests of W. North America and mountain forests of Central America. Winters in South America as far south as Peru and Bolivia.

large eye

upright, watchful posture

long tail

DISTRIBUTION

short legs

Plumage Sexes alike	Habitat	Migration Migrant

Family TYRANNIDAE	Species *Empidonax difficilis*	Length 13.5cm (5¼in)

PACIFIC SLOPE FLYCATCHER

broad-based bill

large eye

A small, inconspicuous flycatcher, this bird perches in an upright posture, occasionally waving its fanned tail up and down ("flirting"), and swooping to seize insects in the air or on foliage. It frequents woodland on mountain slopes, as well as wooded canyons.
• **NEST** A cup nest formed from plant materials, built in a hollow or cavity.
• **DISTRIBUTION** Breeds in W. Canada and USA. Migrates as far south as W. Mexico in winter.

short legs

long wings

long tail

DISTRIBUTION

Plumage Sexes alike	Habitat	Migration Migrant

Family TYRANNIDAE	Species *Sayornis phoebe*	Length 17cm (6¾in)

EASTERN PHOEBE

Named in imitation of its "fee bee" call, the Eastern Phoebe lives in open woodland and farmland, hunting insects from an open perch, usually near water. It has also adapted itself successfully to urban habitats, where it nests readily on buildings. While perched, it frequently bobs its tail up and down.
• **NEST** A stout cup nest made of mud and plant materials, on a sheltered ledge. New nests are sometimes built on top of old ones.
• **DISTRIBUTION** Breeds in C. and E. North America. Winters in S.E. USA and Mexico.

broad, flat bill

long wings

long, balancing tail

DISTRIBUTION

Plumage Sexes alike	Habitat	Migration Migrant

Family TYRANNIDAE	Species *Sayornis nigricans*	Length 19cm (7½in)

BLACK PHOEBE

Known for its "fee-bee" call, the Black Phoebe is quite tame and is often seen perched on a boulder in mid-river. It sallies short distances over the water surface to catch flying insects, returning to the same perch. The upright posture of the perched bird, and its wagging tail, are useful identifying features in the field.
• **NEST** A cup nest made of mud pellets and grass, on a rocky ledge near water.
• **DISTRIBUTION** From S.W. USA through Central America and the Andes to Bolivia and N.W. Argentina.

large eye

slim bill for catching insects

DISTRIBUTION

long tail

JUVENILE

Plumage Sexes alike	Habitat 〰 〰	Migration Non-migrant

Family TYRANNIDAE	Species *Pyrocephalus rubinus*	Length 15cm (6in)

VERMILION FLYCATCHER

Easily the most vividly coloured of the tyrant flycatchers, this species lives in scattered trees and shrubs or open woodland, often in semi-arid country but usually near water. It feeds on insects caught either at rest or in flight.
• **NEST** A shallow cup nest in a tree fork.
• **DISTRIBUTION** Breeding range extends from USA to Argentina; also Galapagos Islands. Southern populations winter in Amazonia, northern ones in Central America.

intense, crimson crown

slender bill

crimson underparts

DISTRIBUTION

FEMALE

Plumage Sexes differ	Habitat 🌳 🌳	Migration Partial migrant

Family TYRANNIDAE	Species *Ochthoeca cinnamomeiventris*	Length 13cm (5in)

SLATY-BACKED CHAT-TYRANT

This squat, dark, short-billed bird occurs in forests on mountain slopes. Slaty-backed Chat-Tyrants are often seen along streams. The species is highly sedentary – birds normally spend their whole life within a small locality. They are usually seen in pairs, hunting insects and other invertebrates in low vegetation.
• **NEST** An open cup nest, built on a ledge on a rock face, near water.
• **DISTRIBUTION** Through the Andes from Venezuela to Bolivia, at altitudes where the climate is subtropical.

white streak above the eye

DISTRIBUTION

broad, rufous belly

Plumage Sexes alike	Habitat 🌳🌳🌳 ⛰ 〰 🪨	Migration Non-migrant

Family TYRANNIDAE	Species *Colonia colonus*	Length 23cm (9in)

LONG-TAILED TYRANT

Two long tail feathers make this bird conspicuous in flight or in the prominent places where it tends to perch. It spends much of the day on an exposed vantage point in the tree canopy at the outer fringes of lowland rainforest or isolated woodlands. Favoured perches are on dead or dying trees, bare branches, and snags. Long-tailed Flycatchers nearly always perch in pairs, and each pair tends to use a particular perch or series of perches habitually. They watch for flying insects and make quick outward flights to seize them, usually returning faithfully to the same perch. Stingless bees are among the commonest prey items.
• **NEST** A loose nest of plant materials is placed in a hole in a dead branch.
• **DISTRIBUTION** From Honduras to Colombia; S. Brazil and N.E. Argentina; and the Guianas.

large, watchful eye

• *white head stripe*

• *elongated central tail feathers*

DISTRIBUTION

Plumage Sexes alike	Habitat	Migration Non-migrant

Family TYRANNIDAE	Species *Fluvicola nengeta*	Length 13cm (5in)

MASKED WATER TYRANT

A distinctively pied tyrant, this bird is usually seen on or near the ground, often on vegetation or rocks close to water. Its diet consists of insects, which it gleans from the foliage.
• **NEST** An oval construction with a side entrance, made of grass and plant down, lined with feathers, and placed on a branch tip, low over water.
• **DISTRIBUTION** Two populations: one in W. Ecuador and Peru, and one in E. Brazil.

• *black eyestripe*

DISTRIBUTION

• *vivid, black-and-white tail is often turned up at a jaunty angle*

Plumage Sexes alike	Habitat	Migration Non-migrant

Family TYRANNIDAE	Species *Hirundinea ferruginea*	Length 18cm (7in)

CLIFF FLYCATCHER

A slender bird with noisy, twittering and chattering calls, this species sits on conspicuous perches. It frequents rocky places and is often seen at road cuttings, flying out to catch an insect in flight before returning to its perch. Telephone wires are also used as perches. In addition to its original nest sites on cliffs and outcrops, the Cliff Flycatcher now commonly nests on buildings in villages and farms.
• **NEST** A cup nest, placed on a ledge on a cliff or wall.
• **DISTRIBUTION** Andean highlands from Venezuela to Argentina; also from the Guianas through Brazil to Uruguay.

warm reddish-brown plumage

long wings for aerial agility

DISTRIBUTION

Plumage Sexes alike	Habitat	Migration Non-migrant

Family TYRANNIDAE	Species *Machetornis rixosus*	Length 19cm (7½in)

CATTLE TYRANT

Adapted to life in an open-country habitat, this slender bird can run considerable distances across the ground. It also perches on rocks, low vegetation, and even on the backs of cattle and other grazing animals. The diet consists of insects, which the birds catch on the ground, on the animals, or in the air.
• **NEST** A large, ball-shaped structure of plant materials, sited in low vegetation. Also uses old nests of other grassland bird species.
• **DISTRIBUTION** Lowlands from Venezuela to Colombia, from N.E. Brazil to S. Brazil, and from E. Bolivia to N. Argentina.

faint eyestripe

muted yellow underside

long legs for foraging on the ground

DISTRIBUTION

Plumage Sexes alike	Habitat	Migration Partial migrant

Family TYRANNIDAE	Species *Pitangus sulphuratus*	Length 23cm (9in)

GREAT KISKADEE

A large and noisy, tree-dwelling tyrant flycatcher, this species is seen in open country with scattered trees, often beside water or around human habitations. It hunts from a perch, using its strong, predatory bill to pounce on small creatures on the ground, including insects, worms, and even small vertebrates such as mice, frogs, and lizards. The Great Kiskadee also plunge-dives to catch fish, and hawks insects in the air.
• **NEST** A large and loosely domed nest with a wide side entrance, or sometimes an open cup nest, made of plant materials and situated in a tree.
• **DISTRIBUTION** From S. USA (S. Texas) as far south as C. Argentina. Introduced in Bermuda.

striped head

stout, hooked bill

large wings

broad tail

DISTRIBUTION

Plumage Sexes alike	Habitat	Migration Non-migrant

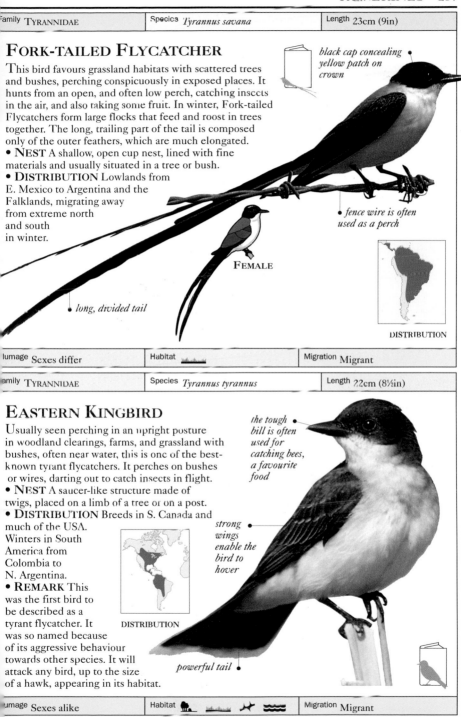

| Family TYRANNIDAE | Species *Tyrannus savana* | Length 23cm (9in) |

FORK-TAILED FLYCATCHER

This bird favours grassland habitats with scattered trees and bushes, perching conspicuously in exposed places. It hunts from an open, and often low perch, catching insects in the air, and also taking some fruit. In winter, Fork-tailed Flycatchers form large flocks that feed and roost in trees together. The long, trailing part of the tail is composed only of the outer feathers, which are much elongated.
• **NEST** A shallow, open cup nest, lined with fine materials and usually situated in a tree or bush.
• **DISTRIBUTION** Lowlands from E. Mexico to Argentina and the Falklands, migrating away from extreme north and south in winter.

black cap concealing yellow patch on crown

fence wire is often used as a perch

FEMALE

long, divided tail

DISTRIBUTION

| Plumage Sexes differ | Habitat | Migration Migrant |

| Family TYRANNIDAE | Species *Tyrannus tyrannus* | Length 22cm (8½in) |

EASTERN KINGBIRD

Usually seen perching in an upright posture in woodland clearings, farms, and grassland with bushes, often near water, this is one of the best-known tyrant flycatchers. It perches on bushes or wires, darting out to catch insects in flight.
• **NEST** A saucer-like structure made of twigs, placed on a limb of a tree or on a post.
• **DISTRIBUTION** Breeds in S. Canada and much of the USA. Winters in South America from Colombia to N. Argentina.
• **REMARK** This was the first bird to be described as a tyrant flycatcher. It was so named because of its aggressive behaviour towards other species. It will attack any bird, up to the size of a hawk, appearing in its habitat.

the tough bill is often used for catching bees, a favourite food

strong wings enable the bird to hover

DISTRIBUTION

powerful tail

| Plumage Sexes alike | Habitat | Migration Migrant |

Family TYRANNIDAE	Species *Pachyramphus versicolor*	Length 13cm (5in)

BARRED BECARD

Living in forested mountainsides
at altitudes where the climate is
subtropical, this small bird feeds
on insects and fruit. It forages
at all levels in the vegetation,
usually in pairs and often in
mixed-species flocks.
• **NEST** A rounded, woven
structure, with the entrance near
the bottom, built in a tree fork.
• **DISTRIBUTION** Costa Rica
to W. Venezuela and W. Bolivia.

white streaks on wings

DISTRIBUTION

FEMALE

round, plump body

Plumage Sexes differ	Habitat	Migration Non-migrant

Family TYRANNIDAE	Species *Tityra cayana*	Length 22cm (8½in)

BLACK-TAILED TITYRA

This species is conspicuous for its black-
and-white plumage and for its way
of perching on exposed branch-ends.
The stout bill is adapted for eating
fruit and large insects. Usually in
pairs, it frequents the canopy at
forest edge or beside clearings.
• **NEST** A cup nest on top of
a pile of leaf litter, stuffed into a
woodpecker hole or other cavity.
• **DISTRIBUTION** Lowland
rainforest from Colombia and
Venezuela to N. Argentina.

bare skin surrounding the eye

large bill

DISTRIBUTION

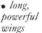

FEMALE

long, powerful wings

Plumage Sexes differ	Habitat	Migration Non-migrant

Family PIPRIDAE	Species *Schiffornis turdinus*	Length 16.5cm (6½in)

THRUST-LIKE SCHIFFORNIS

This plain-looking bird lives
in rainforests, feeding on insects
and fruit. It is very furtive in
its behaviour and hides in the
undergrowth, but has a loud,
whistling song by which it can be identified.
• **NEST** A bulky, open cup nest made of
plant materials, usually placed on the
stub of a broken branch or in a tree fork.
• **DISTRIBUTION** Central America,
N.W. South America; and E. Brazil.
• **REMARK** Probably more closely related to the
tyrant flycatchers rather than to the manakin family.

large eye

short, stubby bill

DISTRIBUTION

low-key plumage for camouflage

Plumage Sexes alike	Habitat	Migration Non-migrant

Family PIPRIDAE	Species *Machaeropterus regulus*	Length 9cm (3½in)

STRIPED MANAKIN

This tiny bird occurs in the lower and middle levels of rainforest and secondary woodland (regrown after forest clearance). It is less conspicuous than other manakins. Males perform courtship displays at specially reserved sites known as "leks". The species feeds on small fruits and insects.
• **NEST** Not scientifically recorded, but probably a cup nest in a bush.
• **DISTRIBUTION** Lowlands in Columbia, Venezuela, E. Ecuador, N.E. Peru; also W. and E. Brazil.

• *scarlet crown*

DISTRIBUTION

FEMALE

• *striped underside*

Plumage Sexes differ	Habitat	Migration Non-migrant

Family PIPRIDAE	Species *Manacus vitellinus*	Length 10cm (4in)

GOLDEN-COLLARED MANAKIN

A colourful bird of the undergrowth, this species occurs at rainforest edges and in secondary woodland (regrown after rainforest clearance). Males perform courtship displays at special sites known as "leks", in which they puff out their throats, utter "snapping" calls, and fly back and forth between perches. The diet consists of fruits and insects.
• **NEST** A small cup nest made of plant materials, situated in a twig fork.
• **DISTRIBUTION** Lowlands from Panama to W. Colombia.

• *shallow, black crown*

DISTRIBUTION

• *strong legs and feet*

FEMALE

Plumage Sexes differ	Habitat	Migration Non-migrant

Family PIPRIDAE	Species *Ilicura militaris*	Length 12cm (4¾in)

PIN-TAILED MANAKIN

This bird lives in the lower and middle levels of rainforest and mature secondary woodland (regrown after rainforest clearance). It feeds on small fruits and insects. Males display to females in a group, calling and ruffling their scarlet rump feathers. Females build the nest and perform all parental duties unaided by the male.
• **NEST** A small cup nest, situated in a twig fork.
• **DISTRIBUTION** Lowlands and foothills in S.E. Brazil.

short, rounded wings •

DISTRIBUTION

tail extends to a sharp • *point*

FEMALE

Plumage Sexes differ	Habitat	Migration Non-migrant

Family PIPRIDAE	Species *Chiroxiphia caudata*	Length 15cm (6in)

SWALLOW-TAILED MANAKIN

This manakin is a brilliantly coloured inhabitant of the undergrowth in rainforest and secondary woodland (where trees have regrown after rainforest clearance). Although Swallow-tailed Manakins usually hide themselves away, males are noticeable when they gather together to perform collective displays to attract females. These displays, at sites called "leks", are characteristic behaviour of the manakin family and are usually accompanied by a variety of rasping, buzzing, and rattling sounds. The diet consists of small fruits and some insects.
• NEST A small cup nest of grass and plant fibres, placed in the fork of a bush.
• DISTRIBUTION Lowland and subtropical zones of S.E. Brazil, E. Paraguay, and N.E. Argentina.

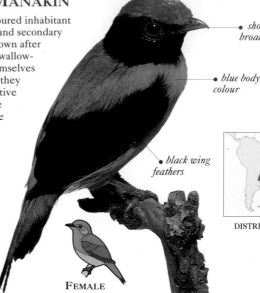

• short, broad bill

• blue body colour

• black wing feathers

DISTRIBUTION

long display feathers •

FEMALE

Plumage Sexes differ	Habitat 🌳	Migration Non-migrant

Family PIPRIDAE	Species *Pipra filicauda*	Length 13cm (5in)

WIRE-TAILED MANAKIN

Although gaudily marked, Wire-tailed Manakins are easily overlooked in the dense foliage of their rainforest habitat. Males take part in communal displays, at special sites called "leks", in which they perform side-jumps, brief flights, and various calls, using their tail filaments to tickle the faces and throats of the females. Calls are simple, but unusual noises are made by rapid vibration of feathers. The Wire-tailed Manakin's short, broad bill is suited to its mixed diet of fruits and insects.
• NEST A cup-shaped nest, made of various types of plant fibres, with excess material hanging below, located in a small tree.
• DISTRIBUTION N. South America, east of the Andes.
• REMARK As in most manakins, the brightly coloured male contrasts with the green female.

• bare white skin around black eye

• yellow underparts

DISTRIBUTION

filamentous tail feathers •

FEMALE

Plumage Sexes differ	Habitat 🌳 🌿	Migration Non-migrant

Family PIPRIDAE	Species *Pipra mentalis*	Length 10cm (4in)

RED-CAPPED MANAKIN

This boldly coloured manakin lives in both rainforest and the secondary woodland that grows after rainforest clearance. It is seen in the middle levels of the forest, feeding mainly on berries, which it plucks in hovering flight, and sometimes taking small insects.
• NEST A shallow cup nest attached to a horizontal fork in a tree.
• DISTRIBUTION From S.E. Mexico to W. Colombia and W. Ecuador.

broad bill

white eye-ring

DISTRIBUTION

buff coloured leg featherings

Plumage Sexes differ	Habitat	Migration Non-migrant

Family COTINGIDAE	Species *Phoenicircus nigricollis*	Length 24cm (9½in)

BLACK-NECKED RED COTINGA

Mainly inhabiting the lower growth of rainforest, this cotinga also ascends to forage in the upper branches for large insects or fruits. The brightly coloured males gather in noisy, spectacular, communal displays at special sites known as "leks", but otherwise the species is generally shy and inconspicuous.
• NEST Details have not been scientifically recorded.
• DISTRIBUTION Lowlands from S. Colombia, S.W. Venezuela, south to N.E. Peru and W. Brazil.

red, bristly crest

red-and-black wings

DISTRIBUTION

FEMALE

black tail tip

Plumage Sexes differ	Habitat	Migration Non-migrant

Family COTINGIDAE	Species *Cotinga amabilis*	Length 20cm (8in)

LOVELY COTINGA

This beautiful blue cotinga sometimes perches on exposed, high branches, but usually remains concealed within the canopy or in the vegetation at the edge of the rainforest. It feeds on fruit and sometimes insects. Males fly with a whirring sound as part of their courtship display behaviour.
• NEST A shallow cup nest, sometimes hidden in foliage, close to the trunk.
• DISTRIBUTION From S. Mexico to Panama, on Caribbean slope.

curved bill

glossy sky-blue plumage

heart shaped breast patch

DISTRIBUTION

thickly feathered rump

FEMALE

Plumage Sexes differ	Habitat	Migration Non-migrant

Family COTINGIDAE	Species *Querula purpurata*	Length 28cm (11in)

PURPLE-THROATED FRUITCROW

A large cotinga with dark plumage, this species inhabits the middle and upper levels of the rainforest, where it feeds on insects as well as on fruit. Purple-throated Fruitcrows live in small social groups. The members of each of these communities feed and rest together, and care jointly for the young in the nest. In courtship, the male displays by puffing out his ruff of purple throat feathers.

• **NEST** A shallow cup nest made of twigs, located high in a tree.

• **DISTRIBUTION** Lowlands from Costa Rica through much of South America as far south as N. Bolivia and Amazonian Brazil.

• **REMARK** Fruitcrows are the only cotingas that live in social groups. There are three other species: the Red-ruffed, Crimson, and Bare-necked Fruitcrows, all living in South America.

DISTRIBUTION

• *broad-based bill*

• *throat ruff swells out in display*

short, strong legs •

• *long, slender wings for rapid flight*

FEMALE

Plumage Sexes differ	Habitat 🌳🌳🌳	Migration Non-migrant

Family COTINGIDAE	Species *Rupicola peruviana*	Length 30cm (12in)

ANDEAN COCK-OF-THE-ROCK

This vivid bird occurs in forest by streams and in wooded gorges of the Andes, feeding on fruit. The highly coloured males perform noisy, communal courtship displays, at special sites known as "leks", on bare branches in middle and upper vegetation. During display, males extend the crest forwards, completely covering the bill. The shape of the eye also changes from round to narrowly elliptical. The females are cinnamon brown all over and have smaller crests than the males. They visit the lek and watch the displaying males, and eventually each female selects a mate. After mating, they perform all nesting duties and parental care unaided by the males.

• **NEST** A cup-shaped nest made of mud and stuck to a rock face in a sheltered hollow.

• **DISTRIBUTION** Andes from Venezuela to Bolivia at altitudes where the climate is subtropical.

semicircular crest opens out further in full display •

round, staring eye •

enlarged wing coverts •

FEMALE

DISTRIBUTION

Plumage Sexes differ	Habitat 🌿 〰 🦆	Migration Non-migrant

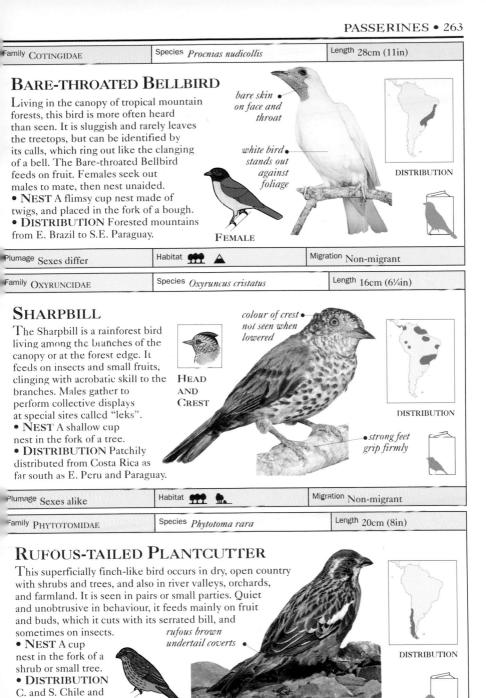

Family COTINGIDAE	Species *Procnias nudicollis*	Length 28cm (11in)

BARE-THROATED BELLBIRD

Living in the canopy of tropical mountain
forests, this bird is more often heard
than seen. It is sluggish and rarely leaves
the treetops, but can be identified by
its calls, which ring out like the clanging
of a bell. The Bare-throated Bellbird
feeds on fruit. Females seek out
males to mate, then nest unaided.
• NEST A flimsy cup nest made of
twigs, and placed in the fork of a bough.
• DISTRIBUTION Forested mountains
from E. Brazil to S.E. Paraguay.

bare skin on face and throat

white bird stands out against foliage

DISTRIBUTION

FEMALE

Plumage Sexes differ	Habitat	Migration Non-migrant

Family OXYRUNCIDAE	Species *Oxyruncus cristatus*	Length 16cm (6¼in)

SHARPBILL

The Sharpbill is a rainforest bird
living among the branches of the
canopy or at the forest edge. It
feeds on insects and small fruits,
clinging with acrobatic skill to the
branches. Males gather to
perform collective displays
at special sites called "leks".
• NEST A shallow cup
nest in the fork of a tree.
• DISTRIBUTION Patchily
distributed from Costa Rica as
far south as E. Peru and Paraguay.

colour of crest not seen when lowered

HEAD
AND
CREST

DISTRIBUTION

strong feet grip firmly

Plumage Sexes alike	Habitat	Migration Non-migrant

Family PHYTOTOMIDAE	Species *Phytotoma rara*	Length 20cm (8in)

RUFOUS-TAILED PLANTCUTTER

This superficially finch-like bird occurs in dry, open country
with shrubs and trees, and also in river valleys, orchards,
and farmland. It is seen in pairs or small parties. Quiet
and unobtrusive in behaviour, it feeds mainly on fruit
and buds, which it cuts with its serrated bill, and
sometimes on insects.
• NEST A cup
nest in the fork of a
shrub or small tree.
• DISTRIBUTION
C. and S. Chile and
adjacent parts
of Argentina.

rufous brown undertail coverts

FEMALE

DISTRIBUTION

Plumage Sexes differ	Habitat	Migration Non-migrant

Family PITTIDAE	Species *Pitta erythrogaster*	Length 16cm (6¼in)

RED-BELLIED PITTA

This pitta is usually seen on the rainforest floor, hopping from place to place and also making short flights. It feeds on small invertebrates (hammering snails on stones) and small fruits. It sometimes ascends the trees to sing, and may roost in the branches as well.
• **NEST** Dome with a side entrance, on the ground, on a tree stump, or in a vine tangle.
• **DISTRIBUTION** Philippines, E. Indonesia, New Guinea, and N. Australia. Some limited migration.

squat, hunched pose

large eye

DISTRIBUTION

long legs for ground-feeding

Plumage Sexes alike	Habitat	Migration Partial migrant

Family PITTIDAE	Species *Pitta guajana*	Length 22cm (8½in)

BANDED PITTA

Shady rainforests are the main habitat of this pitta, but it can also be found in secondary woodland (regrown after rainforest has been cleared). It can be seen hopping along the ground in search of snails, worms, beetles, and other large insects. Its call is loud and penetrating.
• **NEST** A ball-shaped, hollow structure made of vegetation and placed in a bush.
• **DISTRIBUTION** Malay Peninsula, Sumatra, Borneo, Java, and Bali.

big eyes for vision in poor light

white wing patch

DISTRIBUTION

FEMALE

Plumage Sexes differ	Habitat	Migration Non-migrant

Family PITTIDAE	Species *Pitta brachyura*	Length 20cm (8in)

INDIAN PITTA

The habitat of this pitta extends from tropical into subtropical forests and thick scrub. Its flight is limited, although it ascends trees to roost and sing. It travels in springy hops, looking for fruit, insects, and seeds.
• **NEST** A large, domed nest at ground level, with a side entrance.
• **DISTRIBUTION** Indian subcontinent. Migrant populations winter in S. India and Sri Lanka.

large head and eye

powerful bill for digging

DISTRIBUTION

agile, bounding legs

BLUE WING PATCH

Plumage Sexes alike	Habitat	Migration Partial migrant

Family PITTIDAE	Species *Pitta caerulea*	Length 29cm (11½in)

GIANT PITTA

This shy bird is rarely seen, but its distinctive calls are easily heard. It is at its most common in the lowland rainforests, but has also been recorded in mountain rainforests. The diet consists mainly of land snails and earthworms.
• **NEST** A domed structure of dead leaves and twigs, hidden in undergrowth, with a side entrance.
• **DISTRIBUTION** Malay Peninsula, Sumatra, and Borneo.

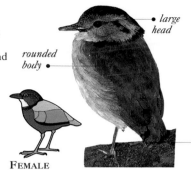

• *large head*

rounded body •

• *short tail*

DISTRIBUTION

FEMALE

Plumage Sexes alike	Habitat 🌳	Migration Non-migrant

Family ACANTHISITTIDAE	Species *Acanthisitta chloris*	Length 8cm (3¼in)

RIFLEMAN

Also known as the Titipounamou, this tiny forest bird uses its sharp bill to search crevices in bark and probe mosses and lichens for insects. It has a high-pitched call.
• **NEST** A loosely woven, domed nest with a side entrance, in a tree hollow or sometimes in a bank.
• **DISTRIBUTION** New Zealand.
• **REMARK** A threatened species due to forest destruction.

DISTRIBUTION

broad head •

• *short, rounded wings*

Plumage Sexes alike	Habitat 🌳	Migration Non-migrant

Family PHILEPITTIDAE	Species *Neodrepanis coruscans*	Length 10cm (4in)

SUNBIRD-ASITY

Living in dense rainforest, this species feeds at all levels from ground to canopy, taking insects and probing flowers, possibly for nectar. It can adapt to secondary forest (regrown after rainforest clearance). This quiet, rather sluggish bird is usually solitary, or lives in small family groups. After breeding, males moult to resemble females.
• **NEST** A spherical nest covered with moss and lined with leaves, generally suspended from the end of a branch.
• **DISTRIBUTION** E. Madagascar.

decorative eye wattle •

long, probing bill

DISTRIBUTION

FEMALE

Plumage Sexes differ	Habitat 🌳	Migration Non-migrant

Family MENURIDAE	Species *Menura novaehollandiae*	L. 90cm (35in)/80cm(32in)

SUPERB LYREBIRD

Resembling a pheasant both in size and lifestyle, the Superb Lyrebird is a ground-dwelling species living in moist eucalyptus forests. It scratches the ground with its long, strong legs to reveal insects and other invertebrates. The male develops a unique, lyre-shaped tail that features in courtship dances performed on a special display mound, which he scrapes together out of damp soil. The dancing male vibrates his spread tail above his back, and the display also includes a highly developed song, with elements of astonishingly clever mimicry.

tail arched • over body in display

• **NEST** A large, domed nest with a side entrance, made of sticks, bark, fern fronds, and moss, and lined with rootlets. The nest may be located on the ground or on a stump, tree fern, or rock.

• **DISTRIBUTION** S.E. Australia.

• **REMARKS** The lyre-shaped tail of the adult male accounts for the 10cm (4in) length difference between the sexes.

FEMALE

DISTRIBUTION

Plumage Sexes differ	Habitat 🌳🌳	Migration Non-migrant

Family ATRICHORNITHIDAE	Species *Atrichornis clamosus*	Length 20cm (8in)

NOISY SCRUB-BIRD

brown plumage for camouflage against • bare ground

This shy, secretive, and almost flightless bird lives in eucalyptus scrub. It seeks its food among dead leaves and ground litter, taking mainly small invertebrates and occasionally small lizards and frogs. Males sing loudly to proclaim their territories.

short, weak • wings

• **NEST** A domed nest in thick vegetation, placed a little above the ground.

strong legs •

• **DISTRIBUTION** S.W. Australia.

• **REMARK** Endangered species.

DISTRIBUTION

FEMALE

Plumage Sexes differ	Habitat ✈	Migration Non-migrant

Family ALAUDIDAE	Species *Eremoptryx verticalis*	Length 13cm (5in)

GREY-BACKED FINCH-LARK

A lark of bare, dry places, this species is often seen walking or running on the ground. Occasionally it settles on a branch after a short, low flight. The diet consists of seeds, plants, and small invertebrates.
• **NEST** A cup nest sunk in the ground, beside a stone or tuft.
• **DISTRIBUTION** Parts of southern Africa.

white ear patch

FEMALE

grey feather edges on back

DISTRIBUTION

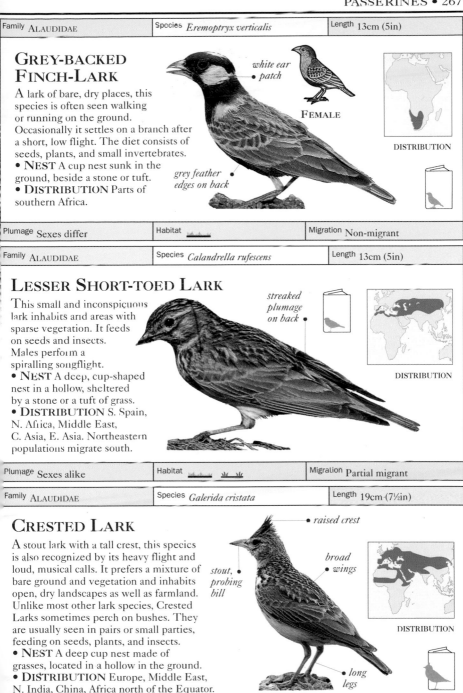

Plumage Sexes differ	Habitat	Migration Non-migrant

Family ALAUDIDAE	Species *Calandrella rufescens*	Length 13cm (5in)

LESSER SHORT-TOED LARK

This small and inconspicuous lark inhabits arid areas with sparse vegetation. It feeds on seeds and insects. Males perform a spiralling songflight.
• **NEST** A deep, cup-shaped nest in a hollow, sheltered by a stone or a tuft of grass.
• **DISTRIBUTION** S. Spain, N. Africa, Middle East, C. Asia, E. Asia. Northeastern populations migrate south.

streaked plumage on back

DISTRIBUTION

Plumage Sexes alike	Habitat	Migration Partial migrant

Family ALAUDIDAE	Species *Galerida cristata*	Length 19cm (7½in)

CRESTED LARK

A stout lark with a tall crest, this species is also recognized by its heavy flight and loud, musical calls. It prefers a mixture of bare ground and vegetation and inhabits open, dry landscapes as well as farmland. Unlike most other lark species, Crested Larks sometimes perch on bushes. They are usually seen in pairs or small parties, feeding on seeds, plants, and insects.
• **NEST** A deep cup nest made of grasses, located in a hollow in the ground.
• **DISTRIBUTION** Europe, Middle East, N. India, China, Africa north of the Equator.

raised crest

broad wings

stout, probing bill

DISTRIBUTION

long legs

Plumage Sexes alike	Habitat	Migration Non-migrant

Family ALAUDIDAE	Species *Lullula arborea*	Length 15cm (6in)

WOODLARK

This small lark is usually found on heaths or mountain grassland: its habitat sometimes includes scattered trees on which it often perches. It feeds on the ground, taking seeds and insects. The male sings from a perch, or in a long, slow songflight.
• **NEST** A deep cup nest in a hollow among grass tufts.
• **DISTRIBUTION** Europe, N. Africa, Middle East; northeastern populations migrate west and south.

lowered crest

broad wings

RAISED CREST

short tail

DISTRIBUTION

Plumage Sexes alike	Habitat	Migration Partial migrant

Family ALAUDIDAE	Species *Alauda arvensis*	Length 18cm (7in)

SKYLARK

A grassland lark famous for its aerial songflight, the Skylark prefers short grass such as pasture. Like all larks it walks, as opposed to hopping. It feeds on plants, seeds, and insects. Outside the breeding season, Skylarks live communally in flocks.
• **NEST** A deep cup nest in a hollow, partly hidden by grass.
• **DISTRIBUTION** Grasslands across Eurasia and N. Africa. Northern populations migrate southwards in winter.

streaked plumage

typical upright posture

broad wings

strong, walking legs

DISTRIBUTION

Plumage Sexes alike	Habitat	Migration Partial migrant

Family ALAUDIDAE	Species *Eremophila alpestris*	Length 17cm (6¾in)

SHORE LARK

This lark forages on bare, stony, or cultivated ground for seeds, plants, and insects. Males give a weak, high-pitched song in an overhead songflight in spring.
• **NEST** A cup nest in a hollow.
• **DISTRIBUTION** Breeds in Eurasia, N. and S. America. Migrates to south of breeding range (Eurasia), or to north (S. America), or to ocean shores (W. Europe and N. America).

horn-like tufts (lost in winter)

white belly

long wings

WINTER PLUMAGE

DISTRIBUTION

Plumage Sexes alike	Habitat	Migration Partial migrant

Family HIRUNDINIDAE	Species *Tachycineta bicolor*	Length 15cm (6in)

TREE SWALLOW

A hole nesting swallow, this bird is common in thinly wooded habitats near water, where it forages over open country catching small insects in flight. Large flocks gather to migrate.
• **NEST** A lining of plant materials in a cavity, in a tree, post, or building.
• **DISTRIBUTION** Breeds in North America. Winter range extends as far south as Colombia.

large eye

long, slender wings

DISTRIBUTION

JUVENILE

Plumage Sexes alike	Habitat	Migration Migrant

Family HIRUNDINIDAE	Species *Progne subis*	Length 19cm (7½in)

PURPLE MARTIN

This dark swallow flies over a variety of open habitats, hunting insects in the air by gliding in circles, with periods of flapping flight.
• **NEST** Tree holes lined with mud and sticks, often in nest boxes in east of range.
• **DISTRIBUTION** Breeds in USA. Winters in S.E. Brazil.

large eye

blue sheen on upper body

short, forked tail

DISTRIBUTION

FEMALE

Plumage Sexes differ	Habitat	Migration Migrant

Family HIRUNDINIDAE	Species *Riparia riparia*	Length 12cm (4¾in)

SAND MARTIN

A small, drab swallow, the Sand Martin hunts insects by rivers, lakes, and sand pits near to its nesting colonies.
• **NEST** A cup nest is built of plant materials and feathers in a tunnel in a bank or cliff.

powerful, slender wings for long-distance flight

short, blunt tail

DISTRIBUTION

• **DISTRIBUTION** Breeds in North America and Eurasia. Winters in South America, Africa, N. India, and S.E. Asia.

Plumage Sexes alike	Habitat	Migration Migrant

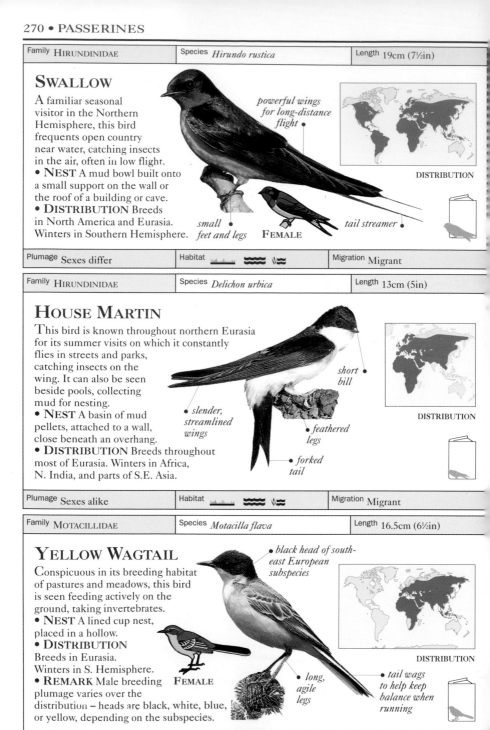

Family HIRUNDINIDAE	Species *Hirundo rustica*	Length 19cm (7½in)

SWALLOW

A familiar seasonal
visitor in the Northern
Hemisphere, this bird
frequents open country
near water, catching insects
in the air, often in low flight.
• **NEST** A mud bowl built onto
a small support on the wall or
the roof of a building or cave.
• **DISTRIBUTION** Breeds
in North America and Eurasia.
Winters in Southern Hemisphere.

*powerful wings
for long-distance
flight*

DISTRIBUTION

*small
feet and legs* **FEMALE**

tail streamer

Plumage Sexes differ	Habitat	Migration Migrant

Family HIRUNDINIDAE	Species *Delichon urbica*	Length 13cm (5in)

HOUSE MARTIN

This bird is known throughout northern Eurasia
for its summer visits on which it constantly
flies in streets and parks,
catching insects on the
wing. It can also be seen
beside pools, collecting
mud for nesting.
• **NEST** A basin of mud
pellets, attached to a wall,
close beneath an overhang.
• **DISTRIBUTION** Breeds throughout
most of Eurasia. Winters in Africa,
N. India, and parts of S.E. Asia.

*short
bill*

DISTRIBUTION

*slender,
streamlined
wings*

*feathered
legs*

*forked
tail*

Plumage Sexes alike	Habitat	Migration Migrant

Family MOTACILLIDAE	Species *Motacilla flava*	Length 16.5cm (6½in)

YELLOW WAGTAIL

Conspicuous in its breeding habitat
of pastures and meadows, this bird
is seen feeding actively on the
ground, taking invertebrates.
• **NEST** A lined cup nest,
placed in a hollow.
• **DISTRIBUTION**
Breeds in Eurasia.
Winters in S. Hemisphere.
• **REMARK** Male breeding
plumage varies over the
distribution – heads are black, white, blue,
or yellow, depending on the subspecies.

*black head of south-
east European
subspecies*

DISTRIBUTION

FEMALE

*long,
agile
legs*

*tail wags
to help keep
balance when
running*

Plumage Sexes differ	Habitat	Migration Migrant

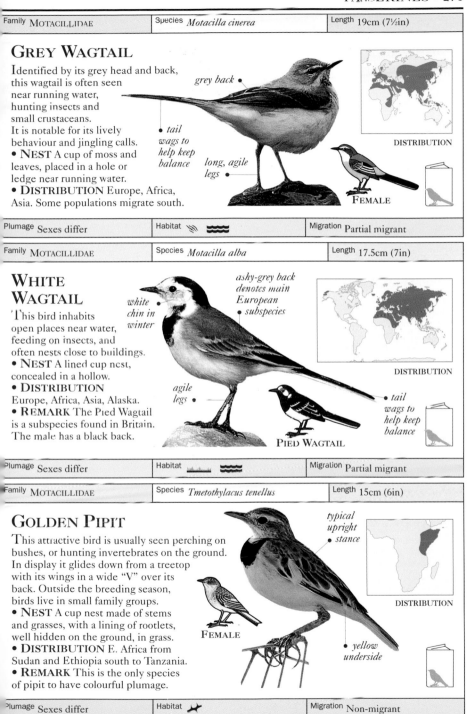

Family MOTACILLIDAE	Species *Motacilla cinerea*	Length 19cm (7½in)

GREY WAGTAIL

Identified by its grey head and back,
this wagtail is often seen
near running water,
hunting insects and
small crustaceans.
It is notable for its lively
behaviour and jingling calls.
• **NEST** A cup of moss and
leaves, placed in a hole or
ledge near running water.
• **DISTRIBUTION** Europe, Africa,
Asia. Some populations migrate south.

grey back •

• *tail*
wags to
help keep
balance long, agile
legs •

DISTRIBUTION

FEMALE

Plumage Sexes differ	Habitat	Migration Partial migrant

Family MOTACILLIDAE	Species *Motacilla alba*	Length 17.5cm (7in)

WHITE WAGTAIL

This bird inhabits
open places near water,
feeding on insects, and
often nests close to buildings.
• **NEST** A lined cup nest,
concealed in a hollow.
• **DISTRIBUTION**
Europe, Africa, Asia, Alaska.
• **REMARK** The Pied Wagtail
is a subspecies found in Britain.
The male has a black back.

ashy-grey back
denotes main
European
• subspecies

white
chin in
winter

agile
legs •

PIED WAGTAIL

DISTRIBUTION

• tail
wags to
help keep
balance

Plumage Sexes differ	Habitat	Migration Partial migrant

Family MOTACILLIDAE	Species *Tmetothylacus tenellus*	Length 15cm (6in)

GOLDEN PIPIT

This attractive bird is usually seen perching on
bushes, or hunting invertebrates on the ground.
In display it glides down from a treetop
with its wings in a wide "V" over its
back. Outside the breeding season,
birds live in small family groups.
• **NEST** A cup nest made of stems
and grasses, with a lining of rootlets,
well hidden on the ground, in grass.
• **DISTRIBUTION** E. Africa from
Sudan and Ethiopia south to Tanzania.
• **REMARK** This is the only species
of pipit to have colourful plumage.

typical
upright
• stance

FEMALE

DISTRIBUTION

• yellow
underside

Plumage Sexes differ	Habitat	Migration Non-migrant

Family MOTACILLIDAE	Species *Anthus pratensis*	Length 14.5cm (5¾in)

MEADOW PIPIT

A streaked, brown bird of grassland and
moors, the Meadow Pipit has a weak,
jerky flight and squeaky calls. It runs
and walks on open ground, taking
insects, worms, and seeds.
It performs a songflight
with a parachuting fall.
• **NEST** A cup nest made
of grass stems and blades, lined and
tucked into a hollow in the ground.
• **DISTRIBUTION** From Greenland
to C. Asia. Some birds migrate to N. Africa.

• *slender, insect-eater's bill*

• *streaked plumage*

DISTRIBUTION

Plumage Sexes alike	Habitat	Migration Partial migrant

Family CAMPEPHAGIDAE	Species *Lalage sueurii*	Length 18cm (7in)

WHITE-WINGED TRILLER

Normally an inconspicuous brown bird with streaky
wings, this species gets its name from the male's
dashing, pied breeding plumage and loud, trilling
song. Pairs often nest close to one another in a
semi-colonial arrangement. White-winged
Trillers feed on insects, taken either from
foliage or while walking on the ground.
• **NEST** A shallow, saucer-shaped
nest made of roots and grass, bound
to a tree fork with spiders' webs.
• **DISTRIBUTION** Australia.
Winters in N. Australia, New Guinea,
and the island of Timor in Indonesia.

white wing bar

DISTRIBUTION

FEMALE

• *long wings for rapid flight*

Plumage Sexes differ	Habitat	Migration Migrant

Family CAMPEPHAGIDAE	Species *Pericrocotus flammeus*	Length 23cm (9in)

SCARLET MINIVET

This slender, vivid bird flits restlessly in the
rainforest canopy, making short, quick chases
after insects. This species is usually seen in
flocks of up to 20 or more, often associating
with mixed-species hunting parties.
• **NEST** A cup nest made of lichens,
bound with spiders' webs, and ornamented
with bark flakes. Usually high in the trees.
• **DISTRIBUTION** Indian subcontinent,
S. China, and much of S.E. Asia.
• **REMARK** The scarlet plumage of the
males is replaced by orange in the Indian
subcontinent south of the Himalayas.

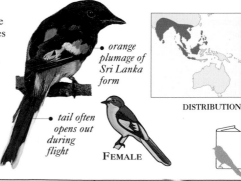

• *orange plumage of Sri Lanka form*

DISTRIBUTION

FEMALE

• *tail often opens out during flight*

Plumage Sexes differ	Habitat	Migration Non-migrant

Family CAMPEPHAGIDAE	Species *Coracina novaehollandiae*	Length 33cm (13in)

BLACK-FACED CUCKOO-SHRIKE

A slender, tree-dwelling bird of thinly spaced woodland, this species has an undulating style of flight and a habit of shuffling its wings just after alighting. The "cuckoo" in its name refers to the long, slender body shape. The "shrike" refers to its style of feeding, taking large insects and their larvae from foliage or the ground, and sometimes eating berries. The call is either a grating "kaark" or a gentler, whistling sound.
• **NEST** A small, saucer-shaped nest made of dry twigs and bark, fixed together with spiders' webs, and built in the fork of a tree branch.
• **DISTRIBUTION** Australia; migrant populations winter in northern states and New Guinea.
• **REMARK** Migration varies between local populations. Some travel to New Guinea, some a shorter distance, while others merely roam nomadically within Australia. These birds settle in places where recent rain has resulted in fresh growth of plants, flowers, and insects. If conditions are suitable, the birds breed.

DISTRIBUTION

slender wings for long-distance flight •

Plumage Sexes alike	Habitat 🌳🌳 🌿🌿	Migration Partial migrant/nomadic

Family PYCNONOTIDAE	Species *Pycnonotus zeylanicus*	Length 28cm (11in)

STRAW-HEADED BULBUL

The largest of all the bulbuls, this bird is usually found in trees and bushes. It occurs at the rainforest edge and in secondary growth (areas where trees have regrown after rainforest clearance). Its food consists chiefly of fruit, buds, and berries, which it supplements with some insects. The song is loud and strong, consisting of a clear, melodious warbling. This species is shy and inconspicuous, more often heard than seen. Among its own flocks, which usually consist of half-a-dozen birds, it behaves in a quarrelsome manner, constantly uttering a harsh and noisy chatter. When excited, the birds raise the short, bristly feathers on the front of their crowns to form a small, straw-coloured crest.
• **NEST** A shallow, cup-shaped nest of rootlets, grass, and leaves, placed in a bush or low tree.
• **DISTRIBUTION** Malay Peninsula, Borneo, Sumatra, and Java.
• **REMARK** This bird has become rare in much of its range as a result of trapping for the local cagebird trade.

• *lowered crest*

black • *moustache*

• *large, heavily built body for a bulbul*

DISTRIBUTION

Plumage Sexes alike	Habitat 🌳🌳 🌿	Migration Non-migrant

Family PYCNONOTIDAE	Species *Pycnonotus jocosus*	Length 20cm (8in)

RED-WHISKERED BULBUL

An agile, active, and sometimes noisy bird, this
bulbul is commonly seen in orchards, gardens,
town parks, and secondary woodland (regrown
after forest clearance). It searches for insects,
fruit, and buds, making characteristically
short, jerky flights and often working in pairs.
• **NEST** A shallow, neat cup nest of twigs
and dead leaves, with finer lining, bound
with spiders' webs, placed in a tree.
• **DISTRIBUTION** Parts of India,
China, and S.E. Asia. Introduced
in USA and Australia.

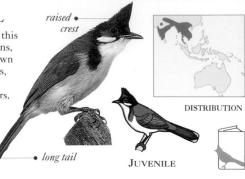

raised •
crest

• long tail

JUVENILE

DISTRIBUTION

Plumage Sexes alike	Habitat	Migration Non-migrant

Family PYCNONOTIDAE	Species *Alophoixus phaeocephalus*	Length 20cm (8in)

YELLOW-BELLIED BULBUL

A common bulbul of lowland
rainforest, this species is recognized
by its combination of a puffy white
throat, yellow underparts, and the
absence of a crest. Being relatively
tame, it is easy to approach. Normally
a solitary bird, it keeps to the lower
levels of the rainforest, where it feeds
mainly on berries and small beetles.
• **NEST** A shallow cup nest made of
plant fibres, lined with fine coconut hairs,
and placed low above ground in a bush or tree.
• **DISTRIBUTION** Malay Peninsula, Sumatra, and Borneo.

grey
• collar

fluffed •
feathers

rufous brown •
rump

DISTRIBUTION

Plumage Sexes alike	Habitat	Migration Non-migrant

Family PYCNONOTIDAE	Species *Hypsipetes leucocephalus*	Length 23cm (9in)

BLACK BULBUL

Loose-plumaged, nervously active
and noisy, the Black Bulbul inhabits oak,
pine, and rhododendron forests in mountains,
feeding on berries and larger fruits. At higher
altitudes it occurs only as a summer visitor.
• **NEST** A neat, flimsy cup made of
grass, leaves, and moss, in a tree fork.
• **DISTRIBUTION** Indian subcontinent
and parts of China and S.E. Asia. Northern
populations migrate southwards in winter.
• **REMARK** There are several distinct
geographical forms of this bird, the one
shown here being the Himalayan subspecies.

• shaggy,
black crest

• long
wings
for agile
flight

• red feet
and legs

forked
• tail

DISTRIBUTION

Plumage Sexes alike	Habitat	Migration Partial migrant

Family IRENIDAE	Species *Aegithina tiphia*	Length 14cm (5½in)

COMMON IORA

This small, active bird is seen either
in pairs or in mixed hunting parties. It
searches for insects and caterpillars among
foliage in rainforests and plantations. In
display, the male fluffs out his rump and
flank feathers, jumps into the air,
and glides back down to his perch.
• **NEST** A neat cup nest
made of plant material, coated
with spiders' webs, in a twig fork.
• **DISTRIBUTION** India and
S.E. Asia to Borneo and Java.

yellow head and neck

vividly streaked wings

DISTRIBUTION

short, square tail

FEMALE

Plumage Sexes differ	Habitat	Migration Non-migrant

Family IRENIDAE	Species *Chloropsis hardwickii*	Length 19cm (7½in)

ORANGE-BELLIED LEAFBIRD

This acrobatic species is often seen in pairs or
small parties high in the foliage canopy, mainly
in hill forest. The Orange-bellied Leafbird
commonly joins other bird species to visit
blossoming trees, where it feeds on insects
and spiders, as well as taking nectar
with its special brush-tipped tongue.
• **NEST** A cradle of roots
and fibres, suspended between
twigs near the end of a tree branch.
• **DISTRIBUTION**
From the eastern Himalayas and
S. China to the Malay Peninsula.

long, curved bill

pale orange belly

DISTRIBUTION

blue tail and flight feathers

FEMALE

Plumage Sexes differ	Habitat	Migration Non-migrant

Family IRENIDAE	Species *Irena puella*	Length 27cm (10½in)

ASIAN FAIRY BLUEBIRD

Though not always noticed in the
tree shade, this is a common bird of
both deciduous and evergreen forest.
It is often seen in small groups,
feeding on fruits in the tops of tall
trees. Its presence is given away
by its flowing, musical calls.
• **NEST** A mossy cup nest on
a twig base, lined with rootlets,
placed in the fork of a twig.
• **DISTRIBUTION** S.W. India;
and from E. Himalayas through
S.E. Asia to Borneo and Java.

stout, fruit-eating bill

DISTRIBUTION

long tail coverts

FEMALE

Plumage Sexes differ	Habitat	Migration Non-migrant

Family LANIIDAE	Species *Eurocephalus anguitimens*	Length 9½in (24cm)

SOUTHERN WHITE-CROWNED SHRIKE

An unusually sociable shrike, this species is usually seen in pairs or small parties. It perches conspicuously on top, or on the outer branches, of trees in woodlands or savanna (tropical or subtropical grassland). Like other shrikes it forages for insects and other prey by dropping from a perch to the ground, as well as feeding on berries. Its flight is strong and direct, with shallow, quick wingbeats.
• **NEST** A thick-walled cup nest, made of plant fibres and bound with spiders' webs, located in a tree.
• **DISTRIBUTION** Parts of southern Africa.

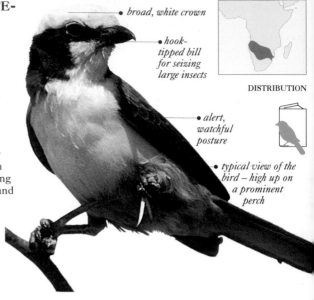

• *broad, white crown*

• *hook-tipped bill for seizing large insects*

DISTRIBUTION

• *alert, watchful posture*

• *typical view of the bird – high up on a prominent perch*

Plumage Sexes alike	Habitat	Migration Non-migrant

Family LANIIDAE	Species *Corvinella melanoleuca*	Length 45cm (17½in)

MAGPIE-SHRIKE

Unmistakable with its long, black tail, this species inhabits open, semi-arid woodland, often of acacia trees, and scrub. Unusually sociable for a shrike, it is generally seen in noisy groups of up to a dozen individuals. The Magpie-Shrike perches on the tops of trees and bushes, dropping down to seize its prey, which consists of insects and small reptiles.
• **NEST** A bulky, cup-shaped nest made of twigs, grass stems, and roots, lined with finer rootlets and the stems and tendrils of creepers, and placed in a tree.

DISTRIBUTION

• **DISTRIBUTION** Eastern and southern Africa from Kenya to Mozambique.
• **REMARKS** This bird is also known as the Long-tailed Shrike. It is one of a range of open-country birds using a long tail as a display feature.

• *broad, domed head*

• *bold white bars (often concealed)*

• *stout body*

• *long tail impresses females as well as warning other males to stay off the territory*

Plumage Sexes alike	Habitat	Migration Non-migrant

Family LANIIDAE	Species *Prionops plumatus*	Length 20cm (8in)

WHITE HELMET-SHRIKE

Unlike many shrikes, this species
is exceptionally gregarious at all times,
forming groups of up to 20 birds, usually
consisting of siblings from several broods. It
forages at all levels, from the forest canopy to
the ground, taking insects and spiders. Groups
roost together on branches in huddled rows.
• **NEST** A compact cup nest made of
bark shreds, bound on the outside with
spiders' webs, and placed in a tree fork.
• **DISTRIBUTION** Parts of
Africa south of the Sahara.

crest
projects
over bill

yellow
wattle
around
the eye

short,
rounded
wings

DISTRIBUTION

Plumage Sexes alike	Habitat	Migration Non-migrant

Family LANIIDAE	Species *Tchagra senegala*	Length 22cm (8½in)

BLACK-CROWNED TCHAGRA

Like most shrikes, this bird is usually solitary
or seen in pairs. It forages for invertebrates and
other small animals on or near the ground,
and flies low between bushes in
fluttering flight. In its display
flight it rises from a bush,
calling, then glides down.
• **NEST** A shallow cup nest
of fine twigs and roots, lined
with finer rootlets, in a bush.
• **DISTRIBUTION** N.W. Africa;
parts of Africa south of the
Sahara; S.W. Arabian Peninsula.

rufous
plumage on
back and
wings

DISTRIBUTION

Plumage Sexes alike	Habitat	Migration Non-migrant

Family LANIIDAE	Species *Laniarius atrococcineus*	Length 23cm (9in)

CRIMSON-BREASTED GONOLEK

This vividly coloured shrike is
secretive in behaviour. It lives in open
woodland, foraging for insects on
the ground or in trees. Calls
are loud and bell-like, and
mating pairs often sing
together in "duets".
• **NEST** A bark
bowl, secured with spiders'
webs and lined with fibres, in a tree.
• **DISTRIBUTION** Parts of southern Africa.

JUVENILE

hooked bill

white
wing stripe

DISTRIBUTION

Plumage Sexes alike	Habitat	Migration Non-migrant

Family LANIIDAE	Species *Telephorus zeylonus*	Length 23cm (9in)

BOKMAKIERIE

This shrike perches in conspicuous places on bushy hillsides with rocks, in river-valley scrub, and in gardens. It hunts low in the undergrowth for insects and small animals. Pairs sing "duetting" calls all year round.
• **NEST** A bulky bowl made of twigs and stems, usually in a dense bush.
• **DISTRIBUTION** Parts of southern Africa.

typical "duetting" posture

pairs sing from the tops of bushes

DISTRIBUTION

JUVENILE

Plumage Sexes alike	Habitat	Migration Non-migrant

Family LANIIDAE	Species *Lanius collurio*	Length 18cm (7in)

RED-BACKED SHRIKE

This predator-like songbird is seen in bushes and scrub, watching from a vantage point and swooping on prey. It feeds mainly on insects, sometimes on birds and other small animals.
• **NEST** A deep cup nest of grass and rootlets, placed in a dense bush.
• **DISTRIBUTION** Breeds in Eurasia from S.E. Britain to W. Siberia. Migrates southwards, some birds reaching South Africa.

black eyestripe

rich rufous back

alert, upright pose

FEMALE

DISTRIBUTION

Plumage Sexes differ	Habitat	Migration Migrant

Family LANIIDAE	Species *Lanius ludovicianus*	Length 22cm (8½in)

LOGGERHEAD SHRIKE

Thinly wooded, open country is the main habitat of this shrike. It moves about in short flights from one lookout perch to another, feeding by swooping to the ground to seize prey, mainly insects.
• **NEST** A well-lined, bulky cup nest made of twigs, weed stems, and rootlets, placed in a thick shrub or low tree.
• **DISTRIBUTION** From S. Canada to Mexico. Northern populations migrate southwards.

black eyestripe

hooked bill

JUVENILE

black wings

DISTRIBUTION

Plumage Sexes alike	Habitat	Migration Migrant

Family VANGIDAE	Species *Schetba rufa*	Length 20cm (8in)

RUFOUS VANGA

Strictly a rainforest species, the Rufous Vanga is usually seen in family groups of four to eight birds. It is a rather inactive hunter, often spending long intervals watching from a low branch before swooping to seize prey. It feeds on a variety of insects but will also take lizards if available.
• **NEST** Details have not been scientifically recorded.
• **DISTRIBUTION** Madagascar.
• **REMARK** Belongs to a family of birds that are found only in Madagascar.

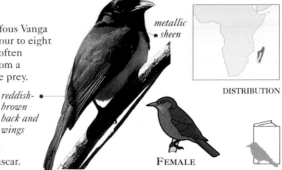

metallic sheen

reddish-brown back and wings

DISTRIBUTION

FEMALE

Plumage Sexes differ	Habitat	Migration Non-migrant

Family BOMBYCILLIDAE	Species *Bombycilla garrulus*	Length 20cm (8in)

BOHEMIAN WAXWING

Normally found in northern forests, where it eats berries and insects, this bird expands its range in exceptional years, appearing in towns and gardens.
• **NEST** A cup nest on a conifer branch, usually hidden in thick foliage.
• **DISTRIBUTION** Breeds in Canada, N.W. USA, and N. Eurasia. Southern limits of the winter range vary from year to year.

raised crest

DISTRIBUTION

waxy blobs on secondary feather tips

JUVENILE

Plumage Sexes differ slightly	Habitat	Migration Migrant

Family BOMBYCILLIDAE	Species *Bombycilla cedrorum*	Length 18cm (7¼in)

CEDAR WAXWING

This species is plainer in colour than the Northern Waxwing, and lives in a wider variety of habitats including both broadleaved and coniferous forest, open woodland, and thickets. It feeds on a variety of small fruits, and sometimes also catches insects in gliding flight above the trees.
• **NEST** A stout cup nest hidden in dense foliage, often high in a tree.
• **DISTRIBUTION** Breeds in Canada and much of USA. Winter range extends from S. Canada to N. South America.

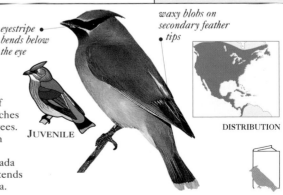

eyestripe bends below the eye

waxy blobs on secondary feather tips

DISTRIBUTION

JUVENILE

Plumage Sexes differ slightly	Habitat	Migration Migrant

Family BOMBYCILLIDAE	Species *Phainopepla nitens*	Length 20cm (8in)

PHAINOPEPLA

Recognized by its direct,
buoyant flight, this bird
breeds either in semi-
desert or in riverside
areas in deserts. It feeds
on mistletoe and buckthorn
berries, also catching insects.
• **NEST** A well-concealed
cup nest made of plant fibres,
strengthened with small twigs.
• **DISTRIBUTION** Breeds in S.W.
USA and W. Mexico. Winters in Mexico.

sharp crest

FEMALE

DISTRIBUTION

wings conceal a white patch, revealed in flight

Plumage Sexes differ	Habitat	Migration Migrant

Family CINCLIDAE	Species *Cinclus cinclus*	Length 18cm (7in)

DIPPER

This species lives and nests on fast-running
streams, especially in hill country. It walks
and even swims underwater in its search
for prey, which consists of insect larvae and
crustaceans. The name is derived from its
frequent "bobbing" movements.
• **NEST** Large and spherical
with a side entrance, built
over running water and
made of moss, grass, and leaves.
• **DISTRIBUTION** Mainly
mountainous and hilly regions
of Eurasia and N.W. Africa.

stout but streamlined body

short, stiff tail

DISTRIBUTION

JUVENILE

Plumage Sexes alike	Habitat	Migration Partial migrant

Family TROGLODYTIDAE	Species *Campylorhynchus brunneicapillus*	Length 22cm (8½in)

CACTUS WREN

Living in arid landscapes, this bird
often sings from the top of a cactus.
It feeds on the ground, taking insects
and invertebrates, and makes short,
slow flights with whirring wingbeats.
• **NEST** Spherical, made
of dry vegetation, with an
entrance tunnel at the side,
in a cactus or thorny bush.
• **DISTRIBUTION** Parts of
S.W. USA and Mexico.
• **REMARK** The largest
North American wren.

stout build

intricate, flecked pattern

top of cactus

DISTRIBUTION

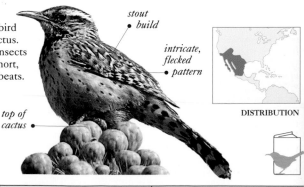

Plumage Sexes alike	Habitat	Migration Non-migrant

Family TROGLODYTIDAE	Species *Donacobius atricapillus*	Length 23cm (9in)

BLACK-CAPPED DONACOBIUS

This marsh-dwelling bird feeds on insects. It is
usually hidden in the vegetation, but when disturbed,
it flies to a prominent perch and boldly scolds the
intruder. In display, pairs sing together while
each bird bobs its head and wags its tail.
• **NEST** A deep, bulky structure made
of marsh vegetation, usually built
in the foliage, low over water.
• **DISTRIBUTION**
From extreme tip of
E. Panama to N.E. Argentina.
• **REMARK** This is the
largest wren species
in the world.

staring •
eye

stout, •
strong
bill

• *typical
alert pose*

• *very long legs*

leg feathering •

• long tail
wags vigorously
in display

DISTRIBUTION

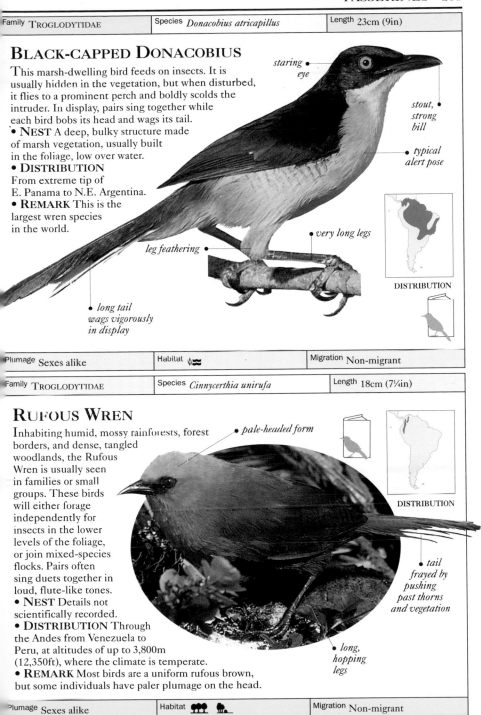

Plumage Sexes alike	Habitat 〰️	Migration Non-migrant

Family TROGLODYTIDAE	Species *Cinnycerthia unirufa*	Length 18cm (7¼in)

RUFOUS WREN

Inhabiting humid, mossy rainforests, forest
borders, and dense, tangled
woodlands, the Rufous
Wren is usually seen
in families or small
groups. These birds
will either forage
independently for
insects in the lower
levels of the foliage,
or join mixed-species
flocks. Pairs often
sing duets together in
loud, flute-like tones.
• **NEST** Details not
scientifically recorded.
• **DISTRIBUTION** Through
the Andes from Venezuela to
Peru, at altitudes of up to 3,800m
(12,350ft), where the climate is temperate.
• **REMARK** Most birds are a uniform rufous brown,
but some individuals have paler plumage on the head.

• *pale-headed form*

DISTRIBUTION

• tail
frayed by
pushing
past thorns
and vegetation

• long,
hopping
legs

Plumage Sexes alike	Habitat 🌳🌳 🪨	Migration Non-migrant

Family TROGLODYTIDAE	Species *Thryomanes bewickii*	Length 13cm (5in)

BEWICK'S WREN

Common but not easily seen, Bewick's
Wren is a small bird with reddish-brown or
grey-brown plumage and a long, narrow stripe
above the eye. It has a characteristic habit of
flicking its tail sideways as it works through
the undergrowth, feeding on insects.
• **NEST** A bulky, deep cup nest,
made from plant material, feathers, and wool,
placed in a crevice or often in a bird box.
• **DISTRIBUTION** Breeds in much of USA
and N. Mexico. Some northern populations
migrate south within this range in winter.

*slender
bill*

*reddish-
brown
form*

DISTRIBUTION

*tail often
flicks from
side to side*

Plumage Sexes alike	Habitat	Migration Partial migrant

Family TROGLODYTIDAE	Species *Thryothorus ludovicianus*	Length 14.5cm (5¾in)

CAROLINA WREN

A medium-sized wren,
this bird hides in the
undergrowth, where it
searches for insects. Its
habitats include gardens,
woods, farmland, and scrub. The
song, consisting of a short, musical
phrase repeated with endless
variations, is heard all year round.
• **NEST** A bulky structure of
leaves, grasses, and feathers, usually
located in a hole, brushpile, or cranny.
• **DISTRIBUTION** E. USA and Mexico.

*long stripe
above the eye*

*uptilted
tail*

DISTRIBUTION

*crouched
posture*

Plumage Sexes alike	Habitat	Migration Non-migrant

Family TROGLODYTIDAE	Species *Troglodytes troglodytes*	Length 8cm (3¼in)

NORTHERN WREN

This tiny bird, with its slender bill
and secretive manner, is found in
forests, woods, farmlands, grassland,
and gardens. It is usually seen singly
as it busily seeks insects in tangled
cover. The explosive song is loud
for a bird of this diminutive size.
• **NEST** A dome made of leaves, grass,
and moss, with a side entrance, and
placed in a crevice or sheltered site.
• **DISTRIBUTION** A widespread
species in the temperate zone
of the Northern Hemisphere.

*large
head*

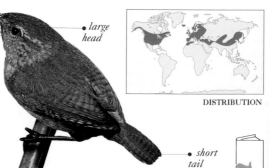

DISTRIBUTION

*short
tail*

Plumage Sexes alike	Habitat	Migration Non-migrant

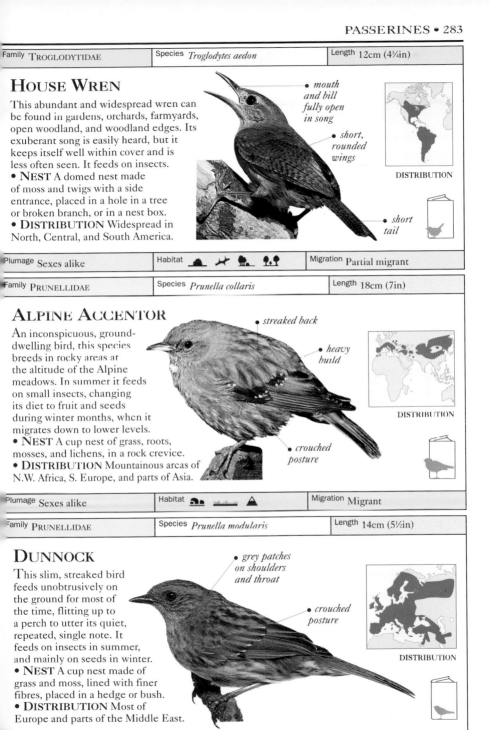

| Family TROGLODYTIDAE | Species *Troglodytes aedon* | Length 12cm (4¾in) |

HOUSE WREN

This abundant and widespread wren can be found in gardens, orchards, farmyards, open woodland, and woodland edges. Its exuberant song is easily heard, but it keeps itself well within cover and is less often seen. It feeds on insects.
• **NEST** A domed nest made of moss and twigs with a side entrance, placed in a hole in a tree or broken branch, or in a nest box.
• **DISTRIBUTION** Widespread in North, Central, and South America.

mouth and bill fully open in song

short, rounded wings

DISTRIBUTION

short tail

| Plumage Sexes alike | Habitat | Migration Partial migrant |

| Family PRUNELLIDAE | Species *Prunella collaris* | Length 18cm (7in) |

ALPINE ACCENTOR

An inconspicuous, ground-dwelling bird, this species breeds in rocky areas at the altitude of the Alpine meadows. In summer it feeds on small insects, changing its diet to fruit and seeds during winter months, when it migrates down to lower levels.
• **NEST** A cup nest of grass, roots, mosses, and lichens, in a rock crevice.
• **DISTRIBUTION** Mountainous areas of N.W. Africa, S. Europe, and parts of Asia.

streaked back

heavy build

DISTRIBUTION

crouched posture

| Plumage Sexes alike | Habitat | Migration Migrant |

| Family PRUNELLIDAE | Species *Prunella modularis* | Length 14cm (5½in) |

DUNNOCK

This slim, streaked bird feeds unobtrusively on the ground for most of the time, flitting up to a perch to utter its quiet, repeated, single note. It feeds on insects in summer, and mainly on seeds in winter.
• **NEST** A cup nest made of grass and moss, lined with finer fibres, placed in a hedge or bush.
• **DISTRIBUTION** Most of Europe and parts of the Middle East.

grey patches on shoulders and throat

crouched posture

DISTRIBUTION

| Plumage Sexes alike | Habitat | Migration Partial migrant |

Family MIMIDAE	Species *Dumetella carolinensis*	Length 22cm (8½in)

GREY CATBIRD

The catbird is so named because of its descending, cat-like "mew" call. It is furtive, but is a moderately common bird of dense thickets in deciduous woodlands, often living in gardens and town parks. Here it keeps low, often skulking on the ground, feeding on berries, seeds, insects, and invertebrates.

black crown

tail is usually tilted up

- **NEST** A cup nest made of twigs, lined with finer rootlets, and placed in a bush or tangle of undergrowth.
- **DISTRIBUTION** Breeds in S. Canada and much of the USA. Winters in S.E. USA, parts of the Caribbean, and Central America to Panama.
- **REMARK** Like the related Northern Mockingbird, this bird imitates songs of other birds, but its performances are quieter and less varied, and it does not repeat phrases as Mockingbirds do.

DISTRIBUTION

slate-grey plumage above and below

Plumage Sexes alike	Habitat	Migration Migrant

Family MIMIDAE	Species *Mimus polyglottos*	Length 25cm (10in)

NORTHERN MOCKINGBIRD

A bold, noisy, and aggressive bird, this species is willing to live among humans as long as gardens or woods with thickets can be found. It also thrives in semi-desert. This species is a skilful mimic and incorporates memorized phrases as part of its song, typically repeating each one several times over. Its food consists of fruit, berries, and insects.

JUVENILE

- **NEST** An open cup nest made of sticks, lined with rootlets, fine grass, leaves, and plant down, and placed on a low branch in a shrub or thicket.
- **DISTRIBUTION** Parts of USA and most of Mexico. Northern populations migrate south within this range in winter.
- **REMARK** The bird's name is a reference to its mimicry of other birds.

long tail

white wing bars

long legs for foraging on the ground

DISTRIBUTION

Plumage Sexes alike	Habitat	Migration Partial migrant

Family MIMIDAE	Species *Toxostoma rufum*	Length 29cm (11½in)

BROWN THRASHER

Large compared with other birds that live in the undergrowth, the Brown Thrasher is a shy inhabitant of dense thickets and woodland edges. It feeds by flicking back ("thrashing") leaves with its strong bill to disturb and expose its insect prey.
• **NEST** A cup nest made of twigs and lined with finer material, placed in a bush or tangle of thick undergrowth.
• **DISTRIBUTION** Breeds in S. Canada and C. and E. USA. Spends the winter in S.E. USA.
• **REMARK** Often sings from cover, uttering each phrase only twice.

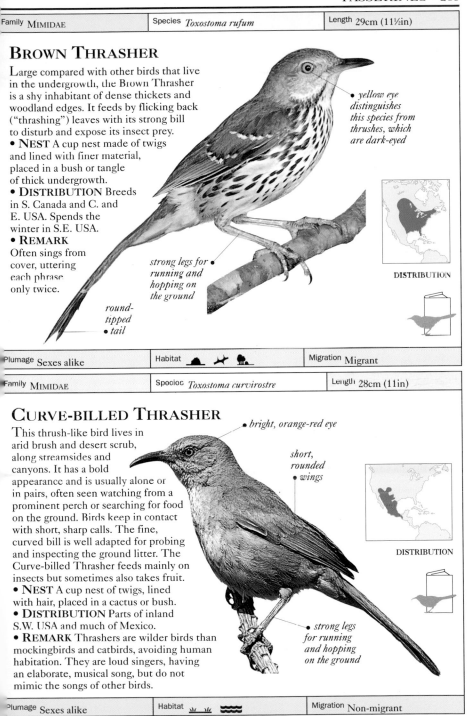

yellow eye distinguishes this species from thrushes, which are dark-eyed

strong legs for running and hopping on the ground

round-tipped tail

DISTRIBUTION

Plumage Sexes alike	Habitat	Migration Migrant

Family MIMIDAE	Species *Toxostoma curvirostre*	Length 28cm (11in)

CURVE-BILLED THRASHER

This thrush-like bird lives in arid brush and desert scrub, along streamsides and canyons. It has a bold appearance and is usually alone or in pairs, often seen watching from a prominent perch or searching for food on the ground. Birds keep in contact with short, sharp calls. The fine, curved bill is well adapted for probing and inspecting the ground litter. The Curve-billed Thrasher feeds mainly on insects but sometimes also takes fruit.
• **NEST** A cup nest of twigs, lined with hair, placed in a cactus or bush.
• **DISTRIBUTION** Parts of inland S.W. USA and much of Mexico.
• **REMARK** Thrashers are wilder birds than mockingbirds and catbirds, avoiding human habitation. They are loud singers, having an elaborate, musical song, but do not mimic the songs of other birds.

bright, orange-red eye

short, rounded wings

DISTRIBUTION

strong legs for running and hopping on the ground

Plumage Sexes alike	Habitat	Migration Non-migrant

| Family TURDIDAE | Species *Chaetops frenatus* | Length 24cm (9½in) |

RUFOUS ROCKJUMPER

Found exclusively on rocky mountain slopes, this bird is designed for life among the boulders, running quickly over rock surfaces and seeking insects and lizards. It has a piping call.
• **NEST** A cup nest made of coarse grass, rushes, lichens, and sticks, lined with roots and hairs, on the ground near a rock.
• **DISTRIBUTION** Part of South Africa.

alert, watchful posture

long tail for balance *strong legs for hopping among boulders*

DISTRIBUTION

FEMALE

| Plumage Sexes differ | Habitat | Migration Non-migrant |

| Family TURDIDAE | Species *Drymodes superciliaris* | Length 22cm (8¾in) |

NORTHERN SCRUB-ROBIN

A slender robin that lives on the rainforest floor, this is an intensely shy and inconspicuous species, often difficult to see in its dark environment. It moves with springy hops and uptilted tail in search of insects. Its call is a loud, shrill whistle, which it will utter in reply if imitated.
• **NEST** A circular depression scratched in the ground, roughly lined with wiry tendrils of plants, fibres, and leaves.
• **DISTRIBUTION** New Guinea and Australia (N.E. Queensland).

soft colours for camouflage

DISTRIBUTION

long tail, often tilted up *long legs for ground-feeding*

| Plumage Sexes alike | Habitat | Migration Non-migrant |

| Family TURDIDAE | Species *Erithacus rubecula* | Length 14cm (5½in) |

EURASIAN ROBIN

Both male and female robins defend territories, display their red breasts, and sing from prominent perches all through winter. Robins are tame in western Europe but in the east they are shy, woodland birds. The diet consists of worms and insects, taken mainly from the ground.
• **NEST** A bulky nest of moss and leaves, lined with hair, in a crevice.
• **DISTRIBUTION** Eurasia to W. Siberia, N. Africa, and the Middle East. Eastern populations migrate south in winter.

DISTRIBUTION

alert posture

JUVENILE

| Plumage Sexes alike | Habitat | Migration Partial migrant |

Family TURDIDAE	Species *Luscinia megarhynchos*	Length 16.5cm (6½in)

NIGHTINGALE

The sober colours and unobtrusive behaviour of the Nightingale are compensated for by its varied, musical song. It inhabits woodland and undergrowth, feeding on insects, berries, and fruit.
• **NEST** A thick cup made of dead leaves, lined with fine grass and hairs, at ground level in a thicket.
• **DISTRIBUTION** Breeds in parts of Europe, N. Africa, Middle East, and C. Asia. Winters in Africa and Arabian Peninsula.

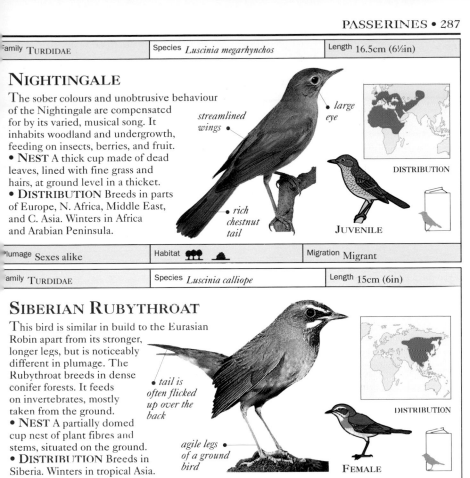

streamlined wings •

• large eye

DISTRIBUTION

• rich chestnut tail

JUVENILE

Plumage Sexes alike	Habitat	Migration Migrant

Family TURDIDAE	Species *Luscinia calliope*	Length 15cm (6in)

SIBERIAN RUBYTHROAT

This bird is similar in build to the Eurasian Robin apart from its stronger, longer legs, but is noticeably different in plumage. The Rubythroat breeds in dense conifer forests. It feeds on invertebrates, mostly taken from the ground.
• **NEST** A partially domed cup nest of plant fibres and stems, situated on the ground.
• **DISTRIBUTION** Breeds in Siberia. Winters in tropical Asia.

• tail is often flicked up over the back

agile legs • of a ground bird

DISTRIBUTION

FEMALE

Plumage Sexes differ	Habitat	Migration Migrant

Family TURDIDAE	Species *Luscinia svecica*	Length 14cm (5½in)

BLUETHROAT

This bird is a type of robin, but is unusually secretive, skulking in the low vegetation. It breeds in forest, forest edges, and willow scrub. Its winter habitat is mainly scrub. The diet consists of insects.
• **NEST** A cup nest on the ground in thick vegetation.
• **DISTRIBUTION** Breeds in Eurasia and Alaska. Winters in Africa and Asia.
• **REMARK** The colour pattern on the throat and breast varies geographically.

tail is often fanned and flicked •

• north European birds have this chestnut spot

DISTRIBUTION

FEMALE

Plumage Sexes differ	Habitat	Migration Migrant

Family TURDIDAE	Species *Phoenicurus ochruros*	Length 15cm (6in)

BLACK REDSTART

A lover of rocky places, also adapted
to urban life, this bird often perches on
a rock or wall. Here it characteristically
bobs up and down, with a shiver
of its tail, before darting to the
ground to pick up an insect.
• **NEST** A cup nest of plant
materials, lined with fine grass, hair,
and feathers, situated in a crevice.
• **DISTRIBUTION** Parts of Europe,
N. and E. Africa, Middle East. Some
southward migration in winter.

grey-black
plumage of
male in
winter

DISTRIBUTION

tail is
frequently
wagged

FEMALE

Plumage Sexes differ	Habitat	Migration Partial migrant

Family TURDIDAE	Species *Cinclidium leucurum*	Length 17cm (6¾in)

WHITE-TAILED ROBIN

A solitary and secretive
robin, this bird is most often
seen on the ground in thick
cover near a forest stream. It
feeds on insects, with berries
in winter. Some pairs breed
high in the Himalayas,
wintering at lower altitudes.
• **NEST** A cup-shaped, domed, or
semi-domed nest of rootlets, dead
leaves, and moss, on the ground.
• **DISTRIBUTION** N.E. India,
S. China, parts of S.E. Asia.

tail fanned
as an alarm
signal

DISTRIBUTION

FEMALE

Plumage Sexes differ	Habitat	Migration Non-migrant

Family TURDIDAE	Species *Sialia sialis*	Length 16.5cm (6½in)

EASTERN BLUEBIRD

This plump, upright bird is a summer
visitor to woodlands, orchards, and farms,
feeding on both insects and fruit. It is
seen in large flocks during migration.
• **NEST** A simple cup nest with a fine
lining, placed in a tree hole or nest-box.
• **DISTRIBUTION** Breeds in
E. North and Central America.
Winters as far south as Nicaragua.
• **REMARK** This species requires
a nest-hole, but competes poorly
with starlings and sparrows. Nest-box
provision has helped its survival.

long wings
and tail

DISTRIBUTION

radiant
blue
plumage

FEMALE

Plumage Sexes differ	Habitat	Migration Partial migrant

Family TURDIDAE	Species *Sialia currucoides*	Length 18cm (7in)

MOUNTAIN BLUEBIRD

Of the three North American bluebird species, this alone lacks chestnut in its plumage. It inhabits open meadows, generally above 1,500m (5,000ft) in summer, often visiting lowlands in winter, forming wandering flocks. It feeds on insects, caught in hovering flight or picked from the ground.
• NEST A loose cup nest, made of plant materials, in a tree hole or nest-box.
• DISTRIBUTION
Breeds in W. North America. Migrates south in winter as far as Mexico.

blue throat, breast, and belly

DISTRIBUTION

wings are long and pointed

FEMALE

Plumage Sexes differ	Habitat	Migration Migrant

Family TURDIDAE	Species *Saxicola torquata*	Length 13cm (5in)

COMMON STONECHAT

This plump, dark-faced bird gets its name from its sharp, scolding call which sounds like two stones being knocked together. It inhabits open heathland, where it perches on the tops of bushes before swooping to take insects on the ground or occasionally in the air.
• NEST A loose cup nest of plant materials, lined and tucked into vegetation on or near ground level.
• DISTRIBUTION Much of Europe, the Middle East, and Africa. Some southward migration in winter.

black head contrasts with white neck patch

DISTRIBUTION

rufous orange breast

FEMALE

Plumage Sexes differ	Habitat	Migration Partial migrant

Family TURDIDAE	Species *Oenanthe oenanthe*	Length 15cm (6in)

NORTHERN WHEATEAR

An inconspicuous bird of bare, open ground, this species forages on the ground, hunting invertebrates. It also catches insects in flight.
• NEST A lined cup nest made of grass and moss, in a cavity.
• DISTRIBUTION
Breeds in Eurasia and N. North America. Winters in Africa.

foraging birds pause to look around

DISTRIBUTION

when taking off, birds expose a black-and-white pattern at the rump

FEMALE

Plumage Sexes differ	Habitat	Migration Migrant

Family TURDIDAE	Species *Enicurus ruficapillus*	Length 18cm (7in)

CHESTNUT-NAPED FORKTAIL

This species lives beside clear-water streams flowing through rainforest.
Here it perches on rocks in mid-stream, running after insects on
the rock or darting after them in the air. It is a wary
bird, always following the
stream-bed when disturbed.
• **NEST** A deep
cup nest, lined
with plant fibres,
and plastered
with a layer
of mud to an
overhanging surface.
• **DISTRIBUTION** Malay
Peninsula, Sumatra, and Borneo.
• **REMARK** There are seven
species of forktail. All are thrushes
of fast-flowing mountain streams,
living in different parts of Asia.
They are all colourfully
marked birds with smartly
forked tails, and are very
sure-footed on the
rocks and in water.

"scaly" plumage on the breast

DISTRIBUTION

forked tail

strong, agile legs

FEMALE

Plumage Sexes differ	Habitat	Migration Non-migrant

Family TURDIDAE	Species *Myiophonus caeruleus*	Length 32cm (12½in)

BLUE WHISTLING THRUSH

Pale feather tips give the violet blue
plumage of this bird a vivid, spangled
effect when seen in motion. Its shy
behaviour, however, and the shaded
habitat, make it hard to see. It lives
in forests alongside mountain streams,
many of them running through ravines
and gorges, overshadowed by rock
walls. It is surefooted enough
to wade through fast-running
water and leap from boulder to
boulder. Pairs stay on territory
all year. The diet consists
of invertebrates and fruit.
• **NEST** A cup-shaped nest
made mainly of moss, often
placed on a ledge in a small cave.
• **DISTRIBUTION** Forests in
Himalayan region, and mountain
ranges of E. and S.E. Asia as far as Java.

silver-blue feather tips sparkle as the bird turns in the light

DISTRIBUTION

the tail is often fanned out, raised, and swayed from side to side

long wings with black-tipped flight feathers

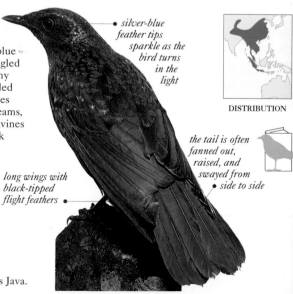

Plumage Sexes alike	Habitat	Migration Non-migrant

Family TURDIDAE	Species *Zoothera interpres*	Length 16cm (6¼in)

CHESTNUT-CAPPED THRUSH

This boldly coloured but shy thrush lives in rainforests, where it is generally seen skulking about on the forest floor. An infrequent singer, it ascends to the mid-height of the trees to perform its song, which is wonderfully musical and varied. Its diet consists of fruits, insects, and other invertebrates such as worms and snails.
• **NEST** A cup-shaped nest in the fork of a slender sapling.
• **DISTRIBUTION** Malaysia and parts of Thailand, Indonesia, and the Philippines.

large eye

spotted belly

DISTRIBUTION

long legs for foraging on the ground

Plumage Sexes alike	Habitat	Migration Non-migrant

Family TURDIDAE	Species *Catharus guttatus*	Length 19cm (7½in)

HERMIT THRUSH

A summer resident in northern forests and on forested mountains, the Hermit Thrush can be identified by the rufous colour of its tail. It is famed for the beauty of its slow, descending song. Berries and insects are its main food.
• **NEST** A compact but bulky cup made of plant materials and mud, usually on the ground under a conifer.
• **DISTRIBUTION** Breeds in North America. Winters as far south as Guatemala.

large eye

typical plump shape

DISTRIBUTION

rufous tail

MOUNTAIN FORM

Plumage Sexes alike	Habitat	Migration Migrant

Family TURDIDAE	Species *Hylocichla mustelina*	Length 20cm (8in)

WOOD THRUSH

A delightfully musical thrush living in woodland habitats, this bird feeds mainly on the ground, taking invertebrates. It also sometimes feeds in the trees, taking insects and fruit.
• **NEST** A cup nest of plant material, with a layer of mud, in a sapling or undergrowth.
• **DISTRIBUTION** Breeds in Canada, W. USA, and New England. Winters in S. USA and Central America.

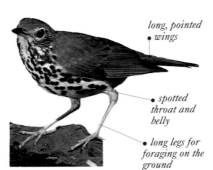

long, pointed wings

spotted throat and belly

DISTRIBUTION

long legs for foraging on the ground

Plumage Sexes alike	Habitat	Migration Migrant

Family TURDIDAE	Species *Turdus merula*	Length 24cm (9½in)

EURASIAN BLACKBIRD

The bold, pure-black plumage of the male – made all the more vivid by his contrasting orange bill and eye-ring – make this bird a very familiar garden species. In the European part of its range, it frequently feeds on lawns. In the East, it is a bird of forest borders and scrub. Everywhere, it feeds chiefly on the ground, scratching and turning leaves to find invertebrates, sometimes taking fruit. The male utters his musical and varied song from a high vantage point.

• *bluntish bill, used for eating fruit as well as probing the ground*

• **NEST** A bulky cup nest made of plant materials and mud, in a tree or bush.
• **DISTRIBUTION** Much of Europe, and parts of N. Africa and Asia. Some southward migration in winter. Introduced in Australia and New Zealand.

FEMALE

DISTRIBUTION

• *athletic legs can run or make rapid, bounding hops*

Plumage Sexes differ	Habitat	Migration Partial migrant

Family TURDIDAE	Species *Turdus pilaris*	Length 25cm (10in)

FIELDFARE

A self-assertive and noisy thrush with a loud, chuckling call, the Fieldfare lives in woodland in small colonies during the breeding season. In winter, roaming flocks often feed and roost in open grassland. Invertebrates form much of the diet; in autumn and winter, birds also eat berries, such as rowan and hawthorn, and fallen fruits such as apples.

• *grey head, nape, and cheeks*

• **NEST** A stout cup nest of plant material *heavy build* • and mud, with a finer inner lining of grass, placed in a tree or bush.
• **DISTRIBUTION** Breeds across N. Eurasia. Winters in Europe and S.W. Asia.
• **REMARK** Birds will aggressively threaten any observer entering their colony.

• *strong legs for bounding and hopping*

DISTRIBUTION

Plumage Sexes alike	Habitat	Migration Migrant

Family TURDIDAE	Species *Turdus philomelos*	Length 23cm (9in)

SONG THRUSH

With its boldly spotted underside and upright stance, the Song Thrush is a familiar bird in well-planted parks and gardens throughout northwest Europe. In the rest of its range it is purely a woodland bird. It feeds on invertebrates, commonly snails. To eat these, Song Thrushes are seen making regular visits to a chosen stone which is used as an "anvil" for breaking the shells open. Berries are another food.
• **NEST** A cup made of plant material, lined with a smooth cup of mud, wood pulp, or clay, in a tree or bush.
• **DISTRIBUTION** Europe, N. Africa, Middle East, and C. Asia. Introduced in Australia and New Zealand.

slender bill

upright posture

spotted breast and belly

long, slender legs

numbered ring indicates that this captive bird is aviary-bred – not caught in the wild

DISTRIBUTION

Plumage Sexes alike	Habitat	Migration Partial migrant

Family TURDIDAE	Species *Turdus viscivorus*	Length 28cm (11in)

MISTLE THRUSH

This large, pale thrush with a bold pattern of spots on its underside is most often seen on the ground, though it sometimes perches in trees. It feeds in pairs or family parties, taking invertebrates on open ground and berries from trees and bushes. Pairs or individual birds can be seen vigorously defending a source of food, such as a fruit tree in winter, from other thrushes. The flight call is a harsh, grating chatter, while the song, which is loud and clear, consists of short, musical phrases.
• **NEST** A cup nest made of grass and moss, usually in the fork of a tree, often higher than nests of other thrushes.
• **DISTRIBUTION** Europe, N.W. Africa, Middle East, and C. Asia. Some populations in east of range migrate.
• **REMARK** Sometimes known as the "storm cock" because of its habit of singing from a treetop in rough weather, early in the year.

strong bill

upright, self-assertive stance

long, powerful legs

DISTRIBUTION

Plumage Sexes alike	Habitat	Migration Partial migrant

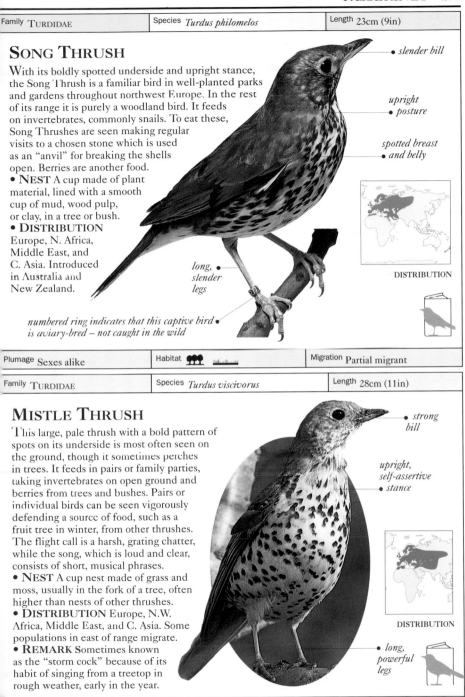

Family TURDIDAE	Species *Turdus migratorius*	Length 25cm (10in)

AMERICAN ROBIN

In its original wild state this bird lived purely in woodland, but it has now become a familiar sight in town parks and suburban gardens. It is primarily a ground-feeding bird and is seen pulling up worms, scratching among leaves, and eating insects and snails. Fruit is taken from orchards. The short, melodious song is heard from early spring.

JUVENILE

DISTRIBUTION

• **NEST** A bulky nest made of twigs, grass, and mud, in a wide variety of situations at any height from ground level to the treetops.
• **DISTRIBUTION** Canada, USA, Mexico, and Guatemala.
• **REMARK** This bird was given the name "robin" by settlers in colonial times because of its "red" breast, but strictly speaking it is a thrush.

strong, hopping • legs

Plumage Sexes alike	Habitat	Migration Partial migrant

Family ORTHONYCHIDAE	Species *Cinclosoma ajax*	Length 23cm (9in)

PAINTED QUAIL-THRUSH

This thrush-like bird rarely leaves the ground and is normally difficult to see in lowland rainforest. Its presence may be more easily detected by its distinctive, thin, whistling call notes. Pairs or small parties walk unhurriedly in the deep shade, searching for insects.
• **NEST** Not scientifically recorded, but closely related birds build open, cup-shaped nests in a depression on the ground.

• short, little-used wings

•**DISTRIBUTION** Lowlands of S. New Guinea.

DISTRIBUTION

• dull brown upper plumage for camouflage against the ground

FEMALE

Plumage Sexes differ	Habitat	Migration Non-migrant

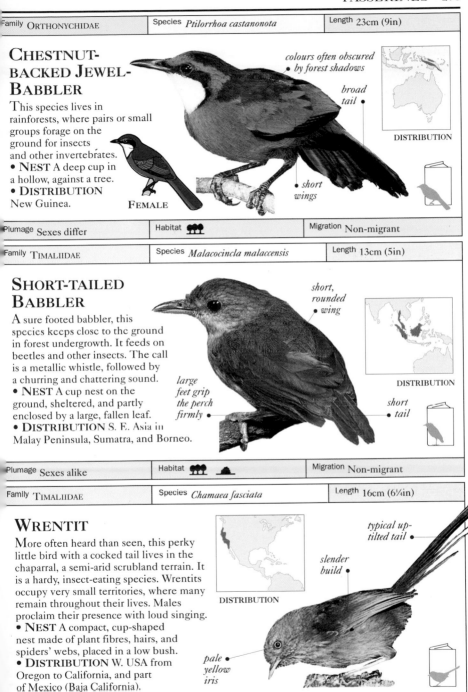

Family ORTHONYCHIDAE	Species *Ptilorrhoa castanonota*	Length 23cm (9in)

CHESTNUT-BACKED JEWEL-BABBLER

This species lives in rainforests, where pairs or small groups forage on the ground for insects and other invertebrates.
• **NEST** A deep cup in a hollow, against a tree.
• **DISTRIBUTION** New Guinea.

colours often obscured by forest shadows

broad tail

DISTRIBUTION

short wings

FEMALE

Plumage Sexes differ	Habitat	Migration Non-migrant

Family TIMALIIDAE	Species *Malacocincla malaccensis*	Length 13cm (5in)

SHORT-TAILED BABBLER

A sure footed babbler, this species keeps close to the ground in forest undergrowth. It feeds on beetles and other insects. The call is a metallic whistle, followed by a churring and chattering sound.
• **NEST** A cup nest on the ground, sheltered, and partly enclosed by a large, fallen leaf.
• **DISTRIBUTION** S. E. Asia in Malay Peninsula, Sumatra, and Borneo.

short, rounded wing

large feet grip the perch firmly

DISTRIBUTION

short tail

Plumage Sexes alike	Habitat	Migration Non-migrant

Family TIMALIIDAE	Species *Chamaea fasciata*	Length 16cm (6¼in)

WRENTIT

More often heard than seen, this perky little bird with a cocked tail lives in the chaparral, a semi-arid scrubland terrain. It is a hardy, insect-eating species. Wrentits occupy very small territories, where many remain throughout their lives. Males proclaim their presence with loud singing.
• **NEST** A compact, cup-shaped nest made of plant fibres, hairs, and spiders' webs, placed in a low bush.
• **DISTRIBUTION** W. USA from Oregon to California, and part of Mexico (Baja California).

typical up-tilted tail

slender build

DISTRIBUTION

pale yellow iris

Plumage Sexes alike	Habitat	Migration Non-migrant

Family TIMALIIDAE	Species *Pomatostomus ruficeps*	Length 22cm (8½in)

CHESTNUT-CROWNED BABBLER

DISTRIBUTION

This is a slim bird with a long tail and a slender, downcurved bill, living in open scrub, semi-desert, and the scrubby woodland formed by mulga trees. It moves about in small flocks, feeding on insects, which
the birds take either
from low
vegetation
or the
ground.
Flocks are shy
of humans. The
birds are lively and
active. They keep up
a constant chattering,
louder when they are
excited, of the type that
gives babblers their name.
• **NEST** A large, domed nest
with a side entrance, composed of
twigs, lined with grass or wool, and
situated in a tree.
• **DISTRIBUTION** Interior of
S.E. Australia.

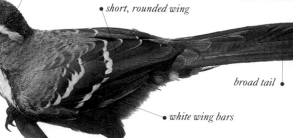

dull brown cap with a white border

short, rounded wing

broad tail

white wing bars

stout, wiry legs

Plumage Sexes alike	Habitat	Migration Non-migrant

Family TIMALIIDAE	Species *Stachyris maculata*	Length 16.5cm (6½in)

CHESTNUT-RUMPED BABBLER

With its strong feet and powerful legs, this babbler is well adapted to a life of clambering about in the undergrowth of lowland rainforests. Small, active parties sometimes leave the cover of the undergrowth to forage in the middle height of the trees. The principal food of this species is insects, but it also takes small fruits when available. Although small, it is a rather noisy bird. Its song consists of a series of
strident phrases, often followed by a long,
trilling note. The calling bird puffs
out its throat, exposing the two
hidden patches of bright
blue, bare skin situated
on the sides of
the neck.

patch of blue skin

DISTRIBUTION

typical crouching posture

• **NEST** A loosely constructed
globe of dead leaves, placed a little
above ground level, in a thick tangle of
dead leaves and creepers. Only one example
of this bird's nest has ever been reliably recorded.
• **DISTRIBUTION** Malay Peninsula, Sumatra, and Borneo.

large, powerful feet

Plumage Sexes alike	Habitat	Migration Non-migrant

Family TIMALIIDAE	Species *Garrulax pectoralis*	Length 28cm (11in)

GREATER NECKLACED LAUGHING-THRUSH

An assertive and inquisitive babbler, this bird goes about in groups, often with other laughing-thrushes. Flocks are seen crossing an open space, gliding one after another. The birds feed mainly on the forest floor, moving with large hops, taking insects, fruit, and seeds. They frequently call to each other with piping and grating notes.
• **NEST** A broad, saucer-shaped nest of plant materials, in a tree or bush.
• **DISTRIBUTION** From E. Himalayas across into S. China and N. Vietnam. Introduced in the Hawaiian Islands.

black "moustache" streak

rufous collar

short, rounded wings

black "necklace"

thick legs and large feet

DISTRIBUTION

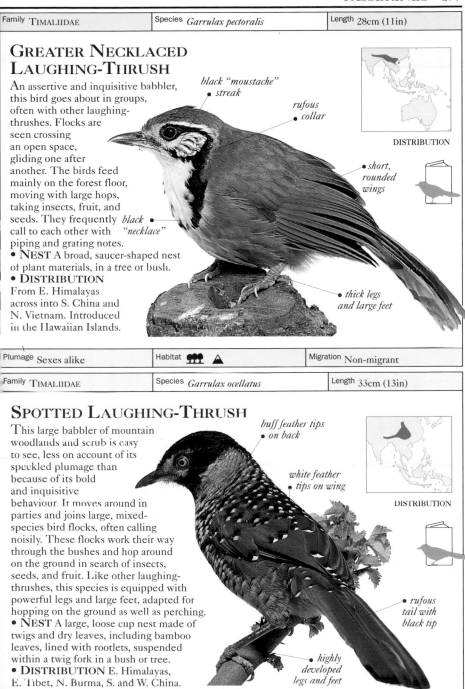

Plumage Sexes alike	Habitat 🌳 ⛰	Migration Non-migrant

Family TIMALIIDAE	Species *Garrulax ocellatus*	Length 33cm (13in)

SPOTTED LAUGHING-THRUSH

This large babbler of mountain woodlands and scrub is easy to see, less on account of its speckled plumage than because of its bold and inquisitive behaviour. It moves around in parties and joins large, mixed-species bird flocks, often calling noisily. These flocks work their way through the bushes and hop around on the ground in search of insects, seeds, and fruit. Like other laughing-thrushes, this species is equipped with powerful legs and large feet, adapted for hopping on the ground as well as perching.
• **NEST** A large, loose cup nest made of twigs and dry leaves, including bamboo leaves, lined with rootlets, suspended within a twig fork in a bush or tree.
• **DISTRIBUTION** E. Himalayas, E. Tibet, N. Burma, S. and W. China.

buff feather tips on back

white feather tips on wing

rufous tail with black tip

highly developed legs and feet

DISTRIBUTION

Plumage Sexes alike	Habitat 🌳 ✈ ⛰	Migration Non-migrant

Family TIMALIIDAE	Species *Leiothrix argentauris*	Length 13cm (5in)

SILVER-EARED MESIA

This small babbler occurs in scrub and secondary scrub (new growth after clearance) in mountains. Flocks of about six to 30 birds search actively for insects in the foliage, calling to each other with chattering notes.
• **NEST** A cup nest of grass, moss, and lichens, lined with rootlets, in a low bush.
• **DISTRIBUTION** From E. Himalayas and S. China as far south as Sumatra.

blunt bill for fruit and insects

strong legs and feet

DISTRIBUTION

FEMALE

Plumage Sexes differ	Habitat ✈ ▲	Migration Non-migrant

Family TIMALIIDAE	Species *Minla cyanouroptera*	Length 15cm (6in)

BLUE-WINGED MINLA

Like many babblers, this species often forms groups of about five to 15 birds, which sometimes form part of the large, roving flocks of mixed bird species occurring in hill forests. They are quick and lively feeders and take insects both by gleaning them in the foliage and by catching them in mid-flight.
• **NEST** A cup nest made of bamboo leaves and rootlets, often wrapped in moss, and hidden in a bush.
• **DISTRIBUTION** Mountain ranges from E. Himalayas to Malay Peninsula.

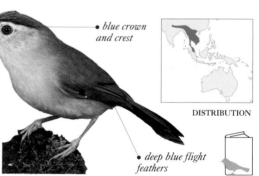

blue crown and crest

deep blue flight feathers

DISTRIBUTION

Plumage Sexes alike	Habitat 🌳 ▲ ✈	Migration Non-migrant

Family TIMALIIDAE	Species *Minla ignotincta*	Length 14cm (5½in)

RED-TAILED MINLA

An insect hunter of the treetops in several types of hill forest, this bird is most common in oak and rhododendron woodland.
• **NEST** A mossy cup nest, lined and situated in a high fork in a tree.
• **DISTRIBUTION** Mountain ranges from E. Himalayas to N. Vietnam.

broad, round wing

vivid white stripe above eye

thick black eyestripe

DISTRIBUTION

PERCHED BIRD

Plumage Sexes alike	Habitat 🌳 🌿 ▲	Migration Non-migrant

| Family TIMALIIDAE | Species *Heterophasia capistrata* | Length 22cm (8½in) |

RUFOUS SIBIA

A slender, active babbler, this bird
is found in the more open types of
mountain woodland, including dwarf
oak forest. When excited, it raises its
shaggy, black cap feathers in a crest.
It is highly acrobatic and hunts
insects high in the upper foliage,
appearing lower down when trees are in fruit.
• NEST A mossy cup nest with a fibrous lining,
built into a twig fork at the end of a branch.
• DISTRIBUTION Through the Himalayas
from N. Pakistan through N. India to S. China.

crest in lowered position

slender, agile build

DISTRIBUTION

long tail

| Plumage Sexes alike | Habitat 🌳🌳🌳 🌳🌳 ⛰ | Migration Non-migrant |

| Family TIMALIIDAE | Species *Yuhina castaniceps* | Length 13cm (5in) |

STRIATED YUHINA

This acrobatic babbler forms flocks of 20 to 30 birds that
hunt among the larger branches. The birds feed mainly
on insects, gleaned from the foliage, but will take
berries when available. While feeding,
the birds utter constant,
low-pitched contact calls.
• NEST A cup nest
made of fine grass,
moss, roots, and
leaves, in a hollow in a bank.
• DISTRIBUTION
From E. Himalayas and
S. China to N. Vietnam.

bushy, grey crest

streaked plumage

HIMALAYAN
SUBSPECIES

DISTRIBUTION

| Plumage Sexes alike | Habitat 🐿⬛ ⛰ | Migration Non-migrant |

| Family TIMALIIDAE | Species *Yuhina flavicollis* | Length 13cm (5in) |

WHISKERED YUHINA

The combination of a jaunty, pointed
crest and a "moustache" identifies this
babbler, which breeds in mountain forests
and winters in the trees in foothills and
lowlands. It nearly always occurs in small
groups, that often join mixed flocks of babblers.
The diet consists of insects, spiders, berries,
and nectar taken from flowering trees.
• NEST Either domed or cup-shaped, made
of moss and lined with roots, and suspended
from the fork of a twig in a tree.
• DISTRIBUTION From E. Himalayas
and S. China to N. Vietnam.

raised crest

white collar

DISTRIBUTION

square tip of tail

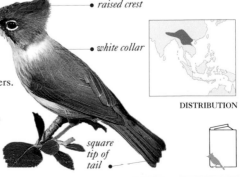

| Plumage Sexes alike | Habitat ⛰ 🌳🌳🌳 | Migration Non-migrant |

Family PANURIDAE	Species *Panurus biarmicus*	Length 16.5cm (6½in)

BEARDED TIT

Living in reedbeds, this bird eats insects in summer, seeds in winter. It flies fast and low over the reeds, calling in distinctive, twanging notes. Flocks search through the reeds for food.
• **NEST** A loosely made cup nest, lined with reed plumes, in reeds, near the ground.
• **DISTRIBUTION** Patchily distributed in Europe, and across Asia to the Pacific.

close-set eyes for accurate focus

DISTRIBUTION

feet grip firmly

FEMALE

Plumage Sexes differ	Habitat	Migration Partial migrant

Family PANURIDAE	Species *Paradoxornis heudei*	Length 18cm (7in)

REED PARROTBILL

A stout bill enables this rare, marsh-dwelling bird to split open reed stems and capture insects sheltering inside. It also eats reed seeds.
• **NEST** A deep cup nest made of reed and sedge leaves, and anchored between stems, just above water.
• **DISTRIBUTION** Mainland E. Asia. Distribution may prove to be continuous between the two areas on the map.

short, rounded wings

DISTRIBUTION

secure grip on stem

long tail

Plumage Sexes alike	Habitat	Migration Non-migrant

Family POLIOPTILIDAE	Species *Polioptila caerulea*	Length 12cm (4¾in)

BLUE-GREY GNATCATCHER

A slender bird that forages restlessly for insects among the trees, this species is seen in large numbers on migration.
• **NEST** A cup nest made of plant down and spiders' silk.
• **DISTRIBUTION** Much of USA, S. Canada, Mexico, Cuba. Northern populations winter in the south of this range.

female bird

DISTRIBUTION

MALE

long tail for balance

Plumage Sexes differ	Habitat	Migration Migrant

Family SYLVIIDAE	Species *Cettia cetti*	Length 14cm (5½in)

CETTI'S WARBLER

A small, squat warbler,
this species usually keeps
out of sight in reedbeds and
waterside thickets, where
it feeds on insects. The
song is brief and explosive.
• **NEST** A bulky, deep cup
nest, made of grass, situated
low in waterside vegetation.
• **DISTRIBUTION** Parts of Europe,
N. Africa, Middle East, and C. Asia. Middle Eastern
and C. Asian populations migrate to N.W. India.

short, wren-like tail

squat build

strongly made feet

DISTRIBUTION

Plumage Sexes alike	Habitat	Migration Partial migrant

Family SYLVIIDAE	Species *Sphenoeacus afer*	Length 22cm (8½in)

CAPE GRASSBIRD

A large warbler, the Cape Grassbird has a
streaked pattern of chestnut, black, and buff
for camouflage in its scrubland and savanna
habitat. Usually solitary or in pairs, it is
shy and secretive, creeping into tangled
vegetation when disturbed. It feeds
in cover, taking insects and spiders, but
often mounts a prominent perch in the
early morning, to sun itself or to sing.
• **NEST** A cup nest made of coarse grass,
lined with fine grass, hidden in a grassy tuft.
• **DISTRIBUTION** Parts of
Zimbabwe, Mozambique, and South Africa.

strongly streaked back

wiry legs and feet

DISTRIBUTION

tail worn thin by thorns

Plumage Sexes alike	Habitat	Migration Non-migrant

Family SYLVIIDAE	Species *Locustella naevia*	Length 13cm (5in)

GRASSHOPPER WARBLER

The male's prolonged, trilling song, uttered
from the top of a bush in the nesting
season, sounds like a grasshopper. For
the most part this bird remains in the
undergrowth, on heaths or in marshy
places, feeding on small insects.
• **NEST** A lined cup nest made
of grass and leaves, hidden in a
depression in thick vegetation.
• **DISTRIBUTION** Breeds
from Europe to W. China.
Winters as far south as
N. Africa and N. India.

slim, streamlined build

faint streaking

DISTRIBUTION

rounded tail

Plumage Sexes alike	Habitat	Migration Migrant

Family SYLVIIDAE	Species *Acrocephalus schoenobaenus*	Length 13cm (5in)

SEDGE WARBLER

One of the noisier warblers, this bird
produces a lively mixture of lilting phrases,
mimicry, and harsh noises. It is not shy
and, when disturbed, sings vigorously.
It is common at the edge of
reedbeds, feeding on insects.
• **NEST** A relatively deep and
bulky nest, bound to stems,
low in waterside vegetation.
• **DISTRIBUTION**
Breeds in Europe and C. Asia.
Winters in tropical southern Africa.

*• streaky
plumage*

DISTRIBUTION

Plumage Sexes alike	Habitat	Migration Migrant

Family SYLVIIDAE	Species *Acrocephalus stentoreus*	Length 19cm (7½in)

CLAMOROUS REED WARBLER

A bulkier version of its northern relative the
Common Reed Warbler, this insect-eating
bird is found in papyrus swamps and
mangroves as well as in reedbeds,
across a huge range from Africa almost to
Australia. Its song is loud and melodious.
• **NEST** A large, neat cup nest, made
of reed leaves or similar materials, lined
and slung between stems slightly
above the surface of the water.
• **DISTRIBUTION** From N.E.
Africa through Asia to New Guinea.
Some populations migrate.

*• plain
plumage*

DISTRIBUTION

NEST

Plumage Sexes alike	Habitat	Migration Partial migrant

Family SYLVIIDAE	Species *Hippolais pallida*	Length 13cm (5in)

OLIVACEOUS WARBLER

Confident in bearing, this
warbler is often seen feeding
in exposed situations, such as
on a thornbush in open grassland.
While gleaning insects, it may
utter "chuck" notes; the song is
musical. It usually breeds in scrub.
• **NEST** A neat cup nest made
of grass, twigs, hair, and spiders'
webs, placed in a low bush or shrub.
• **DISTRIBUTION** Breeding range
is from S. Portugal, Spain, and N. Africa
to C. Asia. Winters in tropical Africa.

*long
• wings*

DISTRIBUTION

Plumage Sexes alike	Habitat	Migration Migrant

Family SYLVIIDAE	Species *Cisticola brunnescens*	Length 11cm (4¼in)

PALE-CROWNED CISTICOLA

Noticeably streaked and short in the tail, this
warbler lives in damp areas of grassland, where
it feeds on ants and other small insects. It is
normally inconspicuous but, in the breeding
season, males perform a diving display
flight, during which they also sing loudly.
• **NEST** An oval nest made of grass that
is still growing, with a side entrance,
bound with spiders' webs, and situated
a short distance above the ground.
• **DISTRIBUTION** Scattered areas
in Africa south of the Sahara.

DISTRIBUTION

• *white
streaks*

• *short
tail*

Plumage Sexes alike	Habitat	Migration Non-migrant

Family SYLVIIDAE	Species *Prinia gracilis*	Length 13cm (5in)

GRACEFUL PRINIA

This is a warbler
of scrub habitats, where
pairs or groups hop on the
ground or leap into the air to
catch insects. In spring, males
sing from bush tops, and
perform display flights with a
distinctly audible, wing-snapping noise.
• **NEST** A dome or upright oval
pouch, with a side entrance, made of
grass and spiders' webs, in low vegetation.
• **DISTRIBUTION** From Egypt and
Somalia through the Middle East to India.

• *slight crest*

*tail
tapers
in steps* •

DISTRIBUTION

• *typical pose –
elegant and
jaunty*

Plumage Sexes alike	Habitat	Migration Non-migrant

Family SYLVIIDAE	Species *Apalis thoracica*	Length 13cm (5in)

BAR-THROATED APALIS

A boldly patterned warbler, this species
inhabits forests, often on hills. Pairs sing
"duetting" songs; at other times
birds join mixed-species flocks.
They forage at all heights in
the forest, taking caterpillars and
mature insects. In behaviour, this
is a bold and inquisitive species.
• **NEST** A long, oval structure made
of plant materials, with a side entrance
near the top, situated in a bush.
• **DISTRIBUTION** From Kenya
south as far as South Africa.

• *long tail
for balance*

*white throat
with dark
grey bar* •

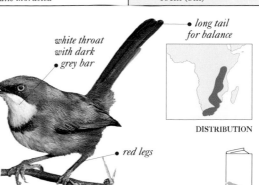

DISTRIBUTION

• *red legs*

Plumage Sexes alike	Habitat	Migration Non-migrant

Family SYLVIIDAE	Species *Orthotomus sericeus*	Length 13.5cm (5¼in)

RUFOUS-TAILED TAILORBIRD

This scrub-dwelling warbler characteristically
carries its tail in a cocked position while
searching the undergrowth for insects. It often
runs rapidly along a branch to seize its prey.
The species has a loud, cheerful song.
• **NEST** The birds "sew" large leaves
together where they are still attached
to the plant, using threads of plant down
and spiders' webs. They then build
a lined cup nest between the leaves.
• **DISTRIBUTION** Malay Peninsula, Sumatra,
Borneo, and small islands in W. Philippines.

vivid crown

sharp bill for piercing leaves

strong feet for acrobatic clinging

DISTRIBUTION

tail is often cocked

Plumage Sexes alike	Habitat	Migration Non-migrant

Family SYLVIIDAE	Species *Sylvietta whytii*	Length 10cm (4in)

RED-FACED CROMBEC

This colourful warbler lives in forest edges, open woodland,
and acacia savanna. It moves in a series of quick hops along
small branches, foraging for insects and small spiders.
• **NEST** A purse-shaped nest with an open top, made
of grass, bark, and plant tendrils, bound together with
spiders' webs, lined
with plant down,
hanging from a twig
in a bush or tree.
• **DISTRIBUTION**
E. Africa from
S. Sudan to
N. Mozambique.

very short tail

large, strong feet for a warbler

DISTRIBUTION

Plumage Sexes alike	Habitat	Migration Non-migrant

Family SYLVIIDAE	Species *Phylloscopus collybita*	Length 11cm (4¼in)

EURASIAN CHIFFCHAFF

A small, dull-green warbler of open
forest and scrub, this species can be
identified by its monotonous "chiff-
chaff, chiff-chaff" song. It gleans actively
in low trees and bushes for insects.
• **NEST** An almost spherical
nest of leaves, moss, and stems, lined
with feathers, on or near the ground.
• **DISTRIBUTION**
Breeds in Europe, C. Asia,
Siberia, and N. Africa.
Winters in Africa south
of the Equator, and India. **SIBERIAN FORM**

faint eyestripe

DISTRIBUTION

**WESTERN
EUROPEAN FORM**

Plumage Sexes alike	Habitat	Migration Migrant

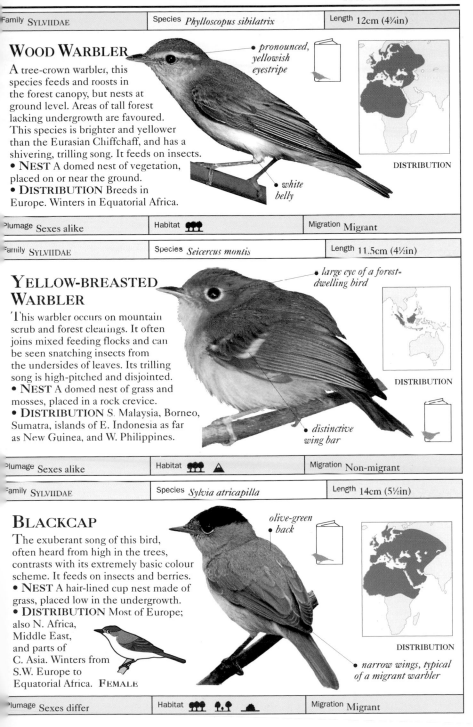

| Family SYLVIIDAE | Species *Phylloscopus sibilatrix* | Length 12cm (4¾in) |

WOOD WARBLER

A tree-crown warbler, this
species feeds and roosts in
the forest canopy, but nests at
ground level. Areas of tall forest
lacking undergrowth are favoured.
This species is brighter and yellower
than the Eurasian Chiffchaff, and has a
shivering, trilling song. It feeds on insects.
• NEST A domed nest of vegetation,
placed on or near the ground.
• DISTRIBUTION Breeds in
Europe. Winters in Equatorial Africa.

*pronounced,
yellowish
eyestripe*

*white
belly*

DISTRIBUTION

| Plumage Sexes alike | Habitat | Migration Migrant |

| Family SYLVIIDAE | Species *Seicercus montis* | Length 11.5cm (4½in) |

YELLOW-BREASTED WARBLER

This warbler occurs on mountain
scrub and forest clearings. It often
joins mixed feeding flocks and can
be seen snatching insects from
the undersides of leaves. Its trilling
song is high-pitched and disjointed.
• NEST A domed nest of grass and
mosses, placed in a rock crevice.
• DISTRIBUTION S. Malaysia, Borneo,
Sumatra, islands of E. Indonesia as far
as New Guinea, and W. Philippines.

*large eye of a forest-
dwelling bird*

*distinctive
wing bar*

DISTRIBUTION

| Plumage Sexes alike | Habitat | Migration Non-migrant |

| Family SYLVIIDAE | Species *Sylvia atricapilla* | Length 14cm (5½in) |

BLACKCAP

The exuberant song of this bird,
often heard from high in the trees,
contrasts with its extremely basic colour
scheme. It feeds on insects and berries.
• NEST A hair-lined cup nest made of
grass, placed low in the undergrowth.
• DISTRIBUTION Most of Europe;
also N. Africa,
Middle East,
and parts of
C. Asia. Winters from
S.W. Europe to
Equatorial Africa. FEMALE

*olive-green
back*

*narrow wings, typical
of a migrant warbler*

DISTRIBUTION

| Plumage Sexes differ | Habitat | Migration Migrant |

Family SYLVIIDAE	Species *Sylvia communis*	Length 14cm (5½in)

WHITETHROAT

A warbler of shrubby growth and steppe, this bird feeds on insects and berries. It can be seen and identified easily when singing – with its white throat puffed out conspicuously – or when performing its dancing songflight.
• **NEST** A lined cup nest, made of grass and hidden in a bush.
• **DISTRIBUTION** Breeds in Europe and also N. Africa, Middle East, and parts of C. Asia. Winters in India and tropical Africa.

rufous-tinted wing feathers

DISTRIBUTION

Plumage Sexes differ slightly	Habitat	Migration Migrant

Family SYLVIIDAE	Species *Sylvia rueppelli*	Length 14cm (5½in)

RUEPPELL'S WARBLER

Hunting insects in thick scrub, often on rocky slopes, this bird is hard to see. It is more often detected by its short, musical song, broken with buzzing, rattling notes.
• **NEST** A cup nest of grass and stalks, in a bush.
• **DISTRIBUTION** Breeds from Greece to S. Israel. Winters in N.E. Africa.

black head and throat patch

heavy, solid build

DISTRIBUTION

FEMALE

Plumage Sexes differ	Habitat	Migration Migrant

Family SYLVIIDAE	Species *Sylvia cantillans*	Length 12cm (4¾in)

SUBALPINE WARBLER

This bird is secretive and difficult to observe, hiding in thorny scrub and thick undergrowth in open woodland. Nonetheless it is a common species throughout the Mediterranean. Its diet consists of insects and their larvae, and berries.
• **NEST** A cup nest of stems and grass, lined with grass or hairs, placed low in a bush.
• **DISTRIBUTION** Mediterranean. Winters in Middle East and N. Africa.

reddish eye-ring

SIBERIAN FORM

DISTRIBUTION

white outer tail feathers

Plumage Sexes differ	Habitat	Migration Migrant

Family SYLVIIDAE	Species *Sylvia undata*	Length 13cm (5in)

DARTFORD WARBLER

A resident (non-migrant) bird in much of
its range, the colourful Dartford Warbler
survives winter frosts by sheltering low in
dense gorse thickets. It sings very musically
in the course of its spring display flight.
Its diet consists of insects and spiders.
• **NEST** A cup nest made of grass, lined
with finer materials, placed low
down in a thick, thorny bush.
• **DISTRIBUTION** Parts of
W. and S. Europe; N.W. Africa.
Some migration within this range.

*shaggy crown
feathers*

long tail

*slim,
elegant
build of a
thicket-
dweller*

DISTRIBUTION

Plumage Sexes differ slightly	Habitat	Migration Partial migrant

Family SYLVIIDAE	Species *Regulus regulus*	Length 9cm (3½in)

GOLDCREST

Usually secretive, this species
becomes more tame
and inquisitive
under winter
conditions. Inhabiting mixed and
coniferous forests, it feeds on insects and
spiders. The voice is thin and high-pitched.
• **NEST** A hammock-like nest of moss and
grass, under a conifer bough.
• **DISTRIBUTION** Europe,
parts of N. Africa, and C. Asia
to Japan. Northern populations
winter in south of this range.

**RAISED
CREST**

*rounded
body*

DISTRIBUTION

Plumage Sexes differ	Habitat	Migration Partial migrant

Family SYLVIIDAE	Species *Regulus satrapa*	Length 9cm (3½in)

GOLDEN-CROWNED KINGLET

This tiny bird is difficult to observe since it tends
to stay high in coniferous trees, often the only clue
being its almost inaudible, high-pitched song. In
winter, northern populations migrate south, and the
birds are more easily seen,
hunting insects in lower cover.
• **NEST** A deep, feather-lined cup
nest of moss and grass, slung below
a branch, usually in a conifer.
• **DISTRIBUTION** Parts of
Canada, much of USA, parts of
Mexico and Guatemala. Some
migration within this range.

*vivid, white
stripe above
the eye*

FEMALE

*pale
wing bar*

DISTRIBUTION

Plumage Sexes differ	Habitat	Migration Partial migrant

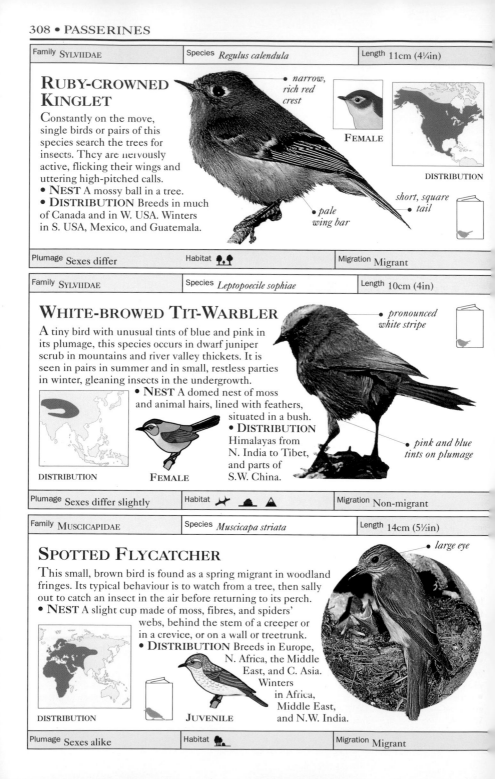

Family SYLVIIDAE	Species *Regulus calendula*	Length 11cm (4¼in)

RUBY-CROWNED KINGLET

Constantly on the move, single birds or pairs of this species search the trees for insects. They are nervously active, flicking their wings and uttering high-pitched calls.
• **NEST** A mossy ball in a tree.
• **DISTRIBUTION** Breeds in much of Canada and in W. USA. Winters in S. USA, Mexico, and Guatemala.

• *narrow, rich red crest*

FEMALE

DISTRIBUTION

short, square tail

• *pale wing bar*

Plumage Sexes differ	Habitat	Migration Migrant

Family SYLVIIDAE	Species *Leptopoecile sophiae*	Length 10cm (4in)

WHITE-BROWED TIT-WARBLER

A tiny bird with unusual tints of blue and pink in its plumage, this species occurs in dwarf juniper scrub in mountains and river valley thickets. It is seen in pairs in summer and in small, restless parties in winter, gleaning insects in the undergrowth.
• **NEST** A domed nest of moss and animal hairs, lined with feathers, situated in a bush.
• **DISTRIBUTION** Himalayas from N. India to Tibet, and parts of S.W. China.

• *pronounced white stripe*

• *pink and blue tints on plumage*

DISTRIBUTION   **FEMALE**

Plumage Sexes differ slightly	Habitat	Migration Non-migrant

Family MUSCICAPIDAE	Species *Muscicapa striata*	Length 14cm (5½in)

SPOTTED FLYCATCHER

This small, brown bird is found as a spring migrant in woodland fringes. Its typical behaviour is to watch from a tree, then sally out to catch an insect in the air before returning to its perch.
• **NEST** A slight cup made of moss, fibres, and spiders' webs, behind the stem of a creeper or in a crevice, or on a wall or treetrunk.
• **DISTRIBUTION** Breeds in Europe, N. Africa, the Middle East, and C. Asia. Winters in Africa, Middle East, and N.W. India.

• *large eye*

DISTRIBUTION   **JUVENILE**

Plumage Sexes alike	Habitat	Migration Migrant

Family MUSCICAPIDAE	Species *Ficedula hypoleuca*	Length 13cm (5in)

PIED FLYCATCHER

A spring migrant to deciduous woodlands, orchards, or gardens, the Pied Flycatcher is less secretive than the Spotted. When perching, it has a distinctive habit of briefly lifting up one of its wings.
• **NEST** A loose cup nest of moss, bark, and rootlets, lined with feathers, in a tree hole.
• **DISTRIBUTION** Europe, N.W. Africa, and S.W. Siberia. Winters in tropical Africa.

large eye •

• *plump body*

DISTRIBUTION

• *white edge of tail shows when spread*

FEMALE

Plumage Sexes differ	Habitat	Migration Migrant

Family MUSCICAPIDAE	Species *Ficedula strophiata*	Length 13cm (5in)

RUFOUS-GORGETED FLYCATCHER

This bluish-grey flycatcher is found in mixed forests, often in mountains. It is usually seen solitarily or in pairs. Like other flycatchers, it feeds by catching insects in flight. In winter, mountain populations migrate to lower altitudes, where they occupy more open habitats.
• **NEST** A loose cup nest made of rootlets and moss, with a finer lining, placed in a bank or tree hole.
• **DISTRIBUTION** Mountains from E. Himalayas to S. Vietnam. Migrant populations winter in the south of this range.

large, dark eye •

• *pale blue forehead stripe*

DISTRIBUTION

• *rufous throat patch*

Plumage Sexes differ slightly	Habitat	Migration Partial migrant

Family MUSCICAPIDAE	Species *Ficedula parva*	Length 12cm (4¾in)

RED-BREASTED FLYCATCHER

Very small for a flycatcher, this bird breeds in deciduous and mixed woodland, both in lowland and mountains, keeping to the thicker foliage. It feeds on insects caught in mid-air. In winter it favours more open habitats, such as forest edges and scrub. Females lack the orange throat seen in males of the species.
• **NEST** A neat cup nest made of root fibres, grass stems, and moss, lined with hair, and placed in a cavity, such as a rotten tree stump.
• **DISTRIBUTION** Breeds in parts of C. Europe and from E. Europe through Asia to Japan. Winters in India, S. China, and parts of S.E. Asia.

• *throat puffed out in song*

DISTRIBUTION

FEMALE

Plumage Sexes differ	Habitat	Migration Migrant

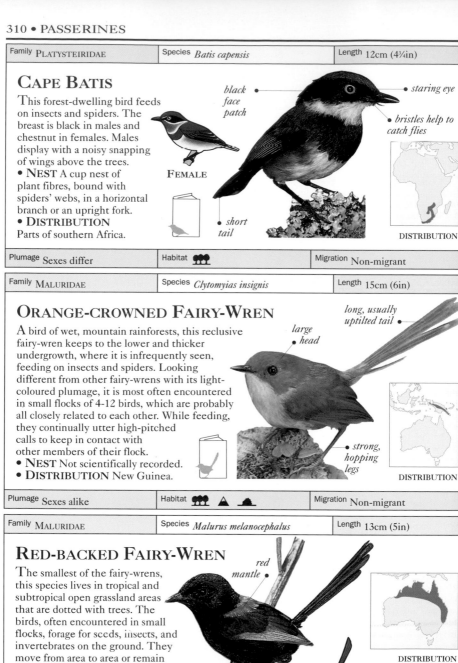

Family PLATYSTEIRIDAE	Species *Batis capensis*	Length 12cm (4¾in)

CAPE BATIS

This forest-dwelling bird feeds on insects and spiders. The breast is black in males and chestnut in females. Males display with a noisy snapping of wings above the trees.
• **NEST** A cup nest of plant fibres, bound with spiders' webs, in a horizontal branch or an upright fork.
• **DISTRIBUTION** Parts of southern Africa.

black face patch

staring eye

bristles help to catch flies

FEMALE

short tail

DISTRIBUTION

Plumage Sexes differ	Habitat	Migration Non-migrant

Family MALURIDAE	Species *Clytomyias insignis*	Length 15cm (6in)

ORANGE-CROWNED FAIRY-WREN

A bird of wet, mountain rainforests, this reclusive fairy-wren keeps to the lower and thicker undergrowth, where it is infrequently seen, feeding on insects and spiders. Looking different from other fairy-wrens with its light-coloured plumage, it is most often encountered in small flocks of 4-12 birds, which are probably all closely related to each other. While feeding, they continually utter high-pitched calls to keep in contact with other members of their flock.
• **NEST** Not scientifically recorded.
• **DISTRIBUTION** New Guinea.

long, usually uptilted tail

large head

strong, hopping legs

DISTRIBUTION

Plumage Sexes alike	Habitat	Migration Non-migrant

Family MALURIDAE	Species *Malurus melanocephalus*	Length 13cm (5in)

RED-BACKED FAIRY-WREN

The smallest of the fairy-wrens, this species lives in tropical and subtropical open grassland areas that are dotted with trees. The birds, often encountered in small flocks, forage for seeds, insects, and invertebrates on the ground. They move from area to area or remain resident, depending on the food supply.
• **NEST** A neat, dome-shaped nest of grass, in a grass tussock or shrub.
• **DISTRIBUTION** N. and E. Australia.

red mantle

DISTRIBUTION

FEMALE

Plumage Sexes differ	Habitat	Migration Non-migrant

Family MALURIDAE	Species *Malurus leucopterus*	Length 12cm (4¾in)

WHITE-WINGED FAIRY-WREN

This bird of arid country is seen in parties comprising a colourful male and his partner, with a retinue of females and subordinate males. They forage for insects on the ground.
• **NEST** A dome of grass and bark, with a side entrance, on the ground under cover.
• **DISTRIBUTION** W. and interior Australia.

FEMALE

• *bold, white wing patch*

• *long legs for foraging on the ground*

DISTRIBUTION

Plumage Sexes differ	Habitat	Migration Non-migrant

Family MALURIDAE	Species *Malurus splendens*	Length 14cm (5½in)

SPLENDID FAIRY-WREN

A bird of scrub and grassland, often near forest edges, this species forms small parties that hop on the ground and search in the undergrowth for seeds and insects. Usually only one male is in blue plumage in each party. Birds make short flights between bushes.
• **NEST** An oval structure with a side entrance, made of grass, placed in a bush.
• **DISTRIBUTION** Australia.
• **REMARK** Plumage pattern varies in the three geographical subspecies.

• *glossy plumage*

• *short, rounded body*

• *short, rounded wings*

FEMALE

DISTRIBUTION

Plumage Sexes differ	Habitat	Migration Non-migrant

Family MALURIDAE	Species *Malurus pulcherrimus*	Length 14cm (5½in)

BLUE-BREASTED FAIRY-WREN

This spectacular bird occurs in woodland and scrub. It is often seen in small parties consisting of a dominant pair with "helpers"; all feed, roost, and nest together. The birds forage in groups on the ground, looking for insects and other small invertebrates.
• **NEST** An oval structure with a side entrance, made of grass and bound together with spiders' webs, lined with plant down or feathers, and placed in a low bush.
• **DISTRIBUTION** S. Western Australia and South Australia.

glossy ear patch

• *long, cocked tail*

FEMALE

• *white belly*

DISTRIBUTION

Plumage Sexes differ	Habitat	Migration Non-migrant

Family ACANTHIZIDAE	Species *Dasyornis brachypterus*	Length 22cm (8¾in)

EASTERN BRISTLEBIRD

Living in scrub and being very shy,
this drab, brown bird is hard to see.
It forages mainly on the ground for
seeds and insects, often carrying its
long tail cocked and slightly fanned.
• **NEST** A round nest with a side
entrance, constructed of coarse grasses
with a finer grass chamber, placed
on the ground or in a grass clump.
• **DISTRIBUTION** S.E. Australian
coastal strip from Brisbane to E. Victoria.
• **REMARK** Endangered species.

short, little-used wings

DISTRIBUTION

Plumage Sexes alike	Habitat	Migration Non-migrant

Family ACANTHIZIDAE	Species *Pycnoptilus floccosus*	Length 17cm (6¾in)

PILOTBIRD

This bird gets its name from its
association with the Superb Lyrebird
(*see p. 268*). The larger Superb Lyrebird
scratches up leaf litter in search of invertebrates,
and the little Pilotbird follows to share in the feast.
The Pilotbird is often surprisingly
tame and may approach a human
observer within arm's reach.
• **NEST** A large, untidy, domed
nest with a side entrance, placed
on the ground or in a bank.
• **DISTRIBUTION**
S.E. Australia.

long tail is often flicked up and down

short, rounded wings

DISTRIBUTION

strong feet for feeding on the ground

Plumage Sexes alike	Habitat	Migration Non-migrant

Family ACANTHIZIDAE	Species *Sericornis frontalis*	Length 11cm (4¼in)

WHITE-BROWED SCRUBWREN

A small, brownish bird, this species is
often found in dense thickets, foraging
just above ground level for seeds and
insects. The underside varies in colour,
from spotted to plain and from
white to buff, according
to geographical area.
• **NEST** A bulky
grass sphere with a side
entrance, placed on the
ground in undergrowth.
• **DISTRIBUTION**
S. and E. Australia.

SOUTHWESTERN FORM

DISTRIBUTION

QUEENSLAND FORM

Plumage Sexes alike	Habitat	Migration Non-migrant

Family ACANTHIZIDAE	Species *Acanthiza pusilla*	Length 10cm (4in)

BROWN THORNBILL

A small, insect-hunting bird with red eyes, this species is found in almost all types of woodland, usually in pairs or small parties. It forages in the undergrowth, rarely on the ground.
• **NEST** An untidy, bulky, oval nest with a side entrance, made of grass, and placed on or near the ground.
• **DISTRIBUTION** Australia, mostly south of Tropic of Capricorn.

chestnut rump

fine streaking

scaly forehead pattern

DISTRIBUTION

Plumage Sexes alike	Habitat	Migration Non-migrant

Family ACANTHIZIDAE	Species *Smicrornis brevirostris*	Length 9cm (3½in)

WEEBILL

This tiny, stubby-billed bird of the trees is tame and inquisitive, but usually stays hidden in the outer foliage. It hovers amid the leaves, gleaning and snatching insects from leaf surfaces. For such a small bird, the Weebill has a loud song.
• **NEST** A neat, dome-shaped nest with a spout-like entrance, constructed of plant down, twigs, and grasses, lined with feathers, and placed high in the outer foliage of a tree.
• **DISTRIBUTION** Most of Australia.

short tail

squat build

DISTRIBUTION

Plumage Sexes alike	Habitat	Migration Non-migrant

Family ACANTHIZIDAE	Species *Aphelocephala leucopsis*	Length 11cm (4¼in)

SOUTHERN WHITEFACE

A mainly ground-dwelling bird with a white forehead, this species forages in open spaces on bare, dry ground for seeds, insects, and other invertebrates. It is often seen in small parties, which may suddenly take flight.
• **NEST** A large, untidy sphere of grass with a side entrance, in a low bush or tree hollow.
• **DISTRIBUTION** Interior of southern half of Australia.

pale edges of flight feathers

chestnut flank denotes western form

DISTRIBUTION

Plumage Sexes alike	Habitat	Migration Non-migrant

| Family ACANTHIZIDAE | Species *Ephthianura tricolor* | Length 11cm (4¼in) |

CRIMSON CHAT

Living in arid places with sparse, low plants, the Crimson Chat supplements its insect diet with nectar from desert flowers. It is nomadic, appearing anywhere where rain has produced fresh plant growth.
• **NEST** A compact, deep cup of grass and twigs, lined with hair and fine rootlets, and placed close to the ground in low cover.
• **DISTRIBUTION** Arid areas of Australia.

FEMALE

pale-edged wing • feathers

DISTRIBUTION

• long legs for foraging on the ground

| Plumage Sexes differ | Habitat | Migration Nomadic |

| Family MONARCHIDAE | Species *Terpsiphone paradisi* | L. 20cm (8in)/50cm (20in) |

ASIAN PARADISE FLYCATCHER

• lowered crest

The male of this species is a remarkable bird with a pale body, deep black head and nape, a vivid blue eye-ring and bill, and a startling tail that culminates in two extra long feathers known as streamers. These are used principally for display to the female in courtship behaviour. When perched, the male often flicks his tail feathers, opening and closing them in a quick, scissor-like movement. His white plumage takes at least four years to develop, immature males resembling females. Birds feed by catching insects in short, aerial chases. They bathe by flying down to water and splashing at the surface, before returning to a perch to tidy and clean their plumage. The call is a short, grating note.
• **NEST** A neat, inverted cone-shaped nest made of grass and plastered with spiders' webs on its outer layer. Inside the structure there is a nesting cup lined with silky down. The nest is placed in a tree, often high above the ground.
• **DISTRIBUTION** Breeds in Indian subcontinent, C. Asia, parts of China, and Korea. Northern populations winter as far south as S. India, Sri Lanka, and parts of E. Indonesia.
• **REMARK** The colour of the male's body and tail plumage varies geographically, the Sri Lankan form never becoming white.

FEMALE

DISTRIBUTION

flexible tail • streamers hang in a graceful curve

| Plumage Sexes differ | Habitat | Migration Partial migrant |

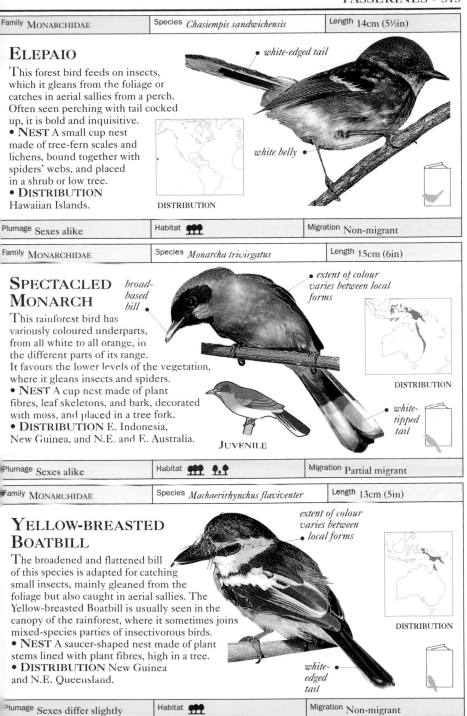

Family MONARCHIDAE	Species *Chasiempis sandwichensis*	Length 14cm (5½in)

ELEPAIO

This forest bird feeds on insects, which it gleans from the foliage or catches in aerial sallies from a perch. Often seen perching with tail cocked up, it is bold and inquisitive.
• **NEST** A small cup nest made of tree-fern scales and lichens, bound together with spiders' webs, and placed in a shrub or low tree.
• **DISTRIBUTION** Hawaiian Islands.

• *white-edged tail*

white belly •

DISTRIBUTION

Plumage Sexes alike	Habitat	Migration Non-migrant

Family MONARCHIDAE	Species *Monarcha trivirgatus*	Length 15cm (6in)

SPECTACLED MONARCH

broad-based bill •

This rainforest bird has variously coloured underparts, from all white to all orange, in the different parts of its range. It favours the lower levels of the vegetation, where it gleans insects and spiders.
• **NEST** A cup nest made of plant fibres, leaf skeletons, and bark, decorated with moss, and placed in a tree fork.
• **DISTRIBUTION** E. Indonesia, New Guinea, and N.E. and E. Australia.

• *extent of colour varies between local forms*

DISTRIBUTION

• *white-tipped tail*

JUVENILE

Plumage Sexes alike	Habitat	Migration Partial migrant

Family MONARCHIDAE	Species *Machaerirhynchus flaviventer*	Length 13cm (5in)

YELLOW-BREASTED BOATBILL

extent of colour varies between • *local forms*

The broadened and flattened bill of this species is adapted for catching small insects, mainly gleaned from the foliage but also caught in aerial sallies. The Yellow-breasted Boatbill is usually seen in the canopy of the rainforest, where it sometimes joins mixed-species parties of insectivorous birds.
• **NEST** A saucer-shaped nest made of plant stems lined with plant fibres, high in a tree.
• **DISTRIBUTION** New Guinea and N.E. Queensland.

DISTRIBUTION

white-edged tail

Plumage Sexes differ slightly	Habitat	Migration Non-migrant

Family MONARCHIDAE	Species *Rhipidura leucophrys*	Length 20cm (8in)

WILLIE WAGTAIL

This ground-dwelling fantail is a common, conspicuous, and tame bird, typically seen holding its spread tail at a low angle. It pivots its body and swings the tail from side to side as it searches the ground for insects and spiders. Insects are also caught on the wing, and in quick, short runs across open ground.

• **NEST** A cup nest made of bark, grass, spiders' webs, and a finer lining, situated in a tree, on a building, or on a post.

• **DISTRIBUTION** Moluccan Islands, New Guinea, Solomon Islands, Australia.

• waving tail frightens insect prey

strong legs for • foraging

DISTRIBUTION

Plumage Sexes alike	Habitat	Migration Non-migrant

Family MONARCHIDAE	Species *Rhipidura rufifrons*	Length 16cm (6¼in)

RUFOUS FANTAIL

This tree-dwelling fantail lives in the middle levels and undergrowth of rainforest and scrub. It hunts by holding its fanned tail high, tilting it and jerking it from side to side to disturb resting insects. In doing this, it reveals its rufous tail and rump.

• **NEST** A compact cup nest of grass and spiders' webs, with a pendant "tail", in a tree fork.

• **DISTRIBUTION** Pacific islands, New Guinea, and N. and E. Australia.

• waving tail frightens insect prey

DISTRIBUTION

Plumage Sexes alike	Habitat	Migration Partial migrant

Family EOPSALTRIIDAE	Species *Microeca fascinans*	Length 14cm (5½in)

JACKY WINTER

A small, grey flycatcher, this species hunts from a perch, often in the cooler parts of the day, such as at dawn and dusk. It flies out to catch insects in the air, or swoops to take invertebrates from the ground. Usually in pairs or small parties, the species is unobtrusive, though its "jacky-winter" call is easily heard.

• **NEST** A shallow cup nest constructed of grass and rootlets, bound with spiders' webs, and lined with lichens. This is placed on a horizontal tree branch, often high above the ground.

• **DISTRIBUTION** Woodland and grassland areas in Australia and S.E. New Guinea.

• pale stripe above eye

• upright posture

white-edged tail •

DISTRIBUTION

Plumage Sexes alike	Habitat	Migration Partial migrant

Family EOPSALTRIIDAE	Species *Petroica multicolor*	Length 12cm (4¾in)

SCARLET ROBIN

This bird of forest and scrubland feeds by perching on a low branch and watching for invertebrates on the ground, on which it pounces. The male advertises himself to either mate or rival with his scarlet breast.
• **NEST** A cup nest made of grass and bark strips, spiders' webs, and lichens, in a hollow, on a branch, or in a fork.
• **DISTRIBUTION** Australia, Solomon Islands, Vanuatu, Fiji, and Samoa.
• **REMARKS** Fifteen subspecies are recognized.

DISTRIBUTION

• *typical upright posture*

FEMALE

Plumage Sexes differ	Habitat	Migration Non-migrant

Family EOPSALTRIIDAE	Species *Petroica macrocephela*	Length 13cm (5in)

TOMTIT

Small and robin-like, this forest-dwelling bird hunts insects on treetrunks, branches, or the ground. It is aggressive and inquisitive in its behaviour, and is not shy of people.
• **NEST** A cup nest of moss and feathers, placed in a tree.
• **DISTRIBUTION** New Zealand.
• **REMARK** Snares Island form is black.

DISTRIBUTION

white wing bar

FEMALE

yellow throat band

Plumage Sexes differ	Habitat	Migration Non-migrant

Family EOPSALTRIIDAE	Species *Eopsaltria australis*	Length 16cm (6¼in)

EASTERN YELLOW ROBIN

This robin of forest undergrowth and scrub is so tame and inquisitive that it is likely to approach any people who appear in its territory. It feeds mainly by pouncing from a branch or stem to seize invertebrates on the ground. Despite its name, it is mostly grey in colour, with yellow only on the underside.
• **NEST** A cup nest of bark and grass, bound with spiders' webs, lined with fine grass and leaves, placed in the fork of a sapling.
• **DISTRIBUTION** E. and S.E. Australia.

• *alert, flycatcher's eye*

• *yellow rump*

DISTRIBUTION

Plumage Sexes alike	Habitat	Migration Non-migrant

Family PACHYCEPHALIDAE	Species *Colluricincla harmonica*	Length 24cm (9½in)

GREY SHRIKE-THRUSH

A heavy, hooked bill and active hunting methods
earn the name "shrike" for this forest bird, which
otherwise resembles a thrush. The species is
unobtrusive but tame, and is seen seeking
prey in undergrowth and scrub. It feeds
on invertebrates and small vertebrates,
such as lizards and bird nestlings.
• **NEST** A grass and bark cup nest
placed just above ground in
vegetation or a crevice.
• **DISTRIBUTION**
Australia and parts of
New Guinea.

*brown patch
on back*

**NORTHWESTERN
FORM**

**EASTERN
FORM**

• **REMARK** The brown
patch on the back is
variable or absent according
to geographical race. It is
largest in northwestern birds.

DISTRIBUTION

Plumage Sexes alike	Habitat	Migration Non-migrant

Family PACHYCEPHALIDAE	Species *Pitohui dichrous*	Length 23cm (9in)

HOODED PITOHUI

A heavily built, fruit-eating bird, this species lives in tropical rainforest and scrub. Its
most unmistakable feature is its coloration – black hood, wings, and tail, and a body
colour between orange and rufous brown. The "hood" refers to the black head,
neck, and breast. It is usually seen in pairs or small parties, in the undergrowth
or the tree canopy, seeking berries as well as larger fruits.
• **NEST** A cup nest constructed of curly vine tendrils,
lined with finer tendrils, and situated
close to ground level in a bush.
• **DISTRIBUTION** New Guinea,
including Japen
Island.

*short,
rounded
wings*

black hood

DISTRIBUTION

*short, springy
legs for hopping
among the twigs*

Plumage Sexes alike	Habitat	Migration Non-migrant

Family PACHYCEPHALIDAE	Species *Pachycephala pectoralis*	Length 16cm (6¼in)

GOLDEN WHISTLER

An insect- and berry-eating bird of rainforest
or scrub, this species may be detected by its
song. This consists of a musical, whistling
phrase ending in a whip-crack note.
• **NEST** A bowl of twigs, bark, grass, and
spiders' webs, placed in the fork of a shrub.
• **DISTRIBUTION** Parts of
Indonesia and Australia,
and islands in S.W. Pacific.
• **REMARK** Has a profusion
of subspecies, all with
different colours.

FEMALE

• *stout head*

• *golden breast and belly*

• *typical upright posture*

DISTRIBUTION

Plumage Sexes differ slightly	Habitat	Migration Partial migrant

Family AEGITHALIDAE	Species *Aegithalos caudatus*	Length 14cm (5½in)

LONG-TAILED TIT

NORTHERN FORM

Constantly active and inquisitive, this
agile species is usually seen in small
flocks that roam the treetops.
The birds continually utter
thin, "zee-zee-zee" notes and
small, explosive calls as they
search out insects and seeds.
• **NEST** A domed nest with
a side entrance, made of a variety
of materials including moss, hair, and
spiders' webs, covered with lichen, lined
with feathers, and often situated in a thorny bush.
• **DISTRIBUTION** Eurasia to Japan.

DISTRIBUTION

Plumage Sexes alike	Habitat	Migration Non-migrant

Family AEGITHALIDAE	Species *Psaltriparus minimus*	Length 11cm (4¼in)

BUSHTIT

• *broad, domed head*

A familiar bird of scrubland,
often on mountainsides, the
Bushtit often forms parties of up
to 20 birds and is frequently seen in
gardens. It feeds on insects and small
seeds. In some areas, the male has
black ear patches, but these vary between
individuals and its significance is unknown.
• **NEST** A finely woven structure
of grasses and other plant materials,
suspended from a branch.
• **DISTRIBUTION** W. Canada,
W. USA, W. Mexico, Guatemala

DISTRIBUTION

• *strong, grasping feet*

SOUTHERN FORM

Plumage Sexes alike	Habitat	Migration Non-migrant

Family REMIZIDAE	Species *Remiz pendulinus*	Length 11cm (4¼in)

PENDULINE TIT

A sprightly, active bird of reedbeds and
thickets, the Penduline Tit feeds on
insects in summer and seeds in winter.
The name refers to its "pendant" nest,
which may take several weeks to build.
• **NEST** A hanging nest made of woolly
willow seeds and down, which the birds
repeatedly peck until the texture is like felt.
The nest, with a round nest-chamber and a vertical
entrance tube, is attached to the tip of a twig on a low tree.
• **DISTRIBUTION** Parts of S. and E. Europe, and through
the Middle East to parts of Siberia, Mongolia, and China.

*• nest
entrance
tube*

DISTRIBUTION

JUVENILE

Plumage Sexes alike	Habitat	Migration Partial migrant

Family REMIZIDAE	Species *Auriparus flaviceps*	Length 10cm (4in)

VERDIN

A small, inconspicuous bird with a sharp,
black bill, the Verdin inhabits brushy
desert valleys and scrub, especially
extensive scrub of *mesquite* bushes. It is
usually seen flitting among the outer twigs or
the undersides of leaves of a desert bush in
search of insect prey. The Verdin is solitary
outside the breeding season. Juveniles lack
the yellow head and brown wing patches.
• **NEST** A ball-shaped nest constructed
of thorny twigs with a side entrance,
and placed in a bush or low in a tree.
• **DISTRIBUTION** S. USA and N. Mexico.

*• largish,
rounded
head*

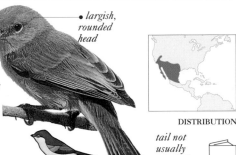

DISTRIBUTION

*tail not
usually
• forked*

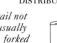

JUVENILE

Plumage Sexes alike	Habitat	Migration Non-migrant

Family PARIDAE	Species *Parus atricapillus*	Length 14cm (5½in)

BLACK-CAPPED CHICKADEE

This tame, acrobatic tit with a distinctive
"chickadee" call is often seen in small groups
that move continuously through woodland. It is
also found in small groves of trees, thickets, and
suburban gardens. Its diet consists of insects, seeds,
and berries. After pairing for the breeding season, birds
form small, noisy flocks in autumn, and these then
team up with similar small flocks of birds of other species.
Black-capped Chickadees are readily attracted to gardens
where sunflower seeds, suet, or peanuts are offered.
• **NEST** A cup nest of plant down, feathers, and hairs, on
a moss base, in a cavity cut in rotting wood or in a nest box.
• **DISTRIBUTION** S. Canada and N. USA.

DISTRIBUTION

*• white outer
tail feathers*

Plumage Sexes alike	Habitat	Migration Non-migrant

Family PARIDAE	Species *Parus ater*	Length 11cm (4¼in)

COAL TIT

Found in all types of woodland in its range, this insect-eating bird feeds in the treetops, but often comes to ground level to nest.
• **NEST** A cup nest made of moss, in a hole in a tree, stump, or bank.
• **DISTRIBUTION** Most of Europe with parts of N.W. Africa, Middle East, Siberia, C. and E. Asia.

DISTRIBUTION

• *white cheek and nape*

EUROPEAN FORM

NORTH AFRICAN FORM

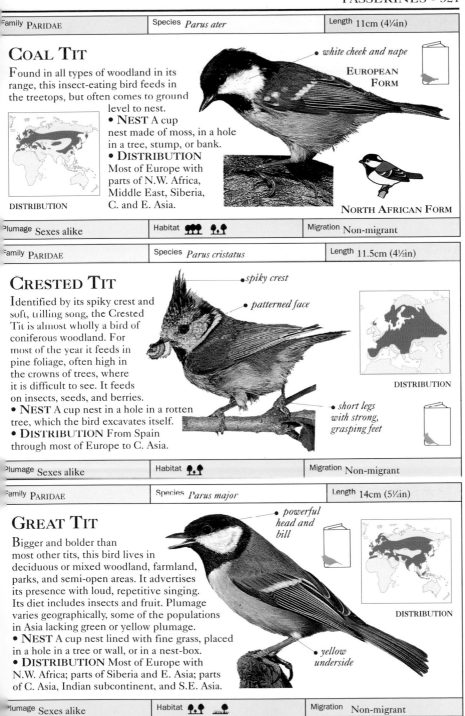

Plumage Sexes alike	Habitat	Migration Non-migrant

Family PARIDAE	Species *Parus cristatus*	Length 11.5cm (4½in)

CRESTED TIT

Identified by its spiky crest and soft, trilling song, the Crested Tit is almost wholly a bird of coniferous woodland. For most of the year it feeds in pine foliage, often high in the crowns of trees, where it is difficult to see. It feeds on insects, seeds, and berries.
• **NEST** A cup nest in a hole in a rotten tree, which the bird excavates itself.
• **DISTRIBUTION** From Spain through most of Europe to C. Asia.

• *spiky crest*

• *patterned face*

DISTRIBUTION

• *short legs with strong, grasping feet*

Plumage Sexes alike	Habitat	Migration Non-migrant

Family PARIDAE	Species *Parus major*	Length 14cm (5¼in)

GREAT TIT

Bigger and bolder than most other tits, this bird lives in deciduous or mixed woodland, farmland, parks, and semi-open areas. It advertises its presence with loud, repetitive singing. Its diet includes insects and fruit. Plumage varies geographically, some of the populations in Asia lacking green or yellow plumage.
• **NEST** A cup nest lined with fine grass, placed in a hole in a tree or wall, or in a nest-box.
• **DISTRIBUTION** Most of Europe with N.W. Africa; parts of Siberia and E. Asia; parts of C. Asia, Indian subcontinent, and S.E. Asia.

• *powerful head and bill*

DISTRIBUTION

• *yellow underside*

Plumage Sexes alike	Habitat	Migration Non-migrant

Family PARIDAE	Species *Parus caeruleus*	Length 11.5cm (4¼in)

BLUE TIT

Well-known as a garden bird, the Blue Tit is also common in woodland. Its food includes insects, seeds, and fruit.
• **NEST** A nest of moss, grass, and twigs, lined with grass and feathers, in a hole in a tree or wall, or in a nest-box.
• **DISTRIBUTION** Europe and parts of N. Africa and the Middle East.
• **REMARK** A readiness to investigate new food sources, and to use nest-boxes, explain the Blue Tit's frequent appearance as a garden bird.

• *blue crown*
• *white stripe*

DISTRIBUTION

• *blue wings and tail*

Plumage Sexes alike	Habitat	Migration Non-migrant

Family PARIDAE	Species *Parus bicolor*	Length 16cm (6¼in)

TUFTED TITMOUSE

Naturally a bird of woodland, forests, and scrub, the Tufted Titmouse is a frequent visitor to gardens, particularly where winter food is provided. It is seen in pairs and small parties, also joining mixed flocks, searching for insects, seeds, fruit, and nuts.
• **NEST** A cup nest made of hair, wool, leaves, and grass, placed in a tree hole, post, or nest-box.
• **DISTRIBUTION** S.E. Canada, E. USA, and N.E. Mexico.

• *small, pointed crest*

SOUTHERN FORM

DISTRIBUTION

EASTERN FORM

Plumage Sexes alike	Habitat	Migration Non-migrant

Family SITTIDAE	Species *Tichodroma muraria*	Length 17cm (6¾in)

WALLCREEPER

Climbing in short hops up rock faces, this bird uses its long, curved bill to probe crevices for insects.
• **NEST** Placed in a rock crevice, the nest is made of roots, grass, and moss, and lined with wool and hair.
• **DISTRIBUTION** From Europe to E. Asia.
• **REMARK** Its jerky, flitting style of flight resembles that of a butterfly.

FEMALE

• *large, scarlet wing patch*

DISTRIBUTION

• *large claws for climbing rock faces*

Plumage Sexes differ	Habitat	Migration Partial migrant

| Family SITTIDAE | Species *Sitta europaea* | Length 14cm (5½in) |

EURASIAN NUTHATCH

Usually seen running along tree branches or up and down the trunk in search of insects, this bird also takes nuts, which it wedges into a crevice and breaks open with blows of its bill.
• **NEST** A cup nest made of bark flakes, in a tree hole. The entrance is often plastered with mud to reduce its size.
• **DISTRIBUTION** Much of Eurasia.

• *short tail*

DISTRIBUTION

SIBERIAN FORM

| Plumage Sexes alike | Habitat | Migration Non-migrant |

| Family SITTIDAE | Species *Sitta carolinensis* | Length 14cm (5½in) |

WHITE-BREASTED NUTHATCH

Common in deciduous woodland and mixed forest areas within its range, the White-breasted Nuthatch characteristically works its way up, down, and across treetrunks in all directions as it forages for small insects. Like other nuthatches, it will also take nuts, which it hammers open with blows from its stout bill. Its song is a series of low, nasal whistles.
• **NEST** A hole in a tree, often lined with bark chippings and softer materials.
• **DISTRIBUTION** Parts of S. Canada, much of USA, and mountains of Mexico.

typical upended • posture

DISTRIBUTION

• *strong, hammering bill*

| Plumage Sexes alike | Habitat | Migration Non-migrant |

| Family NEOSITTIDAE | Species *Daphoenositta chrysoptera* | Length 12cm (4¾in) |

VARIED SITTELLA

NORTHWESTERN FORM

This small and gregarious species forages actively among the branches and twigs of trees, feeding on invertebrates. Plumage colours on the head, back, and wing-stripe vary with the subspecies.
• **NEST** A cup nest made of insect cocoons, spiders' webs, hair, and wool, camouflaged with bark flakes, and built into an upright fork of a tree.
• **DISTRIBUTION** Much of Australia and Highlands of New Guinea.

DISTRIBUTION

EASTERN FORM

| Plumage Sexes differ slightly | Habitat | Migration Non-migrant |

Family CERTHIIDAE	Species *Certhia familiaris*	Length 12cm (4¾in)

COMMON TREECREEPER

This grey-brown bird is usually seen climbing
a treetrunk in short spurts. It pauses to feed,
searching a fissure in the bark for spiders
or insects with its tweezer-like bill. While
stationary, it presses its stiff, spiny tail
against the bark for balance. It then swoops
down low before climbing the next tree.
• **NEST** A pocket-shaped nest made
of plant fibres, placed behind loose
bark, in a split tree, or behind ivy.
• **DISTRIBUTION** Parts of W. Europe
and from E. Europe through C. Asia to Japan.

DISTRIBUTION

*spine-tipped
tail for
• support*

Plumage Sexes alike	Habitat	Migration Non-migrant

Family CERTHIIDAE	Species *Certhia americana*	Length 13cm (5in)

BROWN CREEPER

Like the Common Treecreeper of Eurasia, the
Brown Creeper is adapted to climbing treetrunks,
pressing its stiff tail against the trunk both
for balance and support. It works its way up
one tree after another, searching any crevice
in the bark for its prey of spiders and insects.
• **NEST** A pocket-shaped nest constructed
of plant fibres and flakes of bark,
placed behind loose bark, in a split
tree, or behind a heavy growth of ivy.
• **DISTRIBUTION** W. and S. Canada, most of USA,
and mountains of C. America to Nicaragua. Northern
populations winter in S.E. USA and N. Mexico.

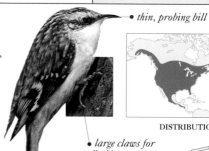

• thin, probing bill

DISTRIBUTION

*• large claws for
climbing*

Plumage Sexes alike	Habitat	Migration Partial migrant

Family CLIMACTERIDAE	Species *Climacteris affinis*	Length 15cm (6in)

WHITE-BROWED TREECREEPER

Although called a treecreeper, this bird
feeds on the ground as much as it does
in trees. It does not use the tail as a support
when climbing, and tends to perch across twigs,
rather than on the treetrunk. Its diet consists
principally of ants. Like other treecreepers,
this species is usually seen singly or in pairs.
• **NEST** A nest made in a hollow
in a tree, usually near ground level,
and lined with animal hairs and grass.
• **DISTRIBUTION** Interior of Australia.

• yellow wing bar

DISTRIBUTION

*• short tail
is not used as
a support in
climbing*

Plumage Sexes alike	Habitat	Migration Non-migrant

Family DICAEIDAE	Species *Melanocharis versteri*	Length 14cm (5½in)

FAN-TAILED BERRYPECKER

This shy, rainforest bird
feeds mainly on berries from
the undergrowth, also taking some
insects. It often hovers to pluck
berries or glean insects from the foliage.
• **NEST** A neat, deep cup nest made
of fibres torn from ferns, decorated with
lichens, and placed in
the fork of a tree or
on a horizontal branch.
• **DISTRIBUTION**
New Guinea.

*white tail patches
are conspicuous
in flight*

FEMALE

DISTRIBUTION

Plumage Sexes differ	Habitat 🌳 🏞 🌿 ⛰	Migration Non-migrant

Family DICAEIDAE	Species *Dicaeum hirundinaceum*	Length 11cm (4¼in)

MISTLETOEBIRD

*sharp, berry-
snatching bill*

This small, short-tailed bird lives in rainforest,
open forest, and scrubland. It feeds particularly
on mistletoe berries (voiding their sticky seeds
unharmed on branches, where they germinate
and grow), and also takes nectar, flower petals,
and insects. Mistletoebirds form small, nomadic
flocks, which move about the foliage from tree
to tree in search of fruiting mistletoe plants.
• **NEST** A domed, hanging
nest of plant down and
spiders' webs, placed in a tree.
• **DISTRIBUTION** Australia
and parts of E. Indonesia.

DISTRIBUTION

FEMALE

*• long
wings for
nomadic
flight*

Plumage Sexes differ	Habitat 🌿 ✈ 🌳	Migration Nomadic

Family DICAEIDAE	Species *Pardalotus punctatus*	Length 9cm (3½in)

SPOTTED PARDALOTE

Usually seen singly or in pairs, this tiny,
brightly coloured bird forages in the upper
foliage of trees for insects which it catches
in passing, often taking them from the
undersides of leaves, in the random method
known as "gleaning". As a treetop
bird, it is more often heard than seen.
• **NEST** A domed nest, made
of bark fragments, either at
the end of a tunnel dug into
a bank, or in a tree stump.
• **DISTRIBUTION**
S. and E. Australia.

• spotted crown

DISTRIBUTION

FEMALE

• short tail

Plumage Sexes differ	Habitat 🌳 🌿 🏞 ✈	Migration Non-migrant

Family DICAEIDAE	Species *Pardalotus striatus*	Length 11cm (4¼in)

STRIATED PARDALOTE

Small and inquisitively active, this
bird hunts and gleans invertebrates
in the outer twigs and leaves of
trees. When not breeding, birds
form flocks that feed together,
uttering constant, short calls.
• **NEST** A domed structure of bark and
grass, lined with finer materials, at the
end of a tunnel, or in a tree hollow.
• **DISTRIBUTION**
Australia. Tasmanian subspecies
winters on mainland.

*white wing
• stripe*

NORTH-
EASTERN
FORM

SOUTHEASTERN FORM

DISTRIBUTION

Plumage Sexes alike	Habitat	Migration Partial migrant

Family NECTARINIIDAE	Species *Nectarinia violacea*	L. 17cm (6¾in)/13cm (5in)

ORANGE-BREASTED SUNBIRD

This small sunbird feeds on
nectar and small insects with its
long, slender bill. It is found on
heathland, where up to 100 birds
will congregate at a food source.
• **NEST** An oval nest of rootlets,
bound with spiders' webs and lined
with seed fluff, usually in a bush.
• **DISTRIBUTION** S. South Africa.
• **REMARK** The male's tail accounts
for the size difference between sexes.

*agile feet cling to small
• twigs to reach flowers*

DISTRIBUTION

FEMALE

Plumage Sexes differ	Habitat	Migration Non-migrant

Family NECTARINIIDAE	Species *Nectarinia senegalensis*	Length 14cm (5½in)

SCARLET-CHESTED SUNBIRD

Identified by the male's brilliant, scarlet breast, this
species is often seen in groups in and around flowering
trees. Females lack the scarlet breast. The diet consists
of insects and nectar, sometimes from the same flower.
• **NEST** A hanging nest of plant fibres and spiders'
webs, with a domed top, a porch, and a dangling
ornament known as a "beard". The
nest is suspended from a thin
twig, often near a wasps' nest.
• **DISTRIBUTION** Parts of
Africa south of the Sahara.

*• iridescent
crown and
"moustache"*

DISTRIBUTION

FEMALE

Plumage Sexes differ	Habitat	Migration Non-migrant

| Family NECTARINIIDAE | Species *Nectarinia famosa* | L. 25cm (10in)/15cm (6in) |

MALACHITE SUNBIRD

Notable for its extremely long tail and bill,
the Malachite Sunbird probes flowers for nectar,
and often also catches insects in hawking flight.
It is an active, aggressive, and territorial species,
and may often be seen in open habitats such
as grassland, defending a feeding site such as
a flowering bush or tree, from other sunbirds.
Adaptable to a wide variety of habitats, it is equally
at home on scrubby mountainsides or in gardens
and parks. It is usually seen in pairs during the
breeding season, but singly at other times of
year. During courtship, the male displays to the
female by shivering his wings and raising his
tail. The song, delivered either out of sight from
within a bush or from a conspicuous perch, consists
of piping call notes, followed by rapid, high-pitched notes.
• **NEST** An oval-shaped structure made of grass and
other vegetable matter, bound with spiders' webs. This
is lined with fine material and placed low down in a bush.
• **DISTRIBUTION** A series of separate areas
in mountain regions from Ethiopia to South Africa.
• **REMARK** The male bird's longer tail accounts
for the length difference between the sexes.

lithe,
athletic
build

long, narrow
wings for
rapid
flight

DISTRIBUTION

long tail for
use in vivid
display

FEMALE

| Plumage Sexes differ | Habitat | Migration Non-migrant |

| Family NECTARINIIDAE | Species *Nectarinia kilimensis* | L. 23cm (9in)/15cm (6in) |

BRONZE SUNBIRD

This bird occurs in clearings, forest edges, and bushy grassland
in tropical mountain ranges. Males are often conspicuous
as they defend their territories, ferociously chasing off
rival males. Bronze Sunbirds utter loud, musical,
piping call notes to maintain contact. They
feed on nectar, insects, and spiders.
• **NEST** An oval structure made of grass,
flowers, lichens, and bark shreds.
The nest is bound with spiders'
webs and situated in a bush.
• **DISTRIBUTION** Mountains
in E. Africa from E. Zaire and
Uganda to Mozambique.
• **REMARK** The male's
longer tail accounts
for the 8cm (3in)
difference in
length between
the sexes.

curved
bill probes
inside
flowers

glittering
bronze tint
shows as
bird turns
in the light

male's long tail
shown off in flight

FEMALE

DISTRIBUTION

| Plumage Sexes differ | Habitat | Migration Non-migrant |

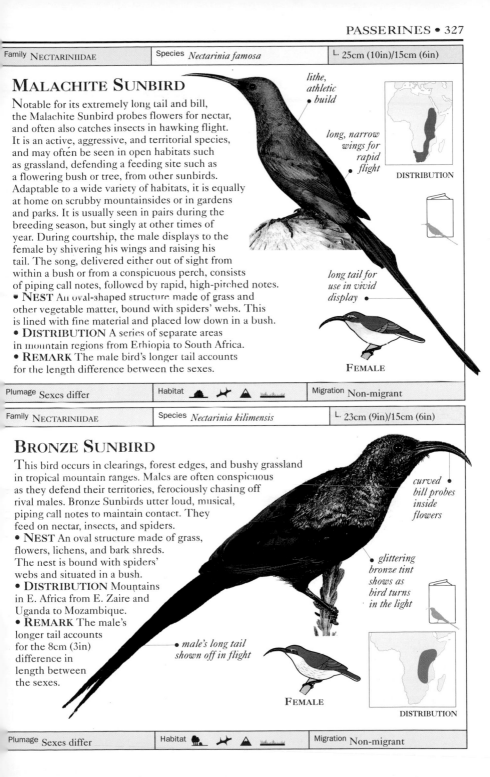

Family NECTARINIIDAE	Species *Aethopyga christinae*	Length 11cm (4¼in)

FORK-TAILED SUNBIRD

This bird occurs in forests and clearings and is commonly seen in tall trees, darting from flower to flower. It lives mainly on nectar and occasionally on insects, usually feeding while perched, but sometimes in hovering flight.

• **NEST** A ball-shaped nest, made of grass, bound with spiders' webs, and placed in a tree.

• **DISTRIBUTION** S. China and N. Vietnam.

glistening plumage

male's finely forked tail tip

DISTRIBUTION

FEMALE

Plumage Sexes differ	Habitat	Migration Non-migrant

Family NECTARINIIDAE	Species *Arachnothera affinis*	Length 17cm (6¾in)

GREY-BREASTED SPIDERHUNTER

A strongly built bird with a short tail and a bill that looks disproportionately large, the Grey-breasted Spiderhunter is seen in the trees and undergrowth of tropical rainforest. The long bill is used for snatching spiders from their webs, for drinking nectar from flowers, and for taking seeds.

• **NEST** A cup-shaped nest of grass stems, decorated with young fern fronds and small flowers, and suspended from the underside of a large leaf.

• **DISTRIBUTION** Malay Peninsula, Borneo, Sumatra, Java, and Bali.

dull olive plumage for camouflage against foliage

streaked breast

short, square tail

DISTRIBUTION

Plumage Sexes alike	Habitat	Migration Non-migrant

Family ZOSTEROPIDAE	Species *Zosterops palpebrosus*	Length 11cm (4¼in)

ORIENTAL WHITE-EYE

Common in open, scrub-covered country and forest edges, this bird is equally at home in bushes and trees. It is usually seen in pairs or small flocks of up to 30 birds, uttering high-pitched calls as they forage quickly through the upper foliage in search of insects, nectar, and fruits.

• **NEST** A cup-shaped nest made of fine roots, leaf ribs, and stems, and placed in a tree or bamboo clump.

• **DISTRIBUTION** Much of Indian subcontinent, S. China, and parts of S.E. Asia.

typical white eye-ring

feet get a firm grip while feeding

DISTRIBUTION

Plumage Sexes alike	Habitat	Migration Non-migrant

Family ZOSTEROPIDAE	Species *Zosterops poliogaster*	Length 11cm (4¼in)

BROAD-RINGED WHITE-EYE

Fairly commonly found in mountain rainforests, this bird occurs in large, noisy flocks that move about in search of food. Its diet consists of a mixture of insects and berries.
• **NEST** A deep cup nest of plant fibres or lichens, lined with finer fibres, and attached to bushes or small trees, sometimes suspended from a twig.
• **DISTRIBUTION** N.E. Africa.

large, white eye-ring

tapering wings

DISTRIBUTION

strong feet for acrobatic perching

Plumage Sexes alike	Habitat	Migration Non-migrant

Family MELIPHAGIDAE	Species *Toxorhamphus poliopterus*	Length 13cm (5in)

GREY-WINGED LONGBILL

This bird is found at the edge of mountain rainforests and in secondary growth (bushes or trees regrown after forest clearance). It feeds on insects and nectar, flitting among the foliage in a nervous manner.
• **NEST** A deep, pouch-like nest of greenish plant material and spiders' webs, decorated with the white cases of spiders' eggs, and placed on the branch of a slender sapling.
• **DISTRIBUTION** New Guinea.

bill is shaped for snatching insects and for probing flowers

DISTRIBUTION

Plumage Sexes alike	Habitat	Migration Non-migrant

Family MELIPHAGIDAE	Species *Certhionyx pectoralis*	Length 14cm (5½in)

BANDED HONEYEATER

This species inhabits woodland and waterside foliage, travelling nomadically in search of nectar, insects, and flowers. Flocks of noisy, aggressive birds are seen feeding in blossoming trees.
• **NEST** A cup nest made of grass and bark, bound with spiders' webs, and suspended in the outer foliage of a tree or bush.
•**DISTRIBUTION** N. Australia.

JUVENILE

DISTRIBUTION

Plumage Sexes alike	Habitat	Migration Nomadic

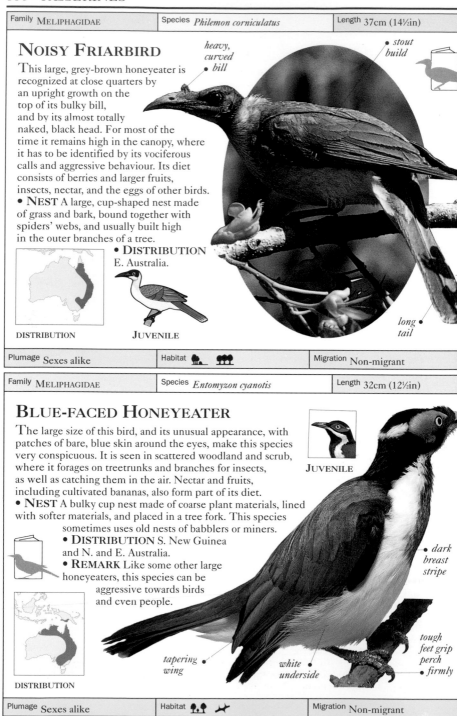

Family MELIPHAGIDAE	Species *Philemon corniculatus*	Length 37cm (14½in)

NOISY FRIARBIRD

heavy, curved bill

stout build

This large, grey-brown honeyeater is recognized at close quarters by an upright growth on the top of its bulky bill, and by its almost totally naked, black head. For most of the time it remains high in the canopy, where it has to be identified by its vociferous calls and aggressive behaviour. Its diet consists of berries and larger fruits, insects, nectar, and the eggs of other birds.
• **NEST** A large, cup-shaped nest made of grass and bark, bound together with spiders' webs, and usually built high in the outer branches of a tree.
• **DISTRIBUTION** E. Australia.

DISTRIBUTION

JUVENILE

long tail

Plumage Sexes alike	Habitat	Migration Non-migrant

Family MELIPHAGIDAE	Species *Entomyzon cyanotis*	Length 32cm (12½in)

BLUE-FACED HONEYEATER

The large size of this bird, and its unusual appearance, with patches of bare, blue skin around the eyes, make this species very conspicuous. It is seen in scattered woodland and scrub, where it forages on treetrunks and branches for insects, as well as catching them in the air. Nectar and fruits, including cultivated bananas, also form part of its diet.

JUVENILE

• **NEST** A bulky cup nest made of coarse plant materials, lined with softer materials, and placed in a tree fork. This species sometimes uses old nests of babblers or miners.
• **DISTRIBUTION** S. New Guinea and N. and E. Australia.
• **REMARK** Like some other large honeyeaters, this species can be aggressive towards birds and even people.

dark breast stripe

tough feet grip perch firmly

DISTRIBUTION

tapering wing

white underside

Plumage Sexes alike	Habitat	Migration Non-migrant

| Family MELIPHAGIDAE | Species *Lichenostomus penicillatus* | Length 18cm (7in) |

WHITE-PLUMED HONEYEATER

A lively, active honeyeater, this species is equally at home in town gardens and forests. Small flocks are seen moving about in open stands of trees, taking nectar from tree blossoms and catching small invertebrates. The courtship display consists of a short, upward, fluttering flight and a shrill "chickowee" call.
• **NEST** A cup nest made of grass, lined with feathers and hairs, bound with spiders' webs, and suspended in a tree or bush.
• **DISTRIBUTION** Through much of Australia.

white ear tuft

slender build

forked tail

DISTRIBUTION

| Plumage Sexes alike | Habitat | Migration Non-migrant |

| Family MELIPHAGIDAE | Species *Phylidonyris novaehollandiae* | Length 18cm (7in) |

NEW HOLLAND HONEYEATER

This noisy, restless bird is nomadic, and flocks will gather at any good source of nectar. Originally a bird of coastal heathlands, it also visits gardens and parks. It feeds on insects.
• **NEST** A cup nest of grass and bark, bound with spiders' webs, with a softer lining, placed in a bush or tree.
• **DISTRIBUTION** S.E. and S.W. Australia.

staring eye with pale iris

bristly feathers

pied plumage

yellow stripe

yellow edge of tail

JUVENILE

DISTRIBUTION

| Plumage Sexes alike | Habitat | Migration Non-migrant/nomadic |

| Family MELIPHAGIDAE | Species *Anthornis melanura* | Length 20cm (8in) |

NEW ZEALAND BELLBIRD

The liquid, bell-like song of the New Zealand Bellbird is heard throughout the year. It is a common forest bird, often seen in large numbers on flowering trees, where it feeds on nectar, fruits, and insects. It also visits gardens near the forest edge where fruit is offered.
• **NEST** A loosely constructed cup nest made of coarse materials, lined with fine grasses and feathers, and placed in the fork of a tree.
• **DISTRIBUTION** New Zealand.
• **REMARK** Only three species of honeyeater occur in New Zealand.

large feet

DISTRIBUTION

| Plumage Sexes differ slightly | Habitat | Migration Non-migrant/nomadic |

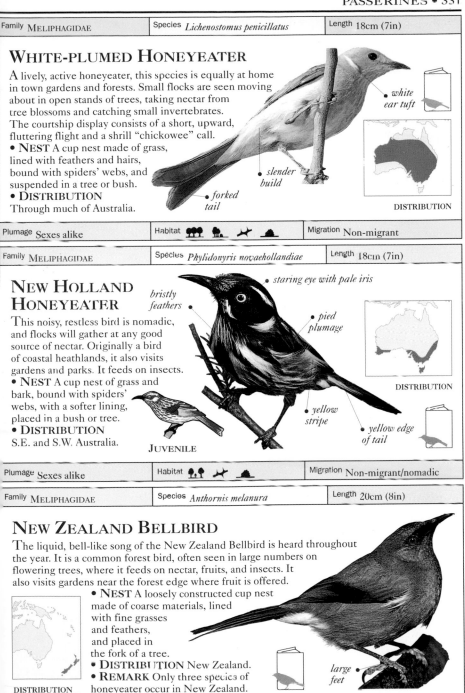

Family MELIPHAGIDAE	Species *Melipotes ater*	Length 32cm (12½in)

SPANGLED HONEYEATER

Although conspicuous because of its large size and colourful appearance, this honeyeater is rather quiet and unobtrusive. Sluggish in general behaviour, it occurs in the upper branches of the higher mountain rainforests, usually singly or in pairs, feeding on fruit such as berries, with occasional insects. Presumably because of this diet it has a short, heavy bill and lacks the brush tongue of nectar-feeding species. The typical call is "chut, chut". The yellow face wattle appears capable of becoming red during sexual displays. Because of its isolated range and retiring habits in a difficult habitat for field work, little is known about it.
• **NEST** A bulky, cup-shaped nest, loosely made out of moss, leaves, and other plant material, hanging from the end of a branch.
• **DISTRIBUTION** Mountains of the Huon Peninsula of W. New Guinea, from 1,200m (3,900ft) to 3,300m (11,000ft).

• *yellow face wattle*

dark • *plumage*

DISTRIBUTION

• *large, powerful feet*

long tail •

Plumage Sexes alike	Habitat 🌳 🌿 ⛰	Migration Non-migrant

Family MELIPHAGIDAE	Species *Manorina flavigula*	Length 28cm (11in)

YELLOW-THROATED MINER

This heavily built, generally grey-brown honeyeater is a sociable and attractive bird, with a strong, yellow-coloured wash on its breast and forehead. It lives in small colonies, often in scattered groups of trees in otherwise open country. Birds probably travel nomadically between such feeding and roosting sites. They feed predominantly on the ground, taking insects and seeds, but they also ascend the trees to take berries, fruit, and sometimes nectar from flowers. Yellow-throated Miners are aggressive birds, with much quarrelling within the colony as well as vigorous defence against birds of other species. Often this defensive behaviour involves the entire flock taking wing and chasing a marauding bird of prey out of its territory, mobbing, and even physically attacking the intruder in flight. There is cooperative care of nestlings within the colony.
• **NEST** A loose cup nest made of grass and twigs, lined with wool and feathers, and placed in a tree fork up to 6m (20ft) from the ground.
• **DISTRIBUTION** Much of Australia.

DISTRIBUTION

• *yellow throat patch*

• *strong wings for vigorous flight*

• *strong legs for feeding on the ground*

Plumage Sexes alike	Habitat 🌳 🌾	Migration Non-migrant

Family MELIPHAGIDAE	Species *Anthochaera paradoxa*	Length 47cm (18½in)

YELLOW WATTLEBIRD

The largest of the honeyeaters, the Yellow Wattlebird is a slender, ungainly bird with characteristic wattles dangling from the cheek. Flocks visit eucalyptus trees to feed on insects and nectar. They also eat fruit from low shrubs and sometimes from orchards, and use garden birdfeeders. This aggressive and noisy bird can be recognized by its harsh, guttural call notes.
• NEST A loose cup nest made of twigs, leaves, and bark, lined with down and feathers, and placed in a high, upward-pointing tree fork.
• DISTRIBUTION Tasmania.

long, tapering tail •

• cheek wattles

• spotted breast

• yellow belly patch

• strong feet for clinging to a tree perch

DISTRIBUTION

Plumage Sexes alike	Habitat	Migration Non-migrant

Family MELIPHAGIDAE	Species *Promerops cafer*	L. 46cm (18in)/23cm (9in)

SUGARBIRD

This is a heathland bird that is seen singly or in pairs during the breeding season, and in small groups, often at a favoured feeding site, at other times of year. The Sugarbird exploits the *Protea* plant in a number of ways. It feeds on *Protea* nectar, which supplements its diet of insects and spiders. The male perches conspicuously on the flower to call and to show his presence to potential rivals for breeding territory.
• NEST An untidy cup nest made of twigs, grass, bracken, roots, and pine needles, neatly lined with *Protea* down, and placed in forked or tangled branches of bushes.
• DISTRIBUTION S. South Africa.
• REMARK Both male and female Sugarbirds have long tails, but the male's much longer tail accounts for the 23cm (9in) length difference between the sexes.

• short legs

DISTRIBUTION

yellowish undertail • coverts

• male's long tail for aerial display

• protea flower

FEMALE

Plumage Sexes differ	Habitat	Migration Non-migrant

Family EMBERIZIDAE	Species *Emberiza citrinella*	Length 16cm (6¼in)

YELLOWHAMMER

This familiar bunting of hedgerows
and farmland is identified by the yellow
head and monotonous song phrase of the male.
The diet consists mainly of insects and seeds,
most of which are taken from the ground.
• **NEST** A neat cup nest of grass, lined with finer
materials, and placed in the base of a hedge, in a low
bush, or on the ground.
• **DISTRIBUTION**
Most of Europe, and
parts of N.W. Africa
and C. Asia.

FEMALE

• *male
displays
yellow
head*

*white •
outer tail
feathers*

DISTRIBUTION

Plumage Sexes differ	Habitat	Migration Partial migrant

Family EMBERIZIDAE	Species *Emberiza flaviventris*	Length 16cm (6¼in)

GOLDEN-BREASTED BUNTING

A brightly coloured bunting of open-country
habitats, this species is recognized by its
deeply undulating flight and a habit, when
alighting, of flicking its tail. It feeds on the
ground, taking seeds and insects. Outside the
breeding season it joins mixed feeding flocks
composed of other buntings and canaries.
• **NEST** A shallow cup nest made of
grass and roots, lined with fine
rootlets, and placed close to the
ground in a low bush or tree.
• **DISTRIBUTION** Open-country
areas of Africa south of the Sahara.

FEMALE

• *black-and-
white head*

• *longish
legs*

*white
outer tail
feathers •*

DISTRIBUTION

Plumage Sexes differ	Habitat	Migration Non-migrant

Family EMBERIZIDAE	Species *Emberiza schoeniclus*	Length 15cm (6in)

REED BUNTING

In spring, males of this species perch on the
tops of reeds or bushes, uttering their three-
note song. In winter, Reed Buntings join
flocks of seed-eating birds on farmland. They
feed on the ground, taking seeds and insects.
• **NEST** A cup nest made of grasses,
placed in vegetation on the ground
or in a bush, usually close by water.
• **DISTRIBUTION** Breeds in
Eurasia from W. Europe to Japan.
Migrant populations winter in
S. Europe, N. Africa, Middle
East, N. China, and N. Japan.

FEMALE

• *white
collar*

• *white
outer tail
feathers*

DISTRIBUTION

Plumage Sexes differ	Habitat	Migration Partial migrant

Family EMBERIZIDAE	Species *Calcarius ornatus*	Length 15cm (6in)

CHESTNUT-COLLARED LONGSPUR

This is a shy, inconspicuous bunting that breeds on the prairies, feeding on seeds and insects. The male performs an attractive display flight, with a warbling song.
• **NEST** A grassy cup in a hollow.
• **DISTRIBUTION** Breeds in C. North America. Winters in S. USA and Mexico.
• **REMARK** The "spur" refers to its long hind claw, an adaptation to ground dwelling.

shortish tail

white outer feathers

FEMALE

DISTRIBUTION

Plumage Sexes differ	Habitat	Migration Migrant

Family EMBERIZIDAE	Species *Plectrophenax nivalis*	Length 17cm (6¾in)

SNOW BUNTING

This species breeds on the tundra and in some mountain areas further south. In winter, large flocks migrate south and out of the mountains, settling on exposed landscapes by the sea. The diet consists of seeds, with insects in summer.
• **NEST** A cup nest in a rock crevice.
• **DISTRIBUTION** Breeds in N. North America and Eurasia. Winters further south.
• **REMARK** Females browner, with less white plumage.

round head

stocky build

DISTRIBUTION

white outer tail feathers

WINTER MALE

Plumage Sexes differ	Habitat	Migration Migrant

Family EMBERIZIDAE	Species *Passerella iliaca*	Length 18cm (7in)

FOX SPARROW

A heavily built bunting with a musical song, this bird feeds in undergrowth on insects and seeds. It sings from an exposed perch, even in winter.
• **NEST** A cup nest, in a thicket, on the ground or in a shrub.
• **DISTRIBUTION** Breeds in Canada and W. USA. Winters from S.W. Canada to S. USA.

rounded head

rufous markings of eastern form

plump body

TYPICAL WESTERN FORM

DISTRIBUTION

Plumage Sexes alike	Habitat	Migration Partial migrant

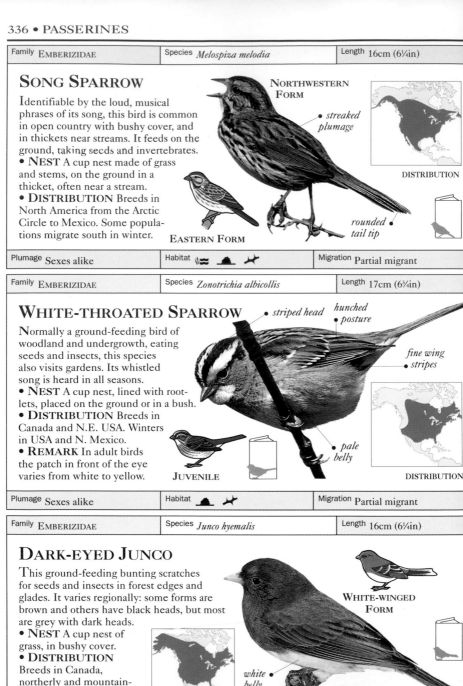

| Family EMBERIZIDAE | Species *Melospiza melodia* | Length 16cm (6¼in) |

SONG SPARROW

Identifiable by the loud, musical phrases of its song, this bird is common in open country with bushy cover, and in thickets near streams. It feeds on the ground, taking seeds and invertebrates.
• **NEST** A cup nest made of grass and stems, on the ground in a thicket, often near a stream.
• **DISTRIBUTION** Breeds in North America from the Arctic Circle to Mexico. Some populations migrate south in winter.

NORTHWESTERN FORM

• *streaked plumage*

DISTRIBUTION

rounded tail tip

EASTERN FORM

| Plumage Sexes alike | Habitat | Migration Partial migrant |

| Family EMBERIZIDAE | Species *Zonotrichia albicollis* | Length 17cm (6¾in) |

WHITE-THROATED SPARROW

Normally a ground-feeding bird of woodland and undergrowth, eating seeds and insects, this species also visits gardens. Its whistled song is heard in all seasons.
• **NEST** A cup nest, lined with rootlets, placed on the ground or in a bush.
• **DISTRIBUTION** Breeds in Canada and N.E. USA. Winters in USA and N. Mexico.
• **REMARK** In adult birds the patch in front of the eye varies from white to yellow.

• *striped head*   *hunched* • *posture*

fine wing • *stripes*

pale belly

JUVENILE

DISTRIBUTION

| Plumage Sexes alike | Habitat | Migration Partial migrant |

| Family EMBERIZIDAE | Species *Junco hyemalis* | Length 16cm (6¼in) |

DARK-EYED JUNCO

This ground-feeding bunting scratches for seeds and insects in forest edges and glades. It varies regionally: some forms are brown and others have black heads, but most are grey with dark heads.
• **NEST** A cup nest of grass, in bushy cover.
• **DISTRIBUTION** Breeds in Canada, northerly and mountainous parts of USA, and N. Mexico. Northern birds migrate south.

WHITE-WINGED FORM

white belly •

DISTRIBUTION

FEMALE OF SLATE-GREY FORM

| Plumage Sexes differ slightly | Habitat | Migration Partial migrant |

Family EMBERIZIDAE	Species *Spizella arborea*	Length 16cm (6¼in)

AMERICAN TREE SPARROW

A bird of open country with bushy cover, this bunting is identified by the dark spot on its grey breast. In winter it joins mixed flocks of ground-feeding birds, taking seeds and invertebrates.

• **NEST** A shallow cup nest of grasses and other coarse vegetable materials, lined with feathers, and placed in a low bush or on the ground.

• **DISTRIBUTION** Breeds in Alaska and N. Canada. Winters in USA as far south as Texas.

DISTRIBUTION

chestnut crown •
white bars •

fluffed plumage •
for winter warmth

Plumage Sexes alike	Habitat	Migration Migrant

Family EMBERIZIDAE	Species *Poospiza nigrorufa*	Length 15cm (6in)

BLACK-AND-RUFOUS WARBLING FINCH

A small and active seed-eater with a short bill, this species inhabits areas of extensive shrubs, sometimes with scattered trees, and is a common bird in this habitat. It is usually found in pairs, which forage on or near the ground for seeds and insects. Males commonly proclaim their territory by singing from an exposed perch and displaying the chestnut breast in the breeding season.

• **NEST** Details have not been scientifically recorded.

• **DISTRIBUTION** River Plate basin in N.E. Brazil, E. Paraguay, Uruguay, and N.E. Argentina.

• white stripe
over eye

• black
back

DISTRIBUTION

• chestnut
breast

Plumage Sexes alike	Habitat	Migration Non-migrant

Family EMBERIZIDAE	Species *Sicalis flaveola*	Length 14cm (5½in)

SAFFRON FINCH

This scrub and grassland bird is easily identified by the intense yellow plumage of the male, with a darker yellow, almost orange, patch at the front of the crown. Flocks are commonly seen feeding quietly on the ground, taking small seeds.

• **NEST** In cavities or abandoned nests of other scrub and grassland birds.

• **DISTRIBUTION** Scattered areas in South America. Also Trinidad. Introduced in Panama, Jamaica, and Puerto Rico.

• **REMARK** A popular cage bird.

JUVENILE

DISTRIBUTION

• strong
legs

slightly forked tail •

Plumage Sexes differ slightly	Habitat	Migration Non-migrant

Family EMBERIZIDAE	Species *Tiaris canora*	Length 11cm (4¼in)

CUBAN GRASSQUIT

yellow collar •

This boldly coloured little seed-eater inhabits the shrubby edges of areas of open grassland. Flocks are often seen on the ground, feeding on small seeds. The song is soft and pleasant.
• **NEST** A spherical nest made of grass, with a side entrance, situated low in a bush or tree.
• **DISTRIBUTION** Cuba. Introduced population in New Providence Island in the Bahamas.

DISTRIBUTION

FEMALE

Plumage Sexes differ	Habitat	Migration Non-migrant

Family EMBERIZIDAE	Species *Geospiza fuliginosa*	Length 11cm (4¼in)

SMALL GROUND FINCH

• male is blacker than the female

Common within its restricted island range, this unobtrusive but lively little finch feeds both on small seeds and insects. It is the smallest of three species of ground finch, and sometimes forms mixed flocks together with these and other finches.
• **NEST** A loose cup made of twigs, grasses, and pieces of bark, lined with lichen, feathers and cottonheads, located in a bush or cactus.
• **DISTRIBUTION** Galapagos Islands (off the Pacific coast of Ecuador).
• **REMARK** One of 14 Galapagos finch species featured in Charles Darwin's evolutionary studies, with a range of bill shapes adapted to specialized diets.

DISTRIBUTION

Plumage Sexes differ slightly	Habitat	Migration Non-migrant

Family EMBERIZIDAE	Species *Pipilo erythrophthalmus*	Length 22cm (8½in)

RUFOUS-SIDED TOWHEE

white spots of western form •

A seed-eater with a long tail and short legs, this bird is adapted to a terrestrial lifestyle. It feeds on the ground, usually in or close to cover, taking both seeds and insects.
• **NEST** An open, loosely made cup nest, situated on or close to the ground.
• **DISTRIBUTION** S. Canada, USA, and much of Mexico. Northern populations winter in the south of this range.
• **REMARK** Plumage, especially that of female birds, varies geographically.

DISTRIBUTION

white-bordered tail

WESTERN FEMALE

Plumage Sexes differ	Habitat	Migration Migrant

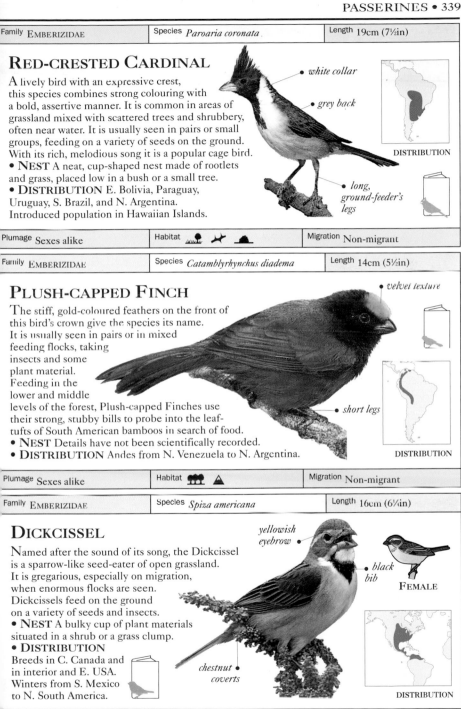

| Family EMBERIZIDAE | Species *Paroaria coronata* | Length 19cm (7½in) |

RED-CRESTED CARDINAL

A lively bird with an expressive crest,
this species combines strong colouring with
a bold, assertive manner. It is common in areas of
grassland mixed with scattered trees and shrubbery,
often near water. It is usually seen in pairs or small
groups, feeding on a variety of seeds on the ground.
With its rich, melodious song it is a popular cage bird.
• NEST A neat, cup-shaped nest made of rootlets
and grass, placed low in a bush or a small tree.
• DISTRIBUTION E. Bolivia, Paraguay,
Uruguay, S. Brazil, and N. Argentina.
Introduced population in Hawaiian Islands.

• white collar

• grey back

DISTRIBUTION

• long,
ground-feeder's
legs

| Plumage Sexes alike | Habitat | Migration Non-migrant |

| Family EMBERIZIDAE | Species *Catamblyrhynchus diadema* | Length 14cm (5½in) |

PLUSH-CAPPED FINCH

The stiff, gold-coloured feathers on the front of
this bird's crown give the species its name.
It is usually seen in pairs or in mixed
feeding flocks, taking
insects and some
plant material.
Feeding in the
lower and middle
levels of the forest, Plush-capped Finches use
their strong, stubby bills to probe into the leaf-
tufts of South American bamboos in search of food.
• NEST Details have not been scientifically recorded.
• DISTRIBUTION Andes from N. Venezuela to N. Argentina.

• velvet texture

• short legs

DISTRIBUTION

| Plumage Sexes alike | Habitat | Migration Non-migrant |

| Family EMBERIZIDAE | Species *Spiza americana* | Length 16cm (6¼in) |

DICKCISSEL

Named after the sound of its song, the Dickcissel
is a sparrow-like seed-eater of open grassland.
It is gregarious, especially on migration,
when enormous flocks are seen.
Dickcissels feed on the ground
on a variety of seeds and insects.
• NEST A bulky cup of plant materials
situated in a shrub or a grass clump.
• DISTRIBUTION
Breeds in C. Canada and
in interior and E. USA.
Winters from S. Mexico
to N. South America.

yellowish
eyebrow •

• black
bib

FEMALE

chestnut •
coverts

DISTRIBUTION

| Plumage Sexes differ | Habitat | Migration Migrant |

| Family EMBERIZIDAE | Species *Pheucticus ludovicianus* | Length 20cm (8in) |

ROSE-BREASTED GROSBEAK

A tree-dweller with a massive bill and a melodious song, this bird lives in open secondary woodland and shrubbery (regrown after forest clearance), eating insects, fruits, seeds, buds, and blossoms.
• **NEST** A loose cup nest of twigs and grass, with a finer lining, in a tree.
• **DISTRIBUTION** Breeds in North America east of the Rockies. Winters in Central and South America.

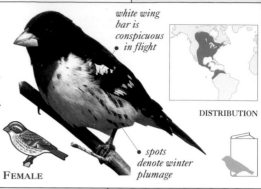

white wing bar is conspicuous in flight

DISTRIBUTION

spots denote winter plumage

FEMALE

| Plumage Sexes differ | Habitat | Migration Migrant |

| Family EMBERIZIDAE | Species *Cardinalis cardinalis* | Length 22cm (8½in) |

COMMON CARDINAL

Well-known for its vivid colours and loud, musical calls, the Common Cardinal has adapted to living in suburban gardens. Throughout its range it lives in undergrowth, where it searches out its diet of insects, fruit, and seeds. Both sexes sing for much of the year.
• **NEST** A coarse cup nest of leaves and twigs, lined with grapevine bark, placed just above the ground in a bush.
• **DISTRIBUTION** C., E., and S. USA, and Mexico.

pointed crest

black face

heavy bill

male is red all over

DISTRIBUTION

FEMALE

| Plumage Sexes differ | Habitat | Migration Non-migrant |

| Family EMBERIZIDAE | Species *Saltator maximus* | Length 20cm (8in) |

BUFF-THROATED SALTATOR

A large, heavy-billed, tree-dwelling bird, this is a wary species with inconspicuous plumage. It often keeps out of sight in dense cover afforded by the foliage of scrub and forest-edge undergrowth. It is common in its range and is usually encountered singly or in pairs. The diet consists of fruits and insects.
• **NEST** A cup-shaped nest constructed of coarse grasses, twigs, and other plant material, and situated in a bush or small tree.
• **DISTRIBUTION** Central America, N. and E. South America.

white eyebrow

bright olive back

DISTRIBUTION

| Plumage Sexes alike | Habitat | Migration Non-migrant |

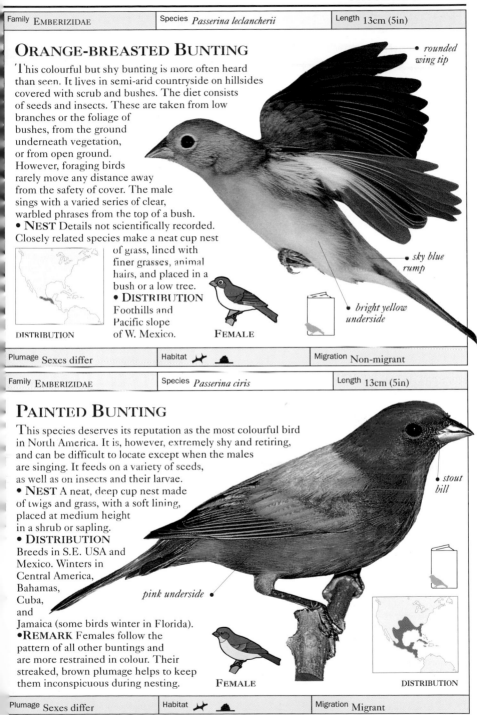

Family EMBERIZIDAE	Species *Passerina leclancherii*	Length 13cm (5in)

ORANGE-BREASTED BUNTING

This colourful but shy bunting is more often heard than seen. It lives in semi-arid countryside on hillsides covered with scrub and bushes. The diet consists of seeds and insects. These are taken from low branches or the foliage of bushes, from the ground underneath vegetation, or from open ground. However, foraging birds rarely move any distance away from the safety of cover. The male sings with a varied series of clear, warbled phrases from the top of a bush.
• **NEST** Details not scientifically recorded. Closely related species make a neat cup nest of grass, lined with finer grasses, animal hairs, and placed in a bush or a low tree.
• **DISTRIBUTION** Foothills and Pacific slope of W. Mexico.

• *rounded wing tip*

• *sky blue rump*

• *bright yellow underside*

DISTRIBUTION

FEMALE

Plumage Sexes differ	Habitat	Migration Non-migrant

Family EMBERIZIDAE	Species *Passerina ciris*	Length 13cm (5in)

PAINTED BUNTING

This species deserves its reputation as the most colourful bird in North America. It is, however, extremely shy and retiring, and can be difficult to locate except when the males are singing. It feeds on a variety of seeds, as well as on insects and their larvae.
• **NEST** A neat, deep cup nest made of twigs and grass, with a soft lining, placed at medium height in a shrub or sapling.
• **DISTRIBUTION** Breeds in S.E. USA and Mexico. Winters in Central America, Bahamas, Cuba, and Jamaica (some birds winter in Florida).
•**REMARK** Females follow the pattern of all other buntings and are more restrained in colour. Their streaked, brown plumage helps to keep them inconspicuous during nesting.

• *stout bill*

pink underside •

FEMALE

DISTRIBUTION

Plumage Sexes differ	Habitat	Migration Migrant

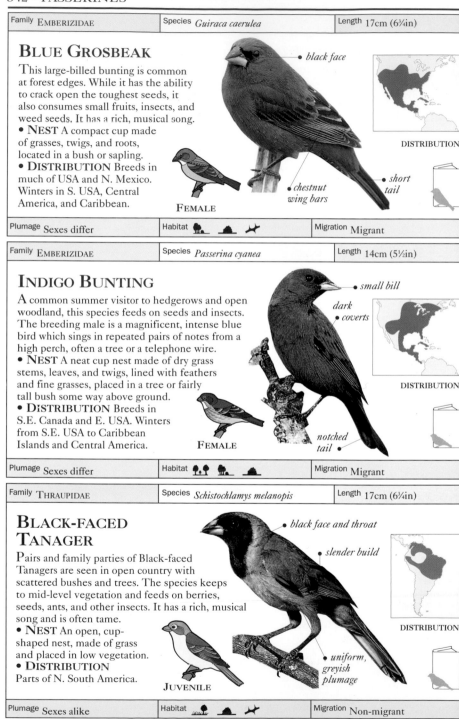

| Family EMBERIZIDAE | Species *Guiraca caerulea* | Length 17cm (6¾in) |

BLUE GROSBEAK

This large-billed bunting is common at forest edges. While it has the ability to crack open the toughest seeds, it also consumes small fruits, insects, and weed seeds, It has a rich, musical song.
• **NEST** A compact cup made of grasses, twigs, and roots, located in a bush or sapling.
• **DISTRIBUTION** Breeds in much of USA and N. Mexico. Winters in S. USA, Central America, and Caribbean.

• black face

• short tail

• chestnut wing bars

DISTRIBUTION

FEMALE

| Plumage Sexes differ | Habitat | Migration Migrant |

| Family EMBERIZIDAE | Species *Passerina cyanea* | Length 14cm (5½in) |

INDIGO BUNTING

A common summer visitor to hedgerows and open woodland, this species feeds on seeds and insects. The breeding male is a magnificent, intense blue bird which sings in repeated pairs of notes from a high perch, often a tree or a telephone wire.
• **NEST** A neat cup nest made of dry grass stems, leaves, and twigs, lined with feathers and fine grasses, placed in a tree or fairly tall bush some way above ground.
• **DISTRIBUTION** Breeds in S.E. Canada and E. USA. Winters from S.E. USA to Caribbean Islands and Central America.

• small bill

dark • coverts

DISTRIBUTION

notched tail •

FEMALE

| Plumage Sexes differ | Habitat | Migration Migrant |

| Family THRAUPIDAE | Species *Schistochlamys melanopis* | Length 17cm (6¾in) |

BLACK-FACED TANAGER

Pairs and family parties of Black-faced Tanagers are seen in open country with scattered bushes and trees. The species keeps to mid-level vegetation and feeds on berries, seeds, ants, and other insects. It has a rich, musical song and is often tame.
• **NEST** An open, cup-shaped nest, made of grass and placed in low vegetation.
• **DISTRIBUTION** Parts of N. South America.

• black face and throat

• slender build

DISTRIBUTION

• uniform, greyish plumage

JUVENILE

| Plumage Sexes alike | Habitat | Migration Non-migrant |

| Family THRAUPIDAE | Species *Cissopis leveriana* | Length 27cm (10½in) |

MAGPIE-TANAGER

This bird is easily recognized by its distinctive, black-and-white plumage and long tail. Often in pairs or small groups, it is a noisy and conspicuous species that can usually be located by its loud, metallic calls, or seen perching in open situations. The Magpie-Tanager is a widespread bird in the lowlands of its range, inhabiting areas of very open woodland, where bushes and trees are interspersed with grassland. Feeding mainly on fruit, it forages at all levels in the foliage, but especially in the tree canopy.
• **NEST** A large, cup-shaped nest, constructed from small twigs and grass, with a finer lining inside made of grass, and well concealed in dense foliage.
• **DISTRIBUTION** Parts of tropical South America.

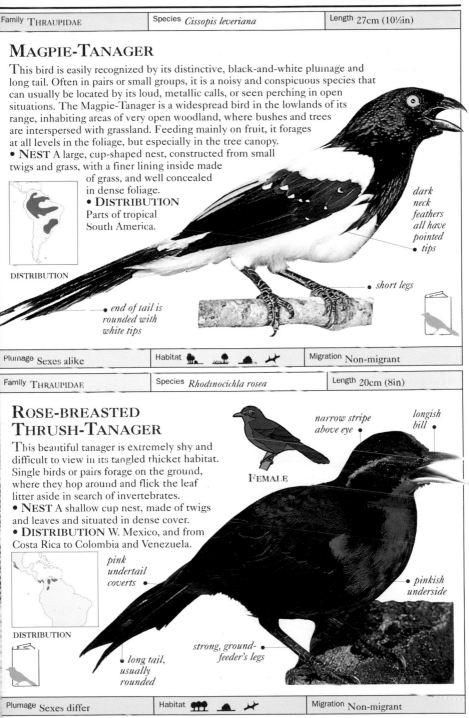

DISTRIBUTION

dark neck feathers all have pointed tips

short legs

end of tail is rounded with white tips

| Plumage Sexes alike | Habitat | Migration Non-migrant |

| Family THRAUPIDAE | Species *Rhodinocichla rosea* | Length 20cm (8in) |

ROSE-BREASTED THRUSH-TANAGER

This beautiful tanager is extremely shy and difficult to view in its tangled thicket habitat. Single birds or pairs forage on the ground, where they hop around and flick the leaf litter aside in search of invertebrates.
• **NEST** A shallow cup nest, made of twigs and leaves and situated in dense cover.
• **DISTRIBUTION** W. Mexico, and from Costa Rica to Colombia and Venezuela.

FEMALE

narrow stripe above eye

longish bill

pink undertail coverts

pinkish underside

DISTRIBUTION

long tail, usually rounded

strong, ground-feeder's legs

| Plumage Sexes differ | Habitat | Migration Non-migrant |

Family THRAUPIDAE	Species *Piranga olivacea*	Length 17cm (6¾in)

SCARLET TANAGER

As it lives and feeds mostly in the upper foliage of trees, this species is more likely to be heard than seen. It breeds in deciduous forest, and winters in the canopy of lowland rainforest. The diet consists of insects and fruit.
• **NEST** A shallow cup nest, lined and placed in a tree.
• **DISTRIBUTION** Breeds in S.E. Canada and E. USA. Winters from Panama as far south as Bolivia.

• scarlet body

black • wings

DISTRIBUTION

black tail •

FEMALE

Plumage Sexes differ	Habitat	Migration Migrant

Family THRAUPIDAE	Species *Piranga ludoviciana*	Length 17cm (6¾in)

WESTERN TANAGER

Yellow wing bars, and a vigorous song, draw attention to this bird. Usually solitary, it forms flocks of up to 30 birds or more on migration. It feeds mostly on insects, but in late summer it also takes fruit, such as berries.
• **NEST** A cup nest, lined with grass and placed in a fir or pine, often high above ground.
• **DISTRIBUTION** Breeds in mountains of S.W. Canada and W. USA. Winters in Central America.

FEMALE

• orange-red colour of head in summer

• yellow underside

short legs •

DISTRIBUTION

Plumage Sexes differ	Habitat	Migration Migrant

Family THRAUPIDAE	Species *Ramphocelus bresilius*	Length 18cm (7in)

BRAZILIAN TANAGER

Chattering groups of this species feed in the shrubby edges of forests, taking fruits, seeds, and insects.
• **NEST** A grass cup nest, placed in a low tree or hidden in marsh grass.
• **DISTRIBUTION** S.E. Brazil, N.E. Argentina.

white bill • patch

glossy red plumage •

DISTRIBUTION

FEMALE

• rounded, black wings

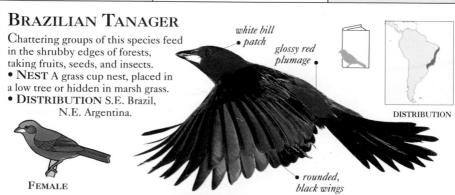

Plumage Sexes differ	Habitat	Migration Non-migrant

Family THRAUPIDAE	Species *Thraupis sayaca*	Length 17cm (6¾in)

SAYACA TANAGER

A bird of scrub and open woodland, this species favours damp areas with thicker vegetation along watercourses. When perched, it has a habit of turning from side to side. It feeds chiefly on fruit, often visits gardens, and can be a pest to commercial fruit growers.
• **NEST** A carefully woven, compact cup nest, well hidden in a low bush or small tree.
• **DISTRIBUTION** Much of Brazil south of the Amazon basin, extending into Bolivia, Paraguay, Uruguay, and N. Argentina.

greyish head and body

pale blue wings and tail

DISTRIBUTION

Plumage Sexes alike	Habitat	Migration Non-migrant

Family THRAUPIDAE	Species *Anisognathus igniventris*	Length 16cm (6¼in)

SCARLET-BELLIED MOUNTAIN-TANAGER

Known for its striking pattern and tinkling song, this mountain bird occurs in woodland and scrub on the Andean uplands, extending upwards into high-altitude pasture and farmland. Usually occurring in pairs or small groups, it feeds on fruit pulp, seeds, leaves, and buds.
• **NEST** A cup nest made of coarse grass, lined with finer grass, in a tree or thicket.
• **DISTRIBUTION** Andes from Venezuela to Bolivia.

scarlet cheek patch

blue shoulder patch

blue rump

DISTRIBUTION

typical short legs of a tanager

Plumage Sexes alike	Habitat	Migration Non-migrant

Family THRAUPIDAE	Species *Anisognathus somptuosus*	Length 17cm (6¾in)

BLUE-WINGED MOUNTAIN-TANAGER

This species occurs in mountain forests and secondary growth (regrown after clearance). It hops about in the outer branches and foliage, plucking fruit and searching for insects.
• **NEST** A cup nest made of grass, probably in a bush or small tree.
• **DISTRIBUTION** Andean forests from Venezuela to Bolivia.

yellow cap

blue shoulder

DISTRIBUTION

light blue feather edges

yellow underside

Plumage Sexes alike	Habitat	Migration Non-migrant

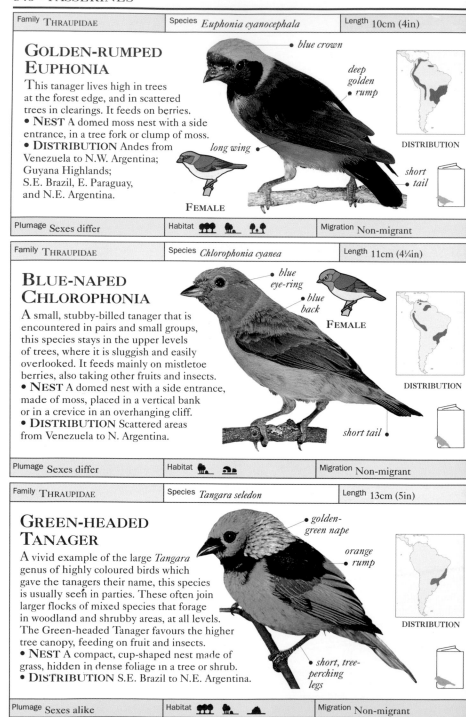

| Family THRAUPIDAE | Species *Euphonia cyanocephala* | Length 10cm (4in) |

GOLDEN-RUMPED EUPHONIA

This tanager lives high in trees at the forest edge, and in scattered trees in clearings. It feeds on berries.
• **NEST** A domed moss nest with a side entrance, in a tree fork or clump of moss.
• **DISTRIBUTION** Andes from Venezuela to N.W. Argentina; Guyana Highlands; S.E. Brazil, E. Paraguay, and N.E. Argentina.

blue crown

deep golden rump

long wing

FEMALE

short tail

DISTRIBUTION

| Plumage Sexes differ | Habitat | Migration Non-migrant |

| Family THRAUPIDAE | Species *Chlorophonia cyanea* | Length 11cm (4¼in) |

BLUE-NAPED CHLOROPHONIA

A small, stubby-billed tanager that is encountered in pairs and small groups, this species stays in the upper levels of trees, where it is sluggish and easily overlooked. It feeds mainly on mistletoe berries, also taking other fruits and insects.
• **NEST** A domed nest with a side entrance, made of moss, placed in a vertical bank or in a crevice in an overhanging cliff.
• **DISTRIBUTION** Scattered areas from Venezuela to N. Argentina.

blue eye-ring

blue back

FEMALE

short tail

DISTRIBUTION

| Plumage Sexes differ | Habitat | Migration Non-migrant |

| Family THRAUPIDAE | Species *Tangara seledon* | Length 13cm (5in) |

GREEN-HEADED TANAGER

A vivid example of the large *Tangara* genus of highly coloured birds which gave the tanagers their name, this species is usually seen in parties. These often join larger flocks of mixed species that forage in woodland and shrubby areas, at all levels. The Green-headed Tanager favours the higher tree canopy, feeding on fruit and insects.
• **NEST** A compact, cup-shaped nest made of grass, hidden in dense foliage in a tree or shrub.
• **DISTRIBUTION** S.E. Brazil to N.E. Argentina.

golden-green nape

orange rump

short, tree-perching legs

DISTRIBUTION

| Plumage Sexes alike | Habitat | Migration Non-migrant |

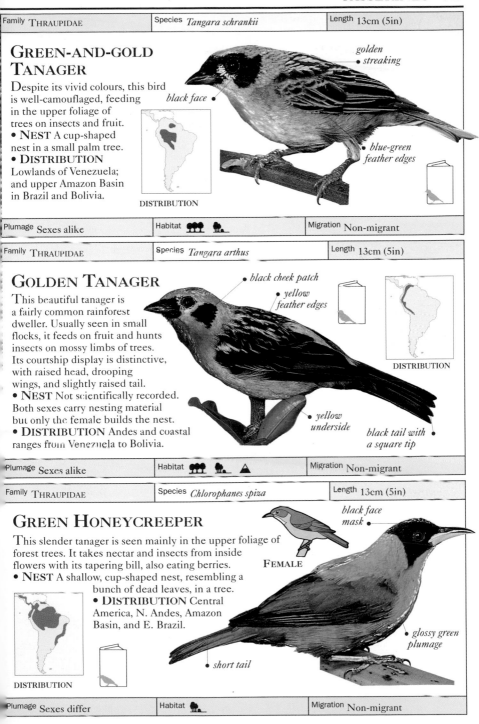

| Family THRAUPIDAE | Species *Tangara schrankii* | Length 13cm (5in) |

GREEN-AND-GOLD TANAGER

Despite its vivid colours, this bird is well-camouflaged, feeding in the upper foliage of trees on insects and fruit.
• **NEST** A cup-shaped nest in a small palm tree.
• **DISTRIBUTION** Lowlands of Venezuela; and upper Amazon Basin in Brazil and Bolivia.

golden streaking

black face

blue-green feather edges

DISTRIBUTION

| Plumage Sexes alike | Habitat | Migration Non-migrant |

| Family THRAUPIDAE | Species *Tangara arthus* | Length 13cm (5in) |

GOLDEN TANAGER

This beautiful tanager is a fairly common rainforest dweller. Usually seen in small flocks, it feeds on fruit and hunts insects on mossy limbs of trees. Its courtship display is distinctive, with raised head, drooping wings, and slightly raised tail.
• **NEST** Not scientifically recorded. Both sexes carry nesting material but only the female builds the nest.
• **DISTRIBUTION** Andes and coastal ranges from Venezuela to Bolivia.

black cheek patch

yellow feather edges

DISTRIBUTION

yellow underside

black tail with a square tip

| Plumage Sexes alike | Habitat | Migration Non-migrant |

| Family THRAUPIDAE | Species *Chlorophanes spiza* | Length 13cm (5in) |

GREEN HONEYCREEPER

This slender tanager is seen mainly in the upper foliage of forest trees. It takes nectar and insects from inside flowers with its tapering bill, also eating berries.
• **NEST** A shallow, cup-shaped nest, resembling a bunch of dead leaves, in a tree.
• **DISTRIBUTION** Central America, N. Andes, Amazon Basin, and E. Brazil.

black face mask

FEMALE

glossy green plumage

short tail

DISTRIBUTION

| Plumage Sexes differ | Habitat | Migration Non-migrant |

| Family THRAUPIDAE | Species *Cyanerpes caeruleus* | Length 10cm (4in) |

PURPLE HONEYCREEPER

Usually seen singly or in pairs, the Purple
Honeycreeper is an active, acrobatic, little
bird with a long, curved bill with which it takes
nectar from flowers. It also snatches small insects
from the leaves and eats fruit such as berries. This
species frequents a variety of wooded habitats,
including gardens and secondary woodland
(regrown after forest clearance).
• NEST A small cup nest, placed
on a stump or at the end of a branch.
• DISTRIBUTION Part of Panama
and parts of N. South America.

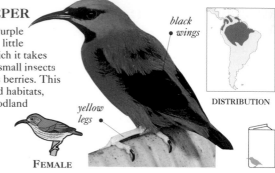

black
• wings

yellow
legs •

FEMALE

DISTRIBUTION

| Plumage Sexes differ | Habitat | Migration Non-migrant |

| Family THRAUPIDAE | Species *Diglossopis cyanea* | Length 15cm (6in) |

MASKED FLOWERPIERCER

This nectar-feeding bird pierces the tubular
corollas of rainforest flowers with
its hooked bill-tip to obtain its food.
Other items in the diet are insects
and small fruits. It inhabits mountain
rainforest, often near the upper
altitude limit for trees, and is usually seen in pairs or
family groups. These keep mainly to the lower vegetation,
sometimes rising to the mid-levels. They feed and move
about actively, never staying still for more than a second.
• NEST A cup-shaped nest made of grass and
moss, probably located in a bush or small tree.
• DISTRIBUTION From N. Venezuela to Bolivia.

• black
face
mask

bill has •
a fine hook
for cutting
flowers

DISTRIBUTION

• slender
legs

| Plumage Sexes alike | Habitat | Migration Non-migrant |

| Family COERIBIDAE | Species *Coereba flaveola* | Length 10cm (4in) |

BANANAQUIT

A tiny, energetic bird, this species is
common in many parts of its extensive
range. It is usually seen alone or in pairs,
feeding in forest or scrub, taking
berries, nectar, and insects.
• NEST An oval-shaped, grassy
ball with a side entrance, placed in a
bush or small tree. Bananaquits also
build nest-like structures which are
known as dummy or dormitory nests.
• DISTRIBUTION
Parts of West Indies, and from
S. Mexico to N.E. Argentina.

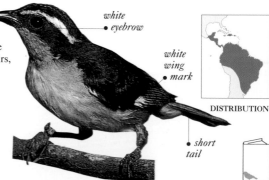

white
• eyebrow

white
wing
• mark

DISTRIBUTION

• short
tail

| Plumage Sexes alike | Habitat | Migration Non-migrant |

Family PARULIDAE	Species *Mniotilta varia*	Length 13cm (5in)

BLACK-AND-WHITE WARBLER

long, tapering wings

FEMALE

This forest and woodland species feeds like a treecreeper (*see p. 324*), moving up trunks and branches, taking insects from crevices or from bark surfaces.
• **NEST** A grass cup nest in a hollow on the ground, often next to a tree.
• **DISTRIBUTION** C. and S.E. Canada, and USA east of the Rockies. Winters in Central and South America as far as Peru.

DISTRIBUTION

Plumage Sexes differ	Habitat	Migration Migrant

Family PARULIDAE	Species *Dendroica petechia*	Length 13cm (5in)

YELLOW WARBLER

ruffled appearance due to wet feathers

This species lives in trees and shrubs, often beside marshes or water. It feeds on insects, which it gleans from the foliage.
• **NEST** A compact cup nest, in a shrub, often close to water.
• **DISTRIBUTION** Canada, USA, Central and South America. Some northern populations migrate southwards.

red streaks on underside

FEMALE

DISTRIBUTION

Plumage Sexes differ	Habitat	Migration Partial migrant

Family PARULIDAE	Species *Dendroica townsendi*	Length 13cm (5in)

TOWNSEND'S WARBLER

black cheek patch

A bird of coniferous forests, Townsend's Warbler is almost always high in the trees, where it forages actively for small insects. The male's black throat contrasts noticeably with the streaked, yellow throat of the female.
• **NEST** A cup nest of fine vegetation, lined with finer plant material, high in a conifer.
• **DISTRIBUTION** Breeds in W. Canada and W. USA. Winters in W. USA and Central America as far south as Nicaragua and Costa Rica.

black throat

DISTRIBUTION

FEMALE

Plumage Sexes differ	Habitat	Migration Migrant

Family PARULIDAE	Species *Dendroica fusca*	Length 13cm (5in)

BLACKBURNIAN WARBLER

This bird is usually seen in the treetops where it feeds on insects. Breeding habitats range from spruce and fir forests to oak woodland. The wintering habitat is tropical forest.
• **NEST** A cup nest of twigs and grasses in a conifer.
• **DISTRIBUTION** Breeds in C. and S.E. Canada and E. USA. Winters from Costa Rica as far south as Peru, and in the West Indies.

DISTRIBUTION

white wing patch

reddish throat

FEMALE

Plumage Sexes differ	Habitat	Migration Migrant

Family PARULIDAE	Species *Dendroica magnolia*	Length 13cm (5in)

MAGNOLIA WARBLER

A common bird of moist, coniferous forest, the Magnolia Warbler is recognized by its musical "weety-weety-weeteo" song. It feeds in the tree-tops, gleaning insects from the leaves. In winter, the male loses its bold head pattern.
• **NEST** A loose, cup-shaped nest of grasses and twigs, placed on a branch in a small tree.
• **DISTRIBUTION** Breeds in Canada and N.E. USA. Winters in Central America as far as Panama.

white eyebrow

white feather edges

yellow underside with black streaks

FEMALE

DISTRIBUTION

Plumage Sexes differ	Habitat	Migration Migrant

Family PARULIDAE	Species *Dendroica coronata*	Length 14cm (5½in)

YELLOW-RUMPED WARBLER

This bird inhabits northern forests, coniferous as well as mixed, feeding on insects. The eastern form (Myrtle Warbler) has a white throat and the western form (Audubon's Warbler) has a yellow throat.
• **NEST** A lined cup nest of grass and small twigs, in a tree.
• **DISTRIBUTION** Breeds in North and Central America. Winters in W. and S. USA, West Indies, and Central America.

yellow crown

yellow rump

DISTRIBUTION

MYRTLE WARBLER

FEMALE

Plumage Sexes differ	Habitat	Migration Migrant

Family PARULIDAE	Species *Setophaga ruticilla*	Length 13cm (5in)

AMERICAN REDSTART

The bright wing and tail patches of this woodland species flash as
it darts after insects among the foliage or hunts them in the air.
• **NEST** A bulky cup in the fork of a sapling or small tree.
• **DISTRIBUTION** Breeds in Canada and E. USA.
Winters in West Indies,
Central America, and
N. South America.

DISTRIBUTION

*orange panel
at side of tail* •

FEMALE

Plumage Sexes differ	Habitat 🌳 🔺	Migration Migrant

Family PARULIDAE	Species *Seiurus aurocapillus*	Length 15cm (6in)

OVENBIRD

A dull, soberly coloured bird of
thick undergrowth in woodland
regions, the Ovenbird walks on the
ground, searching the leaf litter for
small invertebrates. It is common
and is not a shy bird, often sufficiently
curious to approach people quite closely.
• **NEST** A domed structure of leaves,
dry grasses, and weed stems, lined with
tiny rootlets, and placed on the ground.
• **DISTRIBUTION** Breeds S. Canada
and E. USA. Winters in Florida, West
Indies, and south to N.W. South America.

• *rufous
crown stripe*

• *white eye-ring*

DISTRIBUTION

• *long legs of a
ground-feeding
bird*

Plumage Sexes alike	Habitat 🌳 🔺	Migration Migrant

Family PARULIDAE	Species *Geothlypis trichas*	Length 13cm (5in)

COMMON YELLOWTHROAT

Typically a bird of reeds and tall grasses,
the Yellowthroat often moves with its
tail tilted upwards, like that of a wren.
It also inhabits thickets, shrubs, and marsh
vegetation. The diet consists of small insects.
• **NEST** A cup-shaped nest of grass and bark
fragments, lined with finer material, and placed
on or near the ground.
• **DISTRIBUTION** Breeds
in S. Canada, much of USA,
and Mexico. Winters in
S. USA, Central America,
Colombia, and Venezuela.

• *black face mask*
• *pale border*

DISTRIBUTION

• *rounded
tail tip*

FEMALE

Plumage Sexes differ	Habitat 🕊 🔺 〰	Migration Migrant

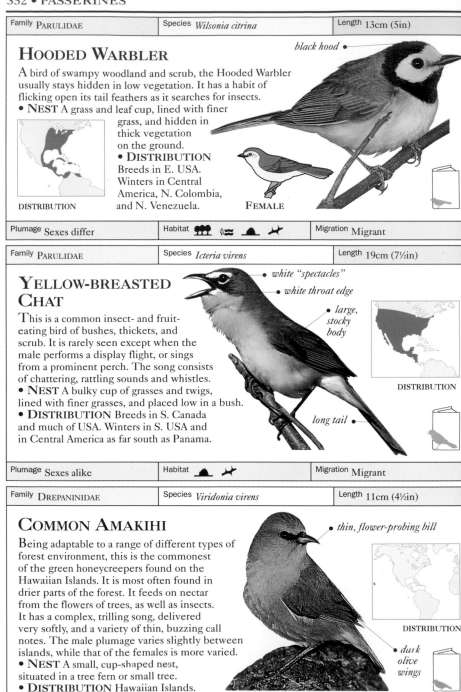

Family PARULIDAE	Species *Wilsonia citrina*	Length 13cm (5in)

HOODED WARBLER

black hood

A bird of swampy woodland and scrub, the Hooded Warbler usually stays hidden in low vegetation. It has a habit of flicking open its tail feathers as it searches for insects.
• **NEST** A grass and leaf cup, lined with finer grass, and hidden in thick vegetation on the ground.
• **DISTRIBUTION** Breeds in E. USA. Winters in Central America, N. Colombia, and N. Venezuela.

DISTRIBUTION

FEMALE

Plumage Sexes differ	Habitat	Migration Migrant

Family PARULIDAE	Species *Icteria virens*	Length 19cm (7½in)

YELLOW-BREASTED CHAT

white "spectacles"
white throat edge
large, stocky body

This is a common insect- and fruit-eating bird of bushes, thickets, and scrub. It is rarely seen except when the male performs a display flight, or sings from a prominent perch. The song consists of chattering, rattling sounds and whistles.
• **NEST** A bulky cup of grasses and twigs, lined with finer grasses, and placed low in a bush.
• **DISTRIBUTION** Breeds in S. Canada and much of USA. Winters in S. USA and in Central America as far south as Panama.

DISTRIBUTION

long tail

Plumage Sexes alike	Habitat	Migration Migrant

Family DREPANINIDAE	Species *Viridonia virens*	Length 11cm (4½in)

COMMON AMAKIHI

thin, flower-probing bill

Being adaptable to a range of different types of forest environment, this is the commonest of the green honeycreepers found on the Hawaiian Islands. It is most often found in drier parts of the forest. It feeds on nectar from the flowers of trees, as well as insects. It has a complex, trilling song, delivered very softly, and a variety of thin, buzzing call notes. The male plumage varies slightly between islands, while that of the females is more varied.
• **NEST** A small, cup-shaped nest, situated in a tree fern or small tree.
• **DISTRIBUTION** Hawaiian Islands.

DISTRIBUTION

dark olive wings

Plumage Sexes differ slightly	Habitat	Migration Non-migrant

| Family DREPANINIDAE | Species *Vestiaria coccinea* | Length 15cm (6in) |

IIWI

white inner wing patch shown in flight •

This distinctive honeycreeper has red body plumage, black wings and tail, and a red bill that curves sharply downwards. A nectar-feeding specialist, it is usually found high in flowering trees, although it keeps well hidden among the foliage. The Iiwi is slow and deliberate in its actions.
• **NEST** An open, loosely made cup, in a tree or bush.
• **DISTRIBUTION** Hawaiian Islands.

DISTRIBUTION

| Plumage Sexes alike | Habitat | Migration Non-migrant |

| Family DREPANINIDAE | Species *Palmeria dolei* | Length 18cm (7in) |

CRESTED HONEYCREEPER

• red nape

Also known as Akohekohe, this species is found only in one mountain locality and is endangered. It is bold and active in behaviour, feeding on nectar in the tops of tall flowers and trees, also taking caterpillars and mature insects. Its calls include a loud whistle.
• **NEST** Not scientifically recorded.
• **DISTRIBUTION** Haleakala Mountain on Maui, Hawaiian Islands.

DISTRIBUTION

• red and blue flecked plumage

| Plumage Sexes alike | Habitat | Migration Non-migrant |

| Family VIREONIDAE | Species *Cyclarhis gujanensis* | Length 15cm (6in) |

RUFOUS-BROWED PEPPERSHRIKE

• large, grey head

NORTH BRAZILIAN FORM

A bull-headed bird with a heavy bill, the Rufous-browed Peppershrike moves about sluggishly in the trees. Always keeping to the thicker parts of the foliage, it is more often heard than seen. Its diet consists of insects and caterpillars.
• **NEST** A thin-walled, grassy cup, usually suspended from the fork of a high branch.
• **DISTRIBUTION** Central America from S.E. Mexico to Panama, and parts of South America as far south as C. Argentina.

DISTRIBUTION

| Plumage Sexes alike | Habitat | Migration Non-migrant |

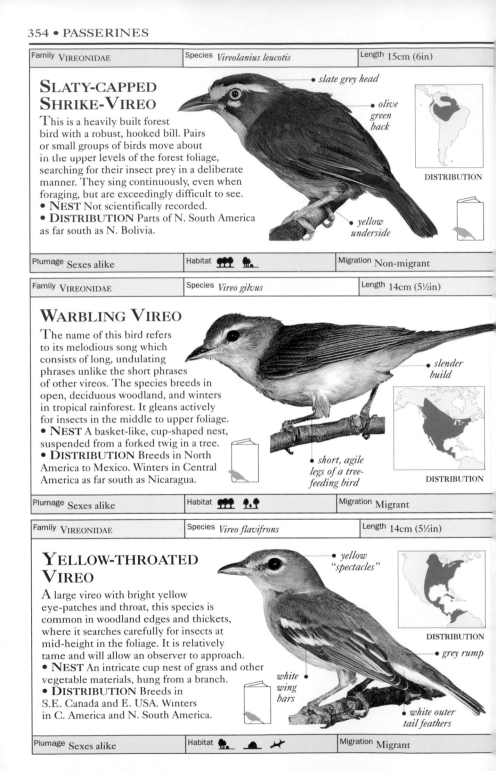

| Family VIREONIDAE | Species *Vireolanius leucotis* | Length 15cm (6in) |

SLATY-CAPPED SHRIKE-VIREO

This is a heavily built forest bird with a robust, hooked bill. Pairs or small groups of birds move about in the upper levels of the forest foliage, searching for their insect prey in a deliberate manner. They sing continuously, even when foraging, but are exceedingly difficult to see.
• **NEST** Not scientifically recorded.
• **DISTRIBUTION** Parts of N. South America as far south as N. Bolivia.

• *slate grey head*

• *olive green back*

DISTRIBUTION

• *yellow underside*

| Plumage Sexes alike | Habitat | Migration Non-migrant |

| Family VIREONIDAE | Species *Vireo gilvus* | Length 14cm (5½in) |

WARBLING VIREO

The name of this bird refers to its melodious song which consists of long, undulating phrases unlike the short phrases of other vireos. The species breeds in open, deciduous woodland, and winters in tropical rainforest. It gleans actively for insects in the middle to upper foliage.
• **NEST** A basket-like, cup-shaped nest, suspended from a forked twig in a tree.
• **DISTRIBUTION** Breeds in North America to Mexico. Winters in Central America as far south as Nicaragua.

• *slender build*

• *short, agile legs of a tree-feeding bird*

DISTRIBUTION

| Plumage Sexes alike | Habitat | Migration Migrant |

| Family VIREONIDAE | Species *Vireo flavifrons* | Length 14cm (5½in) |

YELLOW-THROATED VIREO

A large vireo with bright yellow eye-patches and throat, this species is common in woodland edges and thickets, where it searches carefully for insects at mid-height in the foliage. It is relatively tame and will allow an observer to approach.
• **NEST** An intricate cup nest of grass and other vegetable materials, hung from a branch.
• **DISTRIBUTION** Breeds in S.E. Canada and E. USA. Winters in C. America and N. South America.

• *yellow "spectacles"*

DISTRIBUTION

• *grey rump*

white wing bars

• *white outer tail feathers*

| Plumage Sexes alike | Habitat | Migration Migrant |

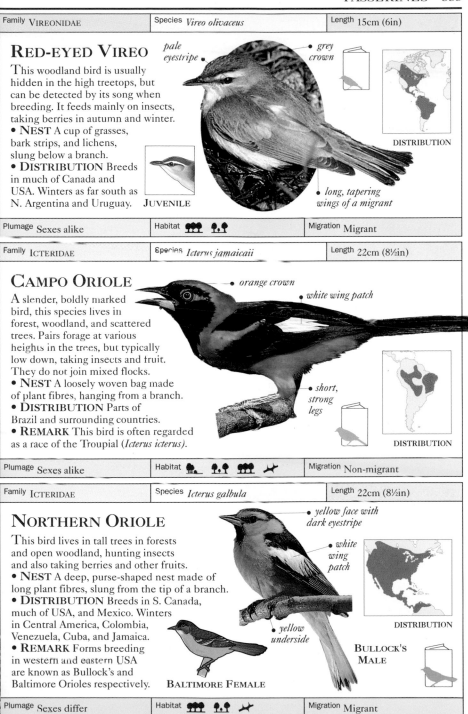

| Family VIREONIDAE | Species *Vireo olivaceus* | Length 15cm (6in) |

RED-EYED VIREO

pale eyestripe

grey crown

This woodland bird is usually hidden in the high treetops, but can be detected by its song when breeding. It feeds mainly on insects, taking berries in autumn and winter.
• **NEST** A cup of grasses, bark strips, and lichens, slung below a branch.
• **DISTRIBUTION** Breeds in much of Canada and USA. Winters as far south as N. Argentina and Uruguay.

DISTRIBUTION

JUVENILE

long, tapering wings of a migrant

| Plumage Sexes alike | Habitat | Migration Migrant |

| Family ICTERIDAE | Species *Icterus jamacaii* | Length 22cm (8½in) |

CAMPO ORIOLE

orange crown

white wing patch

A slender, boldly marked bird, this species lives in forest, woodland, and scattered trees. Pairs forage at various heights in the trees, but typically low down, taking insects and fruit. They do not join mixed flocks.
• **NEST** A loosely woven bag made of plant fibres, hanging from a branch.
• **DISTRIBUTION** Parts of Brazil and surrounding countries.
• **REMARK** This bird is often regarded as a race of the Troupial (*Icterus icterus*).

short, strong legs

DISTRIBUTION

| Plumage Sexes alike | Habitat | Migration Non-migrant |

| Family ICTERIDAE | Species *Icterus galbula* | Length 22cm (8½in) |

NORTHERN ORIOLE

yellow face with dark eyestripe

This bird lives in tall trees in forests and open woodland, hunting insects and also taking berries and other fruits.
• **NEST** A deep, purse-shaped nest made of long plant fibres, slung from the tip of a branch.
• **DISTRIBUTION** Breeds in S. Canada, much of USA, and Mexico. Winters in Central America, Colombia, Venezuela, Cuba, and Jamaica.
• **REMARK** Forms breeding in western and eastern USA are known as Bullock's and Baltimore Orioles respectively.

white wing patch

yellow underside

BULLOCK'S MALE

DISTRIBUTION

BALTIMORE FEMALE

| Plumage Sexes differ | Habitat | Migration Migrant |

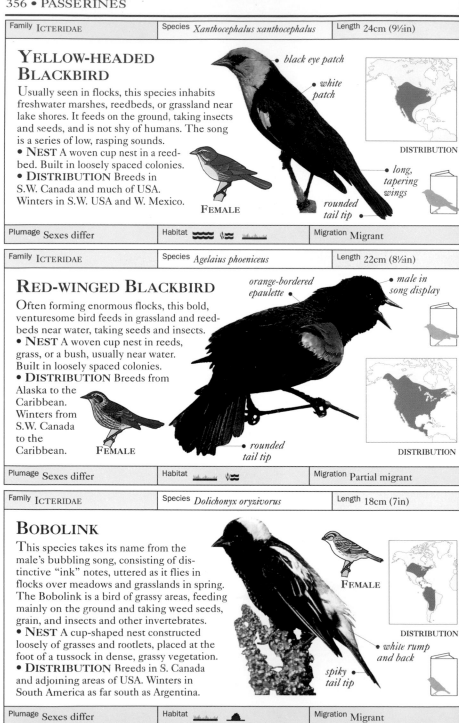

Family ICTERIDAE	Species *Xanthocephalus xanthocephalus*	Length 24cm (9½in)

YELLOW-HEADED BLACKBIRD

Usually seen in flocks, this species inhabits freshwater marshes, reedbeds, or grassland near lake shores. It feeds on the ground, taking insects and seeds, and is not shy of humans. The song is a series of low, rasping sounds.
• **NEST** A woven cup nest in a reed-bed. Built in loosely spaced colonies.
• **DISTRIBUTION** Breeds in S.W. Canada and much of USA. Winters in S.W. USA and W. Mexico.

black eye patch

white patch

long, tapering wings

rounded tail tip

DISTRIBUTION

FEMALE

Plumage Sexes differ	Habitat 〰〰 〰 ⅃⅃⅃	Migration Migrant

Family ICTERIDAE	Species *Agelaius phoeniceus*	Length 22cm (8½in)

RED-WINGED BLACKBIRD

Often forming enormous flocks, this bold, venturesome bird feeds in grassland and reed-beds near water, taking seeds and insects.
• **NEST** A woven cup nest in reeds, grass, or a bush, usually near water. Built in loosely spaced colonies.
• **DISTRIBUTION** Breeds from Alaska to the Caribbean. Winters from S.W. Canada to the Caribbean.

orange-bordered epaulette

male in song display

rounded tail tip

FEMALE

DISTRIBUTION

Plumage Sexes differ	Habitat ⅃⅃⅃ 〰	Migration Partial migrant

Family ICTERIDAE	Species *Dolichonyx oryzivorus*	Length 18cm (7in)

BOBOLINK

This species takes its name from the male's bubbling song, consisting of dis-tinctive "ink" notes, uttered as it flies in flocks over meadows and grasslands in spring. The Bobolink is a bird of grassy areas, feeding mainly on the ground and taking weed seeds, grain, and insects and other invertebrates.
• **NEST** A cup-shaped nest constructed loosely of grasses and rootlets, placed at the foot of a tussock in dense, grassy vegetation.
• **DISTRIBUTION** Breeds in S. Canada and adjoining areas of USA. Winters in South America as far south as Argentina.

FEMALE

DISTRIBUTION

white rump and back

spiky tail tip

Plumage Sexes differ	Habitat ⅃⅃⅃ ▲	Migration Migrant

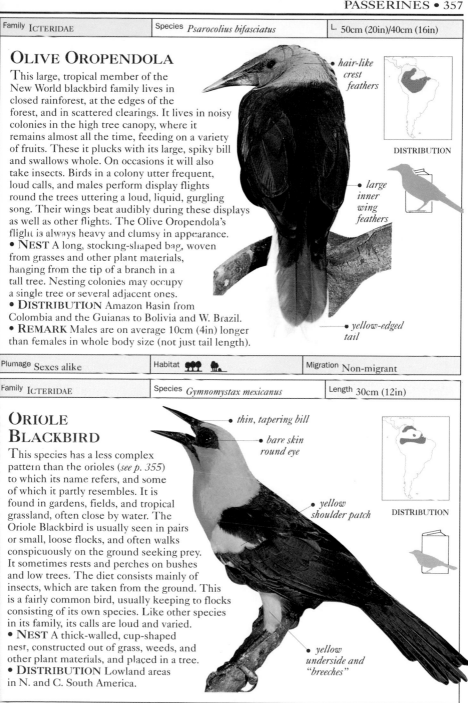

Family ICTERIDAE	Species *Psarocolius bifasciatus*	L. 50cm (20in)/40cm (16in)

OLIVE OROPENDOLA

This large, tropical member of the
New World blackbird family lives in
closed rainforest, at the edges of the
forest, and in scattered clearings. It lives in noisy
colonies in the high tree canopy, where it
remains almost all the time, feeding on a variety
of fruits. These it plucks with its large, spiky bill
and swallows whole. On occasions it will also
take insects. Birds in a colony utter frequent,
loud calls, and males perform display flights
round the trees uttering a loud, liquid, gurgling
song. Their wings beat audibly during these displays
as well as other flights. The Olive Oropendola's
flight is always heavy and clumsy in appearance.
• **NEST** A long, stocking-shaped bag, woven
from grasses and other plant materials,
hanging from the tip of a branch in a
tall tree. Nesting colonies may occupy
a single tree or several adjacent ones.
• **DISTRIBUTION** Amazon Basin from
Colombia and the Guianas to Bolivia and W. Brazil.
• **REMARK** Males are on average 10cm (4in) longer
than females in whole body size (not just tail length).

• *hair-like
crest
feathers*

• *large
inner
wing
feathers*

DISTRIBUTION

• *yellow-edged
tail*

Plumage Sexes alike	Habitat 🌳 🏞️	Migration Non-migrant

Family ICTERIDAE	Species *Gymnomystax mexicanus*	Length 30cm (12in)

ORIOLE BLACKBIRD

This species has a less complex
pattern than the orioles (*see p. 355*)
to which its name refers, and some
of which it partly resembles. It is
found in gardens, fields, and tropical
grassland, often close by water. The
Oriole Blackbird is usually seen in pairs
or small, loose flocks, and often walks
conspicuously on the ground seeking prey.
It sometimes rests and perches on bushes
and low trees. The diet consists mainly of
insects, which are taken from the ground. This
is a fairly common bird, usually keeping to flocks
consisting of its own species. Like other species
in its family, its calls are loud and varied.
• **NEST** A thick-walled, cup-shaped
nest, constructed out of grass, weeds, and
other plant materials, and placed in a tree.
• **DISTRIBUTION** Lowland areas
in N. and C. South America.

• *thin, tapering bill*

• *bare skin
round eye*

• *yellow
shoulder patch*

DISTRIBUTION

• *yellow
underside and
"breeches"*

Plumage Sexes alike	Habitat 🏔️ 🌾 💧 🌊	Migration Non-migrant

Family ICTERIDAE	Species *Sturnella neglecta*	Length 24cm (9½in)

WESTERN MEADOWLARK

With its streaky, brown upperparts
and yellow underparts, the Western
Meadowlark is a distinctive
and familiar bird of grassland and
farmland. Small flocks feed on the ground,
while single birds are often seen perching
on vantage points, such as fence posts.
Meadowlarks have powerful, dagger-like
beaks which they use to work over the turf,
picking up insects and other invertebrates.
• **NEST** A partially domed nest, made
of grass and other plant materials, and
placed on the ground in a concealed spot.
• **DISTRIBUTION** Breeds in W. and C. North
America from S. Canada to C. Mexico.
Winter range extends from S.W. Canada
to C. Mexico.
• **REMARK**
The bubbling, fluty
song contrasts with the
whistling of the Eastern
Meadowlark, which is
similar in appearance. **WINTER PLUMAGE**

tapering head and bill

dark eyestripe

DISTRIBUTION

streaked back

Plumage Sexes alike	Habitat	Migration Partial migrant

Family ICTERIDAE	Species *Quiscalus quiscula*	Length 32cm (12½in)

COMMON GRACKLE

A conspicuous, glossy blackbird, this species
occurs in a range of habitats including
farmland and suburbs. It lives
in flocks throughout the year,
joining huge roosts of mixed
bird species in winter, and
feeds on invertebrates,
seeds, fruit, and nuts.
• **NEST** A bulky,
loose cup nest of grass
and stems, usually
placed low in a tree.
• **DISTRIBUTION**
Breeds in C. and
E. North America
from Alberta as far
south as Texas
and Florida.
Winters within
the southern
half of
this range.

sharp, tapering bill

bronze tinge denotes eastern form

large, strong feet

broad, tapering wings

outer feathers of tail curve upwards, making a concave upper surface

DISTRIBUTION

JUVENILE

Plumage Sexes alike	Habitat	Migration Partial migrant

Family ICTERIDAE	Species *Euphagus cyanocephalus*	Length 23cm (9in)

BREWER'S BLACKBIRD

This is a common, ground-feeding bird of farmland, roadsides, open grassland, and other open habitats. The male is a glossy blackbird with yellow eyes, while the female is dark brown above and lighter brown below. Brewer's Blackbird forages on the ground in large flocks, often in the company of other, similar species. Its diet consists of seeds, insects, and other invertebrates.

• **NEST** A cup-shaped nest made of twigs, lined with grass, and placed on the ground or in a bush or tree. Nests are built in loose colonies.

• **DISTRIBUTION** Breeds in S. Canada west of the Great Lakes, and in W. USA. Winters in N. America from S.W. Canada to Florida and C. Mexico.

purple gloss on head

DISTRIBUTION

green gloss on body revealed as bird turns in light

streamlined, slender build

strong legs for foraging on the ground

FEMALE

Plumage Sexes differ	Habitat	Migration Migrant

Family ICTERIDAE	Species *Molothrus ater*	Length 19cm (7½in)

BROWN-HEADED COWBIRD

Originally living in open woodland and natural grassland, this ground-feeding bird with a stout bill has adapted to farmland and suburban gardens. Flocks often form around livestock or wild herbivores such as bison, catching insects disturbed by, or attracted to, the grazing animals.

• **NEST** Parasitizes the nests of other passerines, including Yellow Warbler (*see p. 349*), Red-eyed Vireo (*p. 355*), and Song Sparrow (*p. 336*).

• **DISTRIBUTION** Breeds in most of North America. Winters from C. USA to Mexico.

dull brown head

short, conical bill

glossy plumage on body

DISTRIBUTION

tail is relatively short, with a blunt tip

strong, tapering wings

JUVENILE

long legs and strong feet of a ground forager

Plumage Sexes differ	Habitat	Migration Migrant

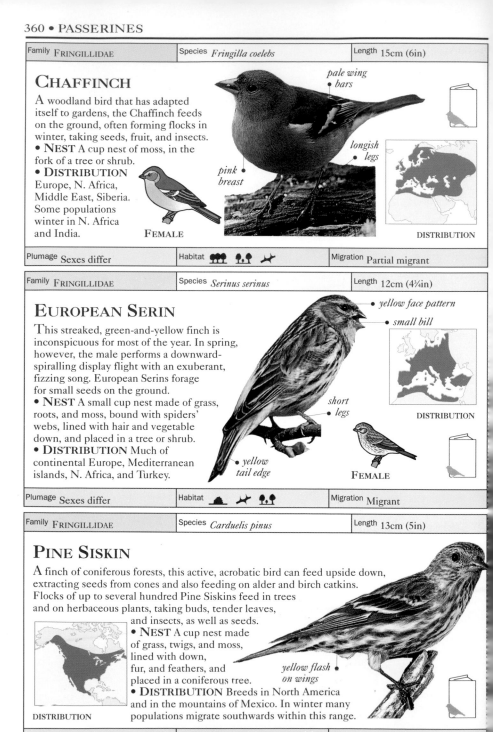

| Family FRINGILLIDAE | Species *Fringilla coelebs* | Length 15cm (6in) |

CHAFFINCH

A woodland bird that has adapted itself to gardens, the Chaffinch feeds on the ground, often forming flocks in winter, taking seeds, fruit, and insects.
• **NEST** A cup nest of moss, in the fork of a tree or shrub.
• **DISTRIBUTION** Europe, N. Africa, Middle East, Siberia. Some populations winter in N. Africa and India.

pale wing bars

longish legs

pink breast

FEMALE

DISTRIBUTION

| Plumage Sexes differ | Habitat | Migration Partial migrant |

| Family FRINGILLIDAE | Species *Serinus serinus* | Length 12cm (4¾in) |

EUROPEAN SERIN

This streaked, green-and-yellow finch is inconspicuous for most of the year. In spring, however, the male performs a downward-spiralling display flight with an exuberant, fizzing song. European Serins forage for small seeds on the ground.
• **NEST** A small cup nest made of grass, roots, and moss, bound with spiders' webs, lined with hair and vegetable down, and placed in a tree or shrub.
• **DISTRIBUTION** Much of continental Europe, Mediterranean islands, N. Africa, and Turkey.

yellow face pattern

small bill

short legs

yellow tail edge

FEMALE

DISTRIBUTION

| Plumage Sexes differ | Habitat | Migration Migrant |

| Family FRINGILLIDAE | Species *Carduelis pinus* | Length 13cm (5in) |

PINE SISKIN

A finch of coniferous forests, this active, acrobatic bird can feed upside down, extracting seeds from cones and also feeding on alder and birch catkins. Flocks of up to several hundred Pine Siskins feed in trees and on herbaceous plants, taking buds, tender leaves, and insects, as well as seeds.
• **NEST** A cup nest made of grass, twigs, and moss, lined with down, fur, and feathers, and placed in a coniferous tree.
• **DISTRIBUTION** Breeds in North America and in the mountains of Mexico. In winter many populations migrate southwards within this range.

yellow flash on wings

DISTRIBUTION

| Plumage Sexes alike | Habitat | Migration Partial migrant |

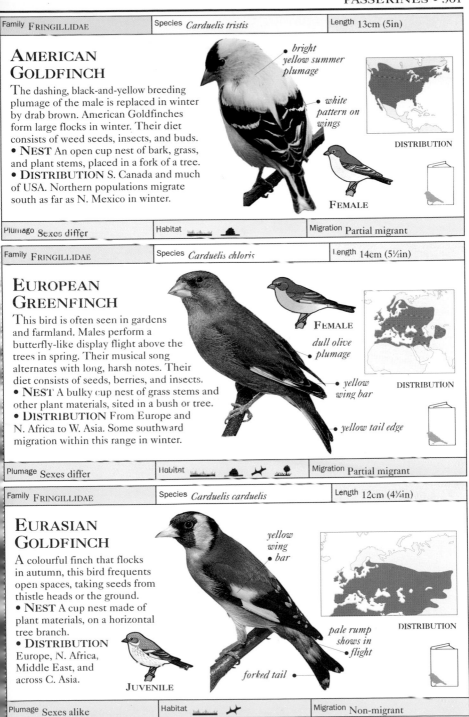

| Family FRINGILLIDAE | Species *Carduelis tristis* | Length 13cm (5in) |

AMERICAN GOLDFINCH

bright
yellow summer
plumage

The dashing, black-and-yellow breeding plumage of the male is replaced in winter by drab brown. American Goldfinches form large flocks in winter. Their diet consists of weed seeds, insects, and buds.
• **NEST** An open cup nest of bark, grass, and plant stems, placed in a fork of a tree.
• **DISTRIBUTION** S. Canada and much of USA. Northern populations migrate south as far as N. Mexico in winter.

white
pattern on
wings

DISTRIBUTION

FEMALE

| Plumage Sexes differ | Habitat | Migration Partial migrant |

| Family FRINGILLIDAE | Species *Carduelis chloris* | Length 14cm (5½in) |

EUROPEAN GREENFINCH

This bird is often seen in gardens and farmland. Males perform a butterfly-like display flight above the trees in spring. Their musical song alternates with long, harsh notes. Their diet consists of seeds, berries, and insects.
• **NEST** A bulky cup nest of grass stems and other plant materials, sited in a bush or tree.
• **DISTRIBUTION** From Europe and N. Africa to W. Asia. Some southward migration within this range in winter.

FEMALE

dull olive
plumage

yellow
wing bar

DISTRIBUTION

yellow tail edge

| Plumage Sexes differ | Habitat | Migration Partial migrant |

| Family FRINGILLIDAE | Species *Carduelis carduelis* | Length 12cm (4¾in) |

EURASIAN GOLDFINCH

A colourful finch that flocks in autumn, this bird frequents open spaces, taking seeds from thistle heads or the ground.
• **NEST** A cup nest made of plant materials, on a horizontal tree branch.
• **DISTRIBUTION** Europe, N. Africa, Middle East, and across C. Asia.

yellow
wing
bar

pale rump
shows in
flight

DISTRIBUTION

forked tail

JUVENILE

| Plumage Sexes alike | Habitat | Migration Non-migrant |

Family FRINGILLIDAE	Species *Carduelis flammea*	Length 12cm (4¾in)

COMMON REDPOLL

red cap •

A tree-dwelling finch, the Common Redpoll feeds among twigs and leaves, sometimes upside down, and sometimes clinging to catkins of silver birch. The diet consists mainly of seeds and insects.
• **NEST** A cup nest of twigs and grasses, lined with finer materials, placed in a bush or tree.
• **DISTRIBUTION** Breeds in N. Canada and USA, S. Greenland, Iceland, and most of Eurasia. Some southward movement in winter.

DISTRIBUTION

• *strong legs for clinging*

FEMALE

Plumage Sexes differ	Habitat	Migration Partial migrant

Family FRINGILLIDAE	Species *Carduelis cannabina*	Length 14cm (5½in)

EURASIAN LINNET

• *red spot on forehead*

Renowned for its sweet, "twangy" song, this species is a finch of open places, particularly gorse-covered heaths. Linnets become sociable in autumn and form huge, wandering flocks, which often move south. They feed mainly on seeds and sometimes on insects.
• **NEST** A cup nest of grass and moss, lined and placed low in a bush or tree.
• **DISTRIBUTION** Most of Europe and N. Africa; parts of the Middle East and C. Asia. Some southward movement in winter.

• *grey head*

DISTRIBUTION

• *white tail edge*

FEMALE

Plumage Sexes differ	Habitat	Migration Partial migrant

Family FRINGILLIDAE	Species *Rhodopechys obsoleta*	Length 14cm (5½in)

DESERT FINCH

• *sandy pink plumage*

This bird inhabits steppe (arid grassland) and semi-desert, its soft, plain colours merging with the bare landscape. Pink, black, and white markings on wing and tail show in flight. Usually seen in pairs, it is not shy and will allow an observer to approach. It feeds on or near the ground, taking seeds and buds.
• **NEST** A cup-shaped nest made of weed stems, grass, and twigs, lined with wool or feathers, and located in a bush or low tree.
• **DISTRIBUTION** Isolated areas in the Middle East, Iran, N.W. Pakistan, C. Asia, and W. China.

DISTRIBUTION

black-and-white tail •

Plumage Sexes differ slightly	Habitat	Migration Partial migrant

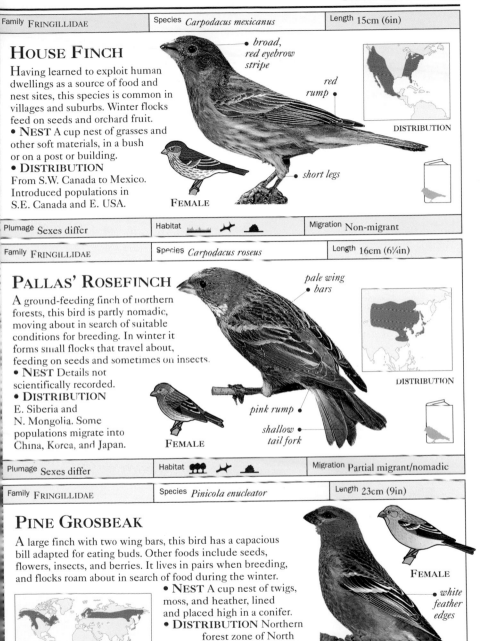

| Family FRINGILLIDAE | Species *Carpodacus mexicanus* | Length 15cm (6in) |

HOUSE FINCH

Having learned to exploit human dwellings as a source of food and nest sites, this species is common in villages and suburbs. Winter flocks feed on seeds and orchard fruit.
• **NEST** A cup nest of grasses and other soft materials, in a bush or on a post or building.
• **DISTRIBUTION** From S.W. Canada to Mexico. Introduced populations in S.E. Canada and E. USA.

- broad, red eyebrow stripe
- red rump
- short legs

DISTRIBUTION

FEMALE

| Plumage Sexes differ | Habitat | Migration Non-migrant |

| Family FRINGILLIDAE | Species *Carpodacus roseus* | Length 16cm (6¼in) |

PALLAS' ROSEFINCH

A ground-feeding finch of northern forests, this bird is partly nomadic, moving about in search of suitable conditions for breeding. In winter it forms small flocks that travel about, feeding on seeds and sometimes on insects.
• **NEST** Details not scientifically recorded.
• **DISTRIBUTION** E. Siberia and N. Mongolia. Some populations migrate into China, Korea, and Japan.

- pale wing bars
- pink rump
- shallow tail fork

DISTRIBUTION

FEMALE

| Plumage Sexes differ | Habitat | Migration Partial migrant/nomadic |

| Family FRINGILLIDAE | Species *Pinicola enucleator* | Length 23cm (9in) |

PINE GROSBEAK

A large finch with two wing bars, this bird has a capacious bill adapted for eating buds. Other foods include seeds, flowers, insects, and berries. It lives in pairs when breeding, and flocks roam about in search of food during the winter.
• **NEST** A cup nest of twigs, moss, and heather, lined and placed high in a conifer.
• **DISTRIBUTION** Northern forest zone of North America, Europe and Siberia. Some birds move south within this range in winter.

FEMALE

- white feather edges

DISTRIBUTION

| Plumage Sexes differ | Habitat | Migration Partial migrant |

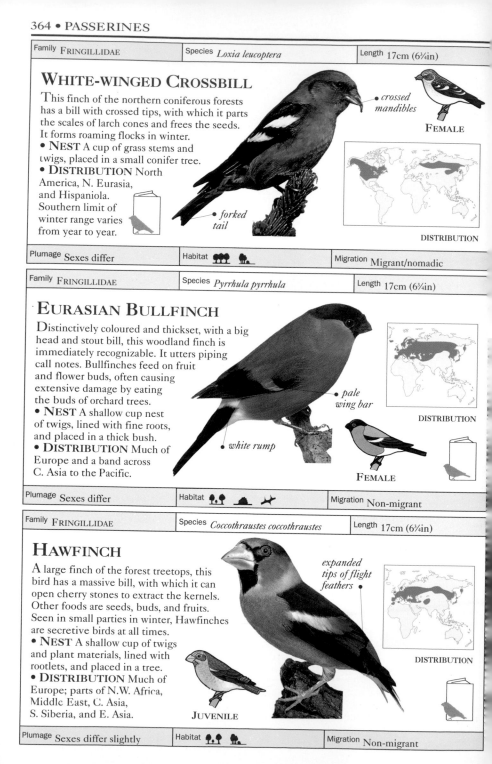

Family FRINGILLIDAE	Species *Loxia leucoptera*	Length 17cm (6¾in)

WHITE-WINGED CROSSBILL

This finch of the northern coniferous forests has a bill with crossed tips, with which it parts the scales of larch cones and frees the seeds. It forms roaming flocks in winter.
• **NEST** A cup of grass stems and twigs, placed in a small conifer tree.
• **DISTRIBUTION** North America, N. Eurasia, and Hispaniola. Southern limit of winter range varies from year to year.

crossed mandibles

FEMALE

forked tail

DISTRIBUTION

Plumage Sexes differ	Habitat	Migration Migrant/nomadic

Family FRINGILLIDAE	Species *Pyrrhula pyrrhula*	Length 17cm (6¾in)

EURASIAN BULLFINCH

Distinctively coloured and thickset, with a big head and stout bill, this woodland finch is immediately recognizable. It utters piping call notes. Bullfinches feed on fruit and flower buds, often causing extensive damage by eating the buds of orchard trees.
• **NEST** A shallow cup nest of twigs, lined with fine roots, and placed in a thick bush.
• **DISTRIBUTION** Much of Europe and a band across C. Asia to the Pacific.

pale wing bar

DISTRIBUTION

white rump

FEMALE

Plumage Sexes differ	Habitat	Migration Non-migrant

Family FRINGILLIDAE	Species *Coccothraustes coccothraustes*	Length 17cm (6¾in)

HAWFINCH

A large finch of the forest treetops, this bird has a massive bill, with which it can open cherry stones to extract the kernels. Other foods are seeds, buds, and fruits. Seen in small parties in winter, Hawfinches are secretive birds at all times.
• **NEST** A shallow cup of twigs and plant materials, lined with rootlets, and placed in a tree.
• **DISTRIBUTION** Much of Europe; parts of N.W. Africa, Middle East, C. Asia, S. Siberia, and E. Asia.

expanded tips of flight feathers

DISTRIBUTION

JUVENILE

Plumage Sexes differ slightly	Habitat	Migration Non-migrant

| Family FRINGILLIDAE | Species *Euphona personata* | Length 23cm (9in) |

JAPANESE GROSBEAK

This large, migratory finch is common in woodland, where it is seen in pairs in the breeding season and in small flocks in winter. Its diet consists of pine nuts, seeds of berries, and insects.
• **NEST** A shallow cup nest made of twigs and lined with finer material, placed in a tree.
• **DISTRIBUTION** Breeds in S.E. Siberia, N. China, and N. Japan. Winters in S. Japan and C. China.

black mask • • massive bill • blue wing patch

DISTRIBUTION

white wing bar

JUVENILE

| Plumage Sexes differ slightly | Habitat | Migration Migrant |

| Family FRINGILLIDAE | Species *Hesperiphona vespertina* | Length 20cm (8in) |

EVENING GROSBEAK

The black-and-yellow plumage of the male, and the white wing patches of both sexes, identify this finch. It is a woodland bird, which visits birdfeeders in winter. Its diet ranges from insect larvae to seeds.
• **NEST** A cup nest of twigs, placed in a tree fork.
• **DISTRIBUTION** Breeds in coniferous zone in S. Canada, W. USA and south to Mexico. Some birds winter in C. and E. USA.

yellow brow •

FEMALE

• massive bill

• stocky build

• short tail

DISTRIBUTION

| Plumage Sexes differ | Habitat | Migration Partial migrant |

| Family ESTRILDIDAE | Species *Uraeginthus ianthinogaster* | Length 14cm (5½in) |

PURPLE GRENADIER

In spite of its gaudy colours this is a secretive bird, living in arid, tropical scrubland. Small flocks feed on the ground, close to cover, taking seeds and insects. The birds utter quiet, indistinct call notes, often heard as they fly past.
• **NEST** A loose, round nest of grass with a side entrance, lined with feathers, low in a shrub.
• **DISTRIBUTION** E. Africa from Ethiopia and Somalia as far south as Tanzania.

purple rump •

FEMALE

long, tapering tail •

DISTRIBUTION

| Plumage Sexes differ | Habitat | Migration Non-migrant |

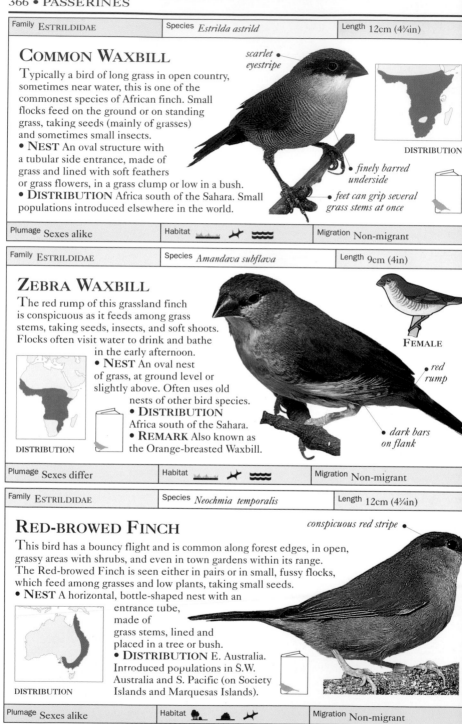

Family ESTRILDIDAE	Species *Estrilda astrild*	Length 12cm (4¾in)

COMMON WAXBILL

Typically a bird of long grass in open country,
sometimes near water, this is one of the
commonest species of African finch. Small
flocks feed on the ground or on standing
grass, taking seeds (mainly of grasses)
and sometimes small insects.
• **NEST** An oval structure with
a tubular side entrance, made of
grass and lined with soft feathers
or grass flowers, in a grass clump or low in a bush.
• **DISTRIBUTION** Africa south of the Sahara. Small
populations introduced elsewhere in the world.

scarlet eyestripe

finely barred underside

feet can grip several grass stems at once

DISTRIBUTION

Plumage Sexes alike	Habitat	Migration Non-migrant

Family ESTRILDIDAE	Species *Amandava subflava*	Length 9cm (4in)

ZEBRA WAXBILL

The red rump of this grassland finch
is conspicuous as it feeds among grass
stems, taking seeds, insects, and soft shoots.
Flocks often visit water to drink and bathe
in the early afternoon.
• **NEST** An oval nest
of grass, at ground level or
slightly above. Often uses old
nests of other bird species.
• **DISTRIBUTION**
Africa south of the Sahara.
• **REMARK** Also known as
the Orange-breasted Waxbill.

FEMALE

red rump

dark bars on flank

DISTRIBUTION

Plumage Sexes differ	Habitat	Migration Non-migrant

Family ESTRILDIDAE	Species *Neochmia temporalis*	Length 12cm (4¾in)

RED-BROWED FINCH

conspicuous red stripe

This bird has a bouncy flight and is common along forest edges, in open,
grassy areas with shrubs, and even in town gardens within its range.
The Red-browed Finch is seen either in pairs or in small, fussy flocks,
which feed among grasses and low plants, taking small seeds.
• **NEST** A horizontal, bottle-shaped nest with an
entrance tube,
made of
grass stems, lined and
placed in a tree or bush.
• **DISTRIBUTION** E. Australia.
Introduced populations in S.W.
Australia and S. Pacific (on Society
Islands and Marquesas Islands).

DISTRIBUTION

Plumage Sexes alike	Habitat	Migration Non-migrant

Family ESTRILDIDAE	Species *Taeniopygia guttata*	Length 12cm (4¾in)

ZEBRA FINCH

So named because of its black-and-white, barred tail, this species lives in semi-desert areas near water, feeding on seeds. It is seen in lively flocks which utter short, nasal notes.
• **NEST** A dome of grass with a side entrance, in a bush or hollow branch.
• **DISTRIBUTION** E. Indonesia and much of Australia.

DISTRIBUTION

• *black-and-white tail*

FEMALE

Plumage Sexes differ	Habitat	Migration Non-migrant

Family ESTRILDIDAE	Species *Taeniopygia bichenovii*	Length 10cm (4in)

DOUBLE-BAR FINCH

This brownish-grey little finch is identified by two black bands across its breast. Small parties feed in short grass or on bare ground, always close to cover, taking small seeds.
• **NEST** A horizontal, bottle-shaped nest made of dried grass, lined with finer grass, and placed in a small bush or in tall grass.
• **DISTRIBUTION** N. and E. Australia.

DISTRIBUTION

speckled wings

• *black-edged, white face*

Plumage Sexes alike	Habitat	Migration Non-migrant

Family ESTRILDIDAE	Species *Erythrura psittacea*	Length 11cm (4¼in)

RED-THROATED PARROT-FINCH

The red-and-green plumage of this finch can be compared with that of a parrot and has given rise to the name. This species occurs in farm-land and open woodland. Seen in pairs in the breeding season, and in flocks at other times, it feeds on grass seeds and sometimes insects.
• **NEST** A round nest of grass with a side entrance, usually in a cavity or recess, or under an overhanging clump of grass.
• **DISTRIBUTION** New Caledonia.

• *green body*

• *red rump*

DISTRIBUTION

Plumage Sexes alike	Habitat	Migration Non-migrant

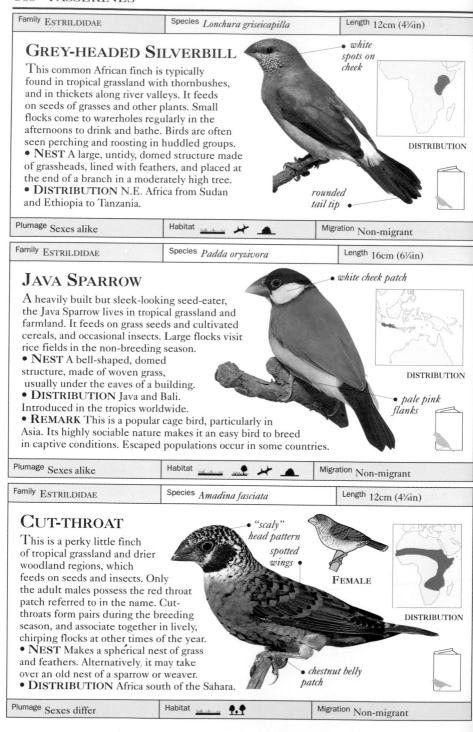

Family ESTRILDIDAE	Species *Lonchura griseicapilla*	Length 12cm (4¾in)

GREY-HEADED SILVERBILL

This common African finch is typically found in tropical grassland with thornbushes, and in thickets along river valleys. It feeds on seeds of grasses and other plants. Small flocks come to waterholes regularly in the afternoons to drink and bathe. Birds are often seen perching and roosting in huddled groups.
• NEST A large, untidy, domed structure made of grassheads, lined with feathers, and placed at the end of a branch in a moderately high tree.
• DISTRIBUTION N.E. Africa from Sudan and Ethiopia to Tanzania.

white spots on cheek

rounded tail tip

DISTRIBUTION

Plumage Sexes alike	Habitat	Migration Non-migrant

Family ESTRILDIDAE	Species *Padda oryzivora*	Length 16cm (6¼in)

JAVA SPARROW

A heavily built but sleek-looking seed-eater, the Java Sparrow lives in tropical grassland and farmland. It feeds on grass seeds and cultivated cereals, and occasional insects. Large flocks visit rice fields in the non-breeding season.
• NEST A bell-shaped, domed structure, made of woven grass, usually under the eaves of a building.
• DISTRIBUTION Java and Bali. Introduced in the tropics worldwide.
• REMARK This is a popular cage bird, particularly in Asia. Its highly sociable nature makes it an easy bird to breed in captive conditions. Escaped populations occur in some countries.

white cheek patch

pale pink flanks

DISTRIBUTION

Plumage Sexes alike	Habitat	Migration Non-migrant

Family ESTRILDIDAE	Species *Amadina fasciata*	Length 12cm (4¾in)

CUT-THROAT

This is a perky little finch of tropical grassland and drier woodland regions, which feeds on seeds and insects. Only the adult males possess the red throat patch referred to in the name. Cut-throats form pairs during the breeding season, and associate together in lively, chirping flocks at other times of the year.
• NEST Makes a spherical nest of grass and feathers. Alternatively, it may take over an old nest of a sparrow or weaver.
• DISTRIBUTION Africa south of the Sahara.

"scaly" head pattern

spotted wings

FEMALE

DISTRIBUTION

chestnut belly patch

Plumage Sexes differ	Habitat	Migration Non-migrant

| Family ESTRILDIDAE | Species *Chloebia gouldiae* | Length 13cm (5in) |

GOULDIAN FINCH

Few species of bird in the world can rival
this bird for sheer splendour of colour. It is
a seed-eater of tropical open woodland and
scrub, feeding in small flocks on the ground.
• **NEST** A loosely built
dome of grass, usually in
a hollow in the ground.
• **DISTRIBUTION** N. Australia.
• **REMARK** There are three
colour phases: Black-headed,
Red-headed, and the rare
Yellow-headed phase.

• *blue-bordered face*

RED-HEADED   **YELLOW-HEADED**

forked tail
• *tip*

DISTRIBUTION

| Plumage Sexes differ slightly | Habitat 🌳 ✈ | Migration Non-migrant |

| Family PLOCEIDAE | Species *Vidua regia* | L. 30cm (12in)/13cm (5in) |

SHAFT-TAILED WHYDAH

An inhabitant of extensive grasslands
in the subtropics, this bird forages
on the ground for fallen seeds. It
does this with an unusual hopping
movement, in which it scratches the
ground whilst jumping up with both
feet. Early in the breeding season, it is seen
in small parties in which males outnumber
females. The males have long tails which they
show off in competitive songflights to attract
females. Once the males have ceased to display,
the long tail is shed and a new plumage is grown,
resembling that of the female. When breeding
is over, the birds gather and feed in large
flocks, which are seen roosting in tall trees.
• **NEST** This bird makes no nest,
but fosters out the care of its young by
laying eggs, cuckoo-fashion, in nests
of Violet-eared Waxbills (*Uraeginthus
granatina*).The young whydahs
resemble young waxbills in mouth
markings and in their calls, and
the nestlings of both species are
reared together by the waxbills.
• **DISTRIBUTION**
Parts of southern Africa.

*male's elaborate tail is present
only during the early stages of
breeding*

expanded tail tips •

• *golden-buff breast*

*red legs
and feet*

• *four elongated
tail shafts*

FEMALE

DISTRIBUTION

| Plumage Sexes differ | Habitat | Migration Non-migrant |

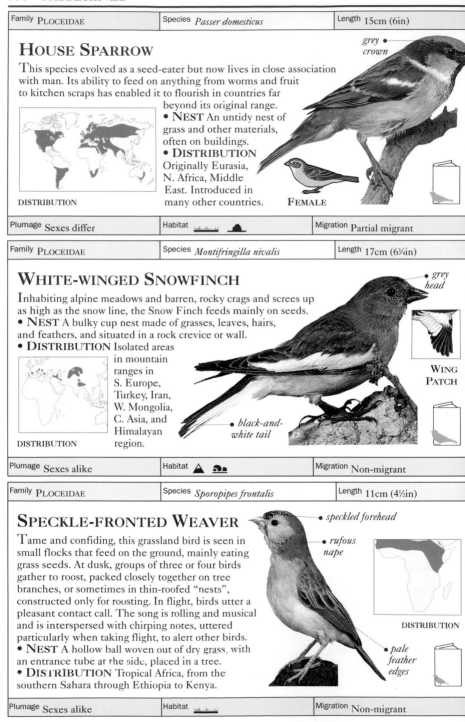

Family PLOCEIDAE	Species *Passer domesticus*	Length 15cm (6in)

HOUSE SPARROW

This species evolved as a seed-eater but now lives in close association with man. Its ability to feed on anything from worms and fruit to kitchen scraps has enabled it to flourish in countries far beyond its original range.
• NEST An untidy nest of grass and other materials, often on buildings.
• DISTRIBUTION Originally Eurasia, N. Africa, Middle East. Introduced in many other countries.

DISTRIBUTION

grey • crown

FEMALE

Plumage Sexes differ	Habitat	Migration Partial migrant

Family PLOCEIDAE	Species *Montifringilla nivalis*	Length 17cm (6¾in)

WHITE-WINGED SNOWFINCH

Inhabiting alpine meadows and barren, rocky crags and screes up as high as the snow line, the Snow Finch feeds mainly on seeds.
• NEST A bulky cup nest made of grasses, leaves, hairs, and feathers, and situated in a rock crevice or wall.
• DISTRIBUTION Isolated areas in mountain ranges in S. Europe, Turkey, Iran, W. Mongolia, C. Asia, and Himalayan region.

DISTRIBUTION

• grey head

WING PATCH

• black-and-white tail

Plumage Sexes alike	Habitat	Migration Non-migrant

Family PLOCEIDAE	Species *Sporopipes frontalis*	Length 11cm (4½in)

SPECKLE-FRONTED WEAVER

Tame and confiding, this grassland bird is seen in small flocks that feed on the ground, mainly eating grass seeds. At dusk, groups of three or four birds gather to roost, packed closely together on tree branches, or sometimes in thin-roofed "nests", constructed only for roosting. In flight, birds utter a pleasant contact call. The song is rolling and musical and is interspersed with chirping notes, uttered particularly when taking flight, to alert other birds.
• NEST A hollow ball woven out of dry grass, with an entrance tube at the side, placed in a tree.
• DISTRIBUTION Tropical Africa, from the southern Sahara through Ethiopia to Kenya.

• speckled forehead

• rufous nape

DISTRIBUTION

• pale feather edges

Plumage Sexes alike	Habitat	Migration Non-migrant

| Family PLOCEIDAE | Species *Ploceus ocularis* | Length 16cm (6¼in) |

SPECTACLED WEAVER

Living in scrub, thickets, and riverside forests, and
spreading into farms and suburban gardens, this shy
species rarely emerges from cover. Pairs creep up and
down stems, foraging for their prey of insects, spiders,
and millipedes, and also taking nectar, seeds, and fruit.
Males hang upside down from the nest in their display.
• **NEST** A rounded, finely woven
nest, suspended from a twig over
water, with a long entrance
tube hanging down below.
• **DISTRIBUTION** Parts of
Africa south of the Sahara.

• *pale eye in black streak*

DISTRIBUTION

• *olive green back*

FEMALE

| Plumage Sexes differ | Habitat | Migration Non-migrant |

| Family PLOCEIDAE | Species *Ploceus cucullatus* | Length 17cm (6¾in) |

VILLAGE WEAVER

black face mask •

Africa's commonest weaver, this
bird forms colonies in trees, often
near villages. It feeds on insects
and seeds. Males display by hanging
below the nest, fluttering their wings.
• **NEST** An oval nest of reeds, sedges,
and grasses, with a nest chamber on one side
and an entrance chamber on the other, with
a vertical entrance tube hanging below.
• **DISTRIBUTION** Much of Africa
south of the Sahara, except in desert areas.

FEMALE

• *yellow feather edges*

DISTRIBUTION

• *golden yellow underside*

| Plumage Sexes differ | Habitat | Migration Non-migrant |

| Family PLOCEIDAE | Species *Quelea cardinalis* | Length 11cm (4¼in) |

CARDINAL QUELEA

This bird is gregarious, sometimes
forming nomadic flocks. It breeds in large
colonies in dense stands of grass and
swamps, and feeds on small seeds. The
male sings from the top of a tall reed,
fluffing out his plumage, quivering
his wings, and jerking his fanned tail.
• **NEST** A compactly woven nest made
of grass, with an entrance at the top on
one side, tied between upright grass stems.
• **DISTRIBUTION** Kenya to Mozambique.
• **REMARK** A relative of the Common
Quelea, which occurs in million-strong flocks.

DISTRIBUTION

FEMALE

| Plumage Sexes differ | Habitat | Migration Partial migrant/nomadic |

Family PLOCEIDAE	Species *Euplectes orix*	Length 12cm (4¾in)

RED BISHOP

This colourful weaver is found in tall grass and reeds in relatively moist areas of savanna. A breeding male may mate with several females, as the species is polygamous. The male displays his black-and-scarlet plumage either from a perch or in slow, jerky, bouncing flight across the reedbeds. His display behaviour includes fluffing out his body and head plumage, and rapidly beating his wings. This eye-catching performance is accompanied by twittering or wheezy calls, uttered both from a perch or during the display flight. Outside the breeding season, birds form large flocks. When feeding, Red Bishops walk in short, deliberate steps while foraging on the ground for seeds, grains, and insects.
• **NEST** An upright, oval nest, woven out of fine grass and reed leaves, with a porched side entrance, attached to a reed stem some 1-2m (3-6ft) above water.
• **DISTRIBUTION** Sub-Saharan Africa, from Kenya and Angola to South Africa.

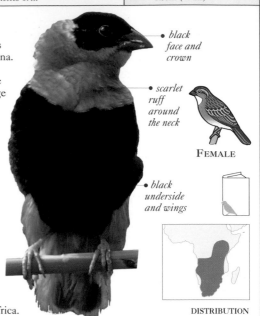

• *black face and crown*

• *scarlet ruff around the neck*

FEMALE

• *black underside and wings*

DISTRIBUTION

Plumage Sexes differ	Habitat	Migration Non-migrant

Family PLOCEIDAE	Species *Euplectes ardens*	L. 28cm (11in)/13cm (5in)

RED-COLLARED WIDOWBIRD

This widowbird of tropical and subtropical grassland is identified by the red neck band on the breeding male's otherwise black plumage. In his territorial display flight the male flutters around in the air over his nesting territory with slow wingbeats, trailing his long, black tail. The female is duller and lacks the long tail, as do immatures. Males outside the breeding season resemble the females and lack the long tail. The species is gregarious at all times, moving about in flocks and visiting bushes and tall grass, often near water. Birds also roost in large flocks, often in tall elephant grass, again close to water. The diet consists of insects and seeds.
• **NEST** An oval nest, made of living grass and lined with dry grass, with an entrance near the top in the form of a covered porch. The nest is placed in a bush or reedbed.
• **DISTRIBUTION** Scattered areas throughout Africa south of the Sahara, except in dense forest or desert areas.

• *buff feather edges in early season*

FEMALE

entire tail is feathered •

DISTRIBUTION

• *tail is long only in the breeding season*

Plumage Sexes differ	Habitat	Migration Non-migrant

Family PLOCEIDAE	Species *Euplectes jacksoni*	L. 33cm (13in)/13cm (5in)

JACKSON'S WIDOWBIRD

This is a common and lively species, living in open, tropical grassland at high altitude. During the breeding season it is easy to see, since the male performs a wild display dance around his own selected tuft of grass, leaping high into the air and arching his long tail over his back. Flocks gather in the post-breeding period and visit farmland, where they feed on seeds and insects, either on the ground or in high grass.
• **NEST** A flimsy nest made of grass and lined with seedheads, with a side entrance. It is placed low in a tuft of grass, with growing blades woven into the structure.
• **DISTRIBUTION** From S.W. Kenya to N. Tanzania.
• **REMARK** The male's long tail accounts for the 20cm (8in) length difference between the sexes.

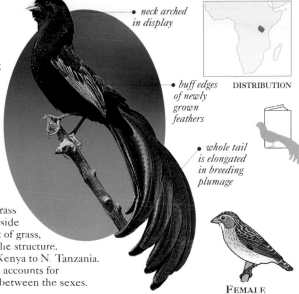

• *neck arched in display*

• *buff edges of newly grown feathers*

DISTRIBUTION

• *whole tail is elongated in breeding plumage*

FEMALE

Plumage Sexes differ	Habitat	Migration Non-migrant

Family PLOCEIDAE	Species *Anomalospiza imberbis*	Length 13cm (5in)

PARASITIC WEAVER

A grassland bird with a short tail and stubby bill, this species is usually found near water. It feeds almost exclusively on seeds. During the breeding season it is seen singly or in pairs, or more rarely in small groups, and males perform a "swizzling" song when displaying. Outside the breeding season, larger flocks gather together. In flight, flocks utter warbling contact notes.
• **NEST** This bird builds no nest of its own but lays eggs in nests of some *Cisticola* and *Prinia* warblers, which foster the young.
• **DISTRIBUTION** Scattered areas throughout Africa south of the Sahara.
• **REMARK** Also popularly known as the Cuckoo-Finch. Its inconspicuous coloration may help it to visit the nests of host birds without being detected.

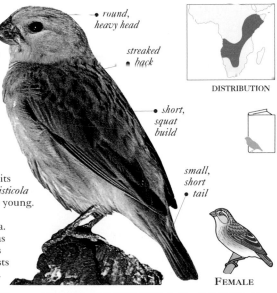

• *round, heavy head*

streaked • *back*

DISTRIBUTION

• *short, squat build*

small, short • *tail*

FEMALE

Plumage Sexes differ	Habitat	Migration Non-migrant

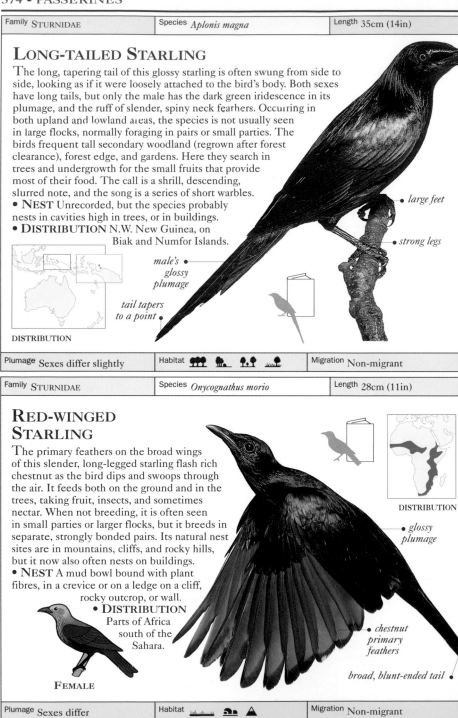

Family STURNIDAE	Species *Aplonis magna*	Length 35cm (14in)

LONG-TAILED STARLING

The long, tapering tail of this glossy starling is often swung from side to side, looking as if it were loosely attached to the bird's body. Both sexes have long tails, but only the male has the dark green iridescence in its plumage, and the ruff of slender, spiny neck feathers. Occurring in both upland and lowland areas, the species is not usually seen in large flocks, normally foraging in pairs or small parties. The birds frequent tall secondary woodland (regrown after forest clearance), forest edge, and gardens. Here they search in trees and undergrowth for the small fruits that provide most of their food. The call is a shrill, descending, slurred note, and the song is a series of short warbles.
• **NEST** Unrecorded, but the species probably nests in cavities high in trees, or in buildings.
• **DISTRIBUTION** N.W. New Guinea, on Biak and Numfor Islands.

• *large feet*

• *strong legs*

male's glossy plumage

tail tapers to a point •

DISTRIBUTION

Plumage Sexes differ slightly	Habitat	Migration Non-migrant

Family STURNIDAE	Species *Onycognathus morio*	Length 28cm (11in)

RED-WINGED STARLING

The primary feathers on the broad wings of this slender, long-legged starling flash rich chestnut as the bird dips and swoops through the air. It feeds both on the ground and in the trees, taking fruit, insects, and sometimes nectar. When not breeding, it is often seen in small parties or larger flocks, but it breeds in separate, strongly bonded pairs. Its natural nest sites are in mountains, cliffs, and rocky hills, but it now also often nests on buildings.
• **NEST** A mud bowl bound with plant fibres, in a crevice or on a ledge on a cliff, rocky outcrop, or wall.
• **DISTRIBUTION** Parts of Africa south of the Sahara.

DISTRIBUTION

• *glossy plumage*

• *chestnut primary feathers*

broad, blunt-ended tail •

FEMALE

Plumage Sexes differ	Habitat	Migration Non-migrant

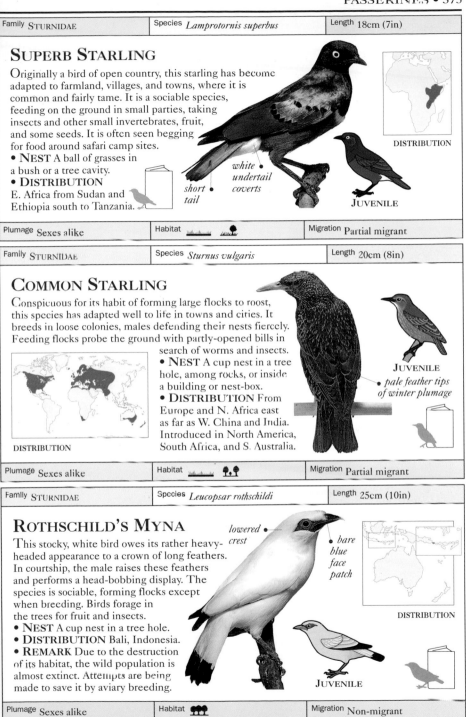

| Family STURNIDAE | Species *Lamprotornis superbus* | Length 18cm (7in) |

SUPERB STARLING

Originally a bird of open country, this starling has become
adapted to farmland, villages, and towns, where it is
common and fairly tame. It is a sociable species,
feeding on the ground in small parties, taking
insects and other small invertebrates, fruit,
and some seeds. It is often seen begging
for food around safari camp sites.
• NEST A ball of grasses in
a bush or a tree cavity.
• DISTRIBUTION
E. Africa from Sudan and
Ethiopia south to Tanzania.

white • undertail coverts

short • tail

DISTRIBUTION

JUVENILE

| Plumage Sexes alike | Habitat | Migration Partial migrant |

| Family STURNIDAE | Species *Sturnus vulgaris* | Length 20cm (8in) |

COMMON STARLING

Conspicuous for its habit of forming large flocks to roost,
this species has adapted well to life in towns and cities. It
breeds in loose colonies, males defending their nests fiercely.
Feeding flocks probe the ground with partly-opened bills in
search of worms and insects.
• NEST A cup nest in a tree
hole, among rocks, or inside
a building or nest-box.
• DISTRIBUTION From
Europe and N. Africa east
as far as W. China and India.
Introduced in North America,
South Africa, and S. Australia.

DISTRIBUTION

JUVENILE

*• pale feather tips
of winter plumage*

| Plumage Sexes alike | Habitat | Migration Partial migrant |

| Family STURNIDAE | Species *Leucopsar rothschildi* | Length 25cm (10in) |

ROTHSCHILD'S MYNA

lowered • crest

This stocky, white bird owes its rather heavy-
headed appearance to a crown of long feathers.
In courtship, the male raises these feathers
and performs a head-bobbing display. The
species is sociable, forming flocks except
when breeding. Birds forage in
the trees for fruit and insects.
• NEST A cup nest in a tree hole.
• DISTRIBUTION Bali, Indonesia.
• REMARK Due to the destruction
of its habitat, the wild population is
almost extinct. Attempts are being
made to save it by aviary breeding.

• bare blue face patch

DISTRIBUTION

JUVENILE

| Plumage Sexes alike | Habitat | Migration Non-migrant |

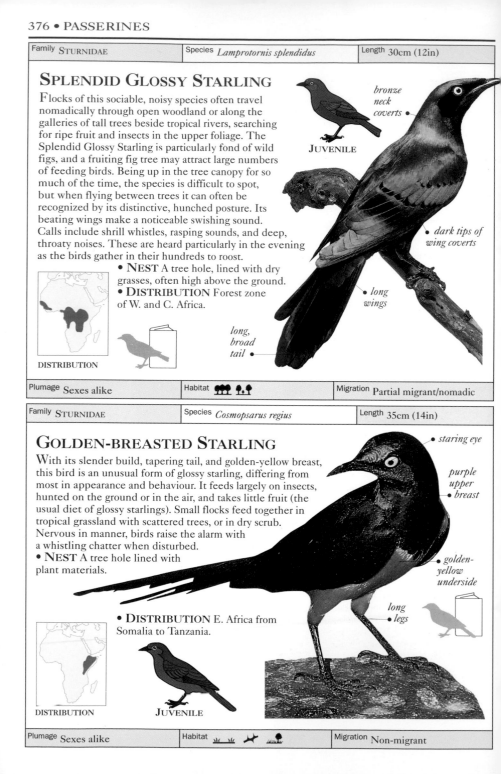

Family STURNIDAE	Species *Lamprotornis splendidus*	Length 30cm (12in)

SPLENDID GLOSSY STARLING

Flocks of this sociable, noisy species often travel nomadically through open woodland or along the galleries of tall trees beside tropical rivers, searching for ripe fruit and insects in the upper foliage. The Splendid Glossy Starling is particularly fond of wild figs, and a fruiting fig tree may attract large numbers of feeding birds. Being up in the tree canopy for so much of the time, the species is difficult to spot, but when flying between trees it can often be recognized by its distinctive, hunched posture. Its beating wings make a noticeable swishing sound. Calls include shrill whistles, rasping sounds, and deep, throaty noises. These are heard particularly in the evening as the birds gather in their hundreds to roost.

• **NEST** A tree hole, lined with dry grasses, often high above the ground.
• **DISTRIBUTION** Forest zone of W. and C. Africa.

bronze neck coverts

JUVENILE

dark tips of wing coverts

long wings

long, broad tail

DISTRIBUTION

Plumage Sexes alike	Habitat	Migration Partial migrant/nomadic

Family STURNIDAE	Species *Cosmopsarus regius*	Length 35cm (14in)

GOLDEN-BREASTED STARLING

With its slender build, tapering tail, and golden-yellow breast, this bird is an unusual form of glossy starling, differing from most in appearance and behaviour. It feeds largely on insects, hunted on the ground or in the air, and takes little fruit (the usual diet of glossy starlings). Small flocks feed together in tropical grassland with scattered trees, or in dry scrub. Nervous in manner, birds raise the alarm with a whistling chatter when disturbed.

• **NEST** A tree hole lined with plant materials.

• **DISTRIBUTION** E. Africa from Somalia to Tanzania.

staring eye

purple upper breast

golden-yellow underside

long legs

DISTRIBUTION

JUVENILE

Plumage Sexes alike	Habitat	Migration Non-migrant

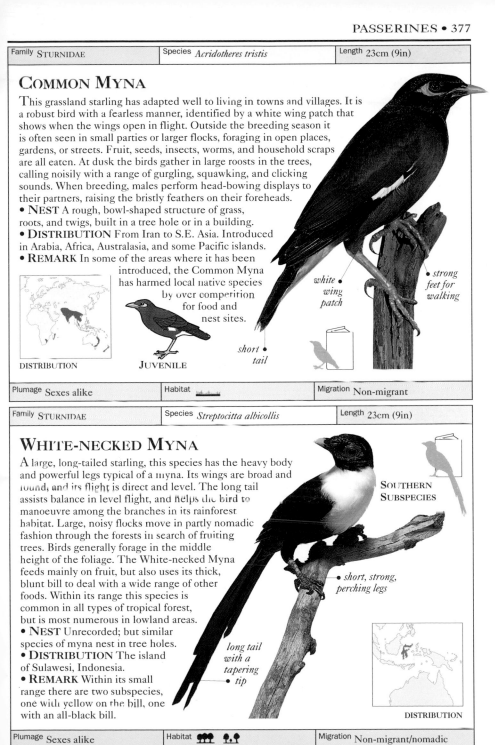

Family STURNIDAE	Species *Acridotheres tristis*	Length 23cm (9in)

COMMON MYNA

This grassland starling has adapted well to living in towns and villages. It is a robust bird with a fearless manner, identified by a white wing patch that shows when the wings open in flight. Outside the breeding season it is often seen in small parties or larger flocks, foraging in open places, gardens, or streets. Fruit, seeds, insects, worms, and household scraps are all eaten. At dusk the birds gather in large roosts in the trees, calling noisily with a range of gurgling, squawking, and clicking sounds. When breeding, males perform head-bowing displays to their partners, raising the bristly feathers on their foreheads.
• **NEST** A rough, bowl-shaped structure of grass, roots, and twigs, built in a tree hole or in a building.
• **DISTRIBUTION** From Iran to S.E. Asia. Introduced in Arabia, Africa, Australasia, and some Pacific islands.
• **REMARK** In some of the areas where it has been introduced, the Common Myna has harmed local native species by over competition for food and nest sites.

white wing patch

strong feet for walking

short tail

DISTRIBUTION

JUVENILE

Plumage Sexes alike	Habitat	Migration Non-migrant

Family STURNIDAE	Species *Streptocitta albicollis*	Length 23cm (9in)

WHITE-NECKED MYNA

A large, long-tailed starling, this species has the heavy body and powerful legs typical of a myna. Its wings are broad and round, and its flight is direct and level. The long tail assists balance in level flight, and helps the bird to manoeuvre among the branches in its rainforest habitat. Large, noisy flocks move in partly nomadic fashion through the forests in search of fruiting trees. Birds generally forage in the middle height of the foliage. The White-necked Myna feeds mainly on fruit, but also uses its thick, blunt bill to deal with a wide range of other foods. Within its range this species is common in all types of tropical forest, but is most numerous in lowland areas.
• **NEST** Unrecorded; but similar species of myna nest in tree holes.
• **DISTRIBUTION** The island of Sulawesi, Indonesia.
• **REMARK** Within its small range there are two subspecies, one with yellow on the bill, one with an all-black bill.

SOUTHERN SUBSPECIES

short, strong, perching legs

long tail with a tapering tip

DISTRIBUTION

Plumage Sexes alike	Habitat	Migration Non-migrant/nomadic

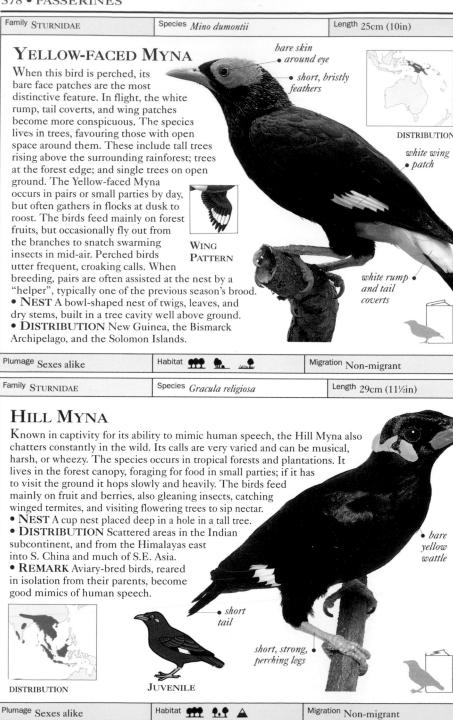

Family STURNIDAE	Species *Mino dumontii*	Length 25cm (10in)

YELLOW-FACED MYNA

When this bird is perched, its bare face patches are the most distinctive feature. In flight, the white rump, tail coverts, and wing patches become more conspicuous. The species lives in trees, favouring those with open space around them. These include tall trees rising above the surrounding rainforest; trees at the forest edge; and single trees on open ground. The Yellow-faced Myna occurs in pairs or small parties by day, but often gathers in flocks at dusk to roost. The birds feed mainly on forest fruits, but occasionally fly out from the branches to snatch swarming insects in mid-air. Perched birds utter frequent, croaking calls. When breeding, pairs are often assisted at the nest by a "helper", typically one of the previous season's brood.
• **NEST** A bowl-shaped nest of twigs, leaves, and dry stems, built in a tree cavity well above ground.
• **DISTRIBUTION** New Guinea, the Bismarck Archipelago, and the Solomon Islands.

bare skin around eye

short, bristly feathers

DISTRIBUTION

white wing patch

WING PATTERN

white rump and tail coverts

Plumage Sexes alike	Habitat	Migration Non-migrant

Family STURNIDAE	Species *Gracula religiosa*	Length 29cm (11½in)

HILL MYNA

Known in captivity for its ability to mimic human speech, the Hill Myna also chatters constantly in the wild. Its calls are very varied and can be musical, harsh, or wheezy. The species occurs in tropical forests and plantations. It lives in the forest canopy, foraging for food in small parties; if it has to visit the ground it hops slowly and heavily. The birds feed mainly on fruit and berries, also gleaning insects, catching winged termites, and visiting flowering trees to sip nectar.
• **NEST** A cup nest placed deep in a hole in a tall tree.
• **DISTRIBUTION** Scattered areas in the Indian subcontinent, and from the Himalayas east into S. China and much of S.E. Asia.
• **REMARK** Aviary-bred birds, reared in isolation from their parents, become good mimics of human speech.

bare yellow wattle

short tail

short, strong, perching logs

DISTRIBUTION

JUVENILE

Plumage Sexes alike	Habitat	Migration Non-migrant

Family STURNIDAE	Species *Buphagus africanus*	Length 22cm (8½in)

YELLOW-BILLED OXPECKER

This grassland bird finds its food on the bodies of large
grazing mammals such as giraffes, rhinoceroses, zebras, and
cattle. It clambers about with its sharp claws, using its tail as a
prop, and removes ticks and other skin parasites with its bill, which
is flattened sideways, with a blunt tip for dislodging the prey. The
oxpecker also probes into skin wounds and sometimes feeds on
wound tissue. If alarmed, the bird dodges around the host's
body to hide. Oxpeckers take the opportunity to drink
when their host visits water. At night they roost in
flocks in trees, in reedbeds, or among rocks.
• **NEST** A pad of feathers, grass, and hair,
placed in a natural hole in a tree.
• **DISTRIBUTION** Africa south
of the Sahara.

JUVENILE

• red
eye

strong claws
for clambering
• on animals

short tail used
• as a prop

DISTRIBUTION

Plumage Sexes alike	Habitat	Migration Non-migrant

Family ORIOLIDAE	Species *Oriolus oriolus*	Length 22cm (8½in)

GOLDEN ORIOLE

Shy and secretive, this species occurs in deciduous woodland, preferring
trees with high, open canopies. Females are well-camouflaged, but even
the bright yellow-and-black male is often hard to see as he searches the
treetop foliage for fruit and insects. Golden Orioles can, however,
be detected by their loud, fluting, three-note calls. They fly
swiftly, often in shallow swoops. Uneasy on the ground, they
stay in the air even to bathe, splashing into water momentarily
before returning to the safety of the trees.
• **NEST** A cup nest slung in a horizontal twig fork,
made of grasses, wool, and strips of bark, finely
lined, and situated high in the outer twigs of a tree.
• **DISTRIBUTION** Breeds in much of Europe,
C. Asia, and N. India. Winters in Africa and India.

• black
eye
streak

long, •
narrow
wing

short tail •

yellow side
panels •

short legs •
of a tree-
dweller

DISTRIBUTION

FEMALE

Plumage Sexes differ	Habitat	Migration Migrant

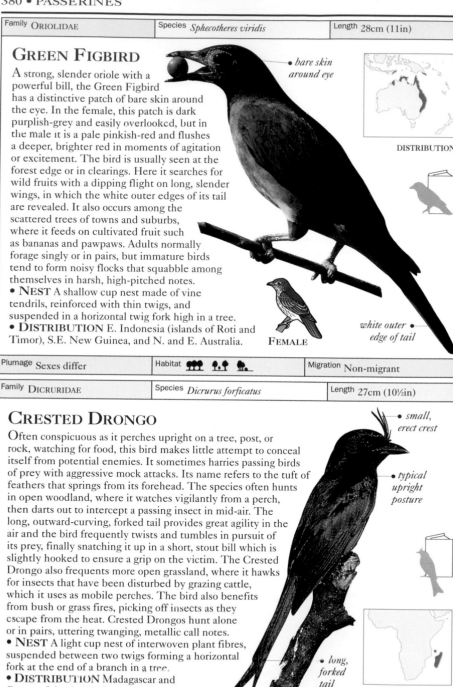

Family ORIOLIDAE	Species *Sphecotheres viridis*	Length 28cm (11in)

GREEN FIGBIRD

A strong, slender oriole with a
powerful bill, the Green Figbird
has a distinctive patch of bare skin around
the eye. In the female, this patch is dark
purplish-grey and easily overlooked, but in
the male it is a pale pinkish-red and flushes
a deeper, brighter red in moments of agitation
or excitement. The bird is usually seen at the
forest edge or in clearings. Here it searches for
wild fruits with a dipping flight on long, slender
wings, in which the white outer edges of its tail
are revealed. It also occurs among the
scattered trees of towns and suburbs,
where it feeds on cultivated fruit such
as bananas and pawpaws. Adults normally
forage singly or in pairs, but immature birds
tend to form noisy flocks that squabble among
themselves in harsh, high-pitched notes.
• **NEST** A shallow cup nest made of vine
tendrils, reinforced with thin twigs, and
suspended in a horizontal twig fork high in a tree.
• **DISTRIBUTION** E. Indonesia (islands of Roti and
Timor), S.E. New Guinea, and N. and E. Australia.

bare skin around eye

DISTRIBUTION

white outer edge of tail

FEMALE

Plumage Sexes differ	Habitat	Migration Non-migrant

Family DICRURIDAE	Species *Dicrurus forficatus*	Length 27cm (10½in)

CRESTED DRONGO

Often conspicuous as it perches upright on a tree, post, or
rock, watching for food, this bird makes little attempt to conceal
itself from potential enemies. It sometimes harries passing birds
of prey with aggressive mock attacks. Its name refers to the tuft of
feathers that springs from its forehead. The species often hunts
in open woodland, where it watches vigilantly from a perch,
then darts out to intercept a passing insect in mid-air. The
long, outward-curving, forked tail provides great agility in the
air and the bird frequently twists and tumbles in pursuit of
its prey, finally snatching it up in a short, stout bill which is
slightly hooked to ensure a grip on the victim. The Crested
Drongo also frequents more open grassland, where it hawks
for insects that have been disturbed by grazing cattle,
which it uses as mobile perches. The bird also benefits
from bush or grass fires, picking off insects as they
escape from the heat. Crested Drongos hunt alone
or in pairs, uttering twanging, metallic call notes.
• **NEST** A light cup nest of interwoven plant fibres,
suspended between two twigs forming a horizontal
fork at the end of a branch in a tree.
• **DISTRIBUTION** Madagascar and
Comoro Islands (northwest of Madagascar).

small, erect crest

typical upright posture

long, forked tail

DISTRIBUTION

Plumage Sexes alike	Habitat	Migration Non-migrant

Family DICRURIDAE	Species *Dicrurus paradiseus*	Length 63cm (25in)

GREATER RACQUET-TAILED DRONGO

This large drongo can be recognized by its two long tail feathers. Each of these is composed of a long, wire-like shaft with a broad vane, known as a racquet, at its tip. In flight, the racquets ripple and bounce as they trail behind the bird. Another recognition feature is the loose, backward-drooping crest on the crown of the head. The species is common in rainforest and bamboo jungle, and feeds almost exclusively on insects, caught on the wing or picked from twigs and foliage. It can use its versatile feet to clamp a large insect to the perch, or to grasp and raise the prey to its bill. Greater Racquet-tailed Drongos hunt by flying out repeatedly from the same perch, or by moving from tree to tree, either alone or in small parties. Such parties often associate with birds of other species, to form large hunting flocks. These flocks flush insects out of the vegetation as they pass, making them easy to catch. Like other drongos, the Greater Racquet-tail is boldly aggressive towards predators. It utters metallic calls, as well as a song that includes musical, whistling sounds and skilful mimicry of other birds.
• **NEST** A deep, loose cup nest made of fine twigs, bark strips, grass stems, and spiders' webs, bound by its outer rim to a horizontally forked twig, and situated high in a tree.
• **DISTRIBUTION** Much of India and through the Himalayan region to S. China, and south as far as Borneo, Java, and Bali.
• **REMARK** This bird is the largest species of drongo, not only on account of tail length but in overall body size too.

DISTRIBUTION

• *forked tail*

• *long-shafted outer tail feathers*

racquets are always • *twisted*

Plumage Sexes alike	Habitat 🌳	Migration Non-migrant

Family CALLAEATIDAE	Species *Creadion carunculatus*	Length 25cm (10in)

SADDLEBACK

Identified by its fleshy wattles, this forest bird lives mainly in the trees, probing bark for insects, and taking fruit and nectar. It makes only brief flights. Pairs remain together.
• **NEST** A cup nest in a tree hole or dense foliage.
• **DISTRIBUTION** New Zealand; once widespread, now only on a few small islands.

chestnut "saddle" • *on the back*

DISTRIBUTION

SOUTH ISLAND JUVENILE

Plumage Sexes alike	Habitat ✈ 🌳	Migration Non-migrant

Family GRALLINIDAE	Species *Grallina cyanoleuca*	Length 27cm (10½in)

MAGPIE-LARK

Although common on farmland and even in towns, the Magpie-Lark is essentially a bird of pond and lake margins, which it visits to collect mud for its nest, and also to look for food. It walks and paddles on long legs, its body and tail well raised, searching the ground and the shallow water for insects, water snails, and other small invertebrates. When it takes *long, broad wings* to the air it flies strongly and directly, steadily flapping its large, rounded wings. After mating, pairs often remain together. They advertise their possession of a territory with a mutual display, in which each bird calls in turn while standing erect and raising its wings high.

strong legs for walking and • wading

FEMALE

• **NEST** A mud bowl, lined with fine grasses and sometimes feathers, built on a horizontal branch in a tree.
• **DISTRIBUTION** Australia, and part of S. New Guinea.

DISTRIBUTION

Plumage Sexes differ	Habitat 🌳🌳 ✈ 〜〜	Migration Non-migrant

Family CORCORACIDAE	Species *Struthidea cinerea*	Length 32cm (12½in)

APOSTLEBIRD

A ground-dwelling bird with a long tail, the Apostlebird has a busy, fussing manner and harsh, chattering calls. It does not fly strongly and feeds mainly on the ground, walking, running, and hopping in search of insects and other invertebrates, and also taking small seeds. The name of this bird is a biblical reference to the 12 apostles, since the birds often live in sociable family groups consisting of this number of birds. Foraging as a group, they preen each other and huddle together to rest and roost in trees. They also cooperate to build the nest, incubate the clutch, and feed the young. Usually there is only one breeding female in the group, but sometimes two or more will lay their eggs in the same nest.

short • wings

• **NEST** A mud bowl reinforced with grass and lined with finer grasses, on a horizontal branch up to 15m (49ft) above the ground.
• **DISTRIBUTION** N. and E. Australia.

DISTRIBUTION

Plumage Sexes alike	Habitat 🌳🌳 ✈	Migration Non-migrant

| Family ARTAMIDAE | Species *Artamus cinereus* | Length 18cm (7in) |

BLACK-FACED WOODSWALLOW

Despite its stout, heavy-headed appearance, the Black-faced Woodswallow is very agile in the air, flying easily on long, tapering wings in pursuit of its insect prey. Found in open country with scattered trees, it watches alertly from a high, bare branch, darting out to ambush passing insects. At other times it circles or glides in prolonged aerial hunts, catching insects in its broad-based bill. It usually occurs in pairs or small flocks, which huddle together to roost. The birds are sociable when breeding, and the nesting pair can often rely on help from other family members.

EASTERN FORM

• **NEST** A cup nest made of twigs and rootlets, built inside a shrub or a hollow stump.

• **DISTRIBUTION** Timor, S. New Guinea, and Australia.

black undertail coverts of western form

DISTRIBUTION

| Plumage Sexes alike | Habitat | Migration Non-migrant |

| Family CRACTICIDAE | Species *Cracticus torquatus* | Length 27cm (10½in) |

GREY BUTCHERBIRD

A long, powerful bill with a hooked tip indicates the predatory nature of this species. Its flight is strong and fast. It feeds on small birds, insects, lizards, and mice, swooping down from a perch to snatch them. Unlike true birds of prey it cannot hold down its victims with its foot. Instead, it carries prey back to the perch and wedges it in a twig fork or impales it on a thorn to tear at it. This behaviour probably explains the bird's name. Pairs live in permanent territories and boldly attack predators that threaten the nest. The species utters musical, whistling calls, and pairs sing "duets" while repeatedly bowing to each other.

strong bill with a hooked tip

• **NEST** A well-built cup nest made of small twigs, lined with rootlets and vine tendrils, and usually placed in a vertical tree fork.

• **DISTRIBUTION** Australia, excluding desert areas.

short legs for perching

feet are not used for holding prey

DISTRIBUTION

JUVENILE

| Plumage Sexes alike | Habitat | Migration Non-migrant |

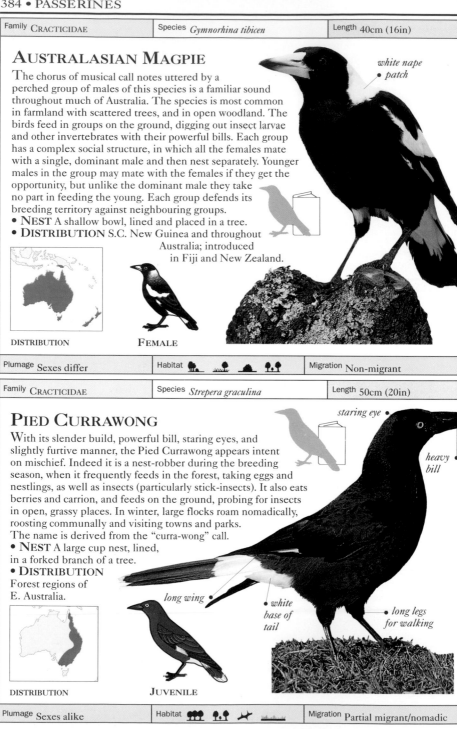

| Family CRACTICIDAE | Species *Gymnorhina tibicen* | Length 40cm (16in) |

AUSTRALASIAN MAGPIE

The chorus of musical call notes uttered by a perched group of males of this species is a familiar sound throughout much of Australia. The species is most common in farmland with scattered trees, and in open woodland. The birds feed in groups on the ground, digging out insect larvae and other invertebrates with their powerful bills. Each group has a complex social structure, in which all the females mate with a single, dominant male and then nest separately. Younger males in the group may mate with the females if they get the opportunity, but unlike the dominant male they take no part in feeding the young. Each group defends its breeding territory against neighbouring groups.
• **NEST** A shallow bowl, lined and placed in a tree.
• **DISTRIBUTION** S.C. New Guinea and throughout Australia; introduced in Fiji and New Zealand.

white nape patch

DISTRIBUTION

FEMALE

| Plumage Sexes differ | Habitat | Migration Non-migrant |

| Family CRACTICIDAE | Species *Strepera graculina* | Length 50cm (20in) |

PIED CURRAWONG

With its slender build, powerful bill, staring eyes, and slightly furtive manner, the Pied Currawong appears intent on mischief. Indeed it is a nest-robber during the breeding season, when it frequently feeds in the forest, taking eggs and nestlings, as well as insects (particularly stick-insects). It also eats berries and carrion, and feeds on the ground, probing for insects in open, grassy places. In winter, large flocks roam nomadically, roosting communally and visiting towns and parks. The name is derived from the "curra-wong" call.
• **NEST** A large cup nest, lined, in a forked branch of a tree.
• **DISTRIBUTION** Forest regions of E. Australia.

staring eye

heavy bill

long wing

white base of tail

long legs for walking

DISTRIBUTION

JUVENILE

| Plumage Sexes alike | Habitat | Migration Partial migrant/nomadic |

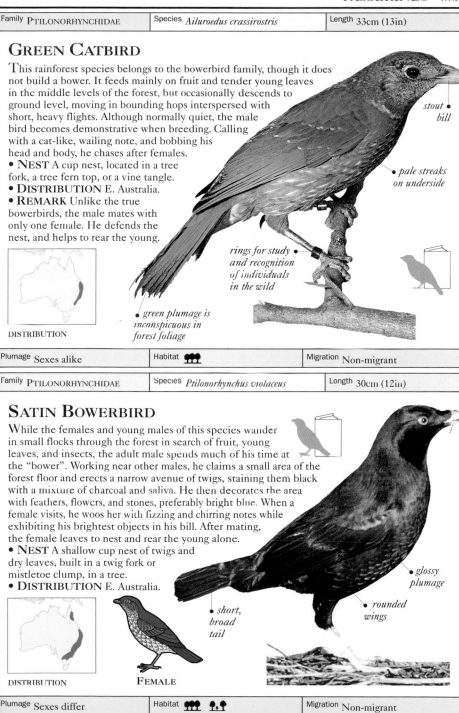

Family PTILONORHYNCHIDAE	Species *Ailuroedus crassirostris*	Length 33cm (13in)

GREEN CATBIRD

This rainforest species belongs to the bowerbird family, though it does not build a bower. It feeds mainly on fruit and tender young leaves in the middle levels of the forest, but occasionally descends to ground level, moving in bounding hops interspersed with short, heavy flights. Although normally quiet, the male bird becomes demonstrative when breeding. Calling with a cat-like, wailing note, and bobbing his head and body, he chases after females.
• **NEST** A cup nest, located in a tree fork, a tree fern top, or a vine tangle.
• **DISTRIBUTION** E. Australia.
• **REMARK** Unlike the true bowerbirds, the male mates with only one female. He defends the nest, and helps to rear the young.

stout bill

• pale streaks on underside

rings for study • and recognition of individuals in the wild

• green plumage is inconspicuous in forest foliage

DISTRIBUTION

Plumage Sexes alike	Habitat	Migration Non-migrant

Family PTILONORHYNCHIDAE	Species *Ptilonorhynchus violaceus*	Length 30cm (12in)

SATIN BOWERBIRD

While the females and young males of this species wander in small flocks through the forest in search of fruit, young leaves, and insects, the adult male spends much of his time at the "bower". Working near other males, he claims a small area of the forest floor and erects a narrow avenue of twigs, staining them black with a mixture of charcoal and saliva. He then decorates the area with feathers, flowers, and stones, preferably bright blue. When a female visits, he woos her with fizzing and chirring notes while exhibiting his brightest objects in his bill. After mating, the female leaves to nest and rear the young alone.
• **NEST** A shallow cup nest of twigs and dry leaves, built in a twig fork or mistletoe clump, in a tree.
• **DISTRIBUTION** E. Australia.

• glossy plumage

• rounded wings

• short, broad tail

DISTRIBUTION

FEMALE

Plumage Sexes differ	Habitat	Migration Non-migrant

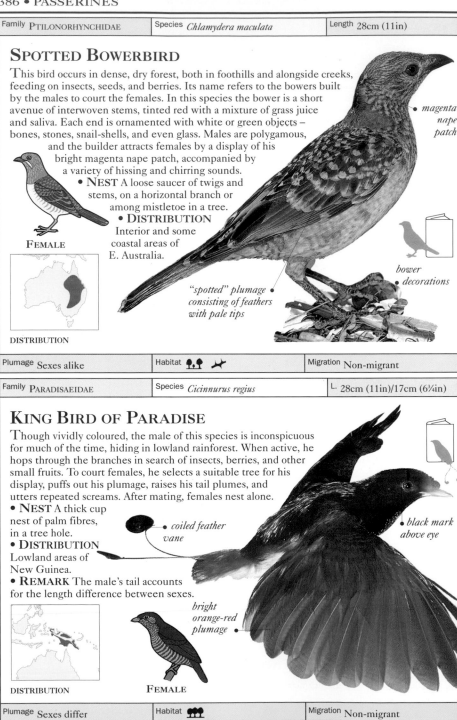

Family PTILONORHYNCHIDAE	Species *Chlamydera maculata*	Length 28cm (11in)

SPOTTED BOWERBIRD

This bird occurs in dense, dry forest, both in foothills and alongside creeks, feeding on insects, seeds, and berries. Its name refers to the bowers built by the males to court the females. In this species the bower is a short avenue of interwoven stems, tinted red with a mixture of grass juice and saliva. Each end is ornamented with white or green objects – bones, stones, snail-shells, and even glass. Males are polygamous, and the builder attracts females by a display of his bright magenta nape patch, accompanied by a variety of hissing and chirring sounds.
• **NEST** A loose saucer of twigs and stems, on a horizontal branch or among mistletoe in a tree.
• **DISTRIBUTION** Interior and some coastal areas of E. Australia.

magenta nape patch

FEMALE

bower decorations

"*spotted" plumage consisting of feathers with pale tips*

DISTRIBUTION

Plumage Sexes alike	Habitat	Migration Non-migrant

Family PARADISAEIDAE	Species *Cicinnurus regius*	L. 28cm (11in)/17cm (6¾in)

KING BIRD OF PARADISE

Though vividly coloured, the male of this species is inconspicuous for much of the time, hiding in lowland rainforest. When active, he hops through the branches in search of insects, berries, and other small fruits. To court females, he selects a suitable tree for his display, puffs out his plumage, raises his tail plumes, and utters repeated screams. After mating, females nest alone.
• **NEST** A thick cup nest of palm fibres, in a tree hole.
• **DISTRIBUTION** Lowland areas of New Guinea.
• **REMARK** The male's tail accounts for the length difference between sexes.

• *coiled feather vane*

• *black mark above eye*

bright orange-red plumage •

DISTRIBUTION   FEMALE

Plumage Sexes differ	Habitat	Migration Non-migrant

Family PARADISAEIDAE	Species *Paradisaea apoda*	L·110cm (43in)/ 40cm (16in)

GREATER BIRD OF PARADISE

Spectacular tufts of plumes on either flank of the male help to identify this rainforest bird. In contrast with other bird of paradise species, he does not display alone but with other males. Groups of males gather on bare branches high in the forest trees, to call and arch their plumes invitingly, advertising their presence with loud, staccato notes. The males then stand motionless while visiting females select a temporary mate. After mating, the female nests alone. Mature males are solitary, while females and young males hunt in small groups. Both sexes feed on fruit and insects.
• **NEST** Not scientifically recorded, but probably a cup nest of twigs, tendrils, and dead leaves, built in a tree.
• **DISTRIBUTION** S.E. New Guinea and Aru islands (off S.W. New Guinea).
• **REMARK** The male's tail streamers account for the length difference between the sexes.

flank feathers

tail streamer

DISTRIBUTION

FEMALE

Plumage Sexes differ	Habitat 🌳🌳🌳	Migration Non-migrant

Family PARADISAEIDAE	Species *Paradisaea rudolphi*	L·63cm (25in)/29cm (11½in)

BLUE BIRD OF PARADISE

This rainforest bird inhabits the foothills of mountainous regions and feeds on tree fruits and insects. Females and young males often forage in small parties, while the mature male usually feeds alone. He also performs his courtship display alone, choosing an open perch as a display site, and uttering a series of plaintive call notes. Then, fanning out his blue belly and flank feathers, he drops upside down and vibrates his body. He also rhythmically expands and contracts a special patch of rust-red and black plumage. While doing this he utters a throbbing, machine-like sound. The female moves along the branch to perch between his feet, looking down on the display, until he swings back upright to stand beside her.
• **NEST** A shallow cup nest, in a low tree.
• **DISTRIBUTION** E. New Guinea.
• **REMARK** The male's long tail streamers account for the 34cm (13½in) length difference between the sexes.

finely divided flank feathers

FEMALE

elongated tail filaments

DISTRIBUTION

Plumage Sexes differ	Habitat 🌳🌳🌳	Migration Non-migrant

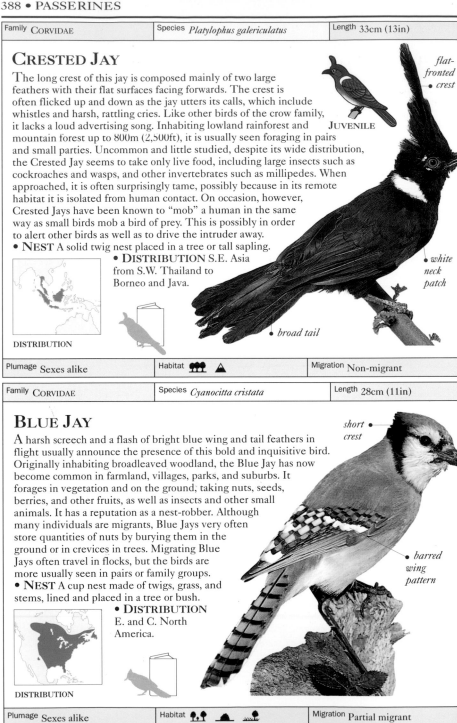

| Family CORVIDAE | Species *Platylophus galericulatus* | Length 33cm (13in) |

CRESTED JAY

The long crest of this jay is composed mainly of two large feathers with their flat surfaces facing forwards. The crest is often flicked up and down as the jay utters its calls, which include whistles and harsh, rattling cries. Like other birds of the crow family, it lacks a loud advertising song. Inhabiting lowland rainforest and mountain forest up to 800m (2,500ft), it is usually seen foraging in pairs and small parties. Uncommon and little studied, despite its wide distribution, the Crested Jay seems to take only live food, including large insects such as cockroaches and wasps, and other invertebrates such as millipedes. When approached, it is often surprisingly tame, possibly because in its remote habitat it is isolated from human contact. On occasion, however, Crested Jays have been known to "mob" a human in the same way as small birds mob a bird of prey. This is possibly in order to alert other birds as well as to drive the intruder away.

• **NEST** A solid twig nest placed in a tree or tall sapling.

• **DISTRIBUTION** S.E. Asia from S.W. Thailand to Borneo and Java.

flat-fronted crest

JUVENILE

white neck patch

broad tail

DISTRIBUTION

| Plumage Sexes alike | Habitat 🌳 ⛰ | Migration Non-migrant |

| Family CORVIDAE | Species *Cyanocitta cristata* | Length 28cm (11in) |

BLUE JAY

A harsh screech and a flash of bright blue wing and tail feathers in flight usually announce the presence of this bold and inquisitive bird. Originally inhabiting broadleaved woodland, the Blue Jay has now become common in farmland, villages, parks, and suburbs. It forages in vegetation and on the ground, taking nuts, seeds, berries, and other fruits, as well as insects and other small animals. It has a reputation as a nest-robber. Although many individuals are migrants, Blue Jays very often store quantities of nuts by burying them in the ground or in crevices in trees. Migrating Blue Jays often travel in flocks, but the birds are more usually seen in pairs or family groups.

• **NEST** A cup nest made of twigs, grass, and stems, lined and placed in a tree or bush.

• **DISTRIBUTION** E. and C. North America.

short crest

barred wing pattern

DISTRIBUTION

| Plumage Sexes alike | Habitat 🌳 🏞 🌿 | Migration Partial migrant |

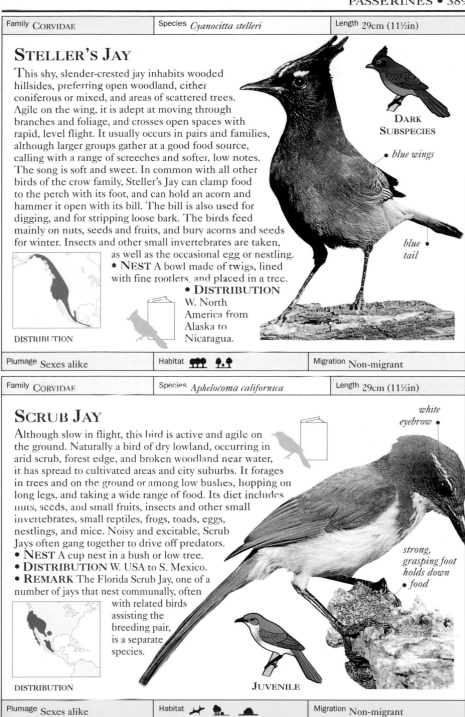

| Family CORVIDAE | Species *Cyanocitta stelleri* | Length 29cm (11½in) |

STELLER'S JAY

This shy, slender-crested jay inhabits wooded hillsides, preferring open woodland, either coniferous or mixed, and areas of scattered trees. Agile on the wing, it is adept at moving through branches and foliage, and crosses open spaces with rapid, level flight. It usually occurs in pairs and families, although larger groups gather at a good food source, calling with a range of screeches and softer, low notes. The song is soft and sweet. In common with all other birds of the crow family, Steller's Jay can clamp food to the perch with its foot, and can hold an acorn and hammer it open with its bill. The bill is also used for digging, and for stripping loose bark. The birds feed mainly on nuts, seeds and fruits, and bury acorns and seeds for winter. Insects and other small invertebrates are taken, as well as the occasional egg or nestling.
• **NEST** A bowl made of twigs, lined with fine rootlets, and placed in a tree.
• **DISTRIBUTION** W. North America from Alaska to Nicaragua.

DARK SUBSPECIES

• *blue wings*

blue tail •

DISTRIBUTION

| Plumage Sexes alike | Habitat | Migration Non-migrant |

| Family CORVIDAE | Species *Aphelocoma californica* | Length 29cm (11½in) |

SCRUB JAY

white eyebrow •

Although slow in flight, this bird is active and agile on the ground. Naturally a bird of dry lowland, occurring in arid scrub, forest edge, and broken woodland near water, it has spread to cultivated areas and city suburbs. It forages in trees and on the ground or among low bushes, hopping on long legs, and taking a wide range of food. Its diet includes nuts, seeds, and small fruits, insects and other small invertebrates, small reptiles, frogs, toads, eggs, nestlings, and mice. Noisy and excitable, Scrub Jays often gang together to drive off predators.
• **NEST** A cup nest in a bush or low tree.
• **DISTRIBUTION** W. USA to S. Mexico.
• **REMARK** The Florida Scrub Jay, one of a number of jays that nest communally, often with related birds assisting the breeding pair, is a separate species.

strong, grasping foot holds down • *food*

DISTRIBUTION

JUVENILE

| Plumage Sexes alike | Habitat | Migration Non-migrant |

Family CORVIDAE	Species *Calocitta colliei*	Length 70cm (28in)

BLACK-THROATED MAGPIE-JAY

With its flamboyant, forward-arching crest and long, tapering tail, this species is exceptionally ornate for a jay. When the bird is excited its crest rises up and extends forward until the tip hangs over the front of the bill. Typically found in open woodland on lower hill slopes and along rivers, it feeds mainly among the trees, taking insects and fruit such as berries. The birds forage in small parties, communicating with a variety of calls and noisily mobbing potential predators. Reports of more than one individual feeding an incubating female suggest that the parties may stay together throughout the year.
• **NEST** A structure made of twigs and lined with rootlets and plant fibres, built in a tree up to 30m (100ft) above the ground.
　　　• **DISTRIBUTION** Pacific region of N.W. Mexico.

DISTRIBUTION

black throat patch

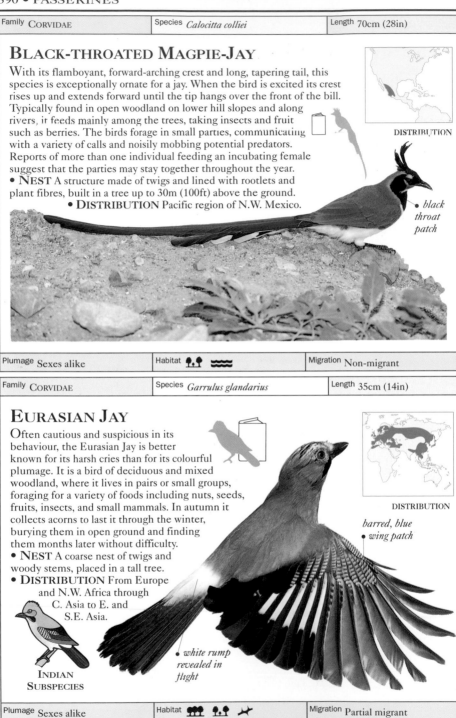

Plumage Sexes alike	Habitat 🌳 〰	Migration Non-migrant

Family CORVIDAE	Species *Garrulus glandarius*	Length 35cm (14in)

EURASIAN JAY

Often cautious and suspicious in its behaviour, the Eurasian Jay is better known for its harsh cries than for its colourful plumage. It is a bird of deciduous and mixed woodland, where it lives in pairs or small groups, foraging for a variety of foods including nuts, seeds, fruits, insects, and small mammals. In autumn it collects acorns to last it through the winter, burying them in open ground and finding them months later without difficulty.
• **NEST** A coarse nest of twigs and woody stems, placed in a tall tree.
• **DISTRIBUTION** From Europe and N.W. Africa through C. Asia to E. and S.E. Asia.

DISTRIBUTION

barred, blue • *wing patch*

white rump revealed in flight

INDIAN SUBSPECIES

Plumage Sexes alike	Habitat 🌳 🌳 ✈	Migration Partial migrant

| Family CORVIDAE | Species *Urocissa erythrorhyncha* | Length 70cm (28in) |

RED-BILLED BLUE MAGPIE

• white crown stripe

The slender, springy, arched tail of the Red-billed Blue Magpie jerks and flicks conspicuously as the bird moves across a forest clearing with typically long, bounding hops. The bird often hunts on the ground, taking centipedes, snails, small mammals, lizards, and even small snakes, but it spends most of the time in the trees of its mountain forest habitat. It forages in small parties for insects, eggs, forest fruits, and even nectar when the trees are in blossom. The Red-billed Blue Magpie moves in level, flapping flight. Like many forest birds it is wary of breaking cover, and a party will cross an open space one at a time in follow-my-leader fashion. In this procedure, each bird is probably testing for danger from a fast-moving predator such as a hawk.

DISTRIBUTION

JUVENILE

• short, strong legs

• glossy blue plumage

• long, arching, graduated tail

• **NEST** A flimsy cup nest of roots, leaves, and twigs, in a tall tree.
• **DISTRIBUTION** From Himalayas east to China and south to Burma and Thailand, in mountain forest at altitudes of up to 2,100m (6,100ft).

| Plumage Sexes alike | Habitat | Migration Non-migrant |

| Family CORVIDAE | Species *Cyanopica cyana* | Length 33cm (13in) |

AZURE-WINGED MAGPIE

• shallow, black cap

This small, graceful, forest magpie has a black cap that can be fluffed up into a crest. The bird raises this crest for display purposes. It is agile on the ground as well as in flight. Aided by fluttering wings, it can hop up treetrunks and other vertical surfaces and even cling upside down beneath branches. Its long tail gives it manoeuvrability in the air, enabling it to weave and dodge between the branches of trees. In the open it usually flies low and level, sometimes swooping, with one bird following another from tree to tree. Azure-winged Magpies are sociable, living in small parties that forage together for insects and other small invertebrates, small fruits, and some seeds. Food items may be hidden and later retrieved. The pairs in each group nest in close proximity, often in adjacent trees.

DISTRIBUTION

• white edges of primary feathers

• long, graduated tail

short, • blue wings

white tail- • tip

• **NEST** A cup nest made of twigs, with a lining of roots, plant fibres, hair, and wool, situated in a tree or bush.
• **DISTRIBUTION** Two separate populations: one in Portugal and S. Spain; the other in E. Asia in Mongolia, China, Korea, and Japan.

| Plumage Sexes alike | Habitat | Migration Non-migrant |

Family CORVIDAE	Species *Pica pica*	Length 48cm (19in)

COMMON MAGPIE

Active and inquisitive, with a swaggering walk and a harsh, chattering call, the Common Magpie originally inhabited scrub or trees with dense foliage, but has now adapted to cultivated and urban areas. Feeding on almost anything it can find, it mainly takes insects and other invertebrates, as well as other small animals, carrion, fruits, and seeds. Its reputation as a nest robber has been greatly exaggerated. Despite its weak flight it can be quite agile in the air, its long tail enabling it to make sudden attacking or evading movements.
• **NEST** A bowl made of twigs and lined with fine rootlets and some mud, roofed with a loose dome of twigs, built in a bush or tree.
• **DISTRIBUTION** N.W. North America, Europe, N.W. Africa, parts of the Middle East, and much of C. and E. Asia.

WING PATTERN

glossy sheen changes from blue to green or purple depending on the light

white shoulder patch

long tail tapers at the tip

DISTRIBUTION

Plumage Sexes alike	Habitat	Migration Non-migrant

Family CORVIDAE	Species *Nucifraga columbiana*	Length 30cm (12in)

CLARK'S NUTCRACKER

The slender, slightly downcurved bill of this species is adapted for probing into pine cones and extracting the seeds. The bird either breaks into the cone on the tree, or pulls the whole cone off and delves into it while holding it down with its foot. It also eats other seeds and fruits when available, as well as robbing nests and probing rotten wood for insects. Pine seeds are the most important food item in its native mountain conifer forests. After collecting seeds in its throat pouch, it carries them to special hoarding sites to ensure a food supply throughout the snow-bound winter. If the seed crop fails the nutcrackers may be forced to make an irruptive migration, appearing in large numbers in lowland forest. Normally each pair lives within its own territory, but also searches outside it for food. The birds communicate with a variety of calls, the commonest being a single, loud note.
• **NEST** A cup nest of twigs, usually at the end of a conifer branch.
• **DISTRIBUTION** W. North America from S. Canada to N. Mexico.

DISTRIBUTION

long, broad wings

Plumage Sexes alike	Habitat	Migration Non-migrant/nomadic

Family CORVIDAE	Species *Pyrrhocorax graculus*	Length 38cm (15in)

ALPINE CHOUGH

The broad wings of the Alpine Chough, with their splayed, finger-like tips, enable it to fly strongly and skilfully in the turbulent mountain winds. Here it soars and glides on air currents and performs aerobatic flights. With its small head, slender bill, and high-pitched, trilling whistle, it is unlike most other members of the crow family. On the ground it walks and runs actively on short legs, probing in rock crevices and open pastures. Although it feeds mainly on insects, snails, and fruit, it will also scavenge on small animal carcases and search for scraps on rubbish tips and picnic sites. The Alpine Chough inhabits high mountains in summer, descending to lowlands in winter. A highly sociable species, it lives in flocks composed mainly of strongly bonded pairs. Flocks roost communally in caves and large crevices, and the pairs often nest in the same sites, though some distance apart.
• **NEST** A mass of sticks and dry roots, located in a rock crevice, on a cave ledge.
• **DISTRIBUTION** Spain and N.W. Africa through S. Europe and Middle East to Asia.

small, slender bill

DISTRIBUTION

long, broad wings

short legs

Plumage Sexes alike	Habitat	Migration Non-migrant

Family CORVIDAE	Species *Corvus monedula*	Length 33cm (13in)

EURASIAN JACKDAW

Sociable, noisy, and confident, this small, bright-eyed crow is a grassland feeder which probes for insects and worms, as well as taking fruit and carrion. It has adapted well to farmland, and also uses buildings as nest sites, forming colonies made up of long-term pairs. The name is derived from its explosive "jack" call.
• **NEST** A lined cup nest made of sticks and stems, placed in a cavity in a tree, cliff, or building.
• **DISTRIBUTION** Eurasia, south to N.W. Africa; northern populations are migratory.

JUVENILE

DISTRIBUTION

grey nape

greyish-black plumage

strong, gripping feet

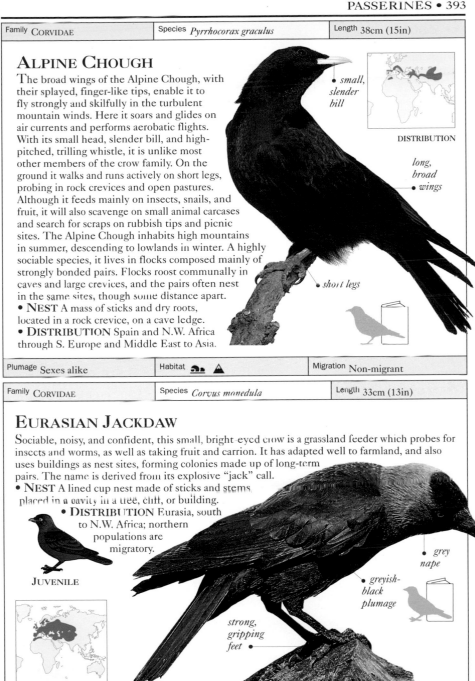

Plumage Sexes alike	Habitat	Migration Partial migrant

Family CORVIDAE	Species *Corvus frugilegus*	Length 47cm (18½in)

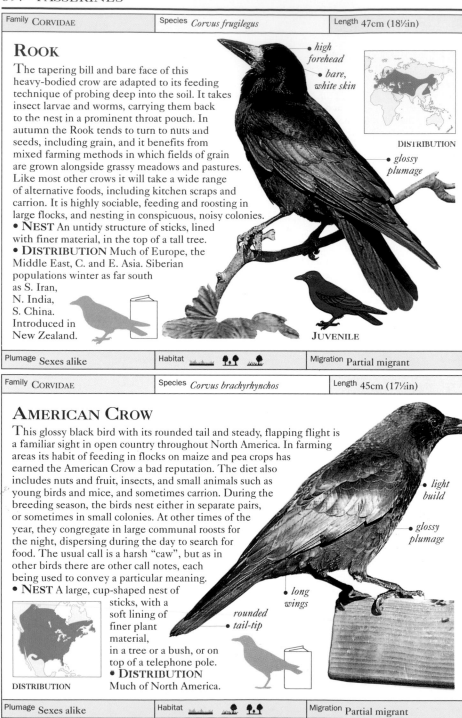

ROOK

The tapering bill and bare face of this heavy-bodied crow are adapted to its feeding technique of probing deep into the soil. It takes insect larvae and worms, carrying them back to the nest in a prominent throat pouch. In autumn the Rook tends to turn to nuts and seeds, including grain, and it benefits from mixed farming methods in which fields of grain are grown alongside grassy meadows and pastures. Like most other crows it will take a wide range of alternative foods, including kitchen scraps and carrion. It is highly sociable, feeding and roosting in large flocks, and nesting in conspicuous, noisy colonies.

• **NEST** An untidy structure of sticks, lined with finer material, in the top of a tall tree.

• **DISTRIBUTION** Much of Europe, the Middle East, C. and E. Asia. Siberian populations winter as far south as S. Iran, N. India, S. China. Introduced in New Zealand.

• *high forehead*
• *bare, white skin*

DISTRIBUTION

• *glossy plumage*

JUVENILE

Plumage Sexes alike	Habitat	Migration Partial migrant

Family CORVIDAE	Species *Corvus brachyrhynchos*	Length 45cm (17½in)

AMERICAN CROW

This glossy black bird with its rounded tail and steady, flapping flight is a familiar sight in open country throughout North America. In farming areas its habit of feeding in flocks on maize and pea crops has earned the American Crow a bad reputation. The diet also includes nuts and fruit, insects, and small animals such as young birds and mice, and sometimes carrion. During the breeding season, the birds nest either in separate pairs, or sometimes in small colonies. At other times of the year, they congregate in large communal roosts for the night, dispersing during the day to search for food. The usual call is a harsh "caw", but as in other birds there are other call notes, each being used to convey a particular meaning.

• **NEST** A large, cup-shaped nest of sticks, with a soft lining of finer plant material, in a tree or a bush, or on top of a telephone pole.

• **DISTRIBUTION** Much of North America.

• *light build*

• *glossy plumage*

• *long wings*

rounded tail-tip

DISTRIBUTION

Plumage Sexes alike	Habitat	Migration Partial migrant

Family CORVIDAE	Species *Corvus corone*	Length 47cm (18½in)

CARRION CROW

This opportunistic species flourishes in a wide variety of habitats, from seashores and forests to towns and refuse tips. It feeds on a huge range of plant and animal foods, including kitchen scraps, carrion, and sometimes shellfish which it drops on to stones to break them. Carrion Crows roost communally outside the breeding season.
• **NEST** A bulky nest of twigs, lined with finer material, in the top of a tree.
• **DISTRIBUTION** Eurasia, the Middle East, and the Nile Valley.
• **REMARK** Subspecies include both "hooded" and black forms.

HOODED CROW

heavy bill •

• *stout build*

• *broad, powerful wings*

DISTRIBUTION

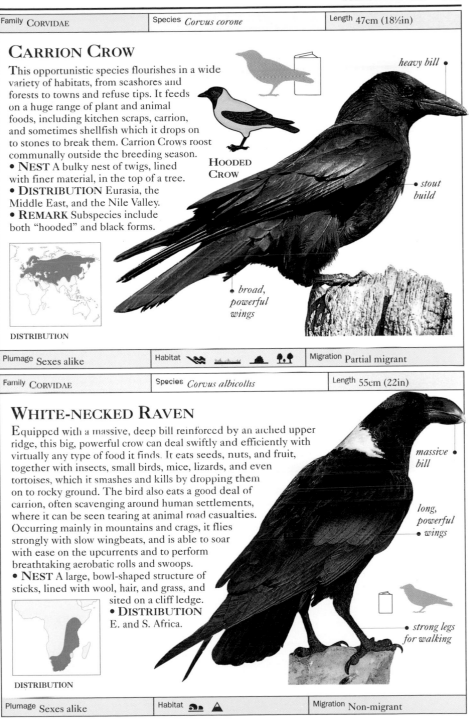

Plumage Sexes alike	Habitat	Migration Partial migrant

Family CORVIDAE	Species *Corvus albicollis*	Length 55cm (22in)

WHITE-NECKED RAVEN

Equipped with a massive, deep bill reinforced by an arched upper ridge, this big, powerful crow can deal swiftly and efficiently with virtually any type of food it finds. It eats seeds, nuts, and fruit, together with insects, small birds, mice, lizards, and even tortoises, which it smashes and kills by dropping them on to rocky ground. The bird also eats a good deal of carrion, often scavenging around human settlements, where it can be seen tearing at animal road casualties. Occurring mainly in mountains and crags, it flies strongly with slow wingbeats, and is able to soar with ease on the upcurrents and to perform breathtaking aerobatic rolls and swoops.
• **NEST** A large, bowl-shaped structure of sticks, lined with wool, hair, and grass, and sited on a cliff ledge.
• **DISTRIBUTION** E. and S. Africa.

massive bill •

long, powerful wings •

• *strong legs for walking*

DISTRIBUTION

Plumage Sexes alike	Habitat	Migration Non-migrant

GLOSSARY

A NUMBER OF the words used in this book may be unfamiliar to some readers. This glossary explains specialist terms both clearly and concisely. Most words defined in the glossary are the names of "types" of birds. Some of these types are bird families, and the scientific name of the family is given in brackets, with an equals sign, e.g. "(= family Anatidae)". Other types are only "parts" of families, and in these cases the family is mentioned either in English in the course of the definition, in bold type, e.g. "a type of falcon", or in brackets at the end, e.g. "(part of family Laridae)". All words that appear in bold type are defined elsewhere in the glossary.

• ACCENTOR
A type of sparrow-like bird with a thin, fine-pointed bill (= family Prunellidae).

• ADAPTATION
Any aspect of a bird's structure or behaviour that has evolved to suit its present environment.

• ADVERTISEMENT
Display behaviour by which a bird signals its presence to other birds.

• ALBATROSS
A type of ocean-going seabird that glides for great distances on long, narrow wings, nesting on islands (= family Diomedeidae).

• ANHINGA
Name for the North American species of darter; alternatively used as a name for all three darter species in the world.

• ANTBIRD
A type of rainforest passerine that feeds on the insects and other invertebrates that become easy to catch when fleeing from army ants (= family Formicariidae).

• AUK
A type of penguin -like seabird that is able to fly and typically hunts under water, propelling itself with its wings rather than its feet (= family Alcidae).

• BABBLER
A type of short-winged, strong-footed passerine of forest or scrub, often occurring in small, noisy groups (= family Timaliidae).

• BARBET
A type of small, sturdy, perching non-passerine with a stout bill, living in trees or bushes (= family Megalaimidae).

• BARN OWL
A type of long-legged owl in which the facial discs form a heart shape (= family Tytonidae).

• BELLBIRD
A type of forest-dwelling bird with loud, bell-like calls; refers to a number of species in the cotinga and honeyeater families.

• BIRD OF PARADISE
A type of forest-dwelling passerine in which the male has strikingly ornate and sometimes extraordinary display plumage (= family Paradisaeidae).

• BIRD OF PREY
A hunting bird; most commonly refers to the day-flying raptors, but sometimes refers to all birds hunting land prey of any size larger than insects, thus including owls, skuas, and shrikes. This phrase generally tends not to be used to refer to insect-eating and fish-eating birds.

• BLACKBIRD
A type of medium-sized passerine which is either all black or mostly black; refers to a few species of Old World thrushes and several New World blackbirds.

• BOWERBIRD
A type of forest-dwelling passerine in which males build elaborate twig "bowers" to which they attract females for mating (= family Ptilonorhynchidae).

• BROADBILL
A type of forest-dwelling passerine with a sturdy body, a wide mouth, and a wide bill (= family Eurylaimidae).

• BULBUL
A type of passerine that feeds mainly on fruit, and has musical calls (= family Pycnonotidae).

• BUNTING
A type of sparrow-like bird with a short, sturdy bill for cracking open husks to feed on seeds (part of family Emberizidae).

• BUSTARD
A type of open-country bird of up to goose size with long, strong legs and small feet, and a long neck (= family Otididae).

• BUTCHERBIRD
A type of passerine bird of trees and shrubs that hunts prey with a strong, hooked bill and either impales it on thorns or wedges it between twigs to feed (= family Cracticidae). Previously also referred to some typical shrikes.

• BUTTON-QUAIL
A type of ground bird the size and shape of a quail but with a slender bill (= family Turnicidae).

• BUZZARD
A type of broad-winged bird of prey that hunts animals and scavenges for carrion (part of family Accipitridae).

• CALL
A short sound used by a bird purely to convey information, as distinct from song.

• CARACARA
A type of falcon that feeds on helpless or slow-moving prey, or scavenges for carrion.

• CARDINAL
A type of sparrow-like bird, often brightly coloured, with a heavy, seed-eating type of bill (part of family Emberizidae).

• CARRION
Carcases or parts of dead animals eaten by birds (or other carrion-eaters) that have not killed them.

• CASQUE
A hard, horn-like feature that projects upwards from the head or bill of a bird.

• CATBIRD
This name is given to birds of various different families that utter sounds like the miaow of a

cat, e.g. Grey Catbird (part of family Mimidae), Green Catbird (part of family Ptilonorhynchidae).

• **CHANTING-GOSHAWK**
A slenderly built **bird of prey** of open country, not particularly resembling a **goshawk**.

• **CHAT**
(i) A type of small **thrush** that typically watches from a low perch or from the ground before swooping on small invertebrates (part of family Turdidae). (ii) A species of American **warbler** (part of family Parulidae).

• **CLAW**
The hard and usually curved tip of a bird's toe.

• **CLUTCH**
The total quantity of eggs incubated by one parent or pair of birds at a time.

• **COCKATOO**
A large and usually crested type of Australasian **parrot**.

• **COLONY**
A group of pairs of birds that nest in close proximity to each other, or the place in which this occurs.

• **COLOUR PHASE**
A type of plumage colour that distinguishes a bird from others of the same **species**, is not related to sex, age, or **subspecies**, and is not a genetic abnormality (**mutation**).

• **COLY**
Another name for a **mousebird**.

• **CONDOR**
A type of **New World vulture**.

• **CONURE**
A popular name sometimes used to refer to some species of South American **parrot**.

• **CONTOUR FEATHER**
A small feather that provides protective cover to the body or wing of a bird.

• **CORMORANT**
A type of slenderly built, web-footed **waterbird** that swims and chases fish under water (= family Phalacrocoracidae).

• **COTINGA**
A type of rainforest passerine, often with display ornaments including **wattles**, bare skin patches, and vividly-coloured or unusually-shaped feathers (= family Cotingidae).

• **COUCAL**
A type of slim-built, non-parasitic **cuckoo** with weak flight, that **skulks** in vegetation and runs on the ground.

• **COURSER**
A type of fast-running **shorebird** with long legs and small feet, living in dry, open landscapes (part of family Glareolidae).

• **COVERTS**
Contour feathers of the wings and around the tail, some overlapping the bases of larger **flight feathers**.

• **COVEY**
A small group of **gamebirds**.

• **CRAKE**
A type of small **rail**, usually living in swamp or grassland vegetation.

• **CRANE**
A type of tall non-passerine with long neck and legs, and a sharp but relatively short bill, occurring in open landscapes, often by water (= family Gruidae).

• **CREEPER**
A type of passerine that hunts insects by running up the trunks and branches of trees (= families Certhiidae, Rhabdornithidae, Climacteridae).

• **CROW**
A type of large passerine, typically black, that often feeds on the ground; alternatively refers to all the birds of the crow family (part or whole of family Corvidae).

• **CUCKOO**
A type of slenderly built, insect-eating non-passerine, living in trees or bushes, or on the ground; many species of cuckoo are nest parasites (= family Cuculidae).

• **CURASSOW**
A type of large, long-tailed, long-legged forest bird resembling a **gamebird**, often perching in trees (part of family Cracidae).

• **CURRAWONG**
A type of large-billed, **crow**-like passerine (part of family Cracticidae).

• **DABBLING DUCK**
A type of **duck** that feeds by filtering food particles from the water in its bill.

• **DARTER**
A type of **waterbird** with a long, snake-like neck, a thin, dagger-like bill, and webbed feet, that swims underwater to catch fish (= family Anhingidae).

• **DISPLAY**
Conspicuous behaviour by which a bird indicates feelings, such as sexual or aggressive excitement.

• **DISTRIBUTION**
The total area in which a bird is regularly seen. In this book,

distribution maps include areas where the bird has been introduced by humans.

• **DIVER**
A type of **waterbird** with a streamlined body and with the feet positioned well back on the body for underwater pursuit of prey (= family Gaviidae).

• **DIVING DUCK**
A type of **duck** that finds food by swimming underwater, propelling itself with webbed feet.

• **DIVING-PETREL**
A type of seabird like a **petrel** that feeds on **plankton** by diving, often plunging through waves (= family Pelecanoididae).

• **DOMESTICATED**
A bird bred in captive or farm conditions to produce a type that is useful, decorative, or otherwise desirable to humans.

• **DOVE**
Alternative name for some (often smaller) species of **pigeon**.

• **DOWN**
A loose-textured feather structure, occurring either as whole feathers or as parts of feathers, that helps to insulate the body and retain heat.

• **DRONGO**
A type of strong-billed, alert and agile passerine, usually black, that hunts insects from a perch (= family Dicruridae).

• **DUCK**
A type of **waterfowl** that spends most of its time on water rather than on land and typically has a broad, flattened bill for extracting food from water or mud.

• **EAGLE**
A type of large, strong **bird of prey** that actively hunts other animals (part of family Accipitridae).

• **ECLIPSE PLUMAGE**
A camouflaged plumage briefly assumed by a male after moulting out of its vivid breeding plumage.

• **EGRET**
A slenderly built type of **heron** that is often pure white and often has fine, loose-textured display plumes when breeding.

• **EURASIA**
The landmass comprising the continents of Europe and Asia, and adjacent islands.

• **EYESTRIPE**
A distinctly-coloured stripe that passes across the side of the head including the area of the eye.

• **EYE-RING**
A narrow and distinctively coloured ring, either of feathers or bare skin, around the eye.

• **FACIAL DISCS**
The two prominent, roughly semicircular shapes made by the feathers on either side of the eyes of most **owl** species.

• **FAIRY-WREN**
A type of small passerine of Australasia with a long tail that is usually carried upright (= family Maluridae).

• **FALCON**
A stoutly built **bird of prey** with tapering wings and a short, strongly-curved bill (= family Falconidae).

• **FANTAIL**
A type of flycatcher of forest or scrub, often hunting insects in foliage, fanning and raising its tail (part of family Monarchidae).

• **FINCH**
A type of sparrow-like bird with a short, stout bill used for cracking seeds (= family Fringillidae); alternatively refers to similar birds of other families, e.g. **waxbills**.

• **FLAMINGO**
A type of wading bird of saline waters with very long legs, wings, and neck, and a short, broad, angled bill used for filtering fine food particles (= family Phoenicopteridae).

• **FLIGHT FEATHERS**
Large, long feathers of wings and tail, used in flight.

• **FLOCK**
A group of birds remaining together for social reasons.

• **FLYCATCHER**
A type of passerine that typically catches aerial prey by flying out from a perch, to which it then returns (= families Monarchidae, Muscicapidae, and Tyrannidae).

• **FORAGE**
To search for food of any kind by hunting over an area.

• **FORM**
A variant of a **species**. This word can refer to (i) a type clearly identifiable as a **subspecies**; (ii) a broader regional type comprising two or more subspecies; or (iii) a **colour phase**.

• **FRANCOLIN**
A type of **gamebird** resembling a **partridge**, usually feeding on the ground and living in open country (part of family Phasianidae).

• **FROGMOUTH**
A type of nocturnal, perching non-passerine with a short, wide bill and huge gape, swooping down to the ground to snatch prey (= family Podargidae).

• **FRUIT-DOVE**
Another name for a **fruit-pigeon**.

• **FRUIT-PIGEON**
A type of **pigeon** living in trees or shrubs and feeding mainly on fruit taken from the branches.

• **FRUITCROW**
A type of crow-like, fruit-eating **cotinga** showing patches of bright plumage colour.

• **GAMEBIRD**
Any bird of the **pheasant** family; these are often hunted for food or sport (= family Phasianidae).

• **GENUS**
A group of closely related **species** that have all evolved from the same ancestor (plural is "genera").

• **GLEANING**
Randomly searching for and picking up food items.

• **GLOSSY STARLING**
A type of **starling** with shiny and often brightly coloured feathers.

• **GNATCATCHER**
A type of small, slender passerine with a thin bill and long tail, that hunts insects in trees and bushes (= family Polioptilidae).

• **GODWIT**
A type of **shorebird** with long, slim legs and neck, and a long, thin bill, which may be either straight or slightly upcurved (part of family Scolopacidae).

• **GOOSE**
A type of **waterfowl** with relatively long legs and a short, strong bill, adapted for walking, grazing, and digging for roots.

• **GOSHAWK**
A type of large, forest-dwelling **hawk** with broad, rounded wings and a long tail.

• **GRACKLE**
A type of slender-bodied, glossy-plumaged **New World blackbird** with a slim, tapering bill and sometimes a long tail. This word has been used to refer to certain species of **myna** and **starling**.

• **GRASSLAND**
Extensive, open areas where the vegetation is dominated by short or tall grasses.

• **GREBE**
A type of thin-necked, fine-billed **waterbird**, almost tailless, that

pursues underwater prey, propelled by feet with lobed toes (= family Podicipedidae).

• **GREEN-PIGEON**
A type of fruit-eating **pigeon** with green plumage for camouflage, living among trees and shrubs.

• **GREGARIOUS**
Preferring to live in social groups.

• **GROSBEAK**
A sparrow-like bird with a very stout, seed-cracking bill. Refers to some birds in the **finch** family (Fringillidae) and some **cardinals** (part of family Emberizidae).

• **GROUSE**
A type of stout, dense-feathered, mainly ground-living **gamebird**.

• **GUAN**
A type of tree-living bird that resembles a **gamebird**, with long, strong legs and often with bare **wattles** (part of Cracidae).

• **GUINEAFOWL**
A type of compactly built **gamebird** with a short tail, living mainly on dry, open ground.

• **GULL**
A type of web-footed **waterbird**, often coastal, with a strong bill; scavenging or partly predatory (part of family Laridae).

• **HABITAT**
The part of the environment in which a **species** normally occurs.

• **HARRIER**
A type of **bird of prey** with long, narrow wings used in low, gliding flight, and with long legs and tail (part of family Accipitridae).

• **HAWK**
A type of **bird of prey** that actively hunts live animals (part of family Accipitridae).

• **HAWK-OWL**
A type of **owl** with a hawk-like shape; alternatively a type of Australasian **owl** with small **facial discs** and a relatively prominent bill (parts of family Strigidae).

• **HELPER**
A bird other than the parents that assists in some stages of nesting.

• **HEMIPODE**
An old name for a **button-quail**, meaning "half-foot" in reference to the absence of a hind toe (= family Turnicidae).

• **HERMIT**
A type of **hummingbird** living solitarily among forest vegetation.

• **HERON**
A type of wading bird with long legs, long neck, broad wings, and

a dagger bill, usually wading to catch fish (= family Ardeidae).

• **HONEYCREEPER**
(i) A type of **tanager** with a slender bill for extracting nectar from flowers (part of family Thraupidae); (ii) a type of finch-like bird belonging to an island group with varied bill-shapes (= family Drepaninidae).

• **HONEYEATER**
A type of small to moderate-sized passerine with a brush-tipped tongue, feeding mostly on nectar from flowers, sometimes also on insects (= family Meliphagidae).

• **HONEYGUIDE**
A type of small, perching non-passerine that feeds by catching insects in the foliage and eating wax from bees' nests (= family Indicatoridae).

• **HOOD**
An area of a single plumage colour extending over the head.

• **HORNBILL**
A type of non-passerine with long wings and tail and a long, curved bill that is usually surmounted by a **casque**. Some hornbills are tree-dwellers (= family Bucerotidae); others feed only on the ground (= family Bucorvidae).

• **HUMMINGBIRD**
A type of tiny, often brightly coloured non-passerine with a thin bill used for feeding on flower nectar, often while hovering (= family Trochilidae).

• **IBIS**
A type of goose-sized wading bird with long legs and neck and a long, downcurved bill (part of family Threskiornithidae).

• **IMPERIAL PIGEON**
A large and often dull-coloured type of **fruit-pigeon**.

• **INCUBATE**
To provide constant warmth for an egg, allowing the embryo inside it to develop.

• **INTRODUCED**
Describes a bird species that has been brought by humans to an area where it would not naturally occur, and is now established.

• **INVERTEBRATE**
A type of small animal having no backbone, such as a worm, insect, spider, snail, shrimp, or crab.

• **IRIDESCENT**
A term describing the glittering appearance of a feather that has a structure that causes it to reflect

different colours according to the direction of the light.

• **JACAMAR**
A type of slender, long-tailed, perching non-passerine with a long, thin bill, that flies out from a perch after insects (= family Galbulidae).

• **JACANA**
A type of small **waterbird** with long legs, toes and claws, that walks on floating waterplants (= family Jacanidae).

• **JAY**
A type of perching passerine of the **crow** family, usually noisy and brightly coloured and often sociable in behaviour.

• **JUVENILE**
A young bird that is not yet mature enough to breed, often having a plumage differing in colour and pattern from adults.

• **KESTREL**
A type of sturdily built **falcon** that usually hovers when hunting and takes small, weak prey.

• **KINGBIRD**
A type of **tyrant flycatcher**, often aggressive enough to harry predators.

• **KINGFISHER**
A type of large-headed, dagger-billed, perching non-passerine that plunge-dives into water in pursuit of insects or fish, some species taking prey from the ground (= family Alcedinidae).

• **KITE**
A type of lightly built **bird of prey** with long wings and often forked tail, and with agile flight, that typically takes weak prey or scavenges for **carrion** (part of family Accipitridae).

• **KOOKABURRA**
A type of large **kingfisher** with noisy calls and a heavy, blunt bill, often living well away from water.

• **LARK**
A type of inconspicuous, ground-living passerine, the male usually advertising itself with prolonged aerial songflights (= family Alaudidae).

• **LAUGHING-THRUSH**
A type of **babbler** that utters laughing calls, often in chorus.

• **LEK**
A communal display-ground used by certain bird species. A number of males display simultaneously and females visit the site in order to mate with a male.

• **LOON**
The North American and Scandinavian name for a **diver**.

• **LORIKEET**
A type of Australasian **parrot** feeding on nectar and pollen.

• **LORY**
A heavily built type of **lorikeet**.

• **LOVEBIRD**
A type of small, slender-billed, short-tailed African **parrot**, usually seen in pairs that keep in close contact with one another.

• **MACAW**
A type of South or Central American **parrot** with a long tail and heavy bill, the best-known species being distinctively large.

• **MALLEE**
Low-growing eucaluptus woodland of semi-arid areas, in which trees are multi-trunked.

• **MANAKIN**
A type of small, brightly coloured, fruit-eating passerine of forest and scrub (= family Pipridae).

• **MANGROVE SWAMP**
A forest habitat in tropical estuaries and lagoons, in which the trees are supported on roots raised above the mud.

• **MARTIN**
Alternative name for some species of **swallow**.

• **MEGAPODE**
A type of chicken-sized ground-bird that builds a mound in which its eggs are incubated, or digs a hole in warm ground for this purpose (= family Megapodiidae).

• **MIGRANT**
A bird that makes regular seasonal movements between breeding and non-breeding areas.

• **MIMICRY**
The ability of a bird to imitate sounds it hears, such as the songs and calls of other bird species, or occasionally other noises.

• **MINER**
A type of moderate-sized, sociable **honeyeater**.

• **MOBBING**
Noisy calling and mock attacks by a group of small birds against a predator, making the presence of the predator known to other small birds in the area.

• **MONARCH FLYCATCHER**
A type of **flycatcher**, often with bright colours, occurring in Africa, Asia, or Australasia, often in the tropics (= family Monarchidae).

• **MOTMOT**
A type of tropical forest non-passerine with a long, drooping tail and a long, strong bill, that watches from a perch to swoop on small prey (= family Momotidae).

• **MOUSEBIRD**
A type of small, plump, mouse-coloured non-passerine with a long tail, mainly eating leaves and buds (= family Coliidae).

• **MUDFLATS**
Level areas of mud created by tidal movements on coasts, in bays, and bordering large rivers.

• **MYNA**
A type of **starling** with a heavy build and a stout bill.

• **NECTAR**
A sugar solution found in small amounts inside flowers.

• **NESTLING**
A very young bird that needs to remain in a nest and to be tended by adults.

• **NEW WORLD BLACKBIRD**
Refers to the varied passerine family to which the American blackbirds belong; the family is also sometimes known as the **troupials** and sometimes as the icterids (= family Icteridae).

• **NEW WORLD VULTURE**
A type of large, bare-headed scavenging bird of the Americas (= family Cathartidae).

• **NIGHTHAWK**
An American type of **nightjar** often flying in daylight. Like other nightjars, it resembles a **hawk** or **falcon** in outline.

• **NIGHTJAR**
A type of non-passerine, usually night-flying, with long wings and tail and a very wide mouth and bill, feeding on insects caught in flight (= family Caprimulgidae).

• **NODDY**
A type of dark sea **tern** with a pale forehead that paired birds show to one another in mutual nodding displays at the nest.

• **NOMADIC**
Having a tendency to wander unpredictably.

• **NON-PASSERINE**
A bird species other than those that consitute the passerine order of mainly perching songbirds (*see also p. 38*).

• **NUNBIRD**
A type of dark, sluggish non-passerine living in forests, that

perches and flies out after insects (part of family Galbulidae).

• **NUTHATCH**
A type of strong-footed, small passerine with a short, strong bill that searches treetrunks and branches for food and hammers open nuts (= family Sittidae).

• **OLD WORLD FLYCATCHER**
A small **flycatcher** of Eurasia or Africa (= family Muscicapidae).

• **OPEN FOREST**
Forest in which trees and undergrowth are well-spread, with spaces between allowing visibility and movement.

• **ORIOLE**
A type of agile, slender-billed passerine of the higher foliage of trees and scrub, feeding on fruit and insects. Refers both to Old World orioles (= family Oriolidae) and New World orioles (part of family Icteridae).

• **OROPENDOLA**
A type of large passerine of tropical forests with a strong, tapering bill, that weaves a long, bag-shaped nest and suspends it from branches of tall trees in colonies (part of family Icteridae).

• **OVENBIRD**
A bird that makes a domed nest with a side entrance resembling an old-fashioned bread oven. Only one species is known as the Ovenbird (part of family Parulidae). Seven species make oven-like mud nests, and the family to which they belong is known as the ovenbird family (= Furnariidae), although these seven species are themselves known as horneros, not ovenbirds.

• **OWL**
A type of predatory bird, usually flying at night, with large eyes set in **facial discs**, strong, grasping feet and claws, and usually silent flight (= families Tytonidae and Strigidae).

• **OWLET-NIGHTJAR**
A type of soft-plumaged non-passerine with a large head, large eyes, and a small but very broad bill, swooping on prey from a perch (= family Aegothelidae).

• **PARADISE-FLYCATCHER**
A type of **monarch flycatcher** with a very long, slender tail.

• **PARAKEET**
Alternative name for a small, long-tailed **parrot**.

• **PARDALOTE**
A type of small, stubby-billed passerine that hunts insects in tree foliage (part of Dicaeidae).

• **PARROT**
A type of non-passerine bird with strong feet for grasping and holding, and with a strong, short, deep bill with a hooked tip, that can manipulate and split open food items (= family Psittacidae).

• **PARROTBILL**
A type of small passerine with a short, stout bill for extracting insects from reed or bamboo stems (= family Panuridae).

• **PARROTLET**
A type of very small, short-tailed **parrot** of South American forests.

• **PARTRIDGE**
A type of stoutly built, ground-dwelling **gamebird** with a short tail and rounded wings.

• **PARTY**
A small group of individual birds.

• **PASSERINE**
A bird belonging to the passerine order of usually perching songbirds (*see also p. 244*).

• **PELICAN**
A type of heavily built **waterbird** with a long, narrow bill and an expandable skin pouch hanging from the bill and throat (= family Pelecanidae).

• **PENGUIN**
A type of flightless seabird with short legs set well back on the body, hunting underwater by swimming with narrow, flipper-like wings, and walking upright on land (= family Spheniscidae).

• **PEPPERSHRIKE**
A type of heavily built **vireo** with a stout, hook-tipped bill.

• **PERCHING BIRD**
A bird with feet adapted for grasping the more level twigs and branches in order to stand or rest, usually living mainly in trees or shrubs. A perching bird is not necessarily a **passerine**.

• **PETREL**
A type of oceanic seabird with nostrils in the form of tubes lying along the top of the bill, with narrow wings and fast flight, usually taking small creatures from or just under the sea surface (part of family Procellariidae).

• **PEWEE**
A type of small, drab-looking **tyrant flycatcher** named after the sound of its usual call note.

• **PHASE**
Another word for **colour phase**.

• **PHOEBE**
A type of **tyrant flycatcher**
named after its "fee-bee" call.

• **PICULET**
A type of tiny **woodpecker**.

• **PIGEON**
A type of non-passerine with
thick, soft plumage, a small,
rounded head, fleshy nostrils, and
cooing calls. Some are perching
birds and others are ground birds,
usually walking with rapid steps
(= family Columbidae).

• **PILEATED**
Refers to a bird in which the
feathers of the whole top of the
head form a crest.

• **PIPIT**
A type of small, inconspicuously
coloured, mainly ground-living
passerine with a slender, insect-
eating bill, usually walking and
running but not hopping (part of
family Motacillidae).

• **PITTA**
A type of forest-floor passerine
with a large head, round body,
very short tail, and long legs
(= family Pittidae).

• **PLANKTON**
A varied community of small
animals and plants swimming or
suspended in seawater or lakes.

• **PLOVER**
A type of **shorebird** with a
rounded head and relatively short
bill. Plovers typically feed in open
places by making short runs and
snatching up small prey that is
visible on the ground surface
(= family Charadriidae).

• **PRATINCOLE**
A type of **shorebird** with a short,
broad bill, large eyes, and often a
forked tail, that catches insects in
flight (part of family Glareolidae).

• **PREENING**
Actions by which a bird grooms its
plumage and maintains it in good
condition by use of bill and claws.

• **PRIMARY FEATHERS**
Long flight feathers on the outer
half of the wing.

• **PUFFBIRD**
A type of stout, loose-plumaged,
perching non-passerine with a
short, stout bill, that flies out from
a perch to seize prey in nearby
vegetation (part of Bucconidae).

• **QUAIL**
A type of small, plump, ground-
living **gamebird** with a short tail.

• **RACE**
Alternative word for **subspecies**.

• **RACQUET**
The expanded and usually
rounded tip of a long feather.

• **RAIL**
A type of slender, long-legged
non-passerine of low vegetation,
marsh, and waterside (= family
Rallidae).

• **RAINFOREST**
Evergreen tropical forest that
depends on constant rainfall all
through the year.

• **RANGE**
Alternative word for **distribution**.

• **RAPTOR**
Alternative word for **bird of prey**.

• **RATITE**
Typically a type of large,
flightless, running bird such as an
Ostrich, lacking the projecting
keel of the breastbone found in all
other birds. The group also
includes **tinamous**.

• **REDSTART**
A type of **chat** with a rufous tail
and rump (part of family
Turdidae); also refers to certain
species of American **warbler** (part
of family Parulidae).

• **RESIDENT**
A bird that normally spends all of
its life within a limited area.

• **ROBIN**
Name often given to a number of
passerine species, mostly small;
most robins resemble a **chat**, and
have a conspicuously orange, red,
or pink breast (part of families
Turdidae and Eopsaltriidae).

• **ROLLER**
A type of stout, big-headed, wide-
billed non-passerine with long
wings, that typically watches from
a perch and swoops to catch prey
on the ground. The name
describes its acrobatic display
flight (= family Coraciidae).

• **ROOST**
(i) To rest or sleep. (ii) A place
where birds do this. (iii) A site
where many birds roost. Day-
flying birds roost by night,
nocturnal birds by day.

• **RUFOUS**
Being of a reddish colour.

• **RUMP**
The lower part of the back of a
bird, above the tail and under the
wingtips when these are closed.

• **SALTMARSH**
Level areas of coastal marsh
where the water is salty.

• **SANDGROUSE**
A type of short-billed, long-
winged non-passerine with
feathered legs that lives on the
ground in dry, open landscapes
and looks like a **gamebird**
(= family Pteroclididae).

• **SANDPIPER**
A type of slender **shorebird**,
usually with long legs, wings,
neck, and bill (part of family
Scolopacidae).

• **SAPSUCKER**
A type of **woodpecker** that feeds
extensively by drinking sweet sap
oozing from rows of holes that it
makes in treetrunks.

• **SCALY PATTERN**
A plumage pattern produced by
the overlapping effect of rounded
feathers that have distinct edges,
either dark or light.

• **SCRAPE**
A nest hollow on the ground
which a bird makes by pressing
its body to the ground, rotating its
body, and kicking backwards with
its feet while doing so.

• **SCREAMER**
A type of large South American
waterbird with big and long-toed
but unwebbed feet, a small,
curved bill, and loud, far-carrying
calls (= family Anhimidae).

• **SCRUB**
A type of vegetation, found over
large or small areas, made up of
shrubs or low trees or a mixture of
the two, often thickly grown, and
frequently with thorns.

• **SECONDARY FEATHERS**
Long flight feathers situated on
the inner wing.

• **SECONDARY FOREST**
Forest that has recently regrown
after the original forest has been
cleared. It is usually less tall and
more uniform in height, thus
offering a different selection of
bird habitats from those in the
original (primary) forest.

• **SEED-EATER**
A type of bird that relies mainly
on seed for its diet and usually
has a short, stout bill adapted for
cracking and removing the husk,
so as to eat the seed inside.

• **SHELDUCK**
A type of long-legged **duck** that
frequently walks on land and
feeds typically by dabbling on the
surface of mudflats or in shallow
water. It is sometimes more like a
goose in its general behaviour.

• **SHOREBIRD**
A type of non-passerine that often walks or runs on the ground, typically with long legs, wings, and neck, and usually lives at the edge of water. Includes **plovers**, **sandpipers**, and similar birds.

• **SHRIKE**
A type of small, fierce passerine with a largish head and short, stout, hook-tipped bill that hunts small animals (= family Laniidae).

• **SKULKING**
Tending to choose to hide in vegetation or other cover whenever the opportunity arises.

• **SNAKEBIRD**
Alternative word for **darter**.

• **SNIPE**
A type of **shorebird** of marshy places with a very long, slender bill for probing deeply for food in mud or soft ground.

• **SOLITARY**
Usually remaining as an isolated individual or pair, rather than joining other birds of its species.

• **SONG**
A usually elaborate sound that a bird utters for the purpose of advertising itself or in display.

• **SONGBIRDS**
Used by many writers to refer to passerines.

• **SPANGLED**
Refers to birds whose plumage is scattered over with conspicuous light marks, usually made up of pale feather tips.

• **SPARROW**
A type of small, dull-coloured passerine with a short, blunt bill for cracking seeds (= family Passeridae, and part of family Emberizidae).

• **SPARROWHAWK**
A type of small **hawk** with short, rounded wings, long tail, and long claws, adapted for hunting and eating small birds.

• **SPECIES**
A group of individuals that are related through a common origin and are capable of freely interbreeding and perpetuating the identity of the group.

• **SPINETAIL**
A type of small passerine with stiff, spiny tips to the shafts of the tail-feathers, that perches; in contrast with the **treecreepers**, spinetails do not use their tails as a support for climbing (part of family Furnariidae).

• **SPOONBILL**
A type of large wading bird of shallow waters with long legs and a long neck, and a long bill whose tip is broad, flat, and rounded, for filtering food from the water (part of family Threskiornithidae).

• **STARLING**
A type of slender passerine, usually with a sharp, tapering bill for eating insects and fruit (= family Sturnidae).

• **STORK**
A type of large bird with long legs and neck and a long, tapering bill. Storks walk on land and wade in shallow water in rivers, lakes, and marshes (= family Ciconiidae).

• **STORM-PETREL**
A type of small **petrel** with low, fluttering flight (= family Hydrobatidae).

• **SUBSPECIES**
A geographical subdivision of a **species** in which all birds show certain features that distinguish them from other subspecies.

• **SUNBIRD**
A type of passerine, usually small and brightly coloured, that perches to feed on nectar from flowers, taken with a very slender bill and fine, tubular tongue (= family Nectariniidae).

• **SWALLOW**
A type of small passerine with a short, broad bill and narrow wings, and usually with a forked tail, that sits on a perch when resting and feeds by pursuing insects in the air (= family Hirundinidae).

• **SWAN**
A type of large, mainly swimming **waterfowl** with a long body, short legs, and a long, slender neck for reaching underwater to pull up waterplants for food.

• **SWIFT**
A type of aerial non-passerine with long, narrow wings and with a short and very wide bill, that feeds by catching insects in the air. Swifts have small feet and can only cling to surfaces rather than perching (= family Apodidae).

• **TAME**
Unafraid of human beings.

• **TANAGER**
A type of passerine, often brightly coloured, of trees and bushes, mostly in the tropics. Most have a seed-cracking type of bill, but use it mainly to feed on fruits (part of family Emberizidae).

• **TEAL**
A type of small, surface-feeding **dabbling duck**.

• **TERN**
A type of sea-going or inland **waterbird** with narrow, tapering wings, a tapering bill, and usually a forked tail, that swoops down or plunge-dives to seize prey in the water (= family Sternidae).

• **TERRITORY**
An area defended by a bird, pair, or small social group, against others, for feeding and often also for nesting, varying in size from the immediate surroundings of an individual bird to several square kilometres.

• **THICK-KNEE**
A type of **shorebird**, usually nocturnal, with a large head and large eyes, occurring in open spaces (= family Burhinidae).

• **THORNBILL**
A type of small, insect-eating passerine, usually with a short, thin bill (= family Acanthizidae).

• **THRASHER**
A type of thrush-like passerine of low vegetation with a slender bill which it uses to probe among leaves and toss leaf litter aside in search of food (part of family Mimidae).

• **THRUSH**
A type of small to moderate-sized passerine with a slender bill and often with a melodious song (= family Turdidae).

• **TINAMOU**
A type of ground-living non-passerine with limited powers of flight, a long neck with small head, and long, strong legs (= family Tinamidae).

• **TIT**
A type of small passerine of trees and shrubs, with a small, strong bill and strong feet for acrobatic feeding (= family Paridae).

• **TITMOUSE**
Alternative word for **tit**.

• **TODY**
A type of tiny, rounded, perching non-passerine with a long, narrow bill that feeds by flying out from a perch to take insects from the air or foliage (= family Todidae).

• **TORPID**
A state of temporary hibernation in which the bird is inactive, maintaining a reduced body temperature, in order to conserve energy when resting or sleeping.

• **TOUCAN**
A type of fruit-eating, perching, forest-dwelling non-passerine with an enlarged, blunt-tipped bill (= family Rhamphastidae).

• **TREE-DUCK**
An alternative name for **whistling-duck**.

TREE-SWIFT
A type of aerial non-passerine with a short, very wide bill, and long wings and tail, feeding on insects caught in the air, and able to perch, rest, and nest in trees (= family Hemiprocnidae).

• **TREECREEPER**
A type of small passerine with a slender, slightly downcurved bill, that climbs treetrunks and branches, some species using the tail as a support (= families Certhiidae and Climacteridae).

• **TROGON**
A type of tree-dwelling non-passerine with a compact body, long tail, and round head with a short, wide bill; it flies out from a perch to snatch insects in mid-air, or to take fruit while hovering (= family Trogonidae).

• **TROUPIAL**
An alternative name referring either to the **New World blackbirds** in general (= family Icteridae) or to a common species of South American **oriole** that belongs to this family.

• **TRUMPETER**
A type of forest-dwelling non-passerine, mainly living on the ground, with a longish neck and round head, long, strong legs, and deep calls (= family Psophiidae).

• **TUNDRA**
A **habitat** consisting of short vegetation, often waterlogged, bordering the polar regions; the underlying soil is frozen in winter, but the surface thaws in summer, allowing some low plant growth.

• **TURACO**
A type of slender, soft-plumaged non-passerine of trees and shrubs with a long tail, rounded wings, and a short, blunt bill for eating fruit (= family Musophagidae).

• **TURKEY-VULTURE**
The commonest species of **New World vulture**; this name is sometimes used for the family (Cathartidae) as a whole.

• **TYRANT FLYCATCHER**
A type of **flycatcher** of the Americas (= family Tyrannidae).

• **VIREO**
A type of small, slender passerine with a short, sturdy bill. Vireos typically hunt insects among the foliage (= family Vireonidae).

• **VULTURE**
A type of scavenging **bird of prey** feeding on **carrion** and lacking or partly lacking feathers on head and neck (= family Cathartidae and part of family Accipitridae).

• **WADER**
(i) A British term, in common use until the 1970s, now generally replaced by the North American term **shorebird**. (ii) A North American term for a large, long-legged wading bird such as a **stork, heron,** or **spoonbill**.

• **WAGTAIL**
A type of slender passerine with a long tail that is flexed up and down when the bird is active (part of family Motacillidae); also refers to certain similar-looking **tyrant** and **monarch flycatchers**.

• **WARBLER**
A type of insect-eating passerine, often with a frequently-used, musical song (families Sylviidae, Parulidae). Also refers to certain species in the **thornbill** family (Acanthizidae).

• **WATERBIRD**
A bird that is usually found in, on, or near water. This term covers a broad range of bird families.

• **WATERFOWL**
A type of web-footed **waterbird** of the **duck, goose,** and **swan** family (= Anatidae).

• **WATTLE**
A prominent or pendant patch of bare skin, usually brightly coloured and often capable of being enlarged in display.

• **WAXBILL**
A type of small or very small passerine with a seed-cracking bill that is often bright red or orange (= family Estrildidae).

• **WEAVER**
A type of small passerine with a seed-cracking bill. Most species weave their nests with strips of fresh plant material (= family Ploceidae).

• **WHEATEAR**
A type of small, ground-living **chat** with a conspicuous, white **rump** (part of family Turdidae).

• **WHISTLER**
A type of passerine with a rounded head and strong or hook-tipped bill, and often a loud, musical song (= family Pachycephalidae).

• **WHISTLING-DUCK**
A type of long-legged and long-necked **duck**, usually **gregarious** and having noisy, whistling calls, some species resting and nesting in trees.

• **WHITE-EYE**
A type of tiny passerine living in trees and shrubs, with a small, thin bill and with a white ring of feathers around each eye (= family Zosteropidae).

• **WHYDAH**
A type of long-tailed **weaver** parasitizing nests of **waxbills**.

• **WIDOWBIRD**
A type of long-tailed **weaver** that is not a nest parasite. The long, black tail gave rise to the "widow" part of this name.

• **WILDFOWL**
Another name for **waterfowl**.

• **WING BAR**
A short, brightly coloured or white band on the wing.

• **WING STRIPE**
A brightly coloured band along the extended wing.

• **WOODCREEPER**
A type of slender-bodied passerine that climbs treetrunks and branches, partly propped up by its tail; bills vary between species, from slender to strong and from long to short (= family Dendrocolaptidae).

• **WOODPECKER**
A type of non-passerine that clambers up treetrunks and branches, partly propped up by its tail, with a strong, tapering bill that can make holes in wood (= family Picidae).

• **WOODSWALLOW**
A type of perching passerine with a large head, short, broad bill, and long wings, that feeds in flocks by chasing insects in the air (= family Artamidae).

• **WREN**
A type of passerine of low vegetation, often small, normally thin-billed, and usually with an upright tail (= family Troglodytidae); or a similar-looking bird of another family (Acanthisittidae, Maluridae, Acanthizidae).

INDEX

ACKNOWLEDGEMENTS

Illustrations: endpapers and pages 6–243, 304– 395 by **Simone End**, pages 244–303 by **Linden Artists**/Steve Lings. **Computer map origination:** Alastair Wardle. **Abbreviations:** *b* = bottom, *t* = top, *c* = centre, *l* = left, *r* = right. Photographs not listed here are copyright Dorling Kindersley, supplied by Cyril Laubscher, Dennis Avon, and Maslowski Photo. **Jacket photographs:** Front: **Jim Battles** *bl*; **Bruce Coleman**/Wayne Lankinen *bc*; **Sharon Cummings** *tl*; **Nature Photographers**/Roger Tidman *cl*; **John Snyder** *c*. Back: **Oxford Scientific Films**/C.W. Helliwell. Front flap: **Paul Doherty**. Back flap: **Jim Battles**. Spine: **VIREO/J.** Dunning. **Inside photographs: Aquila**/Hans Gebuis *56b*; Conrad Greaves *145t, 195t*; Brian Hawkes *153t*; Stuart Horton *189b*; Wayne Lankinen *46b, 140c, 200t , 200b, 216t, 216c, 257b, 279b, 280b, 350b, 356t*; T. Leach *191t*; Robert Maier *73b*; J. Mills *52b*; M Mockler *289c*; A .T . Moffett *392t*; B. Speake *269b*; C. & T. Stuart *64*; M.C. Wilkes *11tl, 39, 56t, 65b, 150t, 152b, 155b, 186b, 393b*; Gary Weber *41*. **Ardea**/Peter Alden *204b*; Dennis Avon *166b, 176c, 221b, 239t, 275b, 278c, 348c, 366b*; J. A.

Bailey *67, 293b*; L.R. Beames *128b, 376b*; Hans and Judy Beste *99t, 136b, 154b, 205b, 311c, 313b*; J.B. & S. Bottomley *161t*; G.K. Brown *137t*; Graeme Chapman *325b*; John Daniels *280c*; Hans Dossenbach *63t*; J.S. Dunning *190t, 247t, 258b, 259t, 259b, 261t, 285t, 352t*; M.D. England *210t, 274b, 283t, 348b*; Jean-Paul Ferrero *49t*; K.W. Fink *42t, 87, 98t, 107b, 111b, 113b, 117t, 143b, 157t, 192b, 194b, 199b, 231t, 289t*; François Gohier *43t*; A. Greensmith *51b, 57t, 124t, 228t, 331b, 338c*; Joanna van Grulsen *209b*; Clem Haagner *276t*; J.L. Mason *244c*; E. McNamara *272c, 312t,*

312c; P. Morris *193t*, *322b*, *387t*; Don Hadden *140b*; Irene Neufeldt *308c*; S. Roberts *217t*, *254t*; Peter Steyn *6tl*, *91b*, *246b*, *286t*, *303b*; W.R. Taylor *314t*; A.D. Trounson & M.C. Clampett *296t*, *331t*, *332b*, *383t*, *383b*; Peter Vaughn *52c*; Alan Weaving *190b*, *276b*; Wardene Weisser *114b*, *282t*, *291c*, *381t*, *390t*. **Jim Battles** *288b*, *339b*, *361t*. **Steve Bentsen** *205c*. **Frank Blackburn** *94t*, *94b*, *144t*, *207t*, *222t*, *241t*, *268t*, *270c*, *282b*, *304b*, *306t*, *307t*, *307c*, *309t*, *319c*, *321t*, *324t*, *334b*; Kevin Carlson *287b*, *304c*, *254c*, *321c*, *372t*; Melvin Grey *80b*, *93b*, *108b*, *139b*, *143c*, *147b*. **BIOS/D.** Halleux *118t*, *227b*; C. Seitre *384b*. **Alan Bovee** *294t*, *323c*, *351t*. **David Broadbent** *55t*, *149b*. **Mike Buxton** *323t*. **Bruce Coleman Ltd** *165t*, *209t*, *266t*, *268b*, *320t*, *325c*, *334c*; Jen & Des Bartlett *58t*, *130b*, *141t*; N.G. Blake *15cr*; B. & C. Calhoun *219b*, *238b*, *253t*, *280t*, *354c*, *358t*, *360b*, *363t*; Brian J. Coates *294b*; Raymond Cramm *130t*; Gerald Cubitt *115b*; Peter Davey *112t*; Ernest Duscher 158b; Inigo Everson *50b*; John Fennell *148t*; C.B. & D.W Frith *167t*, *386t*; Jose Luis Gonzales Grande *188t*, *379b*; Pekka Heto *202t*; Udo Hirsch *146t*; Stephen Kraseman *83t*, *125b*; O. Langrand *265b*, *279t*, *380b*; Gordon Langsbury *7b*, *15cl*, *15bl*, *149t*, *271b*, *279c*; Wayne Lankinen *336c*, *340t*, *341b*, *363b*; Werner Layer *231b*, *287c*, *288t*; Dr Rocco Longo *283c*; L.C Marigo *42b*, *70b*, *97b*, *180t*, *256t*,*256b*; Rinnie van Meurs *156t*, *309b*; Dr Scott Nielson *85t*, *110b*; M.R. Phicton *105b*, *164t*; Dieter & Mary Plage *109t*, *131t*; Dr Eckart Potts *121t*; Mike Price *257t*, *275t*; Hans Reinhard 44, *98b*, *113t*, *165b*, *197b*, *272b*, *295c*, *363c*; Norbert Rosing *138b*; John Shaw *127b*; Norman Tomalin *264c*, *265t*; Joseph van Wormer *212t*, *338b*; Uwe Walz *133t*; Paul R. Wilkinson *203t*; Rod Williams *257t*; Konrad Wothe *53t*, *301t*, *305b*, *360c*; Günter Zeisler *191b*, *218b*, *245b*. **Brian J. Coates** *166t*, *315b*, *380t*. **Bill Coster** *50t*, *86b*, *201b*. **Sharon Cummings** *78b*, *81b*, *108t*, *240b*, *242t*, *320b*, *356c*, *388b*. **Rob Curtis** *269c*, *270t*, *351c*. **R.S. Daniell** *135t*, *163t*, *277t*, *303t*, *379t*. **Peter Davey** *61b*, *66b*, *99b*. **Paul Doherty** *11tr*, *70t*, *74t*, *89t*, *97t*, *103t*, *122t*, *126t*, *132b*, *142b*, *148b*, *151b*, *159t*, *160t*, *160b*, *162t*, *208t*, *220t*, *271c*, *302t*, *303c*, *334t*, *336t*, *362c*. **Brian Gadsby** *82t*, *85b*. **Peter Ginn** *128t*, *229b*, *373b*. **Robert Harding Picture Library** *6tr*. **S.C. Hendricks** *118b*, *225t*, *368b*, *371c*, *377t*. **Jack Jeffery** *315t*, *352b*, *353t*, *353c*. **Zig Koch** *6bc*, *107t*, *122b*, *252c*. **Frank Lane Picture Agency**/R. Austing *95t*; A. R. Hamblin 188b; T. & P. Gardener *310b*; M. Gore *235c*; John Hawkins *395t*; E. & D. Hosking *101b*, *183t*, *186t*, *208b*, *217b*, *224t*, *394b*; F.W. Lane *180b*, *261b*; G. Moon *51t*, *185b*, *381b*; R. van Nostrand *146b*, *187b*; L. Lee Rue *96b*; L. West *337t*; E. Wilmhurst *75b*; M. B. Withers *60*; W. Wisniewski *68t*. **Cyril Laubscher** *11tcl*, *47b*, *164c*, *168t*, *170b*, *171t*, *175t*, *176t*, *177c*, *179b*, *195b*, *234c*, *264b*, *278t*, *298c*, *299t*, *299b*, *326c*, *327t*, *327b*, *331c*, *338t*, *341t*, *347c*, *362b*, *364b*, *369t*, *369b*, *370b*, *385t*. **Nico Myburgh** *76b*, *124b*, *267t*, *301c*, *310t*, *333b*, *371t*. **National Photographic Index of Australian Wildlife**/L.F. Schick *382b*; T.A. Waite *333t*; J.D. Waterhouse *385b*; H. Webster *266c*; Babs & Bert Wells *329b*. **Nature Photographers**/Kevin Carlson *270b*, *382t*; Andrew Cleave *126b*; P Craig-Cooper *65t*, *138t*; Michael Gore *207t*; James Hancock *256c*; M. P. Harris *48*; Hugh Miles *114t*; Paul Sterry *61b*, *115t*, *123t*, *125t*, *359t*; Don Smith *145b*; Roger Tidman *144b*, *284t*, *355t*. **Natural Elements**/Greg Homel *88b*, *131b*, *133t*, *253c*, *300b*, *392b*. **NHPA**/Henry Ausloos *59t*,*198b*; A.P. Barnes *321b*;

George Bernard *102b*; L Campbell *289b*; Stephen Dalton *301b*; Nigel Dennis *233b*, *395b*; Robert Erwin *285b*; Melvin Grey *134b*, *267b*; Helio and Van Ingen *79t*, *89b*; A. Janes *104t*; E.A. Jones *77t*; Rich Kirchner *40*; Stephen J. Kraseman *269t*; Lacz Lemoine *91t*; Michael Morcombe *311b*; Haraldo Palo *88t*, *233t*, *242b*, *248c*, *255b*; Jany Sauvanet *164b*; Philippa Scott *74b*; John Shaw *47t*, *61t*; Morton Strange *132t*, *219t*; Phillip Wayne *119b*; Alan Williams *152t*, *268c*; David Woodfall *193b*. **NHPA/ANT** *45t*/R.J. Allingham *330t*; Anthony Howard *52t*; B. Chudleigh *317c*; I.R. McCann *177t*, *323b*; Frank Park *313c*; Otto Rogge *45b*; M. F. Soper *265c*; Cyril Webster *106t*. **Oxford Scientific Films**/Mike Brown *302b*; Roger Brown *316t*; Ray Coombes *147t*; Michael Fogden *261c*; Jim Frazier & Mantis Wildlife Films *72t*; Max Gibbs *116t*; C.W. Helliwell *157b*; Ben Osborne *49b*; Richard Packwood *58b*; Stan Osolinski *216b*; Tony Tilford *328t*, *328b*; Babs & Bert Wells *324b*; Graham J. Wren *335c*. **OSF/Animals Animals**/Patti Murray *284b*. **OSF/Okapia**/Hans Reinhard *370c*. **William Peckover** *123b*, *155t*, *162b*, *167b*, *170t*, *173b*, *204t*, *273t*, *286c*, *310c*, *317t*, *329c*, *332t*, *378t*, *384t*, *387b*. **J. F. Reynolds** *68b*, *117b*, *121b*, *141b*, *143t*, *224b*, *226t*, *226b*, *228b*, *371b*, *373t*. **T. Robinson** *308b*. **Swan Photographic Agency**/John Buckingham *84b*, *137b*, *153b*, *243b*, *272t*; David M. Cottridge *306c*; Grant Demar *267c*, *292b*, *305t*; Bill Moorcroft *271t*, *360t*; Andrew Ruck *11cc*, *80t*; R. Thomas *201t*; Don Withey *84t*. **John Snyder** *90b*, *106b*, *192t*, *282c*, *340c*. **Roger Steele** *79b*. **Peter Steyn** *277c*. **Swift Picture Library**/Thomas Dressler *230t*. **Roger Tidman** *82b*, *83b*, *86t*, *92b*, *135b*, *142t*, *150b*, *156b*, *238t*, *394t*. **R.E. Viljoen** *9c*, *311t*, *312b*, *313t*, *315c*, *316c*, *316b*, *317b*, *318t*, *326t*, *367c*. **VIREO**/A. Carey *102t*, *112b*; R. & N. Bowers *206b*; R.J. Chandler *136t*; B. Chudleigh *168b*; H. Clarke *295b*, *349b*; H. Cruikshank *335t*; J. Dunning *43b*, *63b*, *206t*, *212b*, *218t*, *232b*, *234t*, *246t*, *246c*, *247t*, *247b*, *248t*, *248b*, *249t*, *249c*, *250t*, *250c*, *250b*, *251t*, *251b*, *252t*, *252c*, *255t*, *258t*, *258c*, *259c*, *263c*, *263b*, *281t*, *281b*, *337c*, *337b*, *339c*, *340b*, *342b*, *343t*, *343b*, *345t*, *345c*, *345b*, *346b*, *347t*, *347b*, *348t*, *353b*, *354t*, *355c*, *357b*; W. Green *78t*, *243t*; C.H. Greenwalt *161b*, *211t*, *211c*, *212c*, *213b*, *214t*, *215c*, *215b*, *223t*, *260b*, *263t*, *295t*, *319t*, *344b*, *346t*, *346c*, *386b*; B. Henry *364t*; D.R. Herr *95b*; J. Hoffman *320c*; Stephen Holt *57b*, *278b*; M.P. Kahl *66t*, *69b*, *71*; A.J. Knystautas *300c*; H.C. Kyllingstad *139t*; P. La Tourrette *319b*; S.J. Lang *356b*; J. Larsen 119t; A. Morris *253b*, *351b*, *352c*; R. Mellon *151t*; T. Parker *203b*; B. Schorre *342c*, *349t*, *349c*, *350t*, *350c*; William Peckover *103b*, *205t*, *221t*, *222b*, *264t*, *302c*, *318b*, *325t*; B. Randall *389b*; M.J. Rauzon *59b*; T.J. Ulrich *127t*, *344c*; D. Wechsler *210c*, *222c*, *223b*, *232t*, *236b*, *238c*, *245t*, *249b*, *251c*, *254b*, *262b*, *213b*, *274c*, *290t*, *296b*, *304t*, *305c*, *314b*; J.R. Woodward *291b*, *322c*, *335b*; D. & M. Zimmerman *55b*, *158t*, *308t*, *389t*. **Alan Weaving** *100*, *225b*. **Alan Wilson** *104b*, *230b*.